Lecture Notes in Computer Science   2034

Edited by G. Goos, J. Hartmanis and J. van Leeuwen

T0188823

Springer
Berlin
Heidelberg
New York
Barcelona
Hong Kong
London
Milan
Paris
Singapore
Tokyo

Maria Domenica Di Benedetto
Alberto Sangiovanni-Vincentelli (Eds.)

Hybrid Systems: Computation and Control

4th International Workshop, HSCC 2001
Rome, Italy, March 28-30, 2001
Proceedings

 Springer

Series Editors

Gerhard Goos, Karlsruhe University, Germany
Juris Hartmanis, Cornell University, NY, USA
Jan van Leeuwen, Utrecht University, The Netherlands

Volume Editors

Maria Domenica Di Benedetto
Università dell'Aquila
Dipartimento di Ingegneria Elettrica
Poggio di Roio, 67040 L'Aquila, Italy
E-mail: dibenede@ing.univaq.it

Alberto Sangiovanni-Vincentelli
University of California at Berkeley
Berkeley, CA 94720
PARADES
Via San Pantaleo, 66, 00186 Roma, Italy
E-mail: alberto@eecs.berkeley.edu

Cataloging-in-Publication Data applied for

Die Deutsche Bibliothek - CIP-Einheitsaufnahme

Hybrid systems : computation and control ; 4th international workshop ;
proceedings / HSCC 2001, Rome, Italy, March 28 - 30, 2001. Maria
Domenica Di Benedetto ; Alberto Sangiovanni-Vincentelli (ed.). -
Berlin ; Heidelberg ; New York ; Barcelona ; Hong Kong ; London ;
Milan ; Paris ; Singapore ; Tokyo : Springer, 2001
   (Lecture notes in computer science ; Vol. 2034)
   ISBN 3-540-41866-0

CR Subject Classification (1998): C.1.m, F.3, C.3, D.2, F.1.2, J.2, I.6

ISSN 0302-9743
ISBN 3-540-41866-0 Springer-Verlag Berlin Heidelberg New York

Springer-Verlag Berlin Heidelberg New York
a member of BertelsmannSpringer Science+Business Media GmbH

http://www.springer.de

© Springer-Verlag Berlin Heidelberg 2001
Printed in Germany

Typesetting: Camera-ready by author, data conversion by PTP Berlin, Stefan Sossna
Printed on acid-free paper   SPIN 10782426   06/3142   5 4 3 2 1 0

Preface

This volume contains the proceedings of the *Fourth Workshop on Hybrid Systems: Computation and Control* (HSCC 2001) held in Rome, Italy on March 28-30, 2001. The Workshop on Hybrid Systems attracts researchers from industry and academia interested in modeling, analysis, synthesis, and implementation of dynamic and reactive systems involving both discrete (integer, logical, symbolic) and continuous behaviors. It is a forum for the discussion of the latest developments in all aspects of hybrid systems, including formal models and computational representations, algorithms and heuristics, computational tools, and new challenging applications.

The Fourth HSCC International Workshop continues the series of workshops held in Grenoble, France (HART'97), Berkeley, California, USA (HSCC'98), Nijmegen, The Netherlands (HSCC'99), and Pittsburgh, Pennsylvania, USA (HSCC 2000). Proceedings of these workshops have been published in the Lecture Notes in Computer Science (LNCS) series by Springer-Verlag.

In line with the beautiful work that led to the design of the palace in which the workshop was held, Palazzo Lancellotti in Rome, resulting from the collaboration of many artists and architects of different backgrounds, the challenge faced by the hybrid system community is to harmonize and extract the best from two main research areas: computer science and control theory. Terminology, mathematical tools, and abstractions are different, problems considered relevant by one community may be considered trivial by the other, yet it is this very difference that may bring new vistas to traditional research fields to escape the trap of routine. The steering committee of the workshop series has been appointed to guide the directions of the research in troubled water balancing the membership among computer scientists, control theorists, and application experts. The technical program committee has been assembled following the same principle. The committee has done a wonderful job in reviewing and discussing 82 submissions (a record number since the inception of the workshop series). All requested reviews were received (a world-wide record among all workshops!). After extended and, at times, intense discussions, 36 papers were selected for presentation at the workshop and publication in this volume. While the technical quality of the papers is excellent, we cannot underestimate the preponderance of control theory papers and the scarcity of application papers. The theory papers are mainly directed at the consolidation of the foundations of the field, a hardly unexpected outcome in an area that is approaching a new level of maturity. However, the lack of relevant application papers is somewhat worrisome. For this reason, we preferred to give emphasis to applications in the invited papers to the workshop: Manfred Morari (ETH Zurich), Costas Pantelides (Imperial College), and Janos Sztipanovits (Vanderbilt University) are all well known for their work in hybrid system applications and in embedded-system design. In addition, we included in the workshop a panel on applications of hybrid systems. The participants to the panel addressed the challenges of using a richly expressive theory, being, as such, relatively poor in computationally affordable synthesis and analysis tools, to yield relevant results in the real-life world. They also addressed the issue of merging knowledge about tools and methods in control and computer science so that we may avoid the risk of re-inventing in one field results that are well known in the other.

We believe that embedded systems will be the main application vehicle for our technology and as such deserve particular attention. Embedded systems will also be the main application domain for electronics in general. Since embedded systems require design methods that guarantee correct and efficient behavior in harsh environments, a strong theoretical approach to synthesis and verification is badly needed. They are hybrid in nature: continuous and discrete mix freely in a variety of application domains. Software and control will play a dominant role. Hence, we believe that our community will be an important constituency in founding the field of embedded system theory and design.

We wish to thank the organizations (PARADES, Progetto Finalizzato Madess II, Consiglio Nazionale delle Ricerche, Army Research Office, National Science Foundation) that financially supported the workshop. Moreover, we acknowledge the contribution of Magneti-Marelli, an automotive electronics company that has put to good use hybrid system technology in its products. In particular, the support and continuous encouragement of Dr. Daniele Pecchini, President and General Manager of Magneti Marelli Powertrain Division, is acknowledged. We thank Prof. Richard Gerber for letting us use START, his software conference manager.

The final remark is dedicated to the Organizing Committee, whose members spent long hours making sure everything was correctly handled, from call for papers to hotel information, and paper submission. In particular, Andrea Balluchi and Luca Benvenuti have spent an inordinate amount of time coping with the software, trying to keep all the web material in synch and making sure authors submitted the correct versions of their papers and the appropriate documents that E-conomy bureaucracy imposes on us.

March 2001   Maria Domenica Di Benedetto and
                                                  Alberto Sangiovanni-Vincentelli

Organization

HSCC 2001 is organized by P.A.R.A.D.E.S. (Project for Advanced Research of Architecture and Design of Electronic Systems), an E.E.I.G established by Cadence, Magneti-Marelli, ST-Microelectronics, and C.N.R. (Italian National Research Council).

Steering Committee

Panos Antsaklis (University of Notre Dame, Notre Dame, IN, USA)
Maria Domenica Di Benedetto (University of L'Aquila, L'Aquila, Italy)
Bruce H. Krogh (Carnegie Mellon University, Pittsburgh, PA, USA)
Mark Greenstreet (University of British Columbia, Vancouver, BC, Canada)
Nancy A. Lynch (Massachusetts Institute of Technology, Cambridge, MA, USA)
Oded Maler (IMAG, Grenoble, France)
Manfred Morari (ETH, Zurich, Switzerland)
Amir Pnueli (Weizmann Institute, Rehovot, Israel)
Anders P. Ravn (Aalborg University, Denmark)
Alberto L. Sangiovanni-Vincentelli (PARADES and University of California at Berkeley, CA, USA)
Claire Tomlin (Stanford University, Stanford, CA, USA)
Frits W. Vaandrager (University of Nijmegen, Nijmegen, The Netherlands)

Program Committee

Rajeev Alur (University of Pennsylvania, Philadelphia, PA, USA)
Eugene Asarin (University of Grenoble, Grenoble, France)
Jean-Pierre Aubin (University of Paris-Dauphine, Paris, France)
Andrea Balluchi (PARADES, Rome, Italy)
Luca Benvenuti (University of Rome "La Sapienza", Rome, Italy)
Antonio Bicchi (University of Pisa, Pisa, Italy)
Gautam Biswas (Vanderbilt University, Nashville, TN, USA)
Rene Boel (Ghent University, Belgium)
Michael Branicky (Case Western Reserve University, Cleveland, OH, USA)
Christos G. Cassandras (Boston University, Boston, MA, USA)
Maria Domenica Di Benedetto (University of L'Aquila, L'Aquila, Italy)
Mark Greenstreet (University of British Columbia, Vancouver, BC, Canada)
Thomas A. Henzinger (University of California at Berkeley, Berkeley, CA, USA)
Stefan Kowalewski (Bosch, Frankfurt, Germany)
Bruce H. Krogh (Carnegie Mellon University, Pittsburgh, PA, USA)
Alexander B. Kurzhanski (Moscow State University, Moscow, Russian Federation)

Gerardo Lafferriere (Portland State University, Portland, OR, USA)
Michael Lemmon (University of Notre Dame, Notre Dame, IN, USA)
Bengt Lennartson (Chalmers University of Technology, Göteborg, Sweden)
Nancy Leveson (Massachusetts Institute of Technology, Cambridge, MA, USA)
John Lygeros (University of Cambridge, Cambridge, United Kingdom)
Oded Maler (VERIMAG, Grenoble, France)
Manfred Morari (Swiss Federal Institute of Technology ETH, Zurich, Switzerland)
George Pappas (University of Pennsylvania, Philadelphia, PA, USA)
Anders Rantzer (Lund Institute of Technology, Lund, Sweden)
Alberto L. Sangiovanni-Vincentelli (PARADES and University of California at Berkeley, CA, USA)
Roberto Segala (University of Bologna, Bologna, Italy)
Eduardo Sontag (Rutgers, State University of New Jersey, Piscataway, NJ, USA)
Claire Tomlin (Stanford University, Stanford, CA, USA)
Stavros Tripakis (VERIMAG, Grenoble, France)
Frits W. Vaandrager (University of Nijmegen, Nijmegen, The Netherlands)
Arjan Van der Schaft (University of Twente, Enschede, The Netherlands)
Jan H. van Schuppen (CWI, Amsterdam, The Netherlands)
Tiziano Villa (PARADES, Rome, Italy)
Howard Wong-Toi (Cadence Berkeley Labs, Berkeley, CA, USA)
Sergio Yovine (VERIMAG, Grenoble, France)

Organizing Committee

Andrea Balluchi (PARADES, Rome, Italy)
Luca Benvenuti (University of Rome "La Sapienza", Rome, Italy)
Maria Domenica Di Benedetto (University of L'Aquila, L'Aquila, Italy)
Alberto Ferrari (PARADES, Rome, Italy)
Antonio Paoletti (University of Rome "Tor Vergata", Rome, Italy and Director PF Madess II, CNR, Italy)
Alberto L. Sangiovanni-Vincentelli (PARADES and University of California at Berkeley, CA, USA)
Donatella Santillo (Cadence Design Systems, Rome, Italy)
Tiziano Villa (PARADES, Rome, Italy)

Additional Referees

Alexandre Bayen	Francesco Cuzzola	Catalin Dima
Calin Belta	Izaias da Silva	Giancarlo Ferrari Trecate
Alberto Bemporad	Thao Dang	Ronojoy Ghosh
Luca Berardi	Jennifer Davoren	Jianghai Hu
Francesco Borrelli	Francesco Delli Priscoli	Inseok Hwang
Ahmed Bouajjani	Stefano Di Gennaro	Gokhan Inalhan

Sponsoring Institutions

P.A.R.A.D.E.S. (Project for Advanced Research of Architecture and Design of Electronic Systems), Cadence, Magneti-Marelli and ST-Microelectronics E.E.I.G, and by C.N.R., the Italian National Research Council, Rome, Italy

Progetto Finalizzato C.N.R. MADESSII SP3.1.2, Italy

Consiglio Nazionale delle Ricerche, Italy

Magneti Marelli S.p.A., Bologna, Italy

Army Research Office, ARL-ERO, USA

National Science Foundation, USA

Table of Contents

Control as an Embedded Technology

Manfred Morari

Automatic Control Laboratory
Swiss Federal Institute of Technology (ETH)
CH-8092 Zurich / Switzerland
morari@aut.ee.ethz.ch, http://control.ethz.ch/~hybrid

Based on work jointly with
Alberto Bemporad, Francesco Borrelli, Francesco Cuzzola, Tobias Geyer,
Domenico Mignone, Fabio Torrisi and Giancarlo Ferrari Trecate

Abstract. We envision the role of control to expand rapidly in two directions. It will impact novel application areas, which have yet to benefit from the power of feedback, and, as an embedded technology, control will extend its reach far beyond the traditional narrow concept to include higher level functions of operation. Our research program is built on this vision. Eventually, these ideas should also radically change what is taught in our class rooms, so that our students can transfer these techniques to industry effectively and reap its benefits.

In all control applications the actual control algorithm is just one tiny part of the overall system designed to ensure safe, reliable and economical operation. Success or failure of "operation" are attributable at least as much to "the rest" as to the control algorithm itself. At the lowest level the control algorithm is endowed with functionality to deal with operating constraints and to switch smoothly between different operating regimes. At the highest levels the control algorithm may be embedded in a scheduling system or even an Enterprise Resource Planning (ERP) system. At all levels this embedding creates a heterogeneous system comprised of many interacting subsystems, typically referred to as a hybrid system.

The integration should eventually lead to a safer, smoother, more responsive and more competitive functioning of the entire system or organization. About three years ago we embarked on a major research program toward this goal. Its objective is the development of new theoretical tools to model, analyze, simulate and control such large complex hybrid systems involving continuous and discrete states, whose behavior is governed by dynamics, logical statements and constraints. In this talk we will summarize the highlights and try to put them in perspective.

Modeling and Simulation: The models should facilitate the analysis and, at the same time, capture the complex behavior, that hybrid systems are known to exhibit. Based on these considerations, we introduced a discrete time description, combining linear dynamics with Boolean variables. This mixed logical dynamical form (MLD) form is capable to model a broad class of systems arising in many applications from the automotive, aircraft, chemical and information technology fields. Supply chains used in

M.D. Di Benedetto, A. Sangiovanni-Vincentelli (Eds.): HSCC 2001, LNCS 2034, pp. 1–2, 2001.
© Springer-Verlag Berlin Heidelberg 2001

business models can be conveniently modeled as MLD systems as well. We defined a new modelling language (HYSDEL) and wrote a compiler to assist the user in the formulation of MLD models.

Controller Synthesis: For controller synthesis we formulate a finite horizon optimal control problem and apply the result in a moving horizon fashion. For MLD models the optimization problem is a mixed-integer linear program (MILP) which must be solved in real time at each sampling time. We have proven that the resulting state feedback control law is piece-wise linear over a polyhedral partition of the state space. As an alternative to on-line optimization, we can determine this control law explicitly by solving a multi-parametric MILP.

State Estimation and Fault Detection: For application of the described control law the system states must be known. Estimation of the states of an MLD system is a complex nonlinear filtering problem. We have defined a moving horizon estimator, where at each time step a mixed integer quadratic program must be solved to arrive at the state estimates. We have proven the convergence of the estimator if certain observability properties are satisfied. Complex fault situations can be modeled accurately in the MLD framework. Fault detection is another application of the new estimator.

Optimisation of Hybrid Processes and Hybrid Controllers

Costas C. Pantelides[1,2]

[1] Centre for Process Systems Engineering
Imperial College of Science, Technology and Medicine, London, UK
[2] Process Systems Enterprise Ltd., London, UK

Abstract. Most processes of practical interest are hybrid in nature, exhibiting both continuous and discrete characteristics. In many cases, the hybrid behaviour is a result of intrinsic physical phenomena that lead to (practically) instantaneous events such as the appearance and disappearance of thermodynamic phases, changes in flow regimes, equipment failures *etc.* All such events effect qualitative changes in the underlying continuous dynamics, thereby leading to hybrid macroscopic behaviour. In other cases, the hybrid nature arises from external discrete actions imposed on the process by its control system. For example, the latter may apply quantisation to convert continuous process measurements into discrete ones and/or continuous control outputs into discrete actions.

Hybrid processes and hybrid controllers, and their combination, can be modelled in terms of State-Transition Networks (STNs). The system behaviour in each state is described by a different set of continuous equations (typically a mixed system of partial and/or ordinary differential and algebraic equations). At any particular time during its operation, the system is in exactly one such state. An instantaneous transition to a different state may take place if a certain logical condition becomes true. Each transition is also characterised by a set of continuous relations that determine unique values for the system variables immediately following the transition in terms of their values immediately preceding it.

In this presentation, we consider mathematical formulations and techniques for the optimisation of hybrid systems described by STNs. This generally seeks to determine the time variation of a set of controls and/or the values of a set of time-invariant parameters that optimise some aspect of the dynamic behaviour of the system. The time horizon of interest may be fixed or variable, subject to specified lower and upper bounds. The equations that determine the system behaviour in each state may be augmented with additional inequality constraints imposing certain restrictions (related to safety or operability) on the acceptable system trajectories. The objective function to be minimised or maximised is usually a combination of fixed contributions (depending on the values of the time-invariant parameters) and variable contributions (depending on the system trajectory, including the variation of the controls).

As an illustration, we start with simple linear systems operating in the discrete time domain, possibly involving uncertain parameters. We then proceed to consider the more complex problem of the optimisation of nonlinear hybrid systems operating in the continuous time domain.

M.D. Di Benedetto, A. Sangiovanni-Vincentelli (Eds.): HSCC 2001, LNCS 2034, p. 3, 2001.
© Springer-Verlag Berlin Heidelberg 2001

Embedded Software and Systems: Challenges and Approaches

Janos Sztipanovits

Department of Electrical Engineering and Computer Science,
Vanderbilt University, Nashville, TN, USA

Abstract. One of the most pervasive applications of computing is information processing tightly integrated with physical processes. Embedded computing rapidly takes over the role of being a universal integrator for physical systems. This trend is based on a fundamental technical reason: digital information processing is uniquely suitable for controlling and implementing complex interactions among physical system components. The expanding integration role of computing challenges the state-of-the-art in both system and software design. First, the traditional separation of related design disciplines is not maintainable. Predictability of the design requires integrated modeling and analysis of physical processes and information processing. Second, the narrow focus of current software technology on functional composition is not sufficient. Essential physical properties of embedded computing systems, such as timing, noise or fault behavior, cut across functional boundaries, which makes software design and implementation extremely hard and expensive. Third, design technologies, which are based on the modeling and analysis of systems with static structure, are becoming inadequate. Although networked embedded computing combined with inexpensive MEMS-based sensors and actuators make the construction of large physical systems with continuously changing structure and physical interactions feasible, their design is an open challenge.

The first part of the talk provides an overview of the unique challenges and new research directions in embedded system and software design. The second part of the talk describes the Model-Integrated Computing (MIC) approach to address some of these challenges. Using the design of structurally adaptive embedded processing systems as example, the following three topics will be covered:

1. Methods and tools for the specification and construction of multiple-view, domain-specific modeling languages and integrated design environments. The MIC approach is based on the application of meta-modeling, meta-programmable modeling tools and model translators that form the foundation for composable design environments.

2. Automated synthesis of processing architectures satisfying multiple functional and physical constraints. The method described is based on symbolic constraint satisfaction.

3. Application of generative programming techniques with special emphasis on model-based software generators.

M.D. Di Benedetto, A. Sangiovanni-Vincentelli (Eds.): HSCC 2001, LNCS 2034, p. 4, 2001.
© Springer-Verlag Berlin Heidelberg 2001

Hybrid Systems Applications: An Oxymoron?

Moderator:
Alberto Sangiovanni-Vincentelli[1,2]

Partecipants:
Thomas A. Henzinger[1], Bruce H. Krogh[3], Oded Maler[4],
Manfred Morari[5], Costas C. Pantelides[6,7], George J. Pappas[8],
Tunc Simsec[1], Janos Sztipanovits[9], Stavros Tripakis[3,10]

[1] EECS Department, University of California at Berkeley, CA, USA
[2] PARADES, Roma, Italy.
[3] ECE Department, Carnegie Mellon University, Pittsburgh, PA, USA
[4] VERIMAG, Centre Equation, Gières, France
[5] Automatic Control Laboratory, ETH, Zurich, Switzerland
[6] Centre for Process Systems Engineering Imperial College, London, United Kingdom
[7] Process Systems Enterprise Ltd., London, United Kingdom
[8] EE Department, University of Pennsylvania, PA, USA
[9] EECS Department, Vanderbilt University, Nashville, TN, USA
[10] CALIFORNIA PATH, University of California at Berkeley, CA, USA

Hybrid systems are richly expressive models for a large variety of potential applications. However, being so rich as to include continuous nonlinear dynamical systems, discrete-event systems and other models of computation (finite-state machines and data flow come to mind here), they are not amenable to computationally attractive techniques for synthesis and analysis and present hard numerical problems to simulation. Hence, applying the methods typical of this technology requires non trivial amount of approximation and abstraction. And approximation and abstraction are effective only if the domain of application is deeply understood. Thus, significant applications of hybrid systems require a great deal of work both to select the right abstraction level and to derive algorithms that exploit the particularities of the domain of application. In addition, one needs to motivate and document convincingly why using hybrid systems can yield better results than other techniques. In this respect, there has been an ongoing debate as to what constitutes a meaningful result in applications: on one hand, novel languages for describing hybrid systems and capturing their properties may be considered sophomoric exercises by experts in languages, on the other, formal verification tools that in general can handle small systems may be seen as toys for who is trying to tame entire chemical plants. On the simulation front, how to deal with discontinuities of trajectories is a major issue. Numerical analysts have been looking at these problems only recently and with a great deal of skepticism as to what can be proven rigorously. Hybrid system researchers are now getting seriously in the simulation arena exploiting what has been done in the numerical analysis arena.

The goal of the panel is to bring experts from the two reference communities of hybrid systems (computer science and control) to debate whether hybrid system applications can indeed be compelling and what can be done to prevent

M.D. Di Benedetto, A. Sangiovanni-Vincentelli (Eds.): HSCC 2001, LNCS 2034, pp. 5–6, 2001.
© Springer-Verlag Berlin Heidelberg 2001

naive work on both sides when straddling across competence domains. Simulation and verification in general will also be discussed in the frame of the work done in numerical analysis. Predicting the outcome of the panel, we would like to end with a positive note: hybrid system technology is relevant to important applications but it has to be handled with great care and pushing the cart all in the same directions will give the hybrid system community the relevance it has the right of aspiring to.

Design of Luenberger Observers for a Class of Hybrid Linear Systems

A. Alessandri[1] and P. Coletta[1,2]

[1] Naval Automation Institute, IAN-CNR National Research Council of Italy,
Via De Marini 6, 16149 Genova, Italy
angelo@ian.ge.cnr.it
[2] Department of Communications, Computer and System Sciences,
DIST–University of Genoa, Via Opera Pia 13, 16145 Genova, Italy
paolo@ian.ge.cnr.it

Abstract. An approach to estimation for a class of hybrid discrete-time linear systems using Luenberger observers is presented. The proposed Luenberger observer for such a kind of systems relies on the switching among different gains. Convergence conditions have been found to ensure the stability of the error dynamics and the related gains may be selected by solving a set of linear matrix inequalities (LMIs). Moreover, this observer may be improved by suitably updating the estimate using the last measures. This update enables one to reduce the norm of the estimation error and is based on the so-called projection method. Simulation results are reported to show the effectiveness of these methods in the estimation for hybrid discrete-time linear systems.

1 Introduction

Hybrid systems have recently gained a great attention and the research in this area has been devoted more to control problems. In this work, the subject is the state estimation for a class of hybrid systems described by switching discrete-time linear equations. Switching systems are well-suited to dealing with applications like, for example, gain scheduling, reconfigurable control, and fault diagnosis, which enable one to point out the importance of constructing observers for such systems.

The problem of estimating the state of a switching system was originally stated in [1]. Later on, a lot of researches investigated the issues related to such a problem in a probabilistic framework, i.e., supposing that the transitions occur according to a model described by a first-order Markov chain. Difficulties may arise in the solution of optimal Bayesian estimation problems and the interested reader is referred, among others, to [2] and [3]. Another relevant topic concerns the so-called multi-model estimation. Such a subject is quite vast and involves many application-oriented problems (for an introduction, see [4]). Summing-up, all the above-mentioned approaches rely on a stochastic setting and the switching event is supposed unknown. Here, we focus on the problem of estimating the state of a switching system by assuming to know both time and mode of the

M.D. Di Benedetto, A. Sangiovanni-Vincentelli (Eds.): HSCC 2001, LNCS 2034, pp. 7–18, 2001.
© Springer-Verlag Berlin Heidelberg 2001

switching. Nevertheless, also in this context, the problem remains hard to solve for the difficulties of both guaranteeing the stability of the estimation error and devising a suitable, efficient observer design procedure. It is worth noting that we will make no assumption on the probabilistic description of the system mode transitions to derive the stability results of the proposed estimation methods.

Gain switching observers for continuous-time nonlinear systems have been considered in [5], where stable switching laws are searched for with different Lyapunov functions for each gain. A different approach based on coprime factorization is proposed in [6] to construct an observer for switching continuous-time linear systems. In the present paper, the goal is to find an estimator with a stable estimation error in the presence of any switching in a given finite set of admissible system modes. Such a problem turns out to be more difficult than the standard design of Luenberger observers for time-invariant linear systems. In this case, a Luenberger observer provides a convergent error dynamics if and only if the gain is chosen such that the poles of the error dynamics are in the strictly stable region. This condition is not sufficient to ensure the stability of the estimation error for a switching linear system. The gain selection of a switching observer is nontrivial as it involves the typical stability issues of the hybrid systems (for an introduction, see [7], [8], and [9]). In our case, the solution of this problem has been addressed by seeking a common Lyapunov function. This, in turn, can be reduced to the fulfillment of linear matrix inequalities (LMIs), which allow one to easily obtain a solution in a computationally feasible way.

An improvement to this Luenberger observer has been made by applying a projection method [10,11] to update the current estimate using the last measures. The resulting estimator exhibits a stable error dynamics if the same LMI relationships found for the first estimator are satisfied. In addition, the new observer results in higher performance, as this update provides a reduction of the estimation error.

The paper is organized as follows. Section 2 is devoted to the problem of constructing a Luenberger observer for switching discrete-time linear systems, with a particular emphasis on the stability of the error dynamics and on the development of an LMI approach to synthesize such observers. In Section 3, a modified Luenberger observer with the related stability analysis is proposed that enables one to estimate the state of the system using also the last available measures. Simulation results are illustrated in Section 4 to show the performance of the proposed estimation methods. The conclusions are drawn in Section 5.

2   Switching Observers for Discrete-Time Linear Systems

Consider the discrete-time linear system

$$\begin{cases} \underline{x}_{t+1} = A_{\sigma(t)}\,\underline{x}_t + B_{\sigma(t)}\,\underline{u}_t \\ \underline{y}_t = C_{\sigma(t)}\,\underline{x}_t \end{cases} \quad , \quad t = 0, 1, \dots \tag{1}$$

where $\underline{x}_t \in \mathbb{R}^n$ is the state vector, $\underline{u}_t \in \mathbb{R}^p$ is the input vector, $\underline{y}_t \in \mathbb{R}^m$ is the measure vector, and $\sigma : \mathbb{N} \longrightarrow \{1, 2, \dots, k\}$ is a function that maps the index time stage into an index set $\{1, 2, \ldots, k\}$. Each of the indices corresponds to a different model of the system and measurement equations, i.e., $A_{\sigma(t)} \in \mathcal{A} \stackrel{\triangle}{=} \{A_1, A_2, \ldots, A_k\}$, $B_{\sigma(t)} \in \mathcal{B} \stackrel{\triangle}{=} \{B_1, B_2, \ldots, B_k\}$, $C_{\sigma(t)} \in \mathcal{C} \stackrel{\triangle}{=} \{C_1, C_2, \ldots, C_k\}$, where $A_i \in \mathbb{R}^{n \times n}$, $B_i \in \mathbb{R}^{n \times p}$, and $C_i \in \mathbb{R}^{m \times n}$ for $i = 1, 2, \ldots, k$. We assume that the matrices $C_i \in \mathbb{R}^{m \times n}$, $i = 1, 2, \ldots, k$, are of full rank $m < n$ and the output of the function $\sigma(\cdot)$ is known at time t. Anyway, it is worth noting that the matrices $B_{\sigma(t)}$ and $C_{\sigma(t)}$ with time-varying dimensions in the number of columns and rows (i.e., of p and m, respectively) are allowed. A switching observer for (1) is the following:

$$\hat{\underline{x}}_{t+1} = A_{\sigma(t)} \, \hat{\underline{x}}_t + B_{\sigma(t)} \, \underline{u}_t + L_{\sigma(t)} \left(\underline{y}_t - C_{\sigma(t)} \, \hat{\underline{x}}_t \right) \quad , \quad t = 0, 1, \ldots \quad (2)$$

where $\hat{\underline{x}}_0 = \bar{\underline{x}}_0$ is chosen "a priori" and $L_{\sigma(t)}$ is the observer gain at the time t, $L_{\sigma(t)} \in \mathcal{L} \stackrel{\triangle}{=} \{L_1, L_2, \ldots, L_k\}$, and $L_i \in \mathbb{R}^{n \times m}$, $i = 1, 2, \ldots, k$. A pictorial representation of such an observer is shown in Fig. 1.

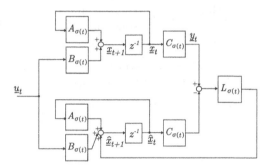

Fig. 1. Scheme of a switching observer.

Note that these gains may change in such a way that the dimension m will vary over time due, for example, to a variable number of available measures at time t. The dynamics of the estimation error (i.e., $\underline{e}_t \stackrel{\triangle}{=} \underline{x}_t - \hat{\underline{x}}_t$) behaves like a switching dynamic system, thus a common Lyapunov function is searched for to ensure stability. Now, we can state the following theorem.

Theorem 1. *Consider the system (1) and assume that the pairs* (A_i, C_i), $i = 1, 2, \ldots, k$, *are observable. If there exists a symmetric positive definite matrix* P *as the solution of the algebraic Lyapunov inequalities*

$$(A_i - L_i C_i)^T P (A_i - L_i C_i) - P < 0 \quad , \quad i = 1, 2, \ldots, k \quad (3)$$

then the observer (2) involves an estimation error asymptotically convergent to zero.

$\square$

Proof of Theorem 1. Let us prove the result stated in Theorem 1. The error dynamics may be computed by means of equations (1) and (2)

$$\underline{e}_{t+1} = \left(A_{\sigma(t)} - L_{\sigma(t)} C_{\sigma(t)}\right) \underline{e}_t \quad , \quad t = 0, 1, \ldots \quad .$$

If we consider the Lyapunov function $V_t = \underline{e}_t^T P \underline{e}_t$, where P is a symmetric positive definite matrix, we obtain $V_{t+1} \le V_t$, $\forall \underline{e}_t \in \mathbb{R}^n$, if

$$\left(A_{\sigma(t)} - L_{\sigma(t)} C_{\sigma(t)}\right)^T P \left(A_{\sigma(t)} - L_{\sigma(t)} C_{\sigma(t)}\right) - P < 0 \quad , \quad t = 0, 1, \ldots \quad ,$$

and then (3) may be easily derived.

■

It is important to recall that the assumption on the observabilty of the pairs (A_i, C_i), $i = 1, 2, \ldots, k$, is necessary to guarantee that each inequality in (3) may admit a solution for a given positive definite matrix P, but the existence of a common P satisfying all the inequalities is required to ensure stability. As it is difficult to find a common Lyapunov function once the gains L_i, $i = 1, 2, \ldots, k$, have been selected, we will try to find the gains and the positive definite matrix P simultaneously. Thus, the goal is to solve the following problem.

Problem 1. Find L_i, $i = 1, 2, \ldots, k$, such that there exists a symmetric positive definite matrix P solving the Lyapunov inequalities

$$(A_i - L_i C_i)^T P (A_i - L_i C_i) - P < 0 \quad , \quad i = 1, 2, \ldots, k \quad . \tag{4}$$

□

The above problem may be reduced to a simpler form that is well-suited to being solved by an LMI method. To this end, let us consider the following lemma.

Lemma 1. *Given a symmetric positive definite matrix P, an inequality*

$$(A_i - L_i C_i)^T P (A_i - L_i C_i) - P < 0 \tag{5}$$

is equivalent to

$$\begin{pmatrix} P & P A_i - Y_i C_i \\ (P A_i - Y_i C_i)^T & P \end{pmatrix} > 0 \tag{6}$$

where $L_i = P^{-1} Y_i$, $i = 1, 2, \ldots, k$.

□

Proof of Lemma 1. Let us recall the well-known Schur complement

$$\begin{pmatrix} Q & S \\ S^T & R \end{pmatrix} > 0 \Leftrightarrow R > 0, Q - S R^{-1} S^T > 0 \Leftrightarrow Q > 0, R - S^T Q^{-1} S > 0$$

where R, S, and Q are matrices of appropriate dimensions. If we apply this result by taking $Q = P$, $S = P A_i - Y_i C_i$, and $R = P$, we can easily verify that (6) gives (5) if $L_i = P^{-1} Y_i$.

∎

To sum up, the solution of Problem 1 can be obtained by solving the following LMI problem.

Problem 2. Find $P > 0$ and Y_i, $i = 1, 2, \ldots, k$, such that

$$\begin{pmatrix} P & P A_i - Y_i C_i \\ (P A_i - Y_i C_i)^T & P \end{pmatrix} > 0 \quad , \quad i = 1, 2, \ldots, k \quad , \tag{7}$$

and take the observer gains $L_i = P^{-1} Y_i$.

□

Problem 2 is simpler than Problem 1, as the former is linear in the unknown parameters, whereas the latter is quadratic at the first glance. Moreover, the formulation of Problem 2 fits the so-called LMI framework [12], which enables one to solve it by means of convex programming algorithms. Efficient numerical methods for convex optimization are available, and the reader is referred to [13] for an introduction on this subject.

3   An Enhanced Projection-Based Luenberger Observer

The Luenberger observer (2) provides an estimate of the state at time $t + 1$ using the measures available at time t by means of $\underline{y}_t$. As a matter of fact, we aim at determining the estimate $\hat{\underline{x}}_{t+1}$ using also $\underline{y}_{t+1}$ like a standard Kalman filter. To this end, a method is proposed and consists in updating the estimate given by the Luenberger observer (2) by means of the projection method [10,11], which allows one to take into account the last measures. More specifically, this estimation method is performed as follows:

$$\begin{cases} \hat{\underline{x}}_{t+1} = A_{\sigma(t)} \hat{\underline{x}}_t^+ + B_{\sigma(t)} \underline{u}_t + L_{\sigma(t)} \left(\underline{y}_t - C_{\sigma(t)} \hat{\underline{x}}_t^+ \right) & , \quad t = 0, 1, \ldots \\ \hat{\underline{x}}_{t+1}^+ = \hat{\underline{x}}_{t+1} + P^{-1} C_{\sigma(t+1)}^T \left(C_{\sigma(t+1)} P^{-1} C_{\sigma(t+1)}^T \right)^{-1} \left(\underline{y}_{t+1} - C_{\sigma(t+1)} \hat{\underline{x}}_{t+1} \right) \end{cases}$$
$$\tag{8}$$

where $\hat{\underline{x}}_0^+ = \bar{\underline{x}}_0$ is chosen "a priori", $L_{\sigma(t)}$ is the observer gain at time t, i.e., $L_{\sigma(t)} \in \mathcal{L} \triangleq \{L_1, L_2, \ldots, L_k\}$, and P is a positive definite matrix. The update that enables one to derive the new estimate $\hat{\underline{x}}_{t+1}^+$ using $\hat{\underline{x}}_{t+1}$ and the last measure vector $\underline{y}_{t+1}$ is based on a simple geometrical idea we will illustrate in the following.

For the sake of notational simplicity, let assume $\underline{x}_{t+1}$ is measured at time $t+1$ by means of $\underline{y}_{t+1} = C \underline{x}_{t+1}$ (i.e., C is used instead of $C_{\sigma(t+1)}$). Moreover, we regard $\hat{x}_{t+1}$ as an "a priori" estimate of x_{t+1} at time $t+1$ and want to determine a new estimate $\hat{x}_{t+1}^{+}$ such that $\|e_{t+1}^{+}\| \leq \|e_{t+1}\|$, where $e_{t+1}^{+} \overset{\triangle}{=} x_{t+1} - \hat{x}_{t+1}^{+}$. The state space can be decomposed into two orthogonal subspaces, like, for example, the null space of C (i.e., $N(C) \overset{\triangle}{=} \{x \in \mathbb{R}^n : Cx = 0\}$) and its orthogonal space $N(C)^{\perp P}$ using the scalar product $<x, z>_P \overset{\triangle}{=} x^T P z$, $x, z \in \mathbb{R}^n$ (this scalar product is well-defined as the matrix P is positive definite). If P is taken equal to the identity matrix, it is easy to verify that $N(C)^{\perp}$ is $R(C^T)$ (i.e., the space spanned by linear combinations of the columns of the matrix C^T).

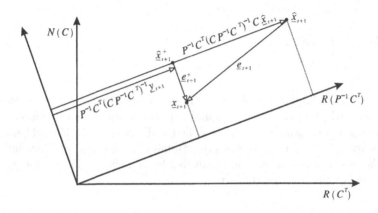

Fig. 2. Sketch to explain the projection method (C replaces $C_{\sigma(t+1)}$).

The decomposition can be accomplished by means of the subspaces given by $R(P^{-1}C^T)$ and its orthogonal complement, instead of $N(C)^{\perp}$ and $N(C)$. The reason for using this subspace decomposition concerns the stability of the estimation error as it will be clarified in the following. Fig. 2 provides a meaningful geometrical interpretation of the projection method and enables one to illustrate the rationale for the proposed approach. As can be noticed in Fig. 2, the projection of x_{t+1} on $R(P^{-1}C^T)$ is equal to $P^{-1}C^T (CP^{-1}C^T)^{-1} C x_{t+1}$, i.e., $P^{-1}C^T (CP^{-1}C^T)^{-1} y_{t+1}$. Note that the projection matrix $P^{-1}C^T (CP^{-1}C^T)^{-1}$ is well-defined as the matrices $C_i \in \mathbb{R}^{m \times n}$, $i = 1, 2, \ldots, k$ (i.e., C in this case) have been assumed of full rank $m < n$. In practice, the estimate of x_{t+1} is obtained by projecting $\hat{x}_{t+1}$ on the subspace corresponding to the new measure y_{t+1}, which provides a new estimate $\hat{x}_{t+1}^{+}$ such that the corresponding estimation error e_{t+1}^{+} is smaller than that of the previous error, i.e., $\|e_{t+1}^{+}\| \leq \|e_{t+1}\|$. A pictorial representation of the observer (8) is shown in Fig. 3.

As far as it concerns the stability of estimation error associated to (8), we can state the following result.

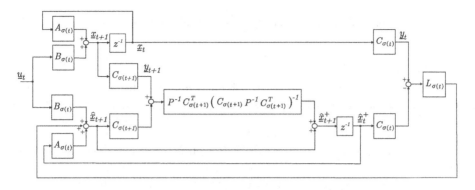

Fig. 3. Scheme of a switching projection-based observer.

Theorem 2. *Consider the system (1) and assume that the pairs* (A_i, C_i), $i = 1, 2, \ldots, k$, *are observable. If there exists a symmetric positive definite matrix* P *as the solution of the algebraic Lyapunov inequalities*

$$(A_i - L_i C_i)^T P (A_i - L_i C_i) - P < 0 \quad , \quad i = 1, 2, \ldots, k \tag{9}$$

then the estimator (8) involves an estimation error asymptotically convergent to zero.

$\square$

Proof of Theorem 2. The estimation error before the projection update is given by

$$\underline{e}_{t+1} = \left(A_{\sigma(t)} - L_{\sigma(t)} C_{\sigma(t)}\right) \underline{e}_t^+ \quad , \quad t = 0, 1, \ldots \quad . \tag{10}$$

As a consequence of the update based on the measure $\underline{y}_{t+1}$, the estimation error becomes $\underline{e}_{t+1}^+ = \left[I - P^{-1} C_{\sigma(t+1)}^T \left(C_{\sigma(t+1)} P^{-1} C_{\sigma(t+1)}^T\right)^{-1} C_{\sigma(t+1)}\right] \underline{e}_{t+1}$. In order to prove that the resulting estimator is stable, consider the Lyapunov functions $V_t = \underline{e}_t^T P \underline{e}_t$ and $V_t^+ = \underline{e}_t^{+T} P \underline{e}_t^+$, where P is a symmetric positive definite matrix. The goal is to demonstrate that the estimation error $\underline{e}_t^+$ converges asymptotically to zero by proving that V_t^+ is decreasing in t, $\forall \underline{e}_t^+ \in \mathbb{R}^n$. To this end, it is sufficient to demonstrate that $V_{t+1}^+ \leq V_{t+1}$, $t = 0, 1, \ldots$ as, from (10), it is obvious that $V_{t+1} \leq V_t^+$, $\forall \underline{e}_t^+ \in \mathbb{R}^n$ if the Lyapunov inequalities (9) are satisfied (see also the proof of Theorem 1). Thus, let us consider

$$V_{t+1}^+ = \left[\underline{e}_{t+1} - P^{-1} C_{\sigma(t+1)}^T \left(C_{\sigma(t+1)} P^{-1} C_{\sigma(t+1)}^T\right)^{-1} C_{\sigma(t+1)} \underline{e}_{t+1}\right]^T P \left[\underline{e}_{t+1}\right.$$
$$\left. - P^{-1} C_{\sigma(t+1)}^T \left(C_{\sigma(t+1)} P^{-1} C_{\sigma(t+1)}^T\right)^{-1} C_{\sigma(t+1)} \underline{e}_{t+1}\right]$$
$$= V_{t+1} - \underline{e}_{t+1}^T C_{\sigma(t+1)}^T \left(C_{\sigma(t+1)} P^{-1} C_{\sigma(t+1)}^T\right)^{-1} C_{\sigma(t+1)} \underline{e}_{t+1}$$

and we can conclude since $-\underline{e}_{t+1}^T C_{\sigma(t+1)}^T \left(C_{\sigma(t+1)} P^{-1} C_{\sigma(t+1)}^T \right)^{-1} C_{\sigma(t+1)} \underline{e}_{t+1} \leq 0$, $\forall \underline{e}_{t+1} \in \mathbb{R}^n$.

∎

The design of the observer (8) can be accomplished by solving the related Problem 2 in order to satisfy (9) as the requirements to apply the projection update are only that P is a positive definite matrix and the matrices $C_i \in \mathbb{R}^{m \times n}$, $i = 1, 2, \ldots, k$, are of full rank.

The projection method has been successfully applied to the estimation of a class of continuous-time nonlinear systems with asynchronous measurements [14]. Moreover, the performance improvements provided by the projection method will be highlighted by means of the simulation results presented in the next section.

4   Simulation Results

In order to show the effectiveness of the proposed estimation methods and the feasibility of the related LMI design procedure, let us consider the simple mechanical system depicted in Fig. 4.

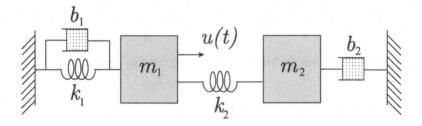

Fig. 4. Simple mechanical system.

The continuous-time dynamics of the system is given by the following equation:

$$\begin{cases} \underline{\dot{x}}(t) = A \underline{x}(t) + B u(t) \\ \underline{y}(t) = C_{\sigma(t)} \underline{x}(t) \end{cases} \tag{11}$$

where $\underline{x}(t) \triangleq [x_1(t), x_2(t), x_3(t), x_4(t)]^T \in \mathbb{R}^4$ is the state vector and $u(t) \in \mathbb{R}$ is the scalar input. More specifically, $x_1(t)$ is the position and of the mass m_1, $x_2(t)$ is the speed of m_1, $x_3(t)$ is the position of the mass m_2, and $x_4(t)$ is the speed of m_2. The matrices A and B are as follows:

$$A \triangleq \begin{pmatrix} 0 & 1 & 0 & 1 \\ -(k_1 + k_2)/m_1 & -b_1/m_1 & -k_2/m_1 & 0 \\ 0 & 0 & 0 & 1 \\ k_2/m_2 & 0 & -k_2/m_2 & -b_2/m_2 \end{pmatrix} \quad B \triangleq \begin{pmatrix} 0 \\ 1/m_1 \\ 0 \\ 0 \end{pmatrix}$$

where the parameters are $k_1 = 0.0642\,Kg/s^2$, $k_2 = 0.1925\,Kg/s^2$, $m_1 = 5.1962\,Kg$, $m_2 = 1.7321\,Kg$, $b_1 = 0.8660\,Kg/s$, and $b_2 = 0.1732\,Kg/s$. The system is switching in that the matrix $C_{\sigma(t)}$ can assume values in the set $\{C_1, C_2, C_3, C_4\}$ with $C_1 = (1,0,0,0,)$, $C_2 = (0,1,0,0)$, $C_3 = (0,0,1,0)$, and $C_4 = (0,0,0,1)$. The choice among the four candidate measurement equations is random, with the same probability of occurrence. The system is observable with any of the four measurement equations. The input $u(t)$ was taken to be equal to a sinusoidal force, i.e., $u(t) = k_u \sin(w\,t)$, where, for each simulation run, k_u and w were randomly chosen in $[0.0, 4.0]\,N$ and $[0.1, 0.6]\,rad/s$, respectively. Moreover, the initial states were randomly Gaussian distributed around $\underline{0}$ with standard deviations $5.0, 2.0, 5.0$, and 2.0 for x_1, x_2, x_3, and x_4, respectively.

A corresponding discrete-time model was obtained for the same system discretizing equation (11) by means of a simple Euleur's approximation with a time step equal to $0.1s$. In the discrete-time setting, the standard routines of the Matlab LMI Control Toolbox [15] provided the following solution to Problem 2:

$$P = 10^3 \begin{pmatrix} 0.1331 & 0.1175 & -0.0873 & -0.0159 \\ 0.1175 & 1.4445 & -0.0371 & -0.1386 \\ -0.0873 & -0.0371 & 0.0960 & 0.0351 \\ -0.0159 & -0.1386 & 0.0351 & 0.8227 \end{pmatrix}$$

$$L_1 = \begin{pmatrix} 1.0028 \\ -0.0623 \\ 0.9016 \\ -0.0280 \end{pmatrix} \quad L_2 = \begin{pmatrix} -1.5816 \\ 1.0246 \\ -1.1822 \\ 0.1874 \end{pmatrix} \quad L_3 = \begin{pmatrix} 0.6846 \\ -0.0325 \\ 1.0065 \\ -0.0386 \end{pmatrix} \quad L_4 = \begin{pmatrix} 0.4669 \\ 0.1131 \\ -0.6561 \\ 0.9940 \end{pmatrix}.$$

The root mean square (RMS) error was considered as a performance index. This error for the scalar variable $x_i(t)$ with respect to its estimate $\hat{x}_i(t)$ at the time t for N different trials is defined as

$$RMS_i(t) \triangleq \sqrt{\sum_{j=1}^{N} \frac{\left[x_i^j(t) - \hat{x}_i^j(t)\right]^2}{N}} \tag{12}$$

where $x_i^j(t)$ is the value of the variable in the j-th run, $\hat{x}_i^j(t)$ is the estimate of $x_i^j(t)$, and $i = 1, 2, 3$, and 4. In Fig. 5, the simulation results obtained with the two proposed observers using the above-written gains and with initial estimated state equal to $\underline{0}$ are shown as far as it regards the RMS estimation error on 500 trials (i.e., $N = 500$) with different choices of k_u, w, initial state vectors, and switching sequences. As can be noticed in Fig. 5, the enhanced Luenberger observer exhibits a faster convergence rate. The trajectories of the true and estimated state variables for a single random-chosen simulation run are shown in Fig. 6.

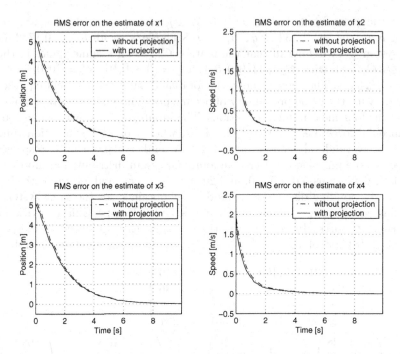

Fig. 5. RMS estimation errors of the switching observers.

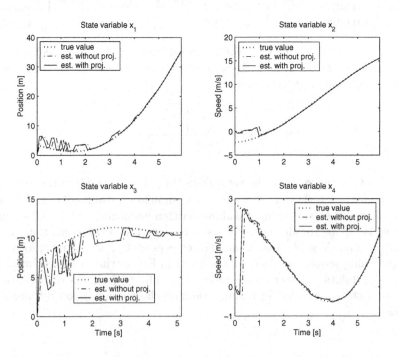

Fig. 6. True values and estimates of the switching observers for a single realization.

5   Conclusions

In this paper, estimation for a class of hybrid systems has been considered. First, we have addressed the problem of designing a Luenberger observer for a class of switching discrete-time linear systems. Conditions ensuring the stability of the error dynamics for such an estimator have been found and an LMI formulation has been presented to synthesize the gains in a straightforward, efficient way. Second, an enhanced Luenberger observer has been proposed to perform estimation using also the last available measures. The stability of the estimation error for this modified Luenberger observer has been proved under conditions that can be ensured by solving the same LMI problem of the first estimator. The simulation results obtained with such observers for a simple mechanical system show both that, as expected, the proposed estimators are stable and that the enhanced Luenberger observer results in higher performance.

Future work will concern the application of the proposed approach to real cases (see [14]), where conventional estimation methods based on Kalman filtering may perform poorly. Moreover, further theoretical investigations will regard the extension of the switching observer to a more general framework, e.g., with noises acting on the system and measurement equations and nonlinearities affecting the dynamics.

References

1. Ackerson, G. A., Fu, K. S.: On state estimation in switching environments. IEEE Trans. on Automatic Control. **15** (1970) 10-17
2. Zhang, Q.: Hybrid filtering for linear systems with non-Gaussian disturbances. IEEE Trans. on Automatic Control. **45** (1999) 50-61
3. Doucet, A., Logothetis, A., and Krishnamurthy, V.: Stochastic sampling algorithms for state estimation of jump markov linear systems. IEEE Trans. on Automatic Control. **45** (2000) 188-202
4. Bar-Shalom, Y., Li, X.: Estimation and Tracking. Artech House, Boston-London (1993)
5. Liu, Y.: Switching observer design for uncertain nonlinear systems. IEEE Trans. on Automatic Control. **42** (1997) 1699-1703
6. Yao, Y. X., Darouach, M., and Schaefers J.: Simultaneous observation of linear systems. IEEE Trans. on Automatic Control. **40** (1995) 696-699
7. Ye, H., Michel, A. N., and Hou, L.: Stability theory for hybrid dynamical systems. IEEE Trans. on Automatic Control, **43** (1998) 461-474
8. Branicky, M. S.: Multiple Lyapunov functions and other analysis tools for switched and hybrid systems. IEEE Trans. on Automatic Control. **43** (1998) 475-482
9. Liberzon, D., Morse, A. S.: Basic problems in stability and design of switched systems. IEEE Control Systems Magazine. **19** (1999) 59-70
10. Sur, J.: State Observers for Linear Systems with Quantized Outputs. PhD thesis, University of California, Santa Barbara (1996)
11. Sur, J., Healey, A. J.: A multi sensor asynchronous projection algorithm filter (PAF) for AUV navigation. in 10th Symposium on Unmanned Untethered Submersible Technology, Durham, New Hampshire, (1997) 88-100

12. Boyd, S., Crusius, C., and Hanson, A.: Control applications of nonlinear convex programming. J. Proc. Control. **8** (1998) 313-324
13. Boyd, S., El Ghaoui, L., Feron, E., and Balakrishnan, V.: Linear Matrix Inequalities in System and Control Theory. Studies in Applied Mathematics. **15** (1994) SIAM, Philadelphia, PA
14. Alessandri, A., Coletta, P.: Navigation for underwater vehicles based on nonlinear asynchronous estimation. Proc. American Control Conference, Chicago, IL (2000) 85-89
15. Gahinet, P., Nemirovski, A., and Laub, A. J., and Chilali, M.: LMI Control Toolbox User's Guide. The Math Works Inc. (1985)

Hybrid Modeling and Simulation of Biomolecular Networks

Rajeev Alur, Calin Belta, Franjo Ivančić, Vijay Kumar, Max Mintz,
George J. Pappas, Harvey Rubin, and Jonathan Schug

University of Pennsylvania
biohybrid@grasp.cis.upenn.edu

Abstract. In a biological cell, cellular functions and the genetic regulatory apparatus are implemented and controlled by a network of chemical reactions in which regulatory proteins can control genes that produce other regulators, which in turn control other genes. Further, the feedback pathways appear to incorporate switches that result in changes in the dynamic behavior of the cell. This paper describes a hybrid systems approach to modeling the intra-cellular network using continuous differential equations to model the feedback mechanisms and mode-switching to describe the changes in the underlying dynamics. We use two case studies to illustrate a modular approach to modeling such networks and describe the architectural and behavioral hierarchy in the underlying models. We describe these models using CHARON [2], a language that allows formal description of hybrid systems. We provide preliminary simulation results that demonstrate how our approach can help biologists in their analysis of noisy genetic circuits. Finally we describe our agenda for future work that includes the development of models and simulation for stochastic hybrid systems.[1]

1 Introduction

In order to survive, organisms continuously monitor their surroundings and, if necessary, adjust traffic through simple or complex combinations of genetic and metabolic networks to respond to alterations in local conditions. Local conditions include both the physical environment, for example, temperature (the heat and cold shock response), nutrient and energy source concentrations (the stringent response), light (circadian rhythms), cell density (quorum sensing response) as well as the molecular environment of individual regulatory components. Examples of the latter include intracellular concentrations of transcription factors and allosteric effectors. The availability of complete genomic information for a wide variety of organisms and the consequent attention on proteomics has dramatically increased the number of systems and components of systems that are involved in these sensing and responding activities [4,10]. Understanding how

---

[1] This research was supported in part by DARPA/ITO Mobies project (grant number F33615-00-C-1707) and NSF grant CDS-97-03220.

M.D. Di Benedetto, A. Sangiovanni-Vincentelli (Eds.): HSCC 2001, LNCS 2034, pp. 19–32, 2001.

these biological systems are integrated and regulated and how the regulation may be influenced, possibly for therapeutic purposes, remains a significant challenge.

In this paper we model and simulate examples of genetic and metabolic networks using a hybrid systems approach that combines concepts and tools from control theory and computer science. First we analyze a previously published plasmid-based genetic network that was designed and synthesized using three repressor transcription factors where one repressor negatively regulates the production of a subsequent repressor [7]. Then we model a biologically important genetic network that controls the quorum sensing response, an adaptive response of certain gram negative bacteria to local population density [13,17]. The quorum sensing response controls the luminescent behavior in certain strains of Vibrio which has been linked to the normal development of the bacterial host [18] as well as to medically important phenomena such as biofilm formation by Pseudomonas aerugenosa, an organism that can cause overwhelming pneumonia and septic shock [11,20].

2   Modeling

The genetic circuits and biomolecular networks considered here and elsewhere are remarkably similar to hybrid systems encountered in engineering, for example embedded systems. In particular, it is worth noting the following three key features:

Concurrency and communication. At the intra-cellular level, proteins and mRNAs are agents communicating with each other and influencing each other's behavior. At the inter-cellular level, cells can be viewed as networked agents interacting with each other via different communication mechanisms.
Discrete and continuous behaviors. At the lowest level, the evolution of entities such as proteins can be described by differential equations. Discreteness arises in two ways. First, a certain activity may be triggered only when the concentration of enabling quantities is above the desired threshold. This leads to discrete switching between active and dormant states. Second, different models may be appropriate at different levels of concentration.
Stochastic behavior. Evolution of entities is not deterministic, and is better captured by stochastic models that allow for uncertainty and noise.

These characteristics are typical of high-level models of embedded software such as autonomous communicating mobile robots. For describing such systems, we have developed the language CHARON [2] which incorporates ideas from concurrency theory (languages such as CSP [12]), object-oriented software design notations (such as Statecharts [9] and UML [3]), and formal models for hybrid systems (such as hybrid automata [1] and hybrid I/O automata [15]). The key features of CHARON are:

Architectural hierarchy. The building block for describing the system architecture is an *agent* that communicates with its environment via shared variables. The language supports the operations of *composition* of agents to model concurrency, *hiding* of variables to restrict sharing of information, and *instantiation* of agents to support reuse.

Behavior hierarchy. The building block for describing flow of control inside an atomic agent is a *mode*. A mode is basically a hierarchical state machine, that is, a mode can have submodes and transitions connecting them. Variables can be declared locally inside any mode with standard scoping rules for visibility. Modes can be connected to each other only via well-defined entry and exit points. We allow *sharing* of modes so that the same mode definition can be instantiated in multiple contexts. Finally, to support *exceptions*, the language allows group transitions from default exit points that are applicable to all enclosing modes.

Discrete updates. Discrete updates are specified by *guarded actions* labeling transitions connecting the modes. Actions can have calls to externally defined Java functions which can be used to write complex data manipulations. It also allows us to mimic stochastic aspects through randomization.

Continuous updates. Some of the variables in CHARON can be declared *analog*, and they flow continuously during continuous updates that model passage of time. The evolution of analog variables can be constrained in three ways: *differential* constraints (e.g. by equations such as $\dot{x} = f(x, u)$), *algebraic* constraints (e.g. by equations such as $y = g(x, u)$), and *invariants* (e.g. $|x - y| \leq \varepsilon$) which limit the allowed durations of flows. Such constraints can be declared at different levels of the mode hierarchy.

Modular features of CHARON allow succinct and structured description of complex systems. Similar features are supported by the languages SHIFT [6] and STATEFLOW (see www.mathworks.com). In CHARON, modularity is not only apparent in syntax, but we are developing analysis tools (such as simulation) that exploit this modularity. Furthermore, CHARON has formal foundations supporting compositional refinement calculus which allows relating different models of the system in mathematically precise manner. A formal mathematical description allows us to develop tools for computing equilibria, for reachability analysis and for analyzing properties like stability and reachability.

In the next two sections, we will briefly describe case studies that we have used to investigate the hybrid systems approach to modeling biological systems, and the applications of CHARON to these systems. We will also illustrate our approach by providing preliminary simulation results.

3   A Repressilator Network

As noted in [5], most biomolecular systems of interest involve many interactions connected through positive and negative feedback loops and an understanding of their dynamics is hard to obtain. In this section we will describe the modeling of a specific biomolecular network. We will model a repressilator system described in [7]. First we provide some biological background information and describe the protein network used in [7], and then describe the models of the protein network, including examples of CHARON models.[2]

3.1   The Basic Phenomena

In the synthetic oscillatory network described in [7], networks of interacting biomolecules carry out many essential functions in living cells. But the design principles of the functioning of such networks still remain poorly understood–even in relatively simple systems [14]. The authors proposed the design and construction of a synthetic protein network implementing a particular function. Their motivation is that such "rational network design" may lead to the engineering of new cellular behaviors and to improved understanding of naturally occuring networks.

The repressilator system described in [7] contains three proteins, namely lacI, tetR, and cI. The protein lacI represses the protein tetR, tetR represses cI, whereas cI represses lacI, thus completing a feedback system called a repressilator system. The dynamics of the network depend on the transcription rates, translation rates, and decay rates of proteins and messenger RNAs. Depending on the values of the different parameters in the model, the system might converge to a stable limit cycle or become unstable.

3.2   Approaches to Modeling

It is well known in mechanics and thermodynamics that there are two different approaches to modeling systems such as the repressilator system. At reasonably high molecular concentrations, one can adopt continuum models which lend themselves to deterministic models involving ordinary and partial differential equations. At lower concentrations, the discrete molecular interactions become important and deterministic models are difficult to obtain [8].

The Deterministic, Continuous Approximation. We will consider the three repressor protein concentrations $p_i, i \in P = \{\text{lacI}, \text{tetR}, \text{cI}\}$ and their corresponding mRNA concentrations $m_i, i \in P$ as continuous dynamic variables. The system kinetics are determined by the following six coupled first-order differential equations.

$$\frac{dm_i}{dt} = -m_i + \frac{\alpha}{1 + p_j^n} + \alpha_0$$

$$\frac{dp_i}{dt} = -\beta(p_i - m_i)$$

$$(i, j) \in \{(\text{lacI,cI}), (\text{tetR,lacI}), (\text{cI,tetR})\}$$

---

[2] For more information on CHARON or sample CHARON code, please check http://www.cis.upenn.edu/mobies/charon/ or contact ivancic@seas.upenn.edu.

The equations use various constants. The leakiness of the promoter α is the number of protein copies per cell produced from a given promoter type during continuous growth in the presence of saturating repressor amounts. During the absence of the repressor, we have $\alpha + \alpha_0$ number of protein copies per cell. The ratio of the protein decay rate to the mRNA decay rate is denoted by β, while n stands for the so called Hill coefficient.

The Stochastic, Discrete Approximation. The continuous analysis neglects the discrete nature of molecular components and the stochastic character of their interaction [7]. Following [7], we adopt the stochastic approximation as described by Gillespie in [8]. The various proteins and mRNAs are modeled by discrete variables corresponding to the number of molecules measuring concentration, and are updated at discrete time intervals by stochastic rules.

3.3   CHARON Model

In this section we will present the repressilator system models as described in [7] using the CHARON language. We will present many of the advantages that the CHARON language has to offer for modeling such biomolecular models.

Our model will define a generic protein model as an agent in CHARON. We will instantiate this agent model to obtain the three proteins lacI, tetR, and cI. The approximation models will be implemented inside the modes of the protein agent. To present another feature of our language, we will also describe a combination of the discrete and the continuous model into one modeling system.

The Protein Agent in the Continuous Approximation. In this section we will describe a CHARON model of a generic protein agent. We have a continuous input variable which represents the repressor protein concentration p_R. This means, that the environment of this protein agent supplies the value of this variable, and it cannot be changed by the protein agent. The protein agent has a continuous private variable representing the messenger RNA concentration. Private variables cannot be seen outside the agent and can be updated internally for internal use only. The output of the protein agent is a continuous variable representing the protein concentration. Output variables are updated by the agent, and can be used as input variables to other agents. The generic protein agent has parameters $\alpha_0, \alpha, \beta, n, p_0$, and m_0. By instantiating these parameters with values, we can obtain instantiated protein agents representing a specific protein. The parameters p_0 and m_0 will be used for initialization purposes and stand for the initial protein concentration and the initial messenger RNA concentration respectively. The following represents the corresponding CHARON code.

```
agent contProtein (real p0 , m0 , alpha0 , alpha , beta , n){
    write analog real p = p0 ; //protein concentration
    read analog real pR ; //repressor protein concentration
    private analog real m = m0 ; //messenger RNA concentration
    mode cont = continuous ( alpha0 , alpha , beta , n ) ; }
```

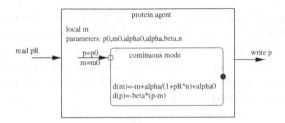

Fig. 1. A generic protein agent for the continuous approximation model

We still need to define the behavior of the agent. The behavior is described by the modes of the agent. The behavior of the generic protein agent is defined in `cont`, which is an instantiation of a generic `continuous` mode defined by the following code. A graphical version of the generic protein model can be found in Figure 1.

```
mode continuous (real alpha0 , alpha , beta , n){
    write analog real p ; //protein concentration
    read analog real pR ; //repressor protein concentration
    private analog real m ; //messenger RNA concentration
    diff mRNA { d(m) = -m + alpha / (1+pR^n) + alpha0 }
    diff proteinConcentration { d(p) = -beta * (p-m) } }
```

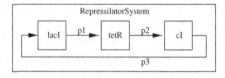

Fig. 2. Composed repressilator system using the instantiated generic protein agent

Instantiation and Concurrency. We defined a generic protein agent in the previous section. We have to instantiate this generic agent model to get the three proteins used in the system. We also want the three proteins lacI, tetR, and cI to run in parallel and to influence each other. Notice the use of renaming of variables to couple the three instantiated protein agents to influence each other. A graphical version of the composed system is illustrated in Figure 2. The following represents the corresponding CHARON code using some values for the parameters. A simulation trace generated by the CHARON tool-set is given in Figure 3.

```
agent RepressilatorSystem (){
    private analog real p1 , p2 , p3 ;
    agent lacI = contProtein ( ... ) [ p , pR := p1 , p3 ] ;
    agent tetR = contProtein ( ... ) [ p , pR := p2 , p1 ] ;
    agent cI   = contProtein ( ... ) [ p , pR := p3 , p2 ] ; }
```

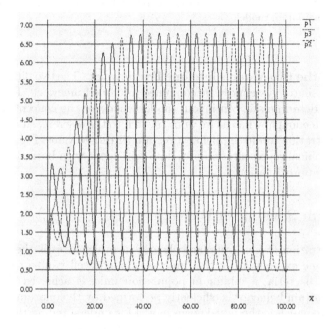

Fig. 3. Simulation trace for the repressilator system showing stable oscillations for the three protein concentration p_1, p_2, p_3 over time.

The Protein Agent in the Discrete Approximation. In this section we will present a possible model for a discrete approximation of a protein agent. As we did it for the continuous case, we will again define a generic protein agent, that can be instantiated to build a system of proteins. Our model works as follows. We have an integer variable n that keeps track of the number of protein molecules which is the output of the agent. The input to the agent is the number of repressor protein molecules n_R. Depending on various parameters, we want to increase or decrease the number of protein molecules by one at a time. The basic idea is to use stochastic simulation as described in [8]. The parameters that influence the stochastic simulation are binding and unbinding of proteins on two-sided promoters, the protein and mRNA decay rates, and translation.

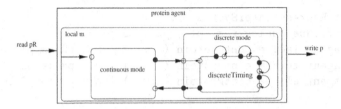

Fig. 4. A generic protein agent for the combined framework using continuous and discrete approximation model

Combining the two Models into one Framework. The two different models for the repressilator system can be combined into one framework. The basic idea is to use the deterministic continuous model whenever the concentration of the protein is high enough, whereas we would switch to the discrete, stochastic model if the concentration would fall below a certain threshold value. Figure 4 gives an intuitive graphical representation of the protein agent with both the continuous and discrete approximation.

4   Quorum Sensing in Bacteria

A good illustration of multicellular behavior in prokaryotes is the cell-density-dependent gene expression. In this process, a single cell is able to sense when a *quorum* of bacteria, a minimum population unit, is achieved. Under these conditions, certain behavior is efficiently performed by the quorum, such as bioluminescence, which is the best known model for understanding the mechanism of cell-density-dependent gene expression. In this section, we will describe a hybrid system model that captures the changes in dynamics of the biochemical reactions observed in the literature [13,16,17].

4.1   The Basic Phenomena

Vibrio fischeri is a marine bacterium that can be found both as a free-living organism and as a symbiont of some marine fish and squid. As a free-living organism, *V. fisheri* exists at low densities (less than 500 cells per ml of seawater) and appears to be non-luminescent. As a symbiont, the bacteria live at high densities and are, usually, luminescent. In a liquid culture, the bacteria's level of luminescence is low until the culture reaches mid to late exponential phase. A dramatic increase in luminescence is observed at that time due to the transcriptional activation of the *lux* genes. Once the bacteria reach stationary phase, the level of luminescence decreases.

The *lux* regulon [17] contains two operons, O_L and O_R (see Figure 5). The left operon O_L contains the *luxR* gene encoding the protein LuxR, a transcriptional activator of the system. The right operon O_R contains seven genes *luxICDABEG*.

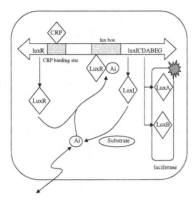

Fig. 5. A portion of DNA emphasizing luxR and luxICDABEG genes and the binding sites for LuxR complex and CRP

Protein LuxI, the product of the *luxI* gene is required for endogenous production of *autoinducer*, a small molecule capable of diffusing in and out of the cell membrane. Genes *luxA* and *luxB* encode two subunits of luciferase. The trio *luxC*, *luxD*, and *luxE* code for the subunits of a protein complex which provides an aldehyde substrate for luciferase. The function of *luxG* is unknown. The autoinducer Ai binds to protein LuxR to form a complex Co. The two operons are separated by a regulatory region that contains a binding site for the cyclic AMP receptor protein CRP and a binding site for the complex Co.

The transcription of *luxR* is regulated by both CRP and Co. We can distinguish among the following three different cases:

- **Case O_L-1** In the absence of the autoinducer, CRP activates O_L expression by initiating two RNA transcripts.
- **Case O_L-2** At low autoinducer concentrations, *luxR* transcription is stimulated by increasing CRP-dependent transcription and by Co-dependent transcription from another transcriptional start site.
- **Case O_L-3** At high autoinducer concentrations, *luxR* transcription is repressed through a second, weaker Co binding site located in *luxD*.

Likewise, transcription of O_R is regulated by both CRP and Co. We distinguish two different cases:

- **Case O_R-1** In the absence of autoinducer, CRP represses O_R transcription.
- **Case O_R-2** In the presence of autoinducer, Co activates transcription of O_R.

These cases will be interpreted as modes as seen later in the paper.

4.2   Mathematical Model

In this section, we develop a mathematical model for the luminescence phenomenon in one bacterium of *V. fischeri*, describing the concentrations of the relevant mRNA's, proteins, and small molecules. As described in Section 4.1 the mechanism of transcription activation of both operons is highly dependent on the concentration of autoinducer, so the time evolution of the system cannot be described by one set of continuous differential equations.[3] Combining cases for O_L and O_R given in the previous section, yields three modes, which we call *OFF*, *POS* and *NEG*. The transitions between modes are governed by the level of internal autoinducer which we represent by [Ai]. Mode *OFF* corresponds to very low or zero concentration of autoinducer ([Ai] $\leq$ [Ai]$_-$) within the bacterium and no luminescence is observed. The system is in mode *POS* when the concentration of internal autoinducer is low ([Ai]$_-$ $\leq$ [Ai] $\leq$ [Ai]$_+$). This mode corresponds to positive growth and increasing concentration of autoinducer. Luminescence is observed, as are higher concentrations of proteins LuxA, LuxB, LuxC, LuxD, and LuxE. The transition to mode *NEG* (negative growth) occurs at high levels of autoinducer ([Ai] > [Ai]$_+$).

We use the following rate equation to describe the concentration for any molecular species (mRNA, protein, protein complex, or small molecule) [19]:

$$\frac{d[x]}{dt} = \text{synthesis} - \text{decay} \pm \text{transformation} \pm \text{transport} \qquad (1)$$

The *synthesis* term represents transcription for mRNA and translation for proteins. The *decay* term represents a first order degradation process. The *transformation* term describes reactions such as cleavage or ligand-binding that do not destroy the protein, but do remove its ability to participate in specific reactions. Finally, molecular species may participate in *transport* processes, like passive diffusion or active transport through a membrane.

The biomolecular system can be described in a nine dimensional state space. The nine variables, $x_1, x_2, \ldots, x_9$, describe the concentrations of different molecules as follows:

x_1 = mRNA transcribed from O_L,
x_2 = mRNA transcribed from O_R,
x_3 = protein LuxR,
x_4 = protein LuxI,
x_5 = protein LuxA,
x_6 = protein LuxB,
x_7 = autoinducer inside the bacterium Ai,
x_8 = LuxR:Ai complex Co,
x_9 = autoinducer outside the bacterium Ai$_{ex}$,

where Ai is the dimensionless version of [Ai].

For simplicity, we have assumed that the concentrations of CRP and of the substrate necessary for endogenous production of Ai are constant. Further, we have neglected the decay rates for chemical compounds. Finally, we assume that

---

[3] In [13], the differential equations for the low autoinducer concentration are described. The model presented here describes a wider range of operating conditions.

the concentrations of LuxC, LuxD, and LuxE are similar to those of LuxA and LuxB.

The (continuous) differential equations for each mode are of the form $\dot{x} = f^i(x)$ where $x = [x_1, x_2, \ldots, x_9]^T \in \mathbb{R}^9$, $f^i = [f_1^i, f_2^i, \ldots, f_9^i]$, and $i \in \{OFF, POS, NEG\}$. The components of the vector fields are explicitly given by:

$$f_1^{OFF} = \eta_1 \left(\frac{1}{2}c - x_1 \right)$$

$$f_1^{POS} = \frac{\eta_1}{4} \left(3c + \frac{x_8^{\nu_{81}}}{\kappa_{81}^{\nu_{81}} + x_8^{\nu_{81}}} - 4x_1 \right)$$

$$f_1^{NEG} = -\eta_1 x_1$$

$$f_2^{OFF} = -\eta_2 x_2$$

$$f_2^{POS} = f_2^{NEG} = \eta_2 \left(\frac{x_8^{\nu_{82}}}{\kappa_{82}^{\nu_{82}} + x_8^{\nu_{82}}} - x_2 \right)$$

$$f_3^i = \eta_3 (x_1 - x_3) - r_{37,Ai} x_3 x_7$$

$$f_4^i = \eta_4 (x_2 - x_4) - r_4 x_4$$

$$f_5^i = \eta_5 (x_2 - x_5)$$

$$f_6^i = \eta_6 (x_2 - x_6)$$

$$f_7^i = -\eta_7 x_7 + r_4 x_4 - r_{mem} (x_7 - x_9) - r_{37,R} x_3 x_7$$

$$f_8^i = -\eta_8 x_8 + r_{37,Ai} x_3 x_7$$

$$f_9^i = -\eta_7 x_9 + r_{mem}(x_7 - x_9) + u$$

where, in the last seven equations f_j^i is independent of the mode. All the quantities in the above model are non-dimensional. $\eta_i = T_0/H_i$ where T_0 is the characteristic time constant of the system and H_i is the half-life (inverse of the decay rate) of molecule x_i. ν_{ij} is a cooperativity coefficient while κ_{ij} describes the potency of the regulation of the transcription of mRNA j by protein i. r denotes transformation and transfer rates. For example r_{mem} is the transfer rate of autoinducer through the membrane of the cell while $r_{37,R}$ and $r_{37,Ai}$ are transformation rates obtained by non-dimensionalizing the binding rate of the reaction between Ai and LuxR in two different ways. c is dependent on the concentration of CRP and its affinity to the corresponding binding site, and, as stated earlier, is assumed to be constant. Finally, u emulates an external source of Ai and is used to simulate the sensitivity of the bacterium to changes of autoinducer concentration in the exterior.

We regard u as an input to our system. Since proteins LuxA and LuxB are subunits of luciferase, which produces luminescence, it is reasonable to assume that the level of luminescence is proportional to the product of the concentrations of LuxA and LuxB, which we choose to be the output of the system.

4.3 CHARON Model

The behavioral hierarchy in CHARON (see Figure 6) is characterized by three different behaviors which are represented by three different modes, namely OFF,

POS, and *NEG*. Many of the differential equations governing the dynamics of the system are shared between the modes. We will introduce the notion of mode hierarchy to extract the shared constraints. Through the notion of submodes and scoping, we can simplify the description of the respective modes *OFF*, *POS*, and *NEG*.

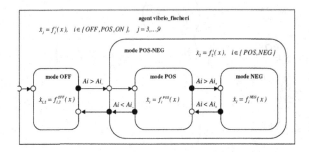

Fig. 6. CHARON structure of the system

Figure 7 illustrates the response (*i.e.*, luminescence) of the bacterium to a perturbation in the concentration of external autoinducer that takes the form of a rectangular pulse. The magnitude of the step has been chosen to make the system go through all three modes. The results confirm the experimental observations [17]: luminescence increases during mode *POS* and decreases in mode *NEG*; there is no luminescence in mode *OFF*. The switch history and the time evolution of the concentrations of the significant molecules in the system are also shown. In mode *OFF*, all molecules decay to zero, except for mRNA O_L and the corresponding protein R, as expected. For a short time, in mode *POS*, all the concentrations increase until the internal autoinducer reaches a high concentration, when the system is switched to mode *NEG*. In this last mode, everything decays to zero, except for internal autoinducer which can reach a stable non-zero value dependent on the size of the step of external autoinducer.

5   Conclusions

In this paper we have shown that biological cellular networks can be naturally modeled as hybrid systems. In particular, the protein repressilator system switches between a continuous deterministic model at high concentrations, and a timed, discrete, stochastic model at low concentrations. Similarly, the luminescence control of *Vibrio fischeri* is naturally modeled as a multi-modal hybrid system, resulting in simulations that are in accordance with experimental observations. The hybrid nature of such protein networks can be very easily expressed and simulated in CHARON, which may offer us better and a more global understanding of biological networks.

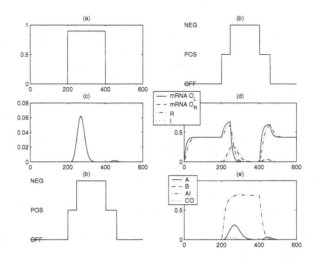

Fig. 7. Increase in external autoinducer produces luminescence: (a)input - external source of autoinducer; (b) switch history; (c) output (luminescence)- product of concentrations of proteins A and B; (d) and (e) time - evolution of concentrations;

The enormous complexity of large scale biological networks will present us with great challenges that we must face. Exploiting the structure of biological systems will be critical for scaling the applicability of the modeling, analysis, and simulation tools. It is therefore extremely encouraging that the two case studies presented in this paper exhibit the architectural paradigms of modern software engineering.

We envision the link between hybrid systems technology, and biology to strengthen. The scalable nature of computational tools like CHARON will enable the unified and improved modeling of biological cellular networks, leading to better understanding, as well as providing us with the opportunity to determine how local biological changes can affect global behavior. Conversely, a good understanding of the robustness of noisy biological networks will lead to new approaches to designing networked embedded systems.

The case studies also highlight the need for developing a theory of *stochastic hybrid systems*, for instance, for modeling rate equations of biochemical reactions. We believe that mathematical and computational tools for the analysis of such systems present a research challenge for the hybrid systems community, while presenting a significant potential for greatly impacting post genomics research.

References

1. R. Alur, C. Courcoubetis, N. Halbwachs, T.A. Henzinger, P. Ho, X. Nicollin, A. Olivero, J. Sifakis, and S. Yovine. The algorithmic analysis of hybrid systems. *Theoretical Computer Science,* 138:3–34, 1995.

2. R. Alur, R. Grosu, Y. Hur, V. Kumar, and I. Lee. Modular specifications of hybrid systems in CHARON In *Hybrid Systems: Computation and Control, Third International Workshop*, volume LNCS 1790, pages 6–19, 2000.
3. G. Booch, I. Jacobson, and J. Rumbaugh. *Unified Modeling Language User Guide*. Addison Wesley, 1997.
4. R. Brent. Genomic biology. *Cell*, 100(1):169–183, January 2000.
5. H. de Jong, M. Page, C. Hernandez, H. Geiselmann, and S. Maza. Modeling and Simulation of Genetic Regulatory Networks. *ERCIM News*, 43, October 2000.
6. A. Deshpande, A. Göllu, and L. Semenzato. SHIFT programming language and run-time systems for dynamic networks of hybrid automata. Technical report, University of California at Berkeley, 1997.
7. M. Elowitz and S. Leibler. Asynthetic oscillatory network of transciptional regulators. *Nature*, 403:335–338, January 2000.
8. D.T. Gillespie. Exact stochastic simulation of coupled chemical reactions. *J. Phys. Chem.*, 81:2340–2361, 1977.
9. D. Harel. Statecharts: A visual formalism for complex systems. *Science of Computer Programming*, 8:231–274, 1987.
10. L.H. Hartwell, J.J. Hopfield, S. Leibler, and A.W. Murray. From molecular to modular cell biology. *Nature*, 402((6761 Suppl)):C47–52, December 1999.
11. D.J. Hassett, J.F. Ma, J.G. Elkins, T.R. McDermott, U.A. Ochsner, S.E. West, C.T. Huand, J. Fredericks, S. Burnett, P.S. Stewart, G. McFeters, L. Passador, and B.H. Iglewski. Quorum sensing in Pseudomonas aeruginosa controls expression of catalase and superoxide dismutase genes and mediates biofilm susceptibility to hydrogen peroxide. *Mol Microbiol*, 34(5):1082–1093, December 1999.
12. C.A.R. Hoare. *Communicating Sequential Processes*. Prentice-Hall, 1985.
13. S. James, P. Nilson, G. James, S. Kjellenberg, and T. Fagerstrom. Luminescence control in the marine bacterium Vibrio fischeri: An analysis of the dynamics of lux regulation. *J Mol Biol*, 296(4):1127–1137, March 2000.
14. D.E. Jr Koshland. The era of pathway quantification. *Science*, 280:852–853, 1998.
15. N. Lynch, R. Segala, F. Vaandrager, and H. Weinberg. Hybrid I/O automata. In *Hybrid Systems III: Verification and Control*, LNCS 1066, pages 496–510, 1996.
16. H. H. McAdams and A. Arkin. Simulation of prokaryotic genetic circuits. *Annu. Rev. Biophys. Biomol. Struct.*, 27:199-224, 1998.
17. D.M. Sitnikov, J.B. Schineller and T.O. Baldwin. Transcriptional regulation of bioluminesence genes from Vibrio fischeri. *Mol Microbiol*, 17(5):801–812, September 1995.
18. K.L. Visick, J. Foster, J. Doino, M. McFall-Ngai and E.G. Ruby. Vibrio fischeri lux genes play an important role in colonization and development of the host light organ. *Bacteriol*, 182(16):4578–4586, August 2000.
19. G. von Dassow, E. Meir, E. M. Munro, and G. M. Odell. The segment polarity network is a robust development module. *Nature*, 406:188-192, July 2000.
20. H. Yang, M. Matewish, I. Loubens, D.G. Storey, J.S. Lam, and S. Jin. migA, a quorum-responsive gene of Pseudomonas aeruginosa, is highly expressed in the cystic fibrosis lung environment and modifies low-molecular-mass lipopolysaccharide. *Microbiology*, 146((Pt 10)):2509–2519, October 2000.

Compositional Refinement for Hierarchical Hybrid Systems[*]

Rajeev Alur[1], Radu Grosu[2], Insup Lee[1], and Oleg Sokolsky[1]

[1] Department of Computer and Information Science, University of Pennsylvania
[2] Department of Computer Science, State University of New York at Stony Brook

Abstract. In this paper, we develop a theory of modular design and refinement of hierarchical hybrid systems. In particular, we present compositional trace-based semantics for the language CHARON that allows modular specification of interacting hybrid systems. For hierarchical description of the system architecture, CHARON supports building complex agents via the operations of instantiation, hiding, and parallel composition. For hierarchical description of the behavior of atomic components, CHARON supports building complex modes via the operations of instantiation, scoping, and encapsulation. We develop an observational trace semantics for agents as well as for modes, and define a notion of *refinement* for both, based on trace inclusion. We show this semantics to be compositional with respect to the constructs in the language.

1 Introduction

Modern software design paradigms promote *hierarchy* as one of the key constructs for structuring complex specifications. We are concerned with two distinct notions of hierarchy. In *architectural hierarchy*, a system with a collection of communicating agents is constructed by parallel composition of atomic agents, and in *behavioral hierarchy*, the behavior of an individual agent is described by hierarchical sequential composition. The former hierarchy is present in almost all concurrency formalisms, and the latter, while present in all block-structured programming languages, was introduced for state-machine-based modeling in STATECHARTS [9], and forms an integral part of modern notations such as UML [5].

A hybrid system typically consists of a collection of digital programs that interact with each other and with an analog environment. Specifications of hybrid systems integrate state-machine models of discrete behavior with differential equations for continuous behavior. This paper is about developing a *formal* and *compositional* semantics of hierarchical hybrid specifications. Formal semantics leads to definitions of *semantic* equivalence (or refinement) of specifications based on their observable behaviors, and compositionality means that semantics of a component can be constructed from the semantics of its subcomponents. Such

---

[*] This research was supported in part by NSF CCR-9988409, ARO DAAG55-98-1-0466, DARPA ITO MOBIES F33615-00-C-1707, DARPA ITO MARS program, grant no. 130-1303-4-534328-xxxx-2000-0000, and ONR N00014-97-1-0505 (MURI).

M.D. Di Benedetto, A. Sangiovanni-Vincentelli (Eds.): HSCC 2001, LNCS 2034, pp. 33–48, 2001.

formal compositional semantics is a cornerstone of concurrency frameworks such as CSP [11] and CCS [14], and is a prerequisite for developing modular reasoning principles such as compositional model checking and systematic design principles such as stepwise refinement.

The main contribution of the paper is a formal compositional semantics for the language CHARON [3] with an accompanying compositional refinement calculus. The building block for describing the system architecture is an *agent* that communicates with its environment via shared variables. The language supports the operations of *composition* of agents to model concurrency, *hiding* of variables to restrict sharing of information, and *instantiation* of agents to support reuse. The building block for describing flow of control inside an atomic agent is a *mode*. A mode is basically a hierarchical state machine, that is, a mode can have submodes and transitions connecting them. Variables can be declared locally inside any mode with standard scoping rules for visibility. Modes can be connected to each other only via well-defined entry and exit points. We allow *sharing* of modes so that the same mode definition can be instantiated in multiple contexts. To support *exceptions*, the language allows group transitions from default exit points that are applicable to all enclosing modes, and to support *history retention*, the language allows default entry transitions that restore the local state within a mode from the most recent exit. Discrete updates are specified by *guarded actions* labeling transitions connecting the modes. Some of the variables in CHARON can be declared *analog*, and they flow continuously during continuous updates that model passage of time. The evolution of analog variables can be constrained in three ways: *differential* constraints (e.g. by equations such as $\dot{x} = f(x, u)$), *algebraic* constraints (e.g. by equations such as $y = g(x, u)$), and *invariants* (e.g. $|x - y| \leq \varepsilon$) which limit the allowed durations of flows. Such constraints can be declared at different levels of the mode hierarchy.

To define the modular semantics for modes, with each mode we associate two relations, one capturing its discrete behavior and one capturing its continuous behavior. Defining the discrete relation is tricky in presence of features such as group transitions, exceptions, and history retention. Our solution relies on a closure construction, inspired by a similar construction for hierarchical discrete systems [2], which allows us to treat the transfer of control between a mode and its environment as a game.

While discrete steps of a mode and its environment are interleaved, continuous steps need to be synchronized as time is a global parameter. In fact, during a flow, all active hierarchically nested modes must participate. To allow flexible and hierarchical specifications, in CHARON, flow constraints can be specified at all levels of the hierarchy. To formalize this feature in a consistent and modular manner, we require that a mode can participate in a flow only when the control is at its default exit point. Then, all applicable constraints are properly used to define permitted flows.

The discrete and continuous relations of a mode allow us to define executions of a mode, and corresponding *traces* are obtained by projecting out the private variables. We show that the set of traces of a mode can be constructed from the traces of its submodes. This compositionality result leads to a compositional notion of refinement for modes. A mode M *refines* a mode N if they have the same interface in terms of entry/exit points and shared variables, and the traces of M is a subset of traces of N. This notion admits modular reasoning in the following manner. Suppose we obtain an implementation design I from a specification design S simply by locally replacing some submode N in S by a submode M. Then, to show I refines S, it suffices to show that M refines N. We illustrate this benefit by a simple example.

Once we have the compositionality results for modes, analogous results for agents are relatively straightforward. We define an observational trace semantics for agents, a resulting notion of refinement, and show it to be compositional with respect to the operations of parallel composition, hiding, and instantiation.

Related work. Early formal models for hybrid systems include phase transition systems [13] and hybrid automata [1]. Models such as hybrid I/O automata [12] and hybrid modules [4] allow compositional treatment of concurrent hybrid behaviors. The notion of hierarchical state machines was introduced in STATECHARTS [9], and is present in many software design paradigms such as UML [5]. Our treatment of hierarchy is closest to hierarchical reactive modules [2] which shows how to define a modular semantics for hierarchical (discrete) modes. Tools such as SHIFT [7], PTOLEMY [6], and STATEFLOW (see www.mathworks.com) allow hierarchical specifications of hybrid behavior, but formal semantics has not been a concern. HYCHARTS [8] presents a hierarchical model with modular operational semantics, but does not consider refinement. Masaccio [10] is a formal model for hierarchical hybrid systems. While same in spirit, it differs from our model in many technically significant aspects: it allows nesting of sequential and parallel composition, and allows a more general form of synchronous communication, but disallows high-level features of CHARON modes such as exceptions, history retention, and specification of constraints at various levels.

2   Motivational Example

In this section, we present a simple example that outlines features, useful in a specification language for hybrid systems. We also point out the difficulties of defining semantics for such a language. Then we give the intuition for our approach to the semantics definition, which allows us to overcome the difficulties.

Our example is a system that controls the level of liquid in a leaky tank. The level is controlled by infusing a flow of liquid into the tank. The level in the tank can be measured directly, but the rate of the leak has to be estimated. The controller has two goals: first, it must make sure that the level is within some critical bounds. If it is not, emergency measures are taken to make the level safe. When the level is safe, the controller should change the infusion rate according to instructions of the user. To do that, the controller periodically recomputes the desired rate of change for infusion and maintains the computed rate until the next update.

We now present a hierarchical description of the system in CHARON. The hierarchy in CHARON is twofold. The *architectural hierarchy* describes how the system agents interact with each other, hiding the details of interaction between sub-agents. The *behavioral hierarchy* describes behavior of each agent, hiding the low-level behavioral details. In our example, we have only one level of architecture description with agents Tank and Controller. There are two variables shared by the agents: level for the level of the liquid, and infusion for the infusion rate.

Both agents are *primitive*, that is, without concurrent sub-agents. Behavior of a primitive agent is given by a *mode*, a hybrid state machine equipped with analog and discrete variables. While a mode stays in a state, its analog variables are updated continuously according to a set of constraints. Taking transitions from one state to another, the mode updates its discrete variables. States of the mode are submodes that can have their own behavior. A mode has a number of *control points*, through which control enters and exits the mode. That is, to perform a computation in one of its submodes, a mode takes a transition to an entry point of that submode. When the computation is complete, a transition from an exit point of the submode is taken. Before the computation of a mode is completed, it may be interrupted by a group transition, originating from a default exit point dx. After an interrupt, control is restored to the mode via a default entry point de. In our example, the behavior of Tank is represented by a single differential equation $d(level) = infusion - leak$, where *leak* is a local variable of Tank. Figure 1 shows the behavior of the agent Controller. The top-level mode of Controller has two submodes, Normal and Emergency. We do not show the details of the mode Emergency. It is activated when the level enters the critical region.

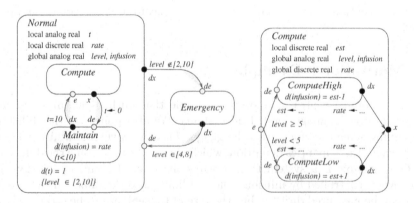

Fig. 1. Behavior of the controller

The mode Normal has two submodes. Submode Maintain is used to maintain the current rate of change for infusion, represented by a local variable *rate*. Every 10 seconds, measured by a local clock t, Maintain makes a call to Submode

Compute that computes a new value of rate. The details of the computation are irrelevant, but we assume that the computation is done differently depending on the level. We therefore introduce two submodes in Compute and show only the constraints for *infusion* in each submode. The exit transition of Compute assigns the computed value to the variable *rate*.

Note that the mode Normal controls the value of the clock t, and its rate of change is the same in all its submodes. By contrast, *infusion* is updated differently in the two submodes. In this case, every submode must provide a constraint for *infusion*. Note also that *rate* is a discrete variable. It is updated only by transitions of Compute.

We use *invariants* to force one of the outgoing transitions. Control can reside in a mode only as long as its invariant is satisfied. As soon as an invariant is violated, control has to leave the mode by taking one of the enabled outgoing transitions. In Figure 1, invariants of the modes are shown in braces. For example, ten time units after entering the mode Maintain the transition to Compute has to be taken.

We distinguish between regular transitions and interrupts. For example, control is transferred from Compute to Maintain only when the computation is complete. When it is time to perform another computation, it will start from the beginning. On the other hand, the transition from Normal to Emergency works as an interrupt. Regardless of which submode of Normal is operating when an interrupt occurs, control is transferred to Emergency. Upon return from the interrupt, the control state of Normal is restored. There is no priority between regular transitions and interrupts[1]. A mode can ignore an enabled interrupt and execute its internal transitions or let time elapse. We use invariants as described above to enforce interrupts (see the invariant of mode Normal). Invariants give the user finer control over interrupts. For example, a situation when an interrupt is optional for some time and then becomes urgent can be easily expressed.

In addition to discrete steps described above, a mode can make *continuous* steps, when time progresses and the analog variables of the mode are updated according to a set of constraints. Because of the hierarchical structure of the mode, the set of applicable constraints consists of the constraints defined in the mode itself and those from the currently active submode. This implies that a mode can engage in a continuous step only when its control properly resides within one of its submodes. For example, we cannot allow time to pass at the control point e of Compute, between executing the transition from Maintain to Compute and a transition to enter ComputeHigh or ComputeLow.

3   Modes

Notation. We will represent modes and agents as tuples of components. If T is a tuple $\langle t_1, \ldots, t_n \rangle$, we identify the component t_i of T as $T.t_i$. We extend this

---

[1] Other treatments of interrupts can be handled equally well within the proposed framework. For example, [2] discuss *weak* interrupts in a similar setting.

notation to sets of tuples. If ST is a set of tuples with the same structure, we write $ST.t_i$ to mean $\bigcup_{T \in ST} T.t_i$.

Given a set V of typed variables, a *valuation* for V is a function mapping variables to their values. We will assume that all valuations are type correct. The set of valuations over V is denoted Q_V. We will use variables s, t, possibly primed or subscripted, to range over valuations. Given a valuation s over V, and a set $W \subseteq V$, $s[W]$ denotes the restriction of s to the variables of W.

A *flow* for a set V of variables is a differentiable function f from a closed interval of non-negative reals $[0, \delta]$ to Q_V. We refer to δ as the *duration* of the flow. We assume that only constant functions are differentiable for non real-valued types. We denote a set of flows for V as $\mathcal{F}_V$.

3.1   Syntax

Definition 1. *(Mode)* A mode M is a tuple $\langle E, X, V, SM, Cons, T \rangle$, where E is a set of entry control points, X is a set of exit control points, V is a set of variables, SM is a set of submodes, $Cons$ is a set of constraints, and T is a set of transitions.

Variables. A mode has a finite set of typed variables V, partitioned into subsets V_a and V_d, the sets of analog and discrete variables, respectively. We also parition V into V_g and V_l, the sets of global and local variables[2]. We assume that there are no conflicts between the names of local variables of different modes.

Submodes. SM is a finite set of submodes. We require that each global variable of a submode is a variable (either global or local) of its parent mode. That is, if $N \in SM$, then $N.V_g \subseteq V$. This induces a natural scoping rule for variables in a hierarchy of modes: a variable introduced as local in a mode is accessible in all its submodes but not in any other mode.

Control points. E is the set of *entry points*; X is the set of *exit points*. There are two distinguished control points representing default entry and exit: $de \in E$ and $dx \in X$. We use C for the set of all control points of the mode: $C = E \cup X \cup SM.E \cup SM.X$.

Constraints. The finite set $Cons$ of constraints defines the flows permitted by M[3]. $Cons$ contains an *invariant* I, which defines when the mode can be active (see the definition of an active mode below). Further, for a variable $x \in V_a$, $Cons$ can contain an *algebraic* constraint A_x, which defines the set of admissible values for x, or a *differential* constraint D_x, which defines admissible values for the derivative of x with respect to time. Every invariant and an algebraic constraint is a predicate $c \subseteq Q_V$ and a differential constraint D_x is a predicate on $Q_{V \cup d(V)}$. A flow f is permitted by the mode if for every t in the domain of f, every variable in $f(t)$ satisfies all constraints in $Cons$. Examples of constraints are $d(x) \leq f(x, y)$ and $g(x, y) \leq 0$.

---

[2] Charon refines the set of global variables further according to allowed read/write access, but we won't make such a distinction in this paper for clarity of presentation.

[3] The semantics does not depend on how sets of flows are specified. Here, we chose one of the possible ways.

Transitions. T is a finite set of transitions of the form (e, α, x), where $e \in E \cup SM.X$, $x \in X \cup SM.E$, and α, the *action* of the transition, is a relation from Q_{V_g} to Q_V if $e \in E$ and from Q_V to Q_V otherwise. A transition connects control points of the mode or its submodes. When a transition is executed, it updates some variables of the mode. Every mode is assumed to have an *identity* transition from de to dx, but we disallow transitions from any non-default control point to dx. A transition that originates at a default exit point of a submode is called a *group transition* of that submode. A group transition can be executed to interrupt the execution of the submode. We require that if a submode has been exited by a group transition, it must be entered again through its default entry point to resume the interrupted execution.

Furthermore, we require that the mode cannot be blocked at any of its non-default control points. Precisely, for every e of M that is not de in M or dx in one of the submodes of M, the union α_e of all actions of the transitions originating at e is complete, that is, for every s there is t such that $(s, t) \in \alpha_e$.

Special modes. We distinguish two kinds of modes that play a special role in the semantic definitions. A mode M is a *leaf* mode if $M.SM = \emptyset$. Leaf modes perform continuous steps according to their constraints. A *top-level* mode has a single non-default entry point *init* and no non-default exit points. Top-level modes are used to describe behavior of agents, as shown in Section 4.

3.2 Semantics

Intuition. A mode can engage in a discrete or continuous behavior. During an execution, the mode and its environment either take turns making discrete steps or take a continuous step together. Discrete and continuous steps of the mode alternate. During a continuous step, the mode follows a flow from the set of flows possible for the current state for the length of its duration, updating its variables according to the flow. Note that the set of flows permitted by the mode's constraints may be further restricted by the mode's environment. A discrete step of the mode is a finite sequence of discrete steps of the submodes and enabled transitions of the mode itself. A discrete step begins in the current state of the mode and ends when it reaches an exit point or when the mode decides to yield control to the environment and let it make the choice of the next step. Note that in the latter case, the decision to break a discrete step is made by the mode itself. Technically, when the mode ends its discrete step in one of its submodes, it returns control to the environment via its default exit point. The closure construction, described below, ensures that the mode can yield control at appropriate moments, and that the discrete control state of the mode is restored when the environment schedules the next discrete step.

State of a mode. We define the state of a mode in terms of all variables of the mode and its submodes. We use $V_* = V \cup SM.V_*$ for the set of all variables.

The state of a mode M is a pair (c, s), where c is the location of discrete control in the mode and $s \in Q_{M.V_*}$. Whenever the mode has control, it resides in one of its control points. In this case, $c \in M.C$. We use special symbol ϵ to denote the case when the mode does not have control. Given a state (c, s) of M, we refer to c as the *control state* of M and to s as the *data state* of M.

Preemption. An execution of a mode can be preempted by a *group* transition. A group transition of a mode originates at the default exit of the mode. During any discrete step of the mode, control can be transferred to the default exit and an enabled group transition can be selected. There is no priority between the transitions of a mode and its group transitions. When an execution of a mode is preempted, the control state of the mode is recorded in a special *history* variable, a new local variable that we introduce into every mode. Then, when the mode is entered through the default entry point next time, the control state of the mode is restored according to the history variable.

The history variable and active submodes. In order to record the location of discrete control during executions, we introduce a new local variable h into each mode that has submodes. The history variable h of a mode M can assume values from the set $SM \cup \epsilon$. A submode N of M is called *active* when the history variable of M has the value N. Every top-level mode is always active.

Closure of a mode. Closure construction is a technical device to allow the mode to interrupt its execution, either to allow the environment to schedule another step or to provide for preemption of the mode execution by group transitions. Transitions of the mode are modified to update h after a transition is executed. In addition, default entry and exit transitions are added to the set of transitions of the mode. These default transitions do not affect the history variable and allow us to interrupt an execution and then resume it later from the same point.

The closure modifies the transitions of M in such a way that, after each transition, h records the active submode. If a transition leads to a control point of a submode N, the resulting state has $h = N$. Otherwise, if the transition leads to a control point of M itself, the value of h after the transition will be ϵ. For each submode N of M, the closure adds a default exit transition from $N.dx$ to $M.dx$. This transition does not change any variables of the mode and is always enabled. Default entry transitions are used to restore the local control state of M. A default entry transition leads from a default entry of the mode to the default entry of every submode N and is enabled if $h = N$. Furthermore, we make sure that the default entry transitions do not interfere with regular entry transitions originating from de. The closure changes each such transition so that it is enabled only if $h = \epsilon$.

Formally, the closure $c(M)$ of a mode $M = \langle E, X, V, SM, Cons, T \rangle$ is defined to be the mode $\langle E, X, V \cup h, c(SM), Cons, c(T) \rangle$, where $h \notin V$ is a new local variable, $c(SM) = \{c(m) \mid m \in SM\}$ is the set of closed submodes of M, and $c(T)$ is the closed set of transitions obtained by extending T with transitions (x, α_x, dx) for every $x \in SM.dx$ and (de, α_x, e) for every $e \in SM.de$, and extending every transition in T such that

- $(s, s) \in \alpha_x$ *iff* $x \in N.E$ for some $N \in SM$ and $s[h] = N$;
- for every transition $(e, \alpha, x) \in T$, the respective closed transition is (e, α', x), where $(s, t) \in \alpha'$ *iff* $(s[V], t[V]) \in \alpha$ and

- if $x \in N.E$ for some $N \in SM$, then $t[h] = N$, otherwise $t[h] = \epsilon$,
- if $e \in N.X$ for some $N \in SM$, then $s[h] = N$, otherwise $s[h] = \epsilon$.

The closure construction for the example introduced in Section 2 is illustrated in Figure 2. To avoid cluttering the figure, we omit the default transitions of the submode ComputeLow, and do not show the variables of the modes.

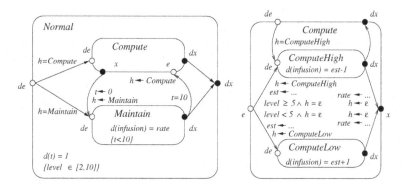

Fig. 2. Closed modes

Before formally defining executions of a mode, we illustrate continuous and discrete steps using the example in Figure 2. Assume that the the controller is in the Maintain mode and none of the invariants is violated. Maintain can voluntarily relinquish control to the environment to let it take a step or advance time by taking the default exit transition to dx of Normal. There, the group transition is not enabled, and the default exit transition of the parent mode is taken. When the control arrives thus at the top level, the environment can schedule a continuous step. The analog variables of all agents are updated according to the constraints of the active modes. The active modes are Maintain, Normal, and Controller. Thus, the applicable constraints are $d(t) = 1$ and $d(infusion) = rate$. The global variable $level$ is updated according to the constraint in Tank. After the continuous step, control returns to Maintain via the chain of default entry transitions. Assume now that the invariant of Normal is violated while control is inside a submode of Compute. Then, control is transferred to dx of Compute and then on to dx of Normal. There, the choice between the group transition to Emergency or the default exit transition is non-deterministic. But since the invariant is violated, a continuous step cannot be taken.

Operational semantics. An operational view of a closed mode M with the set of variables V consists of a *continuous* relation R^C and, for each pair $c_1 \in E$, $c_2 \in X$, a *discrete* relation $R^D_{c_1,c_2}$.

The relation $R^C \subseteq Q_V \times \mathcal{F}_V$ gives, for every data state of the mode, the set of flows from this state. By definition, if the control state of the mode is not at dx, the set of flows for the state is empty. We require that, whenever $(s, f) \in R^C$, $f(0) = s$. In addition, for each s, the set of flows $\mathcal{F}_s = \{f \mid (s, f) \in R^C\}$ is *prefix-closed.* That is, if the domain of $f \in \mathcal{F}_s$ is $[0, \delta]$, then for every $\epsilon < \delta$, a flow $f' : [0, \epsilon]$ that coincides with f on $[0, \epsilon]$ also belongs to $\mathcal{F}_s$. R^C is obtained from the constraints of a mode and relations $SM.R^C$ of its submodes. Given a data state s of a mode M, $(s, f) \in R^C$ iff f is permitted by M and, if N is the active submode at s, $(s[N.V], f[N.V]) \in N.R^C$.

For each $c_1 \in E \cup SM.X$, $c_2 \in X \cup SM.E$, relation $R^D_{c_1, c_2} \subseteq Q_V \times Q_V$ describes the discrete behavior in which control is transferred from c_1 to c_2. The relation $R^D_{e,x}$ comprises *macro-steps* of a mode starting at e and ending at x. A macro step consists of a sequence of *micro-steps*. Each micro-step is either a transition of the mode or a macro-step of one of its submodes. Given the relations $R^D_{e',x'}$, $e' \in SM.E$, $x' \in SM.X$ of macro-steps of the submodes of M, a *micro-execution* of a mode $M = \langle E, X, V, SM, C, T \rangle$ is a sequence of the form $(e_0, s_0), (e_1, s_1), \ldots, (e_n, s_n)$ such that, for all i, $e_i \in C$ and $s_i \in V_*$ and for even i, $((e_i, s_i), (e_{i+1}, s_{i+1})) \in T$, while for odd i, $(s_i, s_{i+1}) \in SM.R^D_{e_i, e_{i+1}}$. Given such a micro execution of M with $e_0 = e \in E$ and $e_n = x \in X$, we have $(s_0, s_n) \in R^D_{e,x}$.

Definition 2. *(Operational semantics) The operational semantics of the mode M consists of its control points $E \cup X$, its variables V and relations R^C and $R^D_{e,x}$.*

The operational semantics of a mode defines a transition system $\mathcal{R}$ over the states of the mode. We write $(e_1, s_1) \overset{o}{\to} (e_2, s_2)$ if $(s_1, s_2) \in R^D_{e_1, e_2}$, and $(dx, s_1) \overset{f}{\to} (dx, s_2)$ if $(s_1, f) \in R^C$, f is defined on the interval $[0, t]$ and $f(t) = s_2$. We extend $\mathcal{R}$ to include *environment* steps. An environment step begins at an exit point of the mode and ends at an entry point. It represents changes to the global variables of the mode by other components while the mode is inactive. Private variables of the mode are unaffected by environment steps. Thus there is an environment step $(x, s) \overset{\varepsilon}{\to} (e, t)$ whenever $x \in X$, $e \in E$, and $s[V_p] = t[V_p]$. We let λ range over $\mathcal{F}_V \cup \{o, \varepsilon\}$. An *execution* of a mode is now a path through the graph of $\mathcal{R}$:

$$(e_0, s_0) \overset{\lambda_1}{\to} (e_1, s_1) \overset{\lambda_2}{\to} \ldots \overset{\lambda_n}{\to} (e_n, s_n).$$

3.3   Trace Semantics

To be able to define a refinement relation between modes, we consider a trace semantics for modes. A *trace* of the mode is a projection of its execution onto the global variables of the mode. That is, a trace is obtained from each execution by replacing every s_i with $s_i[V_g]$, and every f in transition labels with $f[V_g]$. We denote the set of traces of a mode M by L_M.

Definition 3. *(Trace semantics for modes) The trace semantics for M is given by its control points E and X, its global variables V, and its set of its traces L_M.*

In defining compositional and hierarchical semantics, one has to decide, what details of the behavior of lower-level components are observable at higher levels.

In our approach, the effect of a descrete step that updates only local variables of a mode is not observable by its environment, but stoppage of time introduced by such step *is* observable. For example, consider two systems, one of which is always idle, while the other updates a local variable every second. These two systems are different, since the second one does not have flows more than one second long. Defining a modular semantics in a way that such distinction is not made seems much more difficult.

4 Agents

4.1 Syntax

Definition 4. *(Agent) An agent $\langle TM, V, I \rangle$ consists of a set of variables V, a set of initial states, and a set of top-level modes TM.*

The top-level modes collectively define behavior of the agent. The set V is partitioned into *local* variables V_l and *global* variables V_g. We require that $TM.V \subseteq V$, $V_g \subseteq TM.V_g$; that is, all global variables originate in some mode. The set of initial states $I \subseteq Q_V$ specifies possible initializations of the variables of the agent. A *primitive* agent has a single top-level mode. *Composite* agents have many top-level modes and are constructed by parallel composition of other agents as described below.

4.2 Semantics

An execution of an agent follows a trajectory, which starts in one of the initial states and is a sequence of flows interleaved with discrete updates to the variables of the agent. An execution of A is constructed from the relations R^C and R^D of its top-level modes. For a fixed initial state s_0, each mode $M \in TM$ starts out in the state $(init_M, s_M)$, where $init_M$ is the non-default entry point of M and $s_0[M.V] = s_M$. Note that as long as there is a mode M whose control state is at $init_M$, no continuous steps are possible. However, any discrete step of such mode will come from $R^D_{init_M, dx}$ and bring the control state of M to dx. Therefore, any execution of an agent $A = \langle TM, V, I \rangle$ with $|TM| = k$ will start with exactly k discrete initialization steps. At that point, every top-level mode of A will be at its default exit point, allowing an alternation of continuous steps from R^C and discrete steps from $R^D_{de, dx}$. The choice of a continuous step involving all modes or a discrete step in one of the modes is left to the environment. Before each discrete step, there is an environment step, which takes the control point of the chosen mode from dx to de and leaves all the private variables of all top-level modes intact. After that, a discrete step of the chosen mode happens, bringing control back to dx. Thus, an execution of A with $|TM| = k$ is a sequence $s_0 \xrightarrow{o} s_1 \xrightarrow{o} \ldots s_k \xrightarrow{\lambda_1} s_{k+1} \xrightarrow{\lambda_2} \ldots$ such that

- for every $0 \leq i < k$, there is $M \in TM$ such that $(s_i[M.V], s_{i+1}[M.V]) \in M.R^D_{init_M, dx}$. That is, the first k steps initialize the top-level modes of A.

- for every $i \geq k$, one of the following holds:
  - $s_i \xrightarrow{f} s_{i+1}$ such that f is defined on $[0, t]$ and $f(t) = s_{i+1}$, and for every mode $M \in TM$, $(s_i[M.V], f[M.V]) \in M.R^C$; that is, the step is a continuous step, in which every mode takes part;
  - $s_i \xrightarrow{\varepsilon} s_{i+1}$ such that for every mode $M \in TM$, $s_i[M.V_p] = s_{i+1}[M.V_p]$; that is, the step is an environment step;
  - $s_i \xrightarrow{o} s_{i+1}$ with $i > k$, there is $M \in TM$ such that $(s_i[M.V], s_{i+1}[M.V]) \in M.R^D_{de,dx}$; that is, the step is a discrete step by one of the modes.

Note that environment steps in agents and in modes are different. In an agent, an environment step may contain only discrete steps, since all agents participate in every continuous step. The environment of a mode can engage in a number of continuous steps while the mode is inactive.

Definition 5. *(Trace semantics for agents) A trace of A is an execution of A, projected onto the set of its global variables. The denotational semantics of an agent consists of its set of global variables and its set of traces.*

Let A be a primitive agent and $(init, s_0) \xrightarrow{o} (dx, s_1) \xrightarrow{\lambda_1} (c_2, s_2) \xrightarrow{\lambda_2} \ldots \xrightarrow{\lambda_{n-1}} (c_n, s_n)$ be a trace of its top-level mode. It is easy to see that $s_0 \xrightarrow{o} s_1 \xrightarrow{\lambda_1} s_2 \xrightarrow{\lambda_2} \ldots \xrightarrow{\lambda_{n-1}} s_n$ is a trace of A. A similar statement is true for agents with multiple top-level modes.

4.3   Operations on Agents

Variable hiding. The hiding operator makes a set of agent variables private. Given an agent $A = \langle TM, V, I \rangle$, the agent $A \backslash \{V_h\} = \langle TM, V', I \rangle$ with $V'_l = V_l \cup V_h, V'_g = V_g - V_h$. A trace of A, projected onto the set of global variables of $A \backslash \{V_h\}$, is a trace of $A \backslash \{V_h\}$.

Variable renaming. Variable renaming replaces a set of variables in an agent A with another set of variables. Let $V_1 = \{x_1, \ldots, x_n\}, V_2 = \{y_1, \ldots, y_n\}$ be indexed sets of variables with $V_1 \subseteq A.V$. Then, $A[V_1 := V_2]$ is an agent with the set of global variables $(A.V_g - V_1) \cup V_2$. Semantics of the variable renaming operator is given by renaming the variables in the traces of the agent.

Parallel composition. The composition of the two agents $A_1 \| A_2$ is an agent $A = \langle TM, V, I \rangle$ defined as follows: $A.TM = A_1.TM \cup A_2.TM, A.V_g = A_1.V_g \cup A_2.V_g, A.V_l = A_1.V_l \cup A_2.V_l$, and if $s \in A.I$ then $s[A_1.V] \in A_1.I$ and $s[A_2.V] \in A_2.I$.

5   Compositionality Results

We show that our semantics is compositional for both modes and agents. First, the set of traces of a mode can be computed from the definition of the mode itself and the semantics of its submodes. Second, the set of traces of a composite agent can be computed from the semantics of its sub-agents. For the lack of space, we omit the proofs and concentrate on intuitions for the results.

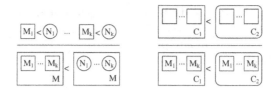

Fig. 3. Compositionality rules for modes

5.1 Compositionality of Modes

In order to show that our trace semantics for modes is compositional, we need to be able to define the semantics of a mode only in terms of the semantics of its submodes.

Compositional Trace Construction. First, we show that every trace of a mode can be constructed using the traces of the submodes.

Theorem 1. *The set of traces of a mode* M *can be computed from the set of traces of its submodes, its closed transition relation* $c(\mathrm{T})$ *and the set of constraints* Cons.

Theorem 1 relies on the following observation. Given a submode N of M, we can "project" a trace σ of M onto N and obtain a trace of N. This projection will 1) restrict all data states and flows to the global variables of N, 2) replace every subsequence of σ where N is inactive into a single environment step, and 3) convert continuous steps of M into continuous steps of N by removing transitions from $N.dx$ to $M.dx$ and from $M.de$ to $N.de$. The critical point in proving this observation is that, whenever the control state is at dx of M, and N is the active submode of M, N has its control state at $N.dx$, since only default exit transitions and the identity transition of the mode can end at dx.

Mode Refinement. The trace semantics leads to a natural notion of refinement between modes: a mode M refines N if it has the same global variables and control points, and every trace of M is a trace of N.

Definition 6. *(Refinement) A mode* M *and a mode* N *are said to be* compatible *if* $M.V_g = N.V_g$, $M.E=N.E$ *and* $M.X=N.X$. *Given two compatible modes* M *and* N, M *refines* N, *denoted* $M \preceq N$, *if* $L_M \subseteq L_N$.

For a finite index set I, we write $\{M_i \mid i \in I\} \preceq \{N_i \mid i \in I\}$ if $M_i \preceq N_i$ for each $i \in I$. The refinement operator is compositional with respect to the encapsulation:

Theorem 2. *(Submode compositionality) Given a mode* N, *suppose* $SM \preceq SN$ *and let* $M = N[SM/SN]$. *Then* $M \preceq N$.

The refinement rule is explained visually in Figure 3, left. If we consider a submode N within a mode M, the remaining submodes of M and the transitions of M can be viewed as an environment or *mode context* for N. In other words, a context for $N_1 \ldots N_k$ is a mode $M[G_1, \ldots G_k]$ with *holes* or *most general sub-modes* G_i, $1 < i < k$ that have the same interface as N_i, have no local variables and put no constraints on the update of global variables. Two contexts are said to be *compatible* if they are compatible as modes and they also are compatible on their holes.

Definition 7. *(Context traces) An* execution *of a mode context C with holes $G_1 \ldots G_k$ is a path*

$$(e_0, s_0) \xrightarrow{\lambda_1} (e_1, s_1) \xrightarrow{\lambda_2} \ldots \xrightarrow{\lambda_n} (e_n, s_n)$$

through the graph of $\mathcal{R}$ of C with $\lambda_i = \epsilon$ for each e_i, e_{i+1} such that e_i is in $C.X$ and e_{i+1} is in $C.E$ or e_i is in $G_j.E$ and e_{i+1} is in $G_j.X$, for $1 < j < k$. A trace of C is obtained by projecting an execution on its global variables.

As with modes, the set of traces of a context C is denoted by L_C and *refinement* is defined by language inclusion. Given a context C with holes $G_1, \ldots G_k$ and a set of modes $N_1, \ldots N_k$ such that $N_i \preceq G_i$ for $1 < i < k$, we write $C[N_1, \ldots N_k]$ the mode obtained by filling the holes G_i of C with N_i. Contexts are also compositional.

Theorem 3. *(Context compositionality) Let C_1 and C_2 be compatible contexts with holes $G_1 \ldots G_k$. If $C_1 \preceq C_2$ then $C_1[N_1, \ldots, N_k] \preceq C_2[N_1, \ldots, N_k]$ for any set $N_i, 1 < i < k$ of modes compatible with the holes, i.e., $N_i \preceq G_i$ for all i.*

A visual representation of this rule is shown in Figure 3, right. The compositionality rules allow us to decompose the proof obligation into refinement of submodes in the most general context, and refinement of contexts under the most general submode.

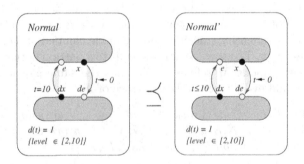

Fig. 4. Refinement example

Consider mode `Normal` in Figure 1 as a two-place context. Let `Normal'` differ from `Normal` only by allowing rate computation to happen more often. The transition to `Compute` has a relaxed guard $t \leq 10$, as shown in Figure 4. By Theorem 3, `Normal[Maintain,Compute]` $\preceq$ `Normal'[Maintain,Compute]`. If `Controller'` is the agent in which `Normal'` replaces `Normal`, then by Theorem 2, `Controller` $\preceq$ `Controller'`.

5.2 Compositionality of Agents

An agent is, in essence, a set of top level modes that interleave their discrete transitions and synchronize their flows, the compositionality results for modes lift in a natural way to agents too. The operations on agents are compositional with respect to refinement.

Definition 8. *(Refinement) An agent A and an agent B are said to be compatible if $A.V_g = B.V_g$. Agent A refines a compatible agent B, denoted $A \preceq B$, if $L_A \subseteq L_B$.*

Theorem 4. *(Agent compositionality) Given compatible agents such that $A \preceq B, A_1 \preceq B_1$ and $A_2 \preceq B_2$. Let $V_1 = \{x_1, \ldots, x_n\}, V_2 = \{y_1, \ldots, y_n\}$ be indexed sets of variables with $V_1 \subseteq A.V$ and let $V_h \subseteq A.V$. Then $A \backslash \{V_h\} \preceq B \backslash \{V_h\}, A[V_1 := V_2] \preceq B[V_1 := V_2]$ and $A_1 \| A_2 \preceq B_1 \| B_2$*

In our example, Tank||Controller $\preceq$ Tank||Controller' by Theorem 4.

6 Conclusions

We have presented a hierarchical modular semantics for hybrid systems. The proposed semantics is compositional both with respect to the system architecture (parallel agents and their subagents) and the system behavior (modes and their submodes). We have introduced the notion of refinement between the system components - both modes and agents - and showed that, in the proposed semantics, composition of components preserves refinement.

We are currently working to build upon the presented compositionality results and provide assume-guarantee proof rules for hybrid systems, extending the results of [2]. The proposed semantics have been used in the modeling language Charon [3] and its toolkit, currently under development by the authors. For further details, see
http://www.cis.upenn.edu/mobies/charon/.

References

1. R. Alur, C. Courcoubetis, N. Halbwachs, T.A. Henzinger, P. Ho, X. Nicollin, A. Olivero, J. Sifakis, and S. Yovine. The algorithmic analysis of hybrid systems. *Theoretical Computer Science*, 138:3–34, 1995.
2. R. Alur and R. Grosu. Modular refinement of hierarchic reactive machines. In *Proceedings of the 27th Annual ACM Symposium on Principles of Programming Languages*, pages 390–402, 2000.
3. R. Alur, R. Grosu, Y. Hur, V. Kumar, and I. Lee. Modular specifications of hybrid systems in CHARON. In *Hybrid Systems: Computation and Control, Third International Workshop*, volume LNCS 1790, pages 6–19, 2000.
4. R. Alur and T.A. Henzinger. Modularity for timed and hybrid systems. In *CONCUR '97: Eighth International Conference on Concurrency Theory*, LNCS 1243, pages 74–88. Springer-Verlag, 1997.

5. G. Booch, I. Jacobson, and J. Rumbaugh. *Unified Modeling Language User Guide.* Addison Wesley, 1997.
6. J. Davis, M. Goel, C. Hylands, B. Kienhuis, E.A. Lee, J. Liu, X. Liu, L. Muliadi, S. Neuendorffer, J. Reekie, N. Smyth, J. Tsay, and Y. Xiong. Overview of the Ptolemy project. Technical Report UCB/ERL M99/37, University of California at Berkeley, 1999.
7. A. Deshpande, A. Göllu, and P. Varaiya. SHIFT: a formalism and a programming language for dynamic networks of hybrid automata. In *Hybrid Systems V*, LNCS 1567. Springer, 1996.
8. R. Grosu, T. Stauner and M. Broy. A Modular Visual Model for Hybrid Systems. In *FTRTFT'98: Formal Techniques in Real Time and Fault Tolerant Systems*, LNCS 1486. Springer-Verlag, 1998.
9. D. Harel. Statecharts: A visual formalism for complex systems. *Science of Computer Programming*, 8:231–274, 1987.
10. T.A. Henzinger. Masaccio: a formal model for embedded components. In *TCS 00: Theoretical Computer Science*, LNCS 1872, pages 549–563. Springer, 2000.
11. C.A.R. Hoare. *Communicating Sequential Processes.* Prentice-Hall, 1985.
12. N. Lynch, R. Segala, F. Vaandrager, and H. Weinberg. Hybrid I/O automata. In *Hybrid Systems III: Verification and Control*, LNCS 1066, pages 496–510, 1996.
13. O. Maler, Z. Manna, and A. Pnueli. From timed to hybrid systems. In *Real-Time: Theory in Practice, REX Workshop*, LNCS 600, pages 447–484. Springer-Verlag, 1991.
14. R. Milner. *A Calculus of Communicating Systems.* LNCS 92. Springer-Verlag, 1980.

Optimal Paths in Weighted Timed Automata[*]

Rajeev Alur[1,2], Salvatore La Torre[1,3], and George J. Pappas[1]

[1] University of Pennsylvania
[2] Bell Labs
[3] Università degli Studi di Salerno
{alur,pappasg}@cis.upenn.edu, latorre@seas.upenn.edu

Abstract. We consider an *optimal-reachability problem* for a timed automaton with respect to a linear cost function which results in a *weighted
timed automaton*. Our solution to this optimization problem consists of
reducing it to a (parametric) shortest-path problem for a finite directed
graph. The directed graph we construct is a refinement of the region automaton due to Alur and Dill. We present an exponential time algorithm
to solve the shortest-path problem for weighted timed automata starting
from a single state, and a doubly-exponential time algorithm to solve
this problem starting from a zone of the state space.

1 Introduction

Timed automata [AD94] are widely accepted as a formalism to model the behaviour of real-time systems: a discrete transition graph is equipped with a finite
set of *clock variables* which are used to express *timing constraints*. Automated
analysis of timed automata relies on the construction of a finite quotient of the
infinite space of clock valuations. In particular, this construction is suitable to
perform *reachability* analysis. Given two states s and t of a timed automaton A,
the reachability problem can be stated as the problem of determining if there
exists a run of A from s to t. Reachability is a core problem in system verification
and directly applies to the verification of *safety* properties.

In the theory of timed automata there are many decision problems which are
undecidable, and decidability is in general hard. In this paper we are interested in
an optimal-reachability problem for timed automata. Time-optimal reachability
was first considered in [CY91], where the problem of computing lower and upper
bounds on time delays in timed automata was solved. Minimal-time reachability
is also considered in [NTY00]. In [ACH93], a weight w is associated with each
location q such that w gives the cost of a unit of time spent in q. Then, given
a cost interval I and two states s and t, the decision problem "is t reachable
from s at a cost $c \in I$?" (*duration-bounded reachability*) is addressed and solved.

---

[*] This work is partially supported by the DARPA/ITO MoBIES grant F33615-00-C-
1707, the NSF Career award CCR97-34115, the SRC award 99-TJ-688, the MURST
grant TOSCA, the DARPA JFACC grant N66001-99-C-8510, and the University of
Pennsylvania Research Foundation.

M.D. Di Benedetto, A. Sangiovanni-Vincentelli (Eds.): HSCC 2001, LNCS 2034, pp. 49–62, 2001.
© Springer-Verlag Berlin Heidelberg 2001

Here we solve a more general optimal-reachability problem, that has been independently solved also in [BHF+]. We consider *weighted timed automata*, that is timed automata with weights (different costs) on both locations and transitions. The cost of a run is given by the sum of costs of the taken switches plus the sum of the costs associated with the visited locations multiplied for the time spent in each of them. Our optimization problem, which we call *optimal-run problem*, can be formalized as a tuple containing a weighted timed automaton, a *source zone* and a *target zone*. If the source zone contains only a state of the automaton, we refer to this problem as the *single-source* optimal-run problem.

Our solution to the optimal-run problem consists of two main steps: first we reduce the optimal-run problem to a shortest-path problem in directed graphs, then we solve the latter. The first step is obtained by constructing a finite graph which is a refinement of the region automaton [AD94]. Each clock region is split into several disjoint subregions relatively to a starting state and to sequences of resets that may occur in "potential" optimal runs. This construction is parameterized on the differences of two consecutive fractional parts from the clock valuation of the starting state. When we consider a general source zone, we leave unspecified these parameters and the above construction reduces the optimal-run problem for weighted timed automata to a parametric shortest-path problem in directed graphs. We give a fix-point computation algorithm to solve this problem, so obtaining a doubly-exponential time algorithm solving the optimal-run problem. In case the input automaton has only one clock variable, this result can be improved to a single exponential by adapting to our case the algorithm given in [KO81,YTO91] for solving a particular case of parametric shortest-path problem. In case the source zone is a singleton we substitutes the parameters with the actual values from the starting state, and thus our optimization problem is reduced to a standard shortest-path problem. Using Dijkstra's algorithm, we obtain an exponential time algorithm for the single-source optimal-run problem.

The optimal-reachability problem is strictly related to other decision problems, and in particular to the problem of synthesizing an optimal controller. The *optimal-control synthesis problem* can be informally stated as the problem of designing a control which is able to drive, at a minimum cost, the system into a given target zone. In the literature, control synthesis problems have been considered in the context of discrete automata [Chu62,Tho95], timed automata [AMP95,MPS95,AM99], linear hybrid automata [WT97], and general hybrid systems [LTS99,SPS00]. The design of an optimal control for hybrid systems is not trivial and in general is undecidable. The approach presented in this paper, can be adapted to solve the optimal-control synthesis problem for weighted timed automata. We observe that this generalizes the results obtained in [AM99] on the synthesis of a time-optimal controller for a timed automaton.

The rest of the paper is organized as follows. In section 2, we define the optimal-run problems and we give some examples. In section 3, we introduce a graph construction to reduce the optimal-run problems to the corresponding shortest-path problems in directed graphs. In section 4, we present our solutions to the single-source optimal-run problem and to the general case.

2 Preliminaries

In this section we define the single-source and the parametric optimal-run problems. We start introducing some notation and the definition of timed automaton.

Given a set C of n variables, a k-zone is a subset of $\mathbb{R}^n$ that can be obtained as a boolean combination of inequalities of the form $x \leq y + c$, $x < y + c$, $x \leq c$, and $x < c$ where $x, y \in C$ and $c \in \{0, 1, \ldots, k\}$. We denote by TRUE the clock constraint which is true for any clock values. We denote by $Z(C)$ the set of all the k-zones, for all $k \in \mathbb{N}$. A function $\lambda : \mathbb{R}^n \longrightarrow \mathbb{R}^n$ is called a reset function if it is equal to the identity on some of the coordinates and zero on the others. We denote by Λ_n the set of all reset functions over $\mathbb{R}^n$. A *timed automaton*[1] A is a tuple $(Q, C, \Delta, \mathrm{Inv})$ where:

- Q is a finite set of locations;
- C is a finite set of n clock variables;
- Δ is a finite subset of $Q \times Z(C) \times \Lambda_n \times Q$;
- $\mathrm{Inv} : Q \longrightarrow Z(C)$ maps each location q to its invariant $\mathrm{Inv}(q)$.

A state is a tuple (q, ν) where $q \in Q$ and $\nu \in \mathbb{R}^n$. We denote by $S = Q \times \mathbb{R}^n$ the set of states for A. A *discrete step* is $(q, \nu) \xrightarrow{e} (q', \nu')$ where $e = (q, \delta, \lambda, q') \in \Delta$, ν satisfies δ, $\nu' = \lambda(\nu)$, and ν' satisfies $\mathrm{Inv}(q')$. A *time step* is $(q, \nu) \xrightarrow{t} (q, \nu')$ where $\nu' = \nu + t$, $t \geq 0$, and $\nu + t'$ satisfies $\mathrm{Inv}(q)$ for all $0 \leq t' \leq t$. A *step* is $(q, \nu) \xrightarrow{t}_{e} (q', \nu')$ where $(q, \nu) \xrightarrow{t} (q, \nu'')$ and $(q, \nu'') \xrightarrow{e} (q', \nu')$, for some $\nu'' \in \mathbb{R}^n$, that is a transition e taken after spending some time t in the current location. A run r of a timed automaton A is a finite sequence $(q_0, \nu_0) \xrightarrow{t_1}_{e_1} (q_1, \nu_1) \xrightarrow{t_2}_{e_2} \cdots \xrightarrow{t_{k-1}}_{e_{k-1}} (q_{k-1}, \nu_{k-1}) \xrightarrow{t_k} (q_k, \nu_k)$. We say that r starts at (q_0, ν_0) and ends at (q_k, ν_k). The definition of r allows time to be spent after taking the last transition e_{k-1}. A *weighted timed automaton* is a timed automaton A with the following cost functions:

- $J_s : \Delta \longrightarrow \mathbb{N}$ (*switch cost*), and
- $J_d : Q \longrightarrow \mathbb{N}$ (*duration cost*).

Given a run r of A and cost functions J_s, and J_d, we associate costs to r as follows:

- $J_s(r) = \sum_{i=1}^{k} J_s(e_i)$, and
- $J_d(r) = \sum_{i=0}^{k-1} t_i \cdot J_d(q_i)$.

The total cost associated to a run r is then $J(r) = J_s(r) + J_d(r)$. We are interested in determining optimal-cost runs for a timed automaton. In the following examples we informally introduce some notions that we will formalize in the rest of the section.

---

[1] The standard definition of timed automata requires also an acceptance condition and a symbol alphabet. Since we are not interested in studying languages accepted by timed automata we omit these features here.

Example 1. Consider the timed automaton defined in Figure 1 such that $J_d(0) = 3$, $J_d(1) = 1$, and the switch costs are all 1. Suppose that we start from state $s = (0, x, y)$ for $0 \leq x, y < 2$ and we want to reach a state in location 2. Possible minimal-cost runs from s to a state $s' = (2, x', y')$ are either $r_1 = (0, x, y) \xrightarrow{t_1}{e_1} (1, x_1, y_1) \xrightarrow{t_2}{e_3} (2, x+2-y, 2)$, or $r_2 = (0, x, y) \xrightarrow{t_3}{e_2} (2, 2, y+2-x)$ for $t_3 = (2 - x)$ (obviously, staying in location 2 longer might only increase the overall cost). According to the cost function J, the cost of r_1 is $J_s(r_1) + J_d(r_1) = 2 + 3t_1 + (2-y-t_1) = 4-y+2t_1$ and the cost of r_2 is $J_s(r_2) + J_d(r_2) = 1 + 3(2-x) = 7 - 3x$. Clearly, $J(r_1)$ is minimized when $t_1 = 0$, that is the transition from 0 to 1 is taken immediately. Moreover, assuming $t_1 = 0$, $J(r_1) \leq J(r_2)$ if $y \geq 3(x-1)$, and $J(r_1) > J(r_2)$, otherwise. Thus, a minimal-cost run from s to a state in location 2 depends on the clock valuation of state s.

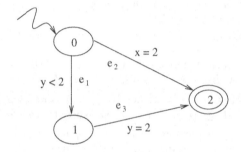

Fig. 1. A timed automaton with more than an optimal run from a same location.

Example 2. Consider the timed automaton defined in Figure 2 such that $J_d(0) = 1$, $J_d(1) = 2$, and the switch costs are all 1. Suppose that we start from state $s = (0, x)$ for $0 \leq x < 2$ and we want to reach a state in location 2. Possible minimal-cost runs from s to a state $s' = (2, x')$ are given by $r_t = (0, x) \xrightarrow{t}{e_1} (1, x_1) \xrightarrow{t'}{e_2} (2, 2)$. Notice that r_t is a run parameterized by t, where t is the time at which the first edge is taken. Thus $J(r_t) = J_s(r_t) + J_d(r_t) = 2 + t + 2(2-t-x) = 6-t-2x$. Hence the cost of r_t is minimized if t is maximized. Since $t < (2-x)$ must hold, the optimal cost for a run starting at s is $(4-x)$, but none of the runs starting at s has such a cost. In fact, for any actual run r_t there exists a $\xi > 0$ such that $t = (2-x-\xi)$, and $J(r_t) = (4-x+\xi)$. Vice-versa, for any $\xi > 0$ there exists a run r such that $J(r) = (4-x+\xi)$. Clearly, there is not a minimal-cost run but we can determine a run whose cost is arbitrarily close to the optimal one.

Now we formalize the notion of optimal cost, optimal run, and approximation of an optimal run. Given a timed automaton A, a state s, and a target zone T, an *optimal cost* for a run from s to T is a J^* such that $J^* \leq J(r)$ for any run r from s to a state in T, and for any $\xi > 0$ there is a run r such that $J(r) \leq J^* + \xi$.

Fig. 2. A timed automaton with no optimal runs from a location.

If there exists a run r^* such that $J(r^*) = J^*$, then r^* is said to be an *optimal run*. As shown in Example 2, sometimes an optimal run from a state s to a target zone T does not exist. In these cases, we are interested in a family R of runs such that all the runs coincide on the sequence of switches and for any $\xi \in \mathbb{R}_+$ there exists a run $r \in R$ such that $J(r) < J^* + \xi$, where J^* is the optimal cost over all runs from s to T. That is we can determine a sequence of runs in R whose costs are arbitrarily close to J^*. We call such a family of runs R an *approximation* of an optimal run. Given a timed automaton A, a source zone S, and a target zone T, we consider the problem of determining an optimal run from a given state $s \in S$ to T, if one exists, or an approximation of an optimal run, otherwise. We call this problem a *single-source optimal-run problem*. We also consider a more general problem, a *zone optimal-run problem*, defined as the problem of determining a symbolic representation of the solution to the single-source optimal-run problem for all states in S. In Example 1, if we consider as target region all the states in location 2 and as only source state $(0, 0, 0)$, then a solution to the corresponding instance of the single-source optimal-run problem is r_1 with $t_1 = 0$. As observed in Example 1, if we consider as source zone the set of states $(0, x, y)$ such that $0 \le x, y \le 1$, then the solution of the corresponding instance of the zone optimal-run problem is r_1 with $t_1 = 0$ if $y \ge 3(x - 1)$, and r_2, otherwise.

We end this section with an example on an air-traffic control problem that we will use subsequently in the paper.

Example 3. Consider the timed automaton in Figure 3. It models a scenario in which two aircraft send a landing request to an airport, and our goal is to allow both the aircraft to land safely and at minimum cost. Safety requires that only one aircraft at a time must be acknowledged for landing, thus there are two possible choices: aircraft 1 waits for the landing of aircraft 2 to be completed, or vice-versa. There are costs c_1 and c_2 to pay for forcing respectively aircraft 1 and aircraft 2 to wait. Moreover, there is also a cost, expressed by w_i, which is related to the time spent waiting. Alternatively, aircraft i can make, at a cost c'_i, a maneuver that allows to spend w'_i instead of w_i per each time unit. This maneuver takes at least time 1. Since it is realistic to reduce the time a runway stays unused, we penalize this event by a cost c_0 per time unit. Finally, we assume that the landing of each aircraft takes at least time 1 since the related acknowledgement was issued by the control tower.

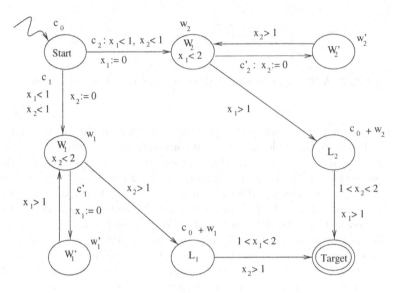

Fig. 3. An air-traffic control problem.

3   The Graph Construction

In this section we give the graph construction underlying the reduction of the single-source optimal-run problem to the shortest-path problem and the zone optimal-run problem to a parametric shortest-path problem. The obtained graph is a refinement of the region automaton [AD94] of a timed automaton, in the sense that each vertex v carries more information than a region. This additional information mainly concerns the sequence of resets needed to reach v from a starting vertex, and the construction preserves the transitions of the region automaton. Via this construction we emphasize the states of the timed automaton that might be visited in some optimal runs. We start by recalling the concepts of labelled directed graph and region automaton, then we describe our graph construction.

Let Θ be a set of real-valued parameters, we denote by D the set of linear expressions over Θ. Given an alphabet Σ, a *D-labelled directed graph* G is a pair (V, E), where V is a set of vertices, and $E \subseteq V \times D \times V$ is a set of D-labelled edges. A path π from v_0 to v_n in G is a sequence $v_0 \xrightarrow{f_1} v_1 \xrightarrow{f_2} \ldots \xrightarrow{f_{n-1}} v_{n-1} \xrightarrow{f_n} v_n$ such that $v_{i-1} \xrightarrow{f_{i-1}} v_i \in E$ for $i = 1, \ldots, n$. For a path π, the cost of π is given by $\sum_{i=1}^{n} f_i$. A path π from v to v' is a *shortest path* if π is the path with minimum cost among those connecting v to v'. Notice that varying the values of parameters in Θ the shortest path of a graph may change, that is to different valuations of parameters may correspond different sets of shortest paths in the graph.

Consider now a timed automaton A. By definition its set of states is infinite. However, they can be partitioned in a finite number of equivalence classes, called *regions*, which are defined by a location and a *clock region*. Denoted by c_x the largest constant in clock constraints involving the clock variable x, a clock region is described by:

- a constraint of type $c - 1 < x < c$, $x > c_x$, or $x = c$ for each clock variable x and $c \leq c_x$;
- the ordering of the fractional parts of the clock variables x such that $x < c_x$.

Thus a clock region denotes a set of clock valuations. Given a clock valuation ν, $[\nu]$ denotes the clock region containing ν. A state (q, ν) belongs to a region $\langle q', \alpha \rangle$ if $q = q'$ and $\nu \in \alpha$. A clock region α is said to be *open* if for any clock variable x and $c \leq c_x$, $x = c$ does not hold in α. Otherwise α is said to be a *boundary* clock region. These definitions apply to regions in an obvious way. The key property of this equivalence, is that all the valuations belonging to a region satisfy the same set of clock constraints from the given timed automaton. Consistently we say that a clock region α satisfies a constraint δ if ν satisfies δ for any $\nu \in \alpha$. A clock region α' is said to be a *time-successor* of a clock region α if and only if for any $\nu \in \alpha$ there is a $d \in \Re_+$ such that $\nu + d \in \alpha'$. The *region automaton* of A is a transition system defined by:

- the set of states $R(S) = \{\langle q, \alpha \rangle \mid q \in Q \text{ and } \alpha \text{ is a clock region for } A\}$;
- the transition rules $R(\Delta)$ such that: $(\langle q, \alpha \rangle, \langle q', \alpha' \rangle) \in R(\Delta)$ if and only if $(q, \lambda, \delta, q') \in \Delta$ and there is a time-successor α'' of α such that α'' satisfies δ and $\alpha' = [\lambda \to 0]\alpha''$.

We denote the region automaton corresponding to A as $R(A)$. For the sake of simplicity, in the following when no confusion can arise we refer to the value of a clock variable x by x itself. With $\overline{x}$ we denote the fractional part of a clock variable x. Let $s = (q, \nu)$ be a state of A and $(0 \approx_1 \overline{x}'_1 \approx_2 \ldots \approx_N \overline{x}'_N \approx_{N+1} 1)$ be the ordering of the fractional parts of the region containing a clock valuation ν (notice that $\approx_i$ is either $=$ or $<$). With $\vartheta(s) = (\vartheta_1, \ldots, \vartheta_{N+1})$ we denote the differences between consecutive values in the above ordering, that is $\vartheta_1 = \overline{x}'_1$, $\vartheta_{N+1} = 1 - \overline{x}'_N$, and $\vartheta_i = \overline{x}'_i - \overline{x}'_{i-1}$ for $i = 2, \ldots, N$. In the following we will use $(\vartheta_1, \ldots, \vartheta_{N+1})$ to denote these differences in the starting state. The graph we are going to define is parameterized over $(\vartheta_1, \ldots, \vartheta_{N+1})$. Moreover, for $i, j \leq N$, we denote by $I(i, j)$ the set of integers $\{i, \ldots, j - 1\}$, if $i < j$, and $\{i, \ldots, N\} \cup \{1, \ldots, j - 1\}$, otherwise.

The region automaton does not carry enough information to solve our optimization problems. Thus we define a labelled directed graph whose vertices correspond to "sub-states" of the region automaton. For a given state $\langle q, \alpha' \rangle$ of the region automaton, a sub-state $\langle q, \alpha \rangle$ is such that α is a convex region contained in α'. Denoted by $(0 \approx_1 \overline{x}'_1 \approx_2 \ldots \approx_h \overline{x}'_h \approx_{h+1} 1)$ the ordering of the fractional parts in a clock region α', we consider sub-regions α of α' such that for some of the $\approx_i$'s which are equal to $<$, the difference between $\overline{x}'_{i-1}$ and $\overline{x}'_i$ is very close to 0. Thus we represent α by α' and specifying in the ordering of the fractional parts if a $<$ is relative to a "small" difference (denoted by $\lesssim$) or to a "large" difference (denoted by $<$). We call each such sub-region α a *boundary sub-region*. Intuitively, the reason we are interested in boundary sub-regions is that the cost functions we consider are linear, and their infimum over a given region is reached on the boundary. Thus optimal runs leave open regions from states which are arbitrarily close to their boundaries. As a consequence optimal runs visit also states characterized by having clocks values either with arbitrarily close fractional parts or with fractional parts which reflects the starting state and the reset history of the computation. For this reason, we add to each boundary sub-region a tuple of indices $(i_1, \ldots, i_k)$ from $\{1, \ldots, n+1\}$ such that: k is the number of large differences in the ordering of the fractional parts, i_l corresponds to the l-th large difference in the ordering of the fractional parts, and there exists a $d \in \{1, \ldots, k\}$ such that $i_{d+h} < i_{d+h+1}$ for $h = 0, \ldots, k-1$, where the sums $(d+h+1)$ and $(d+h)$ are modulo k. We call such tuples *distance tuples*, since they are used to store the difference between two consecutive fractional parts when this difference is "large" (i.e., they are not arbitrarily close). We define the set of vertices V as the set of tuples $\langle q, \alpha, (i_1, \ldots, i_k) \rangle$ where q is a location, α is a boundary sub-region, and $(i_1, \ldots, i_k)$ is a distance tuple from $\{1, \ldots, n+1\}$. For a vertex $\langle q, \alpha, (i_1, \ldots, i_k) \rangle$, the sum $\sum_{l \in I(i_k, i_1)} \vartheta_l$ gives the time to leave the region since this subregion is entered.

The set of edges E contains three types of edges: *immediate switches*, *time edges* and *delayed switches*. Informally, immediate switches correspond to transitions taken in the current state, time edges correspond to letting time elapse until the next region is reached, and delayed switches correspond to transitions taken at the "beginning" or at the "end" of the closest open region (this region if it is an open region, the next otherwise).

Given two vertices $v = \langle q, \alpha, (i_1, \ldots, i_h) \rangle$ and $v' = \langle q', \beta, (j_1, \ldots, j_k) \rangle)$, there is an immediate switch $v \xrightarrow{J_s(e)} v'$ if there exists a transition e of $R(A)$ from $\langle q, \alpha' \rangle$ to $\langle q', \beta' \rangle$, where α' and β' are respectively the regions of $R(A)$ containing α and β, and the sequence $(j_1, \ldots, j_k)$ is obtained from $(i_1, \ldots, i_h)$ by deleting all the indices i_l such that all the clocks between the l-th and the $(l+1)$-th large differences (in the ordering of the fractional parts of α') are reset in e.

Consider a vertex $v = \langle q, \alpha, (i_1, \ldots, i_h) \rangle$ and let $(0 \approx_1 \overline{y}_1 \approx_2 \ldots \approx_k \overline{y}_k \approx_{k+1} 1)$ be the ordering of the fractional parts in α. If we assume that $\alpha(y_k) + 1$ is not larger than the largest constant in the timing constraints involving y_k (i.e., when time elapses the first integer value reached by y_k is at most this constant), we add to E a time edge $v \xrightarrow{c} v'$ for $v' = \langle q, \beta, (j_1, \ldots, j_{h'}) \rangle$ where β is the closest time-successor of α such that the conditions expressed by one of the rows of the following Table 1 are satisfied (where $(0 \approx'_1 \overline{y}'_1 \approx'_2 \ldots \approx'_k \overline{y}'_k \approx_{k+1} 1)$ denotes the ordering of the fractional parts in β, and $l = 2, \ldots, k$):

	$\approx_1$	$\approx_{k+1}$	$\approx'_1$	$\approx'_2$	$\approx'_{l+1}$	$(j_1, \ldots, j_{h'})$	c
1.	$<$	$<$	$=$	$<$	$\approx_l$	$(i_h, i_2, \ldots, i_{h-1})$	$J_d(q) \sum_{l \in I(i_h, i_1)} \vartheta_l$
2.	$\lesssim$ or $=$	$<$	$=$	$<$	$\approx_l$	$(i_h, i_1, \ldots, i_{h-1})$	$J_d(q) \sum_{l \in I(i_h, i_1)} \vartheta_l$
3.	$<$	$\lesssim$	$=$	$<$	$\approx_l$	$(i_1, \ldots, i_h)$	0
4.	$\lesssim$ or $=$	$\lesssim$	$=$	$\lesssim$	$\approx_l$	$(i_1, \ldots, i_h)$	0

In the other case, time edges are defined in the same way except for the fact that the clock y_k does not appear in the ordering of the fractional parts of v' since it has reached its highest constant. To see an example of a time edge, consider a vertex $v = \langle q, \ 0 < x < y < z < 1, \ (1,2,3,4)\rangle$. By row 1 of the above table we have a time edge from v to $\langle q, \ 0 < x < y < 1 \wedge z = 1, \ (4,2,3)\rangle$. The distance tuple $(4,2,3)$ captures the fact that time $(1 - z)$ has elapsed and thus the distance in time from x to 0 is increased by $(1 - z)$, the fractional part of z is now 0, and all the other distances stay unchanged.

Given a vertex $v \in V$ as above, we add to E a delayed switch $v \xrightarrow{c} v''$ for any vertex $v'' \in V$ such that there exists an immediate switch $v' \xrightarrow{J_s(e)} v''$ and $c = c' + J_s(e)$, where $v' = \langle q, \beta, (j_1, \ldots, j_{h'})\rangle$ and β is the closest time-successor of α such that the conditions expressed by one of the rows of the following Table 2 are satisfied (where $(0 \approx'_1 \overline{y}'_1 \approx_2 \ldots \approx'_k \overline{y}'_k \approx_{k+1} 1)$ denotes the ordering of the fractional parts in β, and $l = 2, \ldots, k$):

	$\approx_1$	$\approx_{k+1}$	$\approx'_1$	$\approx'_l$	$\approx'_{k+1}$	$(j_1, \ldots, j_{h'})$	c'
1.	$<$	$<$	$<$	$\approx_l$	$\lessapprox$	$(i_h, i_2, \ldots, i_{h-1})$	$J_d(q) \sum_{l \in I(i_h, i_1)} \vartheta_l$
2.	$\lessapprox$	$<$	$<$	$\approx_l$	$\lessapprox$	$(i_h, i_1, \ldots, i_{h-1})$	$J_d(q) \sum_{l \in I(i_h, i_1)} \vartheta_l$
3.	$=$	$<$	$\lessapprox$	$\approx_l$	$<$	$(i_1, \ldots, i_h)$	0
4.	$=$	$<$	$<$	$\approx_l$	$\lessapprox$	$(i_h, i_1, \ldots, i_{h-1})$	$J_d(q) \sum_{l \in I(i_h, i_1)} \vartheta_l$
5.	$=$	$\lessapprox$	$\lessapprox$	$\approx_l$	$\lessapprox$	$(i_1, \ldots, i_h)$	0

For a given tuple of parameters $\vartheta = (\vartheta_1, \ldots, \vartheta_{N+1})$, we denote by $G_A(\vartheta)$ the D-labelled directed graph (V, E). We recall that for our purposes ϑ represents the differences between the fractional parts of two consecutive clocks in the ordering of the fractional parts in the starting state. The construction of $G_A(\vartheta)$ is general in the sense that it does not depend on the particular source and target zones of the problem, but only on the timed automaton. This allows us to use it for solving both the single-source optimal-run problem (for a fixed ϑ) and the zone optimal-run problem (ϑ belongs to a convex set). As an example of application of the above construction, we discuss a fragment of the graph $G_A(\vartheta)$ for the weighted timed automaton modelling the air-traffic control problem from Example 3 (see Figure 4). For the sake of simplicity, we have marked with $1, \ldots, 5$ the vertices of $G_A(\vartheta)$ in Figure 4, and we refer to them by these numbers. Consider vertex 1. Since in the timed automaton from Figure 3 there is a transition from W_1 to W'_1 resetting clock x_1, we have in $G_A(\vartheta)$ an immediate switch from 1 to 2. Edges from 1 to 3 and from 1 to 4 are delayed switches obtained by the same transition above and respectively rows 3 and 4 of Table 2. The edge from 1 to 5 is a time edge and is defined by row 2 of Table 1. Notice that for a given state $s = (q, \nu)$, we have corresponding vertices of $G_A(\vartheta(s))$ of form $\langle q, \alpha, (i_1, \ldots, i_k)\rangle$, where $\nu \in \alpha$. Moreover, each edge is labelled by the actual cost of the corresponding "activity" in A, that is for immediate switches we have just the cost of the A transition, for time edges the cost of spending the time upto the end of the current region in the current A location, and for delayed switches the cost corresponding to the A transition plus the cost for the time spent in the current location before that the transition is taken. We have the following lemma.

Lemma 1. *Given a timed automaton A, the size of $G_A(\vartheta)$ is exponential in the length of clock constraints of A.*

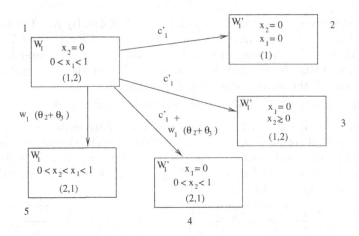

Fig. 4. A fragment of $G_A(\vartheta)$ for the weighted timed automaton in Example 3.

Proof. In [AD94] the authors proved that the size of the region automaton is $O(|A|\, 2^{|\delta(A)|})$, where $|\delta(A)|$ denotes the length of the clock constraints. A simple counting argument gives that the number of ways to substitute $<$ with $\leqslant$ in the ordering of the fractional parts of a clock region is at most 2^{n+1} and the number of tuples of indices we use to represent the relative differences between the fractional parts is at most $n2^n$. Thus the size of $G_A(\vartheta)$ is at most $O(|A|\, n\, 2^{2n+1}\, 2^{|\delta(A)|})$, and since $n = O(|\delta(A)|)$, it is exponential in the length of the clock constraints.

4   Optimal-Runs in Weighted Timed Automata

4.1   Single-Source Case

In this section we prove that the single-source optimal-run problem in timed automata can be reduced to the shortest path problem in a weighted directed graph. To see this we introduce first some notation. Let s_0 be a state (q_0, ν_0) of a weighted timed automaton A and $\vartheta(s_0) = (\vartheta_1, \ldots, \vartheta_{N_0+1})$, we denote by $g(s_0)$ the vertex $\langle q_0, \alpha_0, (i_{0,1}, \ldots, i_{0,N_0})\rangle$ of $G_A(\vartheta(s_0))$ such that $\nu_0 \in \alpha_0$ and $i_{0,j}$ is the j-th largest distance in the ordering of the fractional parts in α_0. Given a positive real $\xi \ll 1$ and a path $\pi = \langle q_0, \alpha_0, (i_{0,1}, \ldots, i_{0,N_0})\rangle \xrightarrow{c_1} \langle q_1, \alpha_1, (i_{1,1}, \ldots, i_{1,N_1})\rangle \xrightarrow{c_2} \ldots \xrightarrow{c_h} \langle q_h, \alpha_h, (i_{h,1}, \ldots, i_{h,N_h})\rangle$ in $G_A(\vartheta(s_0))$, we denote by $R_\pi(\xi)$ the set of runs of A starting at s_0 and obtained by replacing with $(q_j, \nu_j) \xrightarrow[e_j]{t_j} (q_k, \nu_k)$ each portion $\langle q_j, \alpha_j, (i_{j,1}, \ldots, i_{j,N_j})\rangle \xrightarrow{c_{j+1}} \ldots \xrightarrow{c_k} \langle q_k, \alpha_k, (i_{k,1}, \ldots, i_{k,N_k})\rangle$ of π such that:

- $\langle q_{j-1}, \alpha_{j-1}, (i_{j-1,1}, \ldots, i_{j-1,N_{j-1}})\rangle \xrightarrow{c_{j-1}} \langle q_j, \alpha_j, (i_{j,1}, \ldots, i_{j,N_j})\rangle$ is either an immediate or a delayed switch;
- for $l = j \ldots, k - 2$, $\langle q_l, \alpha_l, (i_{l,1}, \ldots, i_{l,N_l})\rangle \xrightarrow{c_{l+1}} \langle q_{l+1}, \alpha_{l+1}, (i_{l+1,1}, \ldots, i_{l+1,N_{l+1}})\rangle$ is a time edge;

- $\langle q_{k-1}, \alpha_{k-1}, (i_{k-1,1}, \ldots, i_{k-1,N_{k-1}}) \rangle \xrightarrow{c_k} \langle q_k, \alpha_k, (i_{k,1}, \ldots, i_{k,N_k}) \rangle$ is either an immediate or a delayed switch. Let $t_j = \tau' + \tau''$ and $\nu_j + \tau' \in \alpha_{k-1}$. In the case of an immediate switch $\tau'' = 0$, while in the other case τ'' is such that:
    - if the delayed switch is obtained by rows 1 and 2 of Table 2, then $\nu_j + t_j \in \alpha_{k-1}$ and the largest fractional part in $\nu_j + t_j$ is greater than $(1 - \xi)$;
    - otherwise, denoted as α' the time-successor of α_{k-1} which is first entered by letting time elapse from a valuation in α_{k-1}, it holds that $\nu_j + t_j \in \alpha'$, moreover if the delayed switch is obtained by rows 4 and 5 of Table 2, the largest meaningful fractional part in $\nu_j + t_j$ is greater than $(1 - \xi)$, and if the delayed switch is obtained by rows 3 and 5 of Table 2, the smallest meaningful fractional part in $\nu_j + t_j$ is less than ξ;
- e_j is the transition corresponding to $\langle q_{k-1}, \alpha_{k-1}, (i_{k-1,1}, \ldots, i_{k-1,N_{k-1}}) \rangle \xrightarrow{c_{k-1}} \langle q_k, \alpha_k, (i_{k,1}, \ldots, i_{k,N_k}) \rangle$.

In the following we assume that ξ is a positive real number such that $\xi \ll 1$. By the definition of $G_A(\vartheta)$ and $R_\pi(\xi)$, we have the following lemma.

Lemma 2. *Given a timed automaton A and a state $s = (q, \nu)$ of A, if π is a path of $G_A(\vartheta(s))$ from $g(s)$ of cost c_π then $R_\pi(\xi)$ is a set of runs of A such that for any $\varepsilon > 0$ there exists an $r \in R_\pi(\xi)$ such that $c_\pi \leq J(r) < c_\pi + \varepsilon$.*

To complete our reduction we need the following lemma.

Lemma 3. *Given a run r of A from a state s to a target zone T, there exists a path π of $G_A(\vartheta(s))$ from $g(s)$ to a vertex corresponding to a state in T such that the cost of π is not larger than $J(r)$.*

Proof. The interesting case is when transitions in r are from states that do not belong to any of the subregions encoded by $G_A(\vartheta(s))$ vertices. Assume that A in run r takes a transition e from an open region α after spending some time in it, and e is the first transition in r with this property. Clearly, upto e, r has a corresponding path π in $G_A(\vartheta(s))$ whose cost is not more than $J(r)$. We observe that by definition there must be two delayed transitions e_1 and e_2 of $G_A(\vartheta(s))$ corresponding respectively to the cases e is taken as soon as α is entered and e is taken just before leaving α. Moreover, consider two A runs r_1 and r_2 that differ from r only for the fact that in r_1 A takes e after an arbitrarily short time spent in α, while in r_2 A takes e after an arbitrarily short time before leaving α. Clearly, $J(r) \geq \min\{J(r_1), J(r_2)\}$ holds. Thus we can add to π the transition corresponding to the run r_i with the least cost between r_1 and r_2. Applying iteratively this argument, we determine a path π in $G_A(\vartheta(s))$ of cost $c \leq J(r)$.

As a direct consequence of Lemmas 2 and 3, we have the following theorems.

Theorem 1. *Given a timed automaton A, a state s of A, a target zone T, π is a shortest path of $G_A(\vartheta(s))$ starting from $g(s)$ to a vertex corresponding to a state in T if and only if $R_\pi(\xi)$ is an approximation of an optimal run of A from s to T.*

Theorem 2. *Given a timed automaton A, a state s of A, a target zone T, there exists an optimal run of A from s to T if and only if for a shortest path π of $G_A(\vartheta(s))$ from $g(s)$ to a vertex corresponding to a state in T there exists a run $r \in R_\pi(\xi)$, such that the cost of π is equal to $J(r)$. Moreover, r is an optimal run of A from s to T.*

Given a timed automaton A, a source state s, and a target zone T, the following algorithm solves the single-source optimal-run problem:

1. Let G be the graph obtained from $G_A(\vartheta(s))$ by collapsing all the vertices corresponding to a state in T in a single vertex v_t.
2. Solve the single-source shortest-path problem on G from $g(s)$.
3. Let π be a shortest path from v_s to v_t. Output[2] $R_\pi(\xi)$ and the cost of π.

Theorem 3. *The single-source optimal-run problem can be solved in time exponential in the size of the timed automaton.*

4.2   The Algorithm for the General Case

In this section we consider the zone optimal-run problem. We give an exponential time algorithm to solve this problem for timed automata with at most 1 clock and a fix-point algorithm in doubly-exponential time, for the general case.

We start considering the general case. Since we want to solve the problem of determining the optimal runs from any state of the source zone S to a state of a target zone T, for parameters ϑ in $G_A(\vartheta)$ we consider only values given by $\vartheta = \vartheta(s)$ for a state in $s \in S$. Thus it holds that $\vartheta_1 + \ldots + \vartheta_{N+1} = 1$ and we can eliminate a parameter by the substitution $\vartheta_{N+1} = 1 - \sum_{i=1}^{N} \vartheta_i$. From now on, we will assume that $\vartheta(s)$ is the tuple $(\vartheta_1, \ldots, \vartheta_N)$ and $G_A(\vartheta(s))$ is the graph obtained after the substitution $\vartheta_{N+1} = 1 - \sum_{i=1}^{N} \vartheta_i$. The algorithm that we are giving, labels the vertices of $G_A(\vartheta)$ with sets of linear expressions on $\vartheta = (\vartheta_1, \ldots, \vartheta_N)$. The meaning of these expressions is that given a state $s \in S$ the minimum over these expressions gives the optimal cost of a run from s. An *expression* is a first-degree polynomial in $\vartheta_1, \ldots, \vartheta_N$, and $(1 - \sum_{i=1}^{N} \vartheta_i)$ with integer coefficients. That is, an expression has the form $f(\vartheta) = a_0 + a_1\vartheta_1 + \ldots + a_N\vartheta_N + a_{N+1}(1 - \sum_{i=1}^{N} \vartheta_i)$, where $a_0, \ldots, a_{N+1}$ are nonnegative integer constants. We denote expressions by $(N + 2)$-tuples of coefficients and write $(a_0, \ldots, a_{N+1})$ for the above expression $f(\vartheta)$. We denote by $\prec$ the natural extension to tuples of the total ordering $<$ over reals. Moreover, let f, f' be two expressions, and v, v' be two vertices of $G_A(\vartheta)$, $(f, v) \prec (f', v')$ if and only if $f \prec f'$. A set X of tuples of type (f, v), for an expression f and a vertex v, is said to be *minimized* (with respect to $\prec$) if for any $(f, v), (f', v') \in X$, (f, v) and (f', v') are not comparable with respect to $\prec$.

---

[2] This step needs a further refinement to distinguish between an approximate solution and an optimal solution. It is not entirely straightforward, but it can be handled at the same complexity. We defer the reader to the full version of the paper.

The algorithm we present computes a labelling function l that maps any vertex u of $G_A(\vartheta)$ to a minimized set of pairs (f, v) for which there exist a path π and a state $s \in S$ such that:

- π is a shortest path of $G_A(\vartheta(s))$ from u to a vertex corresponding to T,
- the first edge e of π connects u to v, and
- the cost of π is given by $f(\vartheta(s))$.

We can summarize our algorithm in the following steps:

1. Initialize l by assigning $l(u) = \{(0, \ldots, 0, u)\}$ for u corresponding to a state in T, and $l(u) = \emptyset$ for all remaining vertices.
2. **repeat**
   $$l' \leftarrow l; l \leftarrow \text{UPDATE(l')}$$
   until $l' = l$
3. Output l.

We just need to specify the function UPDATE. Consider an edge e a vertex $u = \langle q, \alpha, (i_1, \ldots, i_h) \rangle$. We have the following cases:

- e is an immediate switch from u to v: for $(a_0, \ldots, a_{N+1}, v') \in l'(v)$, define $(a'_0, \ldots, a'_{N+1}, v)$ such that $a'_0 = a_0 + c_e$, and $a'_i = a_i$ for $i = 1, \ldots, (N+1)$, where c_e is the cost of e;
- e is a time edge from u to v: for any $(a_0, \ldots, a_{N+1}, v') \in l'(v)$, define $(a'_0, \ldots, a'_{N+1}, v)$ such that if e is obtained by rows 1 and 2 of Table 1 and $i \in I(i_h, i_1)$, then $a'_i = a_i + J_d(q)$, otherwise $a'_i = a_i$;
- the edge e is a delayed switch from u to v: for any $(a_0, \ldots, a_{N+1}, v') \in l'(v)$, define $(a'_0, \ldots, a'_{N+1}, v)$ such that if e is obtained by rows 1, 2 and 4 of Table 2 and $i \in I(i_h, i_1)$, then $a'_i = a_i + J_d(q)$, otherwise $a'_i = a_i$.

Let $l''(u)$ be the set of all the tuples generated for u. After executing $l \leftarrow$ UPDATE(l'), $l(u)$ contains the set obtained deleting from $l'(u) \cup l''(u)$ all the tuples (f, v) such that $f' \prec f$ for some $(f', v') \in l'(u) \cup l''(u)$. Moreover, once the function l is output, it is easy to determine the optimal cost and generate the corresponding solution from l and the graph $G_A(\vartheta)$, given ϑ. We observe that each of the tuples (f, v) belonging to $l(u)$ corresponds to a path from u to a target vertex. Thus the cardinality of $l(u)$ is bounded above by the number of simple paths in $G_A(\vartheta)$. Hence we have the following theorem.

Theorem 4. *The zone optimal-run problem can be solved in doubly-exponential time.*

If we restrict to timed automata with just one clock variable, it is possible to solve the zone optimal-run problem in singly exponential time. We consider the algorithm given in [KO81,YTO91] to solve a particular shortest-path problem with only a parameter ϑ and edge costs given by $(c - \vartheta)$, for constants c. This algorithm runs in polynomial time and can be modified in order to obtain a polynomial time algorithm to solve the parametric shortest-path problem with edge costs given by a first-degree polynomial of ϑ ($\vartheta \in [0, 1]$).

Theorem 5. *The zone optimal-run problem for automata with one clock variable can be solved in exponential time.*

References

ACH93. R. Alur, C. Courcoubetis, and T.A. Henzinger. Computing accumulated delays in real-time system. In *Proc. of the Fifth International Conference on Computer-Aided Verification, CAV'93*, LNCS 697, pages 181 – 193, 1993.

AD94.   R. Alur and D.L. Dill. A theory of timed automata. *Theoretical Computer Science*, 126:183 – 235, 1994.

AM99.   E. Asarin and O. Maler. As soon as possible: Time optimal control for timed automata. In *Proc. of the 2nd International Workshop on Hybrid Systems: Computation and Control*, LNCS 1569, pages 19 – 30, 1999.

AMP95. E. Asarin, O. Maler, and A. Pnueli. Symbolic controller synthesis for discrete and timed systems. In *Proc. of the 2nd International Workshop on Hybrid Systems*, LNCS 999, pages 1 – 20, 1995.

BHF⁺.   G. Behrman, T. Hune, A. Fehnker, K. Larsen, P. Pettersson, R. Romijn, and F. Vaandrager. Minimum-cost reachability for priced timed automata. In *this Volume*.

Chu62. A. Church. Logic, arithmetic, and automata. In *Proc. of the International Congress of Mathematics*, pages 23–35, 1962.

CY91.   C. Courcoubetis and M. Yannakakis. Minimum and maximum delay problems in real-time systems. In *Proc. of the 3rd International Conference on Computer Aided Verification*, LNCS 575, pages 399 – 409, 1991.

KO81.   R. M. Karp and J. R. Orlin. Parametric shortest path algorithm with an application to cyclic staffing. *Discrete Applied Math.*, 3:37 – 45, 1981.

LTS99. J. Lygeros, C. Tomlin, and S.S. Sastry. Controllers for reachability specifications for hybrid systems. *Automatica*, 35(3):349–370, March 1999.

MPS95. O. Maler, A. Pnueli, and J. Sifakis. On the synthesis of discrete controllers for timed systems. In *Proc. of the 12th Annual Symposium on Theoretical Aspects of Computer Science, STACS'95*, LNCS 900, pages 229 – 242, 1995.

NTY00. P. Nierbert, S. Tripakis, and S. Yovine. Minimum-time reachability for timed automata. In *Proc. of the 8-th IEEE Mediterranean Conference on Control and Automation*, 2000.

SPS00. O. Shakernia, G. J. Pappas, and S. Sastry. Decidable controller synthesis for classes of linear systems. In *Proc. of the 3rd International Workshop on Hybrid Systems: Computation and Control, HSCC'00*, LNCS 1790, pages 407 – 420, 2000.

Tho95. W. Thomas. On the synthesis of strategies in infinite games. In Ernst W. Mayr and Claude Puech, editors, *12th Annual Symposium on Theoretical Aspects of Computer Science, STACS'95*, LNCS 900, pages 1 – 13, 1995.

WT97.   H. Wong-Toi. The synthesis of controllers for linear hybrid automata. In *Proc. of the 36th IEEE CDC*, San Diego, CA, December 1997.

YTO91. N. E. Young, R. Tarjan, and J. Orlin. Faster parametric shortest path and minimum balance algorithms. *Networks*, 21 (2):205 – 221, 1991.

Reach Set Computations Using Real Quantifier Elimination

Hirokazu Anai[1] and Volker Weispfenning[2]

[1] Computer System Laboratories, Fujitsu Laboratories Ltd
Kamikodanaka 4-1-1, Nakahara-ku Kawasaki, 211-8588, Japan
anai@jp.fujitsu.com
[2] Fakultät für Mathematik und Informatik, Universität Passau
D-94030 Passau, Germany
weispfen@uni-passau.de

Abstract. Reach set computations are of fundamental importance in control theory. We consider the reach set problem for open-loop systems described by parametric inhomogeneous linear differential systems and use real quantifier elimination methods to get exact and approximate solutions. The method employs a reduction of the forward and backward reach set and control parameter set problems to the transcendental implicitization problems for the components of special solutions of simpler non-parametric systems. For simple elementary functions we give an exact calculation of the cases where exact semialgebraic transcendental implicitization is possible. For the negative cases we provide approximate alternating using discrete point checking or safe estimations of reach sets and control parameter sets. Examples are computed using the REDLOG and QEPCAD packages.

1 Introduction

Today integrated systems which combine physical processes with information systems (*i.e.* digital programs) are in great demand. In fact complex systems which have been designed recently incorporate both differential equations to model the continuous behavior and discrete event systems to model instantaneous state changes in response to events. Systems that are finite state machines with differential equations at each discrete state are called *Hybrid Systems*.

A lot of research effort has been devoted to develop mathematical models, specification formalisms, analysis/design/control methods and tools to help control engineers in building such systems (see [18,30,26]). Most of the applications of hybrid systems are safety critical. Safety is usually encoded as avoidance of an undesirable region of the state space. Consequently, the most important problems for analyzing hybrid systems are verification problems; these are essentially reachability problems, that ask whether trajectories of the hybrid systems reach certain undesirable (unsafe) regions from an initial region.

Computing the reach set of hybrid systems is difficult because hybrid systems have an infinite state space. Due to the difficulty of computing the reach set for

M.D. Di Benedetto, A. Sangiovanni-Vincentelli (Eds.): HSCC 2001, LNCS 2034, pp. 63–76, 2001.
© Springer-Verlag Berlin Heidelberg 2001

systems of differential equations, formal verification methods and tools for hybrid systems have been developed [2,17]. These methods and tools, however, can deal with only very simple continuous models as, *e.g.* $\dot{x} = 1$, $A\dot{x} = b$. What is actually required is to handle hybrid systems with more complicated continuous parts.

Decidability of reachability problem for hybrid systems with linear differential equation of the form $\dot{y} = Ay + Bu$ is discussed in [23,24]. This is a significant class of linear differential equations that is widely used in linear control theory. The results are based on the notion of "o-minimality"[16] from model theory and "quantifier elimination"[11]. O-minimality is used to define a class of hybrid systems "o-minimal hybrid systems" and it is shown that all o-minimal hybrid systems admit finite bisimulations in [22]. To make the bisimulation algorithm computationally feasible, they utilize mathematical logic, in particular, real quantifier elimination, as main tool to represent and manipulate sets symbolically. Since quantifier elimination, in general, is possible for the polynomial theory of reals [11], they have found subclasses of o-minimal hybrid systems that are definable in the theory.

Remark: There are many results that apply quantifier elimination to control theory [6, 15,19,4]. In [28,3] quantifier elimination is used for verification problems (reachability and observability problems) of discrete-time polynomial systems.

In this paper we study in particular reach set problems for continuous open-loop systems described by parametric systems of linear differential equations [21]. Roughly speaking reach set problems are concerned with the relations between possible values of the state variables at some initial time t_0 and the corresponding values at later points in time. The specific problems studied in this paper are the following:

1. Fix a set M of values of the state variables at t_0; what are the possible corresponding values at later points t in time (up to some bound t_1 or ∞). (*Forward reach set*)
2. Fix a set N of "safe" values of the state variables. Find a set M as large as possible of initial values of the state variables at time t_0 that guarantees that the values of the state variables will for all later time points t (up to some bound t_1 or ∞) remain inside N. (*Backward reach set*)
3. Fix a set M of values of the state variables at t_0 and a set N of "safe" values of the state variables. Find a set P as large as possible of the control parameters such that all state variables with initial values at t_0 in M will have values in N for all later time points t (up to some bound t_1 or ∞.) (*Control parameter set*)

Our main tool is the method of real quantifier elimination in computer algebra. This approach was introduced into reach set computations in [29]. In a series of papers they showed how to get exact solutions of the forward reach set problem for certain homogeneous linear differential systems of special type with constant coefficients [23] and for associated inhomogeneous systems with very special right hand side [24]. The exact solutions are always obtained as semialgebraic sets described by a boolean combination of polynomial inequalities.

Here we extend this ad hoc approach for special types of differential systems to a systematic study of the type of results obtainable by an approach via real quantifier elimination. By reducing the approach to its bare essentials, we obtain a much wider systematic framework applicable to a considerably larger class of systems. The main observation is that all the problems mentioned above can be reduced by exact symbolic algorithms to an implicitization problem for certain basic transcendental functions associated with the given system. Exact solutions for implicitization problems with rational parametrizations are well-known [8,27]. Here we deal with the corresponding problem for transcendental parametrizations that has been studied only for special cases *e.g.* in [13,20].

Our main results are as follows: We associate with every parametric linear system of differential equations $\dot{y} = A(t)y + b(t,\underline{r})$ a finite system F of basic functions. Then for semialgebraic sets M, N all three problems can be solved exactly by real quantifier elimination relative to the implicitization problem for the components of the functions in F. Moreover the discrete point version of these problems require only finitely many evaluations of functions in F. We prove a theorem that determines the exact classes of vector-valued functions of the kind arising in linear differential systems with constant coefficients, where exact semialgebraic implicitization is possible. As a corollary we obtain the exact limitations of the approach of [23,24] for linear differential systems with constant coefficients and special right hand sides.

We propose several ways to overcome these limitations by approximate computations: One way is to compute exact reach sets at a finite selection of discrete time points. This is always possible and practically quite efficient, but may lead to underestimation of the true forward reach set, depending on the selection of time points. Another approach separates the common time variable into different time variables. This leads to an overestimation in the implicitization problem resulting in an overestimation of the forward reach set and an underestimation of the backward reach set and the control parameter set: So all three approximations are on the safe side.

We illustrate some problems and solution methods by examples computed in the REDLOG-package of REDUCE [14] and QEPCAD [12]. We expect that our results can be extended to the hybrid systems with linear continuous parts.

2   Reach Sets and Transcendental Implicitization Problem

2.1   Problem Statement

We consider parametric inhomogeneous systems S of linear differential systems of the form $\dot{y} = A(t)y + b(t,\underline{r})$ with an $n \times n$ matrix $A(t)$ of real continuous functions $a_{ij}(t)$ and a vector-valued real continuous function $b(t,\underline{r})$ defined on some interval I. The inhomogeneous part is assumed to be a linear combination $b(t,\underline{r}) = \sum_{i=1}^{k} r_i g_i(t)$ with continuous functions $g_i : I \longrightarrow \mathbb{R}^n$, and real parameters r_i. Such a system can be viewed as an continuous open-loop control system with control parameters $\underline{r} = (r_1, \ldots, r_k)$. Let M be some subset of $\mathbb{R}^n$ and fix an initial time point $t_0 \in I$: Then we denote the set of all solution functions $f : I \longrightarrow \mathbb{R}^n$ of the given system with parameters $\underline{r} = (r_1, \ldots, r_k)$, by F_r, and the set of all solution functions $f \in F_r$ with initial value $f(t_0) \in M$ by $F = F_{M,r}$.

We consider the following *forward reach set problems*:

discrete reach sets Compute for finitely many time points $t_1 < \ldots < t_m$ in I the union of the sets $\{f(t_i) \mid f \in F_{M,r}\}$.

bounded reach set Compute for a given time $t_1 > t_0$ in I the set $\{f(t) \mid f \in F_{M,r}, t_0 \leq t \leq t_1\}$.

unbounded reach set Suppose $I \supseteq [t_0, \infty)$, and compute the set $\{f(t) \mid f \in F_{M,r}, t_0 \leq t\}$.

All computations should be performed in explicit dependence on the control parameters $\underline{r}$. Any solution of the discrete reach sets problem yields an lower estimate for the sets to be computed in the bounded and unbounded reach set problems.

Of equal interest are the corresponding "backward" reach set problems that are a kind of "dual" to the corresponding "forward" problems.

Some *backward reach set problems* are as follows: Let N be a subset of $\mathbb{R}^n$.

backward discrete reach sets Compute for finitely many time points $t_1 < \ldots < t_m$ in I the sets $\{f(t_0) \mid f(t_1), \ldots, f(t_m) \in N\}$.

backward bounded reach set Compute for a given time $t_1 > t_0$ in I the set $\{f(t_0) \mid f(t) \in N \text{ for all } t_0 \leq t \leq t_1\}$.

backward unbounded reach set Suppose $I \supseteq [t_0, \infty)$, and compute the set $\{f(t_0) \mid f(t) \in N \text{ for all } t_0 \leq t\}$.

From the viewpoint of control theory these problems have still other variants concerning the determination of suitable control parameter values $\underline{r} = (r_1, \ldots, r_k)$. Let M as before be a subset of $\mathbb{R}^n$, and let N be another subset of $\mathbb{R}^n$. Then we have the following natural *control parameter set problems*:

discrete point control Compute for finitely many time points $t_1 < \ldots < t_m$ in I the set $\{\underline{r} \in \mathbb{R}^k \mid f(t_i) \in N \text{ for all } f \in F_{M,r}, 1 \leq i \leq m\}$.

bounded interval control Compute for a given time $t_1 > t_0$ in I the set $\{\underline{r} \in \mathbb{R}^k \mid f(t) \in N \text{ for all } f \in F_{M,r}, t_0 \leq t \leq t_1\}$.

unbounded interval control Suppose $I \supseteq [t_0, \infty)$, and compute the set $\{\underline{r} \in \mathbb{R}^k \mid f(t) \in N \text{ for all } f \in F_{M,r}, t_0 \leq t\}$.

In order to make these problems mathematically precise, we need to specify the way in which the input sets M and N, and the output sets should be described. For an approach using symbolic computations it is natural to consider *semialgebraic* sets as possible inputs. These are subsets of $\mathbb{R}^n$ described by a boolean combination $\varphi(x_1, \ldots, x_n)$ of real polynomial inequalities. If in addition all the polynomials involved in $\varphi(x_1, \ldots, x_n)$ are linear, then the set described by φ is called *semilinear* [16,32].

Our goal is to solve the forward and backward reach set and control parameter set problems for semialgebraic input sets as far as possible with descriptions of semialgebraic sets as outputs. This, however, is not always possible. Hence we consider also the computation of overestimating the forward reach sets and underestimating the backward reach set and the control parameter sets by suitable semialgebraic sets.

Our main tool will be a reduction of reach set and control parameter set computations to corresponding implicitization problems for a fixed finite system of functions associated with S, namely a fundamental system $f_1, \ldots, f_n$ for the homogeneous system S_0 associated with S, and special solutions h_i of the parameter-free inhomogeneous system S_i given by $\dot{y} = A(t)y + g_i(t)$ for $1 \le i \le k$. We refer to $\{f_1, \ldots, f_n, h_1, \ldots, h_k\}$ as a system of *basic functions* for S.

Implicitization problems for rational parametrizations of algebraic varieties have been widely considered in computer algebra [8,27]. Here we have to study the corresponding problem for the vector-valued functions $f_1, \ldots, f_n, h_1, \ldots, h_k$, arising from the system S. As these functions will in general be transcendental, we refer to these problems as *transcendental implicitization problems*.

More precisely, we consider the following transcendental implicitization problems for given functions $f_i : I \longrightarrow \mathbb{R}^n$ for $1 \le i \le k$:

discrete points implicitization Compute for finitely many time points $t_1 < \ldots < t_m$ in I the values $(f_1(t_i), \ldots f_k(t_i))$, regarded as points in $\mathbb{R}^{nk}$.
bounded implicitization Compute for a given time $t_1 > t_0$ in I the set $\{(f_1(t), \ldots f_k(t)) \in \mathbb{R}^{nk} \mid t_0 \le t \le t_1\}$.
unbounded implicitization Suppose $I \supseteq [t_0, \infty)$, and compute the set $\{(f_1(t), \ldots f_k(t)) \in \mathbb{R}^{nk} \mid t_0 \le t\}$.

The first problem amounts to simple evaluations of the given functions. Notice that the unbounded and bounded implicitization problem for a single solution of the differential system S is in fact a special case of the unbounded and bounded forward reach set problem for S, respectively, namely for the case of a singleton set M.

2.2   Reduction to Implicitization Problems

Next we show that all reach set computations and control parameter set computations listed above can for semialgebraic input sets M, N be reduced in an exact symbolic way to one of these implicitization problems. All these reductions require real quantifier elimination as fundamental tool. For the case of discrete points forward and backward reach set and control parameter set and semilinear input sets M, N we find moreover that the output sets are also semilinear.

Let $\varphi(x_1, \ldots, x_n)$ and $\psi(x_1, \ldots, x_n)$ be quantifier-free formulas describing the semialgebraic input sets M and N, respectively. Let $\dot{y} = Ay + b(t, \underline{r})$ with $b(t, \underline{r}) = \sum r_i g_i(t)$ be a parametric linear system S with control parameter r_i. Let f_i be a fundamental system of solutions of $\dot{y} = Ay$. Let h_i be a special solution of the system $\dot{y} = Ay + g_i(t)$. Then by the superposition principle, a special solution of the system S is given by $\sum_{i=1}^{k} r_i h_i$. Note that here r_i's may be regarded as constants or as free parameters. Then it is straightforward to write down first-order formulas describing the respective forward and backward reach sets and control parameter sets in terms of evaluations of the basic functions $f_1, \ldots, f_n, h_1, \ldots, h_k$, the given formulas $\varphi(x_1, \ldots, x_n)$, $\psi(x_1, \ldots, x_n)$ and a quantifier-free formula $\mu(y_{11}, \ldots, y_{1n}, \ldots, y_{n1}, \ldots, y_{nn})$ describing the combined range of $(f_1, \ldots, f_n, h_1, \ldots, h_k)$, as a semialgebraic set. All these formulas will involve several quantifiers over real numbers. By real quantifier elimination one can construct equivalent quantifier-free formulas, and thus get the desired semialgebraic descriptions.

We will exhibit concrete first-order formulas for some reach set problems and control parameter set problem. The remaining cases are handled similarly in [5]. The forward discrete reach set problem can be described by the following formula and hence be solved by real quantifier elimination and evaluation of the basic functions at finitely many points.

$$\exists x_1 \ldots \exists x_n (\varphi(\textstyle\sum_i x_i f_i + \sum_i r_i h_i)(t_0) \wedge [\bigwedge_{j=1}^n y_j = (\sum_i x_i f_{ij} + \sum_i r_i h_{ij}(t_1))$$
$$\vee \ldots \vee \bigwedge_{j=1}^n y_j = (\textstyle\sum_i x_i f_{ij} + \sum_i r_i h_{ij})(t_m)]).$$

Next suppose we have a quantifier-free formula $\mu(y_{11}, \ldots, y_{1n}, \ldots, y_{n1}, \ldots,$ $y_{nn}, z_{11}, \ldots, z_{1n}, \ldots, z_{k1}, \ldots, z_{kn})$ describing the combined range of $(f_1, \ldots, f_n,$ $h_1, \ldots, h_k)$ on the interval $[t_0, \infty)$ or $[t_0, t_1]$. So $\mu(y_{11}, \ldots, z_{kn})$ holds for $n(k+n)$-tuple in $\mathbb{R}^{n(k+n)}$ if and only if this tuple is in the combined range of $(f_1, \ldots, f_n,$ $h_1, \ldots, h_k)$ on the given interval. Then the forward bounded and unbounded reach set problem, respectively, can be described by the following formula and hence solved by real quantifier elimination:

$$\exists x_1 \ldots \exists x_n [\varphi(\textstyle\sum_i x_i f_i + \sum_i r_i h_i)(t_0) \wedge \exists y_{11} \ldots \exists y_{nn} \exists z_{11} \ldots \exists z_{kn} (\mu(y_{11}, \ldots, z_{kn})$$
$$\wedge \bigwedge_{j=1}^n y_j = (\textstyle\sum_i x_i y_{ij} + \sum_i r_i z_{ij}))].$$

With the same formula μ, the backward bounded and unbounded reach set problem, respectively, can be described by the following formula and hence solved by real quantifier elimination:

$$\exists x_1 \ldots \exists x_n [\bigwedge_{j=1}^n y_j = (\textstyle\sum_i x_i f_{ij} + \sum_i r_i h_{ij})(t_0)) \wedge \forall y_{11} \ldots \forall y_{nn} \forall z_{11} \ldots \forall z_{kn}$$
$$(\mu(y_{11}, \ldots, z_{kn}) \to \psi(\textstyle\sum_i x_i \underline{y_i} + \sum_i r_i \underline{z_i})(t))].$$

Finally, the bounded interval control problem and the unbounded interval control problem, respectively, can be described by the following formula and hence solved by real quantifier elimination:

$$\exists x_1 \ldots \exists x_n [\varphi(\textstyle\sum_i x_i f_i + \sum_i r_i h_i)(t_0) \wedge \forall y_{11} \ldots \forall y_{nn} \forall z_{11} \ldots \forall z_{kn}$$
$$(\mu(y_{11}, \ldots, z_{kn}) \to \psi(\textstyle\sum_i x_i \underline{y_i} + \sum_i r_i \underline{z_i})(t))].$$

As a corollary to these semialgebraic parametric descriptions of reach sets we also obtain semialgebraic descriptions of the corresponding reach sets, where the control parameters range over a prescribed semialgebraic set C.

Corollary 1. *Let $C \subseteq \mathbb{R}^k$ be a semialgebraic sets of control parameters described by a quantifier-free formula $\gamma(r_1, \ldots, r_k)$. Let $\rho(y_1, \ldots, y_n, r_1, \ldots, r_k)$ be a quantifier-free formula describing a forward/backward reach set relative to the* *control parameters $\underline{r}$. Then the corresponding reach set for arbitrary control parameter values in C is described by the formula $\exists r_1 \ldots \exists r_k(\gamma(\underline{r}) \wedge \rho(\underline{y}, \underline{r}))$, and $\forall r_1 \ldots \forall r_k(\gamma(\underline{r}) \rightarrow \rho(\underline{y}, \underline{r}))$, respectively, and hence is also a semialgebraic set.*

Example 1. Consider the inhomogeneous system [1] $\dot{y} = Ay + b$ with

$$A := \begin{pmatrix} 1 & -3 \\ -2 & 2 \end{pmatrix}, \quad b := r_1 \begin{pmatrix} e^{2t} \\ 0 \end{pmatrix} + r_2 \begin{pmatrix} 0 \\ e^t \end{pmatrix}.$$

Then the basic functions are $\begin{pmatrix} e^{-t} \\ \frac{2}{3}e^{-t} \end{pmatrix}, \begin{pmatrix} -e^{4t} \\ e^{4t} \end{pmatrix}, \begin{pmatrix} 0 \\ \frac{1}{3}e^{2t} \end{pmatrix}, \begin{pmatrix} \frac{1}{2}e^t \\ 0 \end{pmatrix}$. A quantifier-free formula $\mu(y_{11}, y_{12}, y_{21}, y_{22}, z_{11}, z_{12}, z_{21}, z_{22})$ describing the combined range of these functions for $t \in [0, \infty)$ is obtained as follows: Notice that the range of e^{-t} on $[0, \infty)$ is exactly $(0, 1]$, and that $e^t = (e^{-t})^{-1}, e^{4t} = 1/(e^{-t})^4, e^{2t} = 1/(e^{-t})^2$. So μ can be taken as the formula

$$0 < y_{11} \leq 1 \wedge 3y_{12} = 2y_{11} \wedge y_{21}y_{11}^4 = -1 \wedge y_{22}y_{11}^4 = 1 \wedge$$
$$z_{11} = 0 \wedge 3z_{12}y_{11}^2 = 1 \wedge 2z_{21}y_{11} = 1 \wedge z_{22} = 0.$$

3 Exact Transcendental Implicitization

Here we consider cases, where the unbounded and bounded transcendental implicitization problem for given functions $f_i : I \longrightarrow \mathbb{R}^n$ $(1 \leq i \leq k)$ has an exact solution. Notice that the transcendental implicitization problem refers only to the component functions $f_{ij}(t)$ of $f_i(t)$; the grouping of these component functions into vector-valued functions is irrelevant here. So we may assume w.l.o.g. that $k = 1$ and that we deal with a single vector-valued function $f(t) := (f_1(t), \ldots, f_n(t))$. Then the exact transcendental implicitization problem is to determine the range of $f(t)$ on an unbounded interval $[t_0, \infty)$, or a compact interval $[t_0, t_1]$ contained in I. Since the f is continuous, this range is always a connected subset of $\mathbb{R}^n$.

In particular for $n = 1$ the range is a real interval J; moreover J is compact for the bounded implicitization case. In the unbounded implicitization case J is compact iff f is bounded on $[t_0, \infty)$, otherwise it is a closed semiinfinite interval or all of $\mathbb{R}$. In particular J is always a semialgebraic set that can computed explicitly from upper and lower bounds for f. In other words the unbounded and the bounded transcendental implicitization problem always has a positive solution for $n = 1$.

For $n = 2$ there are two well-known cases, where exact unbounded and bounded implicitization is possible, namely the sin-cos-pair and the sinh-cosh-pair: If f has components $f_1 := \cos(p(x)), f_2 := \sin(p(x))$, where $p(x)$ is a real polynomial of positive degree, then the range of $p(x)$ on $[t_0, \infty)$ includes an unbounded interval; consequently the range of f on $[t_0, \infty)$ is exactly the unit circle $\{(x_1, x_2) \mid x_1^2 + x_2^2 = 1\}$. On a bounded interval $[t_0, t_1]$, the range of $p(x)$

---

[1] This is taken from [10] (p.586 example 3.13).

is again a compact interval, and so the range of f is a connected subset of the circle that can be easily computed as semialgebraic set from the range of $p(x)$. For the hyperbolic case, where $f_1 := \cosh(p(x))$, $f_2 := \sinh(p(x))$, the situation is analogous, except that the role of the circle is replaces by the hyperbola $\{(x_1, x_2) \mid x_1^2 - x_2^2 = 1\}$.

The next theorem shows that exact transcendental implicitization is preserved under composition of functions in a very general sense:

Theorem 1. *Let $f(t) := (f_1(t), \ldots, f_k(t))$ be a vector valued function such that the range of f on every compact or unbounded closed interval I is a semialgebraic set described by a quantifier-free formula $\varphi_I(x_1, \ldots, x_k)$. Let g be a continuous real function defined on some compact or upper semiinfinite closed interval I'. Let h_i $(1 \leq i \leq n)$ be semialgebraic real functions defined on some subset of $\mathbb{R}^n$ extending the range of f. Let $\rho_i(x_1, \ldots, x_n, y)$ be quantifier-free formulas defining the graph $\{(x_1, \ldots, x_n, y) \mid y = h_i(x_1, \ldots, x_n)\}$ of h_i. Then the vector-valued function $f^*(t) := (f_1^*(t), \ldots, f_n^*(t))$ with components $f_i^*(t) := h_i(f_1(g(t)), \ldots, f_n(g(t)))$ for $1 \leq i \leq n$ has a semialgebraic range described by the formula $\psi(x_1, \ldots, x_n) := \exists y_1 \ldots \exists y_n (\varphi_J(y_1, \ldots, y_n) \wedge \bigwedge_{i=1}^{n} \rho_i(y_1, \ldots, y_n, x_i))$, where J is the range of $g(t)$ on I'.*

The proof is obvious. Notice that the algorithmic quantifier elimination for the ordered field of real numbers this formula is required in order to transform the formula ψ into an equivalent quantifier-free formula that describes the range of f^* as a semialgebraic set. Typical instances of g and h_i are real polynomials or real rational functions. The method can in particular be applied to the situation, where f consists of a sin-cos-pair or a sinh-cosh-pair as described above. Other interesting examples are pairs $(\wp, \wp')$, where $\wp(t)$ is a Weierstrass $\wp$-function [1]. Then the range of $(\wp, \wp')$, on a large enough interval is a real elliptic curve $\{(x, y) \mid y^2 = 4x^3 - g_2 x - g_3\}$. See [5] for the more examples.

4   Semialgebraic Implicitization for Simple Elementary Functions

In this section we characterize those cases of linear differential systems S with constant coefficients and "simple right hand side", where an exact implicitization of the system of basic functions for S is possible. The condition on the right hand side $b(t)$ of the system is as follows: All components $b_i(t)$ of $b(t)$ are $\mathbb{R}$-linear combinations of functions of the form $t^{d_i} e^{a_i t} \cos(\omega_i t)$, $t^{d_i} e^{a_i t} \sin(\omega_i t)$, where d_i are non-negative integers and a_i, ω_i, α_i are real numbers. Then it is well known that a special solution of the inhomogeneous system and the fundamental solutions of the homogeneous system are again real linear combinations of functions of this kind. We call linear systems of this form *regular* and functions of type $t^d e^{at} \cos(\omega t)$, $t^d e^{at} \sin(\omega t)$, with a, ω, α real numbers *simple elementary functions*. In some special cases of regular systems, it has been shown how to solve the reach set problem by an implicit semialgebraic implicitization of functions of the following type in [23,24,22] : (i) real polynomials $p_i(t)$, (ii) exponential functions $e^{a_i t}$ with rational values of a_i. (iii) trigonometric functions $\cos(\omega_i t)$, $\sin(\omega_i t)$, for rational ω_i.

In the following we show that for simple elementary functions there are only few more cases which allow unbounded exact semialgebraic implicitization; all these cases are covered by Theorem 1 of the last section. In most of the remaining cases the exact semialgebraic implicitization problem is unsolvable. In fact we provide a complete characterization of those cases, where unbounded semialgebraic implicitization is possible.

Let $f(t) := (f_1(t), \ldots, f_n(t))$ with non-constant, pairwise different component functions $f_i(t) := t^{d_i} e^{a_i t} \cos(\omega_i t)$, or $f_i(t) := t^{d_i} e^{a_i t} \sin(\omega_i t)$, where d_i are non-negative integers and a_i, ω_i are real numbers. Moreover we assume that the functions f_i appear in cos-sin-pairs, whenever $\omega_i \neq 0$.

Theorem 2. *Let $f : [t_0, \infty) \longrightarrow \mathbb{R}^n$ be as above and let $n \geq 2$. Then the range of f is a semialgebraic set iff one of the following holds:*

1. *For all $1 \leq i \leq n$, $f_i(t) := t^{d_i}$.*
2. *For all $1 \leq i \leq n$, $d_i = 0$, $f_i(t) := e^{a_i t}$ and $dim_\mathbb{Q}(span(a_1, \ldots, a_n)) \leq 1$.*
3. *For all $1 \leq i \leq n$, $d_i \neq 0$, $a_i \neq 0$, $f_i(t) := t^{d_i} e^{a_i t}$, and $dim_\mathbb{Q}(span(a_1, \ldots, a_n)) \leq 1$, and $\frac{d_i}{d_1} = \frac{a_i}{a_1}$.*
4. *For all $1 \leq i \leq n$, $f_i(t) := \cos(\omega_i t)$, or $f_i(t) := \sin(\omega_i t)$, and $dim_\mathbb{Q}(span(\omega_1, \ldots, \omega_n)) \leq 1$.*

Moreover in these positive cases a quantifier-free formula describing the range of f can be computed algorithmically over the reals.

Idea of the Proof. In the cases mentioned above the unbounded semialgebraic implicitization is always achieved by the methods of the previous section, in particular Theorem 1. It remains to show that in all other cases the range of f is not a semialgebraic set. This requires a case distinction. In each case we show that the assumption that the range of f is semialgebraic leads to a contradiction. Based on the assumption that the range of f is semialgebraic we construct new semialgebraic sets with impossible properties. Either this set is one dimensional such that neither the set nor its complement is a finite union of intervals or it describes the graph of a semialgebraic function with an impossible rate of growth (compare [9]). See [5] for details of the proof.

This theorem clearly shows the limitations of the approach presented in [23, 24]. In fact we have the following immediate corollary:

Corollary 2. *Let $\dot{y} = Ay$ with constant $n \times n$-matrix A be a homogeneous system of linear differential equations. Then exact semialgebraic implicitization is possible for a fundamental system of solutions of the system iff one of the following cases holds:*

1. *All eigenvalues of A are zero, i.e. A is a nilpotent matrix.*
2. *All eigenvalues $\lambda_1, \ldots, \lambda_n$ of A are non-zero, pairwise distinct reals, and $dim_\mathbb{Q}(span(\lambda_1, \ldots, \lambda_n)) \leq 1$.*
3. *All eigenvalues $\lambda_1, \ldots, \lambda_n$ of A are purely imaginary, say of the form $\lambda_i = \mu_i \sqrt{-1}$ with non-zero pairwise distinct reals μ_i, and $dim_\mathbb{Q}(span(\mu_1, \ldots, \mu_n)) \leq 1$.*

5   Approximate Solutions

In this section we study the cases, where an exact semialgebraic unbounded or bounded implicitization is definitely not possible. In these cases we want to find a semialgebraic superset of the true forward reach set and a semialgebraic subset of the true backward reach set or the true control parameter set, both if possible such that the set difference to the true reach set or control parameter set is in some sense "small enough." Then an inspection of the reduction formulas shows that an overestimation of the implicitization problem leads to an overestimation of the forward reach set and an underestimation of the backward reach set and of the control parameter set *i.e.* for "safe" estimations. Hence we are reduced to the problem of finding a semialgebraic superset of the true range of a transcendental vector valued function on a compact or upper semiinfinite closed interval.

One strategy to find overestimations of the range is *separation of variables:* It comes in two flavours: Separation of variables in different components, and separation of variables in products.

Separation of variables in different components :   Let $f(t) = (f_1(t), \ldots, f_n(t))$ be defined on an interval I. Then separation of variables in different components yields the function $g(t) = (f_1(t_1), \ldots, f_n(t_n))$ defined on the cube I^n with range$(g) \supseteq$ range(f). The range of g is easily computed as a box $J_1 \times \cdots \times J_n$, where J_i is the range of f_i. Notice that this box is in fact the smallest box containing the range of f.

Separation of variables in products :   Suppose the component functions of the given functions are products $f_i(t) := f_{i,1}(t) \cdots f_{i,m}(t)$, where each $f_{i,j}(t)$ is defined on the interval I. Put $g_j(t) := (f_{1,j}, \ldots, f_{n,j})^T$. Then each g_j is also defined on the interval I. Let B_j be the range g_j, and put $C := B_1 \cdots B_m$, where the multiplication is performed on the elements componentwise. Then C is obviously a superset of the range of f.

Example 2. Let I be the upper semiinfinite interval $[0, \infty)$.

1. Let $f_1 := \cos(t)$, $f_2 := \sin(t)$. Then the true range of f is the unit circle. Separation of variables in different components yields as overestimation the closed unit square.
2. Let $f_1 := \cosh(t)$, $f_2 := \sinh(t)$. Then the true range of f is the hyperbola $\{(x, y) \mid x^2 - y^2 = 1\}$. Separation of variables in different components yields as overestimation the "quadrant" $\{(x, y) \mid x, y \geq 1\}$.
3. Let $f_1 := e^t \cos(t)$, $f_2 := e^t \sin(t)$. Then the true range of f is an expanding exponential spiral. Separation of variables in different components yields as overestimation the full plane $\mathbb{R}^2$. Separation of variables in products yields as better overestimation the annulus $\{(x, y) \mid x^2 + y^2 \geq 1\}$.
4. Let $f_1 := e^{-t} \cos(t)$, $f_2 := e^{-t} \sin(t)$. Then the true range of f is a contracting exponential spiral. Separation of variables in different components yields as overestimation a closed box $\{(x, y) \mid -e^\pi \leq x \leq 1, -e^{3\pi/2} \leq y \leq e^{\pi/2}\}$. Separation of variables in products yields as overestimation the closed disk $\{(x, y) \mid x^2 + y^2 \leq 1\}$. These approximations are incomparable. So their intersection is a common improvement of both.

6   Complexity

In this section we briefly discuss the complexity of our algorithms. From the results on complexity of quantifier elimination in [7] we can give upper bounds for the asymptotic complexity of our approach:

Discrete point reach set problems are described by purely existential formulas. Hence the complexity of quantifier elimination is at most simply exponential in the dimension of the differential system. For fixed dimension it the computation runs in a polynomial time. The complexity of bounded and unbounded reach set problems is the same as for the discrete reach set problem for a fixed number m of points. The backward discrete reach set problems can be solved in singly exponential time. The complexity of backward bounded and unbounded reach set computation is of type $e^{n^{O(1)}}$ (generalized singly exponential). The upper complexity bounds for the control parameter set problems are same as for the corresponding backward reach set problems.

7   Computational Example in REDLOG and QEPCAD

In this section we report on experimental results in reach set and control parameter set computation. In [5] we have presented experimental results for numerous examples that illustrate the different problem types and solution methods. Here we display only one of these examples with non-constant coefficients to show the generality of the approach. All computations are performed in the REDLOG package [14] of REDUCE 3.7 and QEPCAD [12] [2] . The main algorithm employed is the linear and quadratic quantifier elimination [25,31] of REDLOG and quantifier elimination based on cylindrical algebraic decomposition [12] of QEPCAD.

Example 3. Consider the inhomogeneous system $\dot{y} = Ay + b$ with

$$A := \begin{pmatrix} 0 & 2t \\ -2t & 0 \end{pmatrix}, \quad b := r_1 \begin{pmatrix} 2t\cos(t^2) \\ 2t\sin(t^2) \end{pmatrix}.$$

Then basic functions are $\begin{pmatrix} \sin(t^2) \\ \cos(t^2) \end{pmatrix}, \begin{pmatrix} \cos(t^2) \\ -\sin(t^2) \end{pmatrix}, \begin{pmatrix} \sin(t^2) \\ 0 \end{pmatrix}$. For this system we illustrate the computations in the forward/backward unbounded reach set and the control parameter set problems below (Note that we set $t_0 = 0$):

• **Forward unbounded reach set:** A quantifier-free formula $\mu(y_{11}, y_{12}, y_{21}, y_{22}, z_{11}, z_{12})$ is obtained from the following first-order formula μ_o

$$\mu_o = \exists u \exists v (u^2 + v^2 = 1 \wedge y_{11} = v \wedge y_{12} = u \wedge y_{21} = u \wedge y_{22} = -v \wedge z_{11} = v \wedge z_{12} = 0))$$

by using quantifier elimination. By using REDLOG we have

$$\mu := y_{11}^2 + y_{12}^2 - 1 = 0 \wedge y_{11} + y_{22} = 0 \wedge y_{11} - z_{11} = 0 \wedge y_{12} - y_{21} = 0 \wedge z_{12} = 0$$

---

[2] All the computations are executed on a SUN SPARC station Ultra I (140MHz).

in 10 ms. Then we set $r_1 = 1$ and moreover $\varphi = (0 \leq x_1 \leq 1 \ \wedge \ x_2 = 0)$. Then forward unbounded reach set problem is solved by using real quantifier elimination for the following first-order formula $freach$;

$$freach = \exists x_1(\varphi \wedge \ freachaux)$$

where

$$freachaux = \exists y_{11}\exists y_{12}\exists y_{21}\exists y_{22}\exists z_{11}\exists z_{12}(\mu \wedge y_1 = x_1y_{11} + x_2y_{21} + r_1z_{11}$$
$$\wedge y_2 = x_1y_{12} + x_2y_{22} + r_1z_{12})$$

By using QEPCAD for $freach$ we obtain as an answer for the forward unbounded reach set; $y_1^2 + 4y_2^2 - 4 <= 0$ in 10 ms.

• **Backward unbounded reach set:** μ is the same formula as in forward unbounded reach set. We also set $r_1 = 1$ and $\psi(x_1, x_2) = (-\frac{1}{2} \leq x_1 \leq \frac{1}{2} \wedge -\frac{1}{2} \leq x_1 \leq \frac{1}{2})$. Then the backward unbounded reach set problem is solved by using real quantifier elimination for the following first-order formula $breach$;

$$breach = \exists x_1 \exists x_2(y_1 = x_2 \wedge y_2 = x_1 \wedge breachaux)$$

where

$$breachaux = \forall y_{11}\forall y_{12}\forall y_{21}\forall y_{22}\forall z_{11}\forall z_{12}(\mu \rightarrow (-\frac{1}{2} < x_1y_{11} + x_2y_{21} + r_1z_{11} < \frac{1}{2}$$
$$\wedge -\frac{1}{2} < x_1y_{12} + x_2y_{22} + r_1z_{12} < \frac{1}{2})$$

By using REDLOG for $breach$ we obtain in 420 ms a semialgebraic description of the backward unbounded reach set consisting of 21 atomic formulas.

• **Control parameter set:** The formula μ is the same as in the reach set cases. We also set $\varphi = (0 \leq x_1 \leq 1 \wedge x_2 = 0)$ and $\psi(x_1, x_2) = (-\frac{1}{2} < x_1 < \frac{1}{2} \wedge -\frac{1}{2} < x_1 < \frac{1}{2})$. Then control parameter set problem is solved by using real quantifier elimination for the following first-order formula $pcontrol$;

$$control = \exists x_1(\varphi \wedge control aux)$$

where

$$controlaux = \forall y_{11}\forall y_{12}\forall y_{21}\forall y_{22}\forall z_{11}\forall z_{12}(\mu \rightarrow (-\frac{1}{2} < x_1y_{11} + x_2y_{21} + r_1z_{11} < \frac{1}{2}$$
$$\wedge -\frac{1}{2} < x_1y_{12} + x_2y_{22} + r_1z_{12} < \frac{1}{2})$$

By using REDLOG for $control$ we obtain in 70 ms a semialgebraic description of control parameter set consisting of 12 atomic formulas. It can be simplified to the result $-1 \leq r_1 < \frac{1}{2}$ by hand calculation.

8   Conclusions

In this paper we have studied forward and backward reach set and control parameter set problems for continuous parametric open-loop systems described by a system of parametric linear differential equations with arbitrary coefficients.

The approach using quantifier elimination was introduced into reach set computations in [29]. We extend their ad hoc approach for special types of differential systems to a systematic study of the type of results obtainable by an approach via real quantifier elimination. Thus we obtain a much wider systematic framework applicable to a considerably larger class of systems. The main observation is that all the problems can be reduced by exact symbolic algorithms to an implicitization problem for certain basic transcendental functions associated with the given system.

We have proved a theorem that determines the exact classes of vector-valued functions of the kind arising in linear differential systems with constant coefficients, where exact semialgebraic implicitization is possible. As a corollary we have obtained the exact limitations of the approach of [23,24] for linear differential systems with constant coefficients and simple elementary inhomogeneous part. We have also proposed several ways to overcome these limitations by approximate computations. The problems have been illustrated by examples computed in the REDLOG-package of REDUCE and QEPCAD.

Further research will be concerned with an extension of these results to hybrid systems.

References

1. N. L. Alling. *Real elliptic curves*. North-Holland, 1981.
2. R. Alur, C. Coucoubetis, N. Halbwachs, T. Henzinger, P. Ho, X. Nicolin, A. Olivere, J. Safakis, and S. Yovine. The algorithmic analysis of hybrid systems. *Theoretical Computer Science*, 138:3–34, 1995.
3. H. Anai. Algebraic approach to analysis of discrete-time polynomial systems. In *Proc. of European Control Conference 1999*, 1999.
4. H. Anai and S. Hara. Fixed-structure robust controller synthesis based on sign definite condition by a special quantifier elimination. In *Proceedings of American Control Conference 2000*, pages 1312–1316, 2000.
5. H. Anai and V. Weispfenning. Reach set computation using real quantifier elimination. Technical Report MIP-0012, FMI, Universität Passau, D-94030 Passau, Germany, Oct. 2000.
6. B. Anderson, N. Bose, and E. Jury. Output feedback stabilization and related problems — solution via decision methods. *IEEE Trans. Auto. Control*, 20(1):53–65, 1975.
7. S. Basu, R. Pollack, and M.-F. Roy. On the combinatorial and algebraic complexity of quantifier elimination. *J. ACM*, 43(6):1002–1045, 1996.
8. T. Becker, V. Weispfenning, and H. Kredel. *Gröbner Bases, a Computational Approach to Commutative Algebra*, volume 141 of *Graduate Texts in Mathematics*. Springer, New York, corrected second printing edition, 1998.
9. J. Bochnak, M. Coste, and M.-F. Roy. *Géometrie algébrique réelle*. Springer, Berlin, Heidelberg, New York, 1987.
10. M. Braun. *Differential Equations and Their Applications*, volume 15 of *Applied Mathematical Science*. Springer, 3rd edition, 1983.
11. B. Caviness and J. Johnson, editors. *Quantifier Elimination and Cylindrical Algebraic Decomposition*. Texts and Monographs in Symbolic Computation. Springer, Berlin, Heidelberg, New York, 1998.
12. G. E. Collins and H. Hong. Partial cylindrical algebraic decomposition for quantifier elimination. *Journal of Symbolic Computation*, 12(3):299–328, Sept. 1991.
13. J. Craig. *Introduction to Robotics*. Addison-Wesley, 1986.

14. A. Dolzmann and T. Sturm. REDLOG: Computer algebra meets computer logic. *ACM SIGSAM Bulletin*, 31(2):2–9, June 1997.
15. P. Dorato, W.Yang, and C.Abdallah. Application of quantifier elimination theory to robust multi-object feedback design. *J. Symb. Comp.* **11**, pages 1–6, 1995.
16. L. v. d. Dries. *Tame Topology and o-minimal structures*. Cambridge University Press, 1998.
17. T. Henzinger, P. Kopke, A. Puri, and P. Varaiya. What's decidable about hybrid automata? In *Proceedings of the 27th Annual Symposium on Theory of Computing, STOC'95*, pages 373–382. ACM Press, 1995.
18. T. Henzinger and S. Sastry, editors. *Hybrid Systems : Computation and Control*, volume 1386 of *LNCS*. Springer-Verlag, 1998.
19. M. Jirstrand. Nonlinear control system design by quantifier elimination. *Journal of Symbolic Computation*, 24(2):137–152, Aug. 1997. Special issue on applications of quantifier elimination.
20. P. Kovács. Computer algebra in robot-kinematics. In *Proceeding of the workshop:"Computer Algebra in Science and Engineering", Bielefeld, Aug'94*, pages 303–316, Singapore, 1994. World Scientific.
21. A. Kurzhanski and I. Víyi. *Ellipsoidal Calculus for Estimation and Control*. Birkhäuser, 1997.
22. G. Lafferriere, G. Pappas, and S. Sastry. O-minimal hybrid systems. *Mathematics of control, Signals and Systems*, 13(1):1–21, 2000.
23. G. Lafferriere, G. Pappas, and S. Yovine. A new class of decidable hybrid systems. In *Hybrid Systems: Computation and Control*, volume 1569 of *LNCS*, pages 137–151. Springer, 1999.
24. G. Lafferriere, G. Pappas, and S. Yovine. Reachability computation for linear hybrid systems. In *Proceedings of the 14th IFAC World Congress*, volume E, pages 7–12, Beijin, P.R.China, 1999.
25. R. Loos and V. Weispfenning. Applying linear quantifier elimination. *The Computer Journal*, 36(5):450–462, 1993. Special issue on computational quantifier elimination.
26. N. A. Lynch and B. H. Krogh, editors. *Proceedings Third International Workshop on Hybrid Systems: Computation and Control (HSCC 2000), Pittsburgh, PA, USA*, volume 1790 of *Lecture Notes in Computer Science*. Springer-Verlag, Mar. 2000.
27. D. Manocha and J. Canny. Algorithm for implicitizing rational parametric surfaces. In R. Barnhill and W. Boehm, editors, *Computer Aided Geometric Design*, volume 9. North-Holland, 1992.
28. D. Nešić. Two algorithms arising in analysis of polynomial models. In *Proceedings of 1998 American Control Conference*, pages 1889–1893, 1998.
29. G. Pappas and S. Yovine. Decidable hybrid systems. Technical report, University of California at Berkeley, 1998.
30. F. Vaandrager and J. von Schuppen, editors. *Hybrid Systems : Computation and Control*, volume 1569 of *LNCS*. Springer-Verlag, 1999.
31. V. Weispfenning. Quantifier elimination for real algebra—the quadratic case and beyond. *Applicable Algebra in Engineering Communication and Computing*, 8(2):85–101, Feb. 1997.
32. V. Weispfenning. Semilinear motion planning in REDLOG. Technical report, Universität Passau, D-94030 Passau, May 1999. available at the electronic proceedings of IMACS-ACA'99, http://math.unm.edu/aca.html.

On Hybrid Control of Under-Actuated Mechanical Systems*

Eugene Asarin[1], Sorav Bansal[2], Bernard Espiau[3],
Thao Dang[1], and Oded Maler[1]

[1] VERIMAG, Centre Equation, 2, av. de Vignate, 38610 Gières, France
{asarin,tdang,maler}@imag.fr
[2] Indian Institute of Technology, New Delhi, India
csu97146@cognac.cse.iitd.ernet.in
[3] INRIA Rhône-Alpes, 655, av. de l'Europe, 38334 Montbonnot, France
Bernard.Espiau@inrialpes.fr

Abstract. In this work we present a novel control design methodology for under-actuated mechanical systems. As part of the design process we use the reachability analysis tool **d/dt** [ABDM99,D00] to see whether there is a switching sequence which can drive the system to a desired periodic orbit. Much of the work in the design of the control law is done manually using classical control techniques (unlike the fully-automatic approach advocated in [ABD+00]), and **d/dt** is used to complement these techniques. We hope this work will contribute to the proliferation of reachability-based techniques to the control engineer's tool box.

1 Introduction

The algorithmic approach to the analysis of hybrid systems, first put forward explicitly in [ACH+95], is inspired by a computer science approach to verification of automata. The system under consideration is viewed as a generator of trajectories and the problem of verification consists of checking whether there is an individual trajectory which violates some specification, e.g. reaches a bad state. Likewise, the controller synthesis problem is phrased as restricting systematically the set of all possible behaviors in order to satisfy a property. The algorithmic approach consists in making a *brute-force search* in the state-space, based only on the description of the system dynamics. Initially this approach has been applied to restricted classes of hybrid systems where the continuous dynamics has a constant derivative in every state, see e.g. [AD94] for timed automata, and [ACH+95,AMP95,HHW97] for hybrid automata. More recently attempts have been made to lift this approach to systems with non-trivial dynamics. In particular, some of the authors were involved in the development of **d/dt**, a tool for verification and controller synthesis for hybrid systems with linear continuous dynamics [ABDM99,D00]. The synthesis algorithm implemented

* This work was partially supported by the European Community Esprit-LTR Project 26270 VHS (Verification of Hybrid systems) and the French-Israeli collaboration project 970MAEFUT5 (Hybrid Models of Industrial Plants).

M.D. Di Benedetto, A. Sangiovanni-Vincentelli (Eds.): HSCC 2001, LNCS 2034, pp. 77–88, 2001.
© Springer-Verlag Berlin Heidelberg 2001

in $\mathbf{d/dt}$ [ABD$^+$00,D00] suggested a very idealistic scenario for switching-based control: the user defines the dynamics at the various modes, as well as the control objective, and the tool automatically generates the appropriate conditions for mode switching.

This approach attempts to obtain the *general-purpose* flavor of discrete verification tools and it is still very remote from control engineering practice. In the continuous world, every class of systems has its own special character as well as its corresponding mathematical tricks which are used extensively by engineers during the controller design process. Coordinate transformations, dimensionality reduction, simplifying assumptions or linearization cannot be captured by straightforward reachability analysis.

In this paper we show how reachability-based techniques can be combined with more "knowledge-based" methods in order to derive control strategies for a non-trivial class of dynamical systems, namely under-actuated mechanical systems. We propose a general methodology for designing controllers for such systems and demonstrate it on a double-pendulum example. The complexity of the system as given initially exceeds the current capabilities of reachability-based tools: its dynamics is non-linear and control is done using continuous actuation. Moreover, the system is of dimension n while the dimensionality of the available control is $m < n$. The proposed approach to control this system by switching is based on the following principles.

1. The state-space can be transformed and partitioned via a diffeomorphism ϕ into an m-dimensional part e_1 and an $(n - m)$-dimensional part e_2.
2. Using standard control techniques, e_1 can be controlled to zero. Given this control, the remaining part is a closed system which defines the dynamics of e_2 (called the Zero dynamics).
3. Each diffeomorphism induces a different control law for its zero dynamics and hence a particular "mode" for the dynamics of the the uncontrolled part of the system. We use a parameterized family of diffeomorphisms which becomes finite after discretizing the parameters.
4. The dynamics of e_2 at each mode can be linearized around its equilibrium point. It is possible to choose the parameters so that the linearized system has periodic orbits in every mode. It should be kept in mind that the validity of the linear model is restricted to the neighborhood of the equilibrium.
5. If our goal is to reach a specific periodic orbit, we can achieve it by a sequence of mode switchings. At each mode, however, a different quantity is controlled to zero. Hence, when we switch from controlling e_1 to controlling e_1', the latter should already be close to zero. This restricts the parts of the state-space of the e_2 system where switching is allowed and leads to modeling the system as a hybrid automaton where the transition guards reflect these constraints.

The role of $\mathbf{d/dt}$ is then to check whether, based on the hybrid automaton representation, it is possible to reach from one orbit to another by mode switching and how much time it takes.

2 Control of Under-Actuated Mechanical Systems

2.1 Under-Actuated Mechanical Systems

We consider the class of jointed mechanical systems without flexibilities, the dynamics of which is given by Lagrange equations:

$$M(q)\ddot{q} + N(q,\dot{q}) = W\Gamma \qquad (1)$$

where M is the symmetric positive definite matrix defining the kinetic energy and N gathers generalized gravity, Coriolis and centrifugal forces; q is the n−dimensional vector of generalized (joint) coordinates; Γ includes all external generalized forces and W is a constant matrix.

If we now assume that the generalized forces are only actuation torques/forces (i.e the system is friction-free and no other potential-based actions occur), then the system is called *under-actuated* if rank $(W) < n$. Without loss of generality, we can consider that $W = \begin{pmatrix} I_m \\ 0_{n-m \times n} \end{pmatrix}$ with $m < n$ the number of actuators.

2.2 Zero Dynamics

Let us consider a diffeomorphism ϕ:

$$q \rightarrow \phi(q) = \begin{pmatrix} e_1(q) \\ e_2(q) \end{pmatrix} \qquad (2)$$

where e_1 is m-dimensional. Then, the dynamics (1) projected on the constraint $e_1 = 0$ is called the *zero dynamics* associated with ϕ. It is given by:

$$P(q)(M(q)\ddot{q} + N(q,\dot{q})) = 0 \qquad (3)$$

with $P = I_n - W(J_1 M^{-1} W)^{-1} J_1 M^{-1}$ the projection operator, in which $J_1 = \frac{\partial e_1}{\partial q}$. A control objective can therefore be to bring the system to this zero dynamics, specified by the goal task $e_1 = 0$, and to stabilize it. Since dim $(e_1) =$ dim (Γ), all the available actuation forces/torques have to be used for that purpose. In fact, that can be done trough partial decoupling/feedback linearization: it can be easily seen that using the control

$$\Gamma = (J_1 M^{-1} W)^{-1}(u - \dot{J_1}\dot{q} + J_1 M^{-1} N) \qquad (4)$$

we obtain $\ddot{e}_1 = u$, assumed that $J_1 M^{-1} W$ is nonsingular. It then remains to specify an adequate input u which stabilizes e_1, asymptotically or in finite time, in order to drive the system to the zero dynamics. Once reached, its motion is then governed by eq. (3), which is free, since no more control is available. In many cases, this free motion is a periodic orbit. The idea now is to specify such a periodic orbit as a final goal, recalling that we can consider the choice of ϕ as a way to modify it. The problem addressed in the following is then to study the reachability of this behavior starting from given initial conditions, using a sequence $\phi_1, \phi_2 \ldots$, i.e successive jumps from an orbit to another one.

2.3   Handling the Periodic Orbits

Let us consider the case where $m = n-1$, i.e. the zero dynamics can be expressed using a single coordinate denoted by x_1. When the phase portrait of the system is a closed curve O, this periodic orbit, which characterizes the zero dynamics, can be uniquely specified by a pair (ϕ, X^0) where X^0 is a point on the orbit, for example the initial conditions. Let us assume (assumption A0) that the equation of O in the phase plane is of the form $V(x_1, \dot{x}_1) - \tilde{V} = 0$, the invariance being expressed by $\dot{V} = 0$. V is a so-called *Lyapunov* function. For a non-actuated conservative mechanical system, the natural V is the mechanical energy. Since it is not the case here, $\tilde{V}$ can only be called by analogy the "energy" level of the orbit.

Let us now consider the particular case where the set of ϕ_i consists of functions of given analytical form depending on a k-dimensional vector of real parameters p. Then p can be considered as an auxiliary control of the system. Giving some bounds to the parameters and the variables, so that they range over D_p and D_{X^0}, respectively, the set of all possible orbits for the system is

$$\mathbf{0} = \{O(p, X^0) : p \in D_p \ X^0 \in D_{X^0}\}.$$

When V is known, the set can also be parameterized by p and $\tilde{V}$.

The problem we address now is the following: let us define a desired behavior of the system as a goal orbit O^*; then, given an initial orbit $O_0 \neq O^*$, can we reach O^* by modifying p? We don't consider here related problems of automatic control: existence of the orbits, active stabilization, continuous control of p, which will be addressed in forthcoming papers. Instead, we focus our attention on a *discrete* approach, i.e. to the questions: is there a sequence of intersecting orbits allowing to reach O^* through jumps on the parameters and how long time will it take? Assuming here that these jumps are instantaneous and don't disturb the overall behavior (assumption A1), we can therefore forget the effect of the control (4) and consider for the analysis the related set of zero dynamics uniquely. We are therefore led back to a problem of reachability analysis of a hybrid system: each discrete state is an homogeneous differential equation associated with given values of the parameters; transitions are allowed when orbits of different modes are compatible with each other, i.e. when continuous state variables reach some particular values. We will illustrate the approach on the double pendulum example.

3   The Case of the Double Pendulum

The considered testbed is the double pendulum depicted in Figure 1. The reader is referred to [EGP99] for details on experimental issues. Terms in eq. (1) write for this system as:

$$M = \begin{pmatrix} m_{11} & m_{12} \\ m_{12} & m_{22} \end{pmatrix} \tag{5}$$

and:

$$N = \begin{pmatrix} N_1(q_1, q_2, \dot{q}_1, \dot{q}_2) \\ N_2(q_1, q_2, \dot{q}_1, \dot{q}_2) \end{pmatrix} = \begin{pmatrix} C_{11} & C_{12} \\ C_{21} & C_{22} \end{pmatrix} \begin{pmatrix} \dot{q}_1 \\ \dot{q}_2 \end{pmatrix} + \begin{pmatrix} G_1 \\ G_2 \end{pmatrix} \tag{6}$$

with:

$$
\begin{aligned}
m_{11} &= m_1 l_1^2 + m_2(l_2^2 + L_1^2 + 2L_1 l_2 c2) \\
m_{12} &= m_2(l_2^2 + L_1 l_2 c2) \\
m_{22} &= m_2 l_2^2 \\
C_{11} &= -m_2 L_1 l_2 s2 \dot{q}_2 \\
C_{12} &= -m_2 L_1 l_2 s2(\dot{q}_1 + \dot{q}_2) \\
C_{21} &= m_2 L_1 l_2 s2 \dot{q}_1 \\
C_{22} &= 0 \\
G_1 &= g((m_1 l_1 + m_2 L_1)s1 + m_2 l_2 s12) \\
G_2 &= g m_2 l_2 s12
\end{aligned}
\tag{7}
$$

where $si := sin(q_i)$, $ci := cos(q_i)$, $sij := sin(q_i + q_j)$. We consider the case where only the hip is actuated. Therefore $W = \begin{pmatrix} 1 \\ 0 \end{pmatrix}$. Let us now choose the diffeomorphism ϕ and the control Γ such that

$$e_1 = q_1 - a q_2 - b = 0 \; ; \; e_2 = q_2 \tag{8}$$

where a and b are two real parameters[1]. Therefore the zero dynamics we have to consider is simply:

$$\begin{cases} (m_{22} + a m_{12})\ddot{q}_2 + (a C_{21} + C_{22})\dot{q}_2 + G_2 = 0 \\ q_1 = a q_2 + b \end{cases} \tag{9}$$

where it assumed that $m_{22} + a m_{12} \neq 0$ (assumption A2, satisfied when $-\frac{l_2}{L_1 + l_2} < a < \frac{l_2}{L_1 - l_2}$). This system can be expressed in the single coordinate q_2. It is a second order nonlinear differential equation, for which the natural state vector is $X = \begin{pmatrix} x_1 \\ x_2 \end{pmatrix} = \begin{pmatrix} q_2 - q_2^* \\ \dot{q}_2 \end{pmatrix}$. In order to perform reachability analysis, we have to linearize the system. Its equilibrium points $X^* = \begin{pmatrix} 0 \\ 0 \end{pmatrix}$ are solutions of $G_2(q_2^*) = 0$, i.e, for $a \neq -1$ (assumption A3):

$$q_2^* = -\frac{b + k\pi}{1 + a} \tag{10}$$

We consider in the following only the case $k = 0$. The equation of the system linearized around the center q_2^* is:

$$\dot{x} = Ax = \begin{pmatrix} 0 & 1 \\ -\alpha & 0 \end{pmatrix} x \tag{11}$$

---

[1] Note that expression (8) specifies the desired spatial trajectory of the tip of the double pendulum, while the "energy" level will set the amplitude and the time profile of its motion along this trajectory

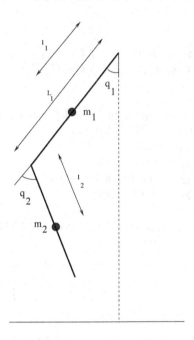

Fig. 1. A double pendulum.

where $\alpha = l_2 + \frac{a}{1+a}L_1 cos(\frac{b}{1+a})$. For ensuring the existence of periodic orbits, the eigenvalues of A have to be imaginary, which implies that α has to be strictly positive (assumption A4). The Lyapunov function associated with the system, i.e the energy level of an orbit is

$$V = \frac{1}{2}(\alpha x_1^2 + x_2^2) \tag{12}$$

For the purpose of reachability analysis it is more comfortable to work with the same system of coordinates in every state, hence we transform the linear dynamics of equation (11) into an affine dynamics over $y = (q_2, \dot{q}_2)$:

$$\dot{y} = Ay + u = \begin{pmatrix} 0 & 1 \\ -\alpha & 0 \end{pmatrix} y + \begin{pmatrix} 0 \\ \alpha q_2^* \end{pmatrix} \tag{13}$$

Finally we have to remember that the system is submitted to physical bounds on the joints: $q_i \in [q_i^{min}, q_i^{max}]$. Introducing them in (8) leads to linear constraints on the parameters.

When we switch from ϕ to ϕ' there might be a transient period until the system settles in the new zero dynamics. In order to make assumption A1 (transitions are immediate) realistic we need to make sure that e_1' and $\dot{e}_1'$ be already close to their zero. For q_1 this means

$$|e_1'| = |q_1 - a'q_2 - b'| < \epsilon_1 \tag{14}$$

Since $q_1 = aq_2 + b$ this reduces to

$$|(a - a')q_2 + (b - b')| < \epsilon_1 \tag{15}$$

For $\dot{q}_2$ we need:

$$|\dot{e}_1'| = |(a - a')\dot{q}_2| < \epsilon_2 \tag{16}$$

These conditions, which form rectangles in the phase-space of the zero dynamics, will be used as transition guards in the hybrid automaton model. Note that these conditions are symmetric, i.e. they are the same, in terms of q_2 and $\dot{q}_2$ for the transitions from (a', b') to (a, b). Of course, their global physical interpretation does depend on the source state of the transition.

The system is modeled as a hybrid automaton with 7 states, each representing a pair (a, b) of parameters (Figure 2). At each state the dynamics is of the form $\dot{x} = Ax + u$ where A and u for the various states are:

s_0		s_1		s_2		s_3		s_4		s_5		s_6	
0	1	0	1	0	1	0	1	0	1	0	1	0	1
−0.0479	0	−0.0878	0	−0.1167	0	−0.1982	0	−0.2326	0	−0.3143	0	−0.3555	0
0		0		0		0		0		0		0	
0.0011		0.0000		−0.0012		0.0000		−0.0039		−0.0090		−0.0140	

The transition guards are computed according to (15) and (16) with $\epsilon_1 = 0.05$ and $\epsilon_2 = 0.02$. In addition, we restrict the transitions to happen between pairs of "close" states, i.e. $|a - a'| \leq 0.15$ and $|b - b'| \leq 0.1$.

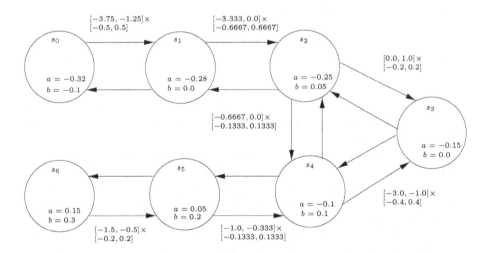

Fig. 2. The hybrid automaton for the double pendulum. The transition guards between pairs of states are written as products of intervals.

In order to facilitate the experimentation with **d/dt** we have augmented the input syntax to include parameters and formulae referring to them. For example, state s_0 and its outgoing transition is specified as:

```
state: 0;
matrixA:
 0.0  1.0,
 [-12-(a0/(1+a0))*L1*cos(b0/(1+a0))]   0.0;
input: type convex_vert
 0.0 [(b0/(1+a0))*(-12-(a0/(1+a0))*L1*cos(b0/(1+a0)))];
transition:
  label go01:
  if in guard:  type rectangle
    [-(-eps1+(b0-b1))/(a0-a1)]  [-(eps1+(b0-b1))/(a0-a1)],
    [eps2/(a0-a1)]  [-eps2/(a0-a1)];
  goto 1;
```

4   Results

The problem we solve with **d/dt** is the following: *given some initial low-energy orbit (more precisely, a connected set of orbits) is there a sequence of switchings that brings the system to its target, a higher-energy set of orbits?* This problem is essentially a controller synthesis problem for the *eventuality* specification, unlike the *safety* controller synthesis that we have treated in [ABD+00]. We are interested in reaching the desired orbit with the least number of mode switchings.

We illustrate informally the synthesis procedure that we employ in order to derive the switching controller. Consider an initial set of orbits characterized by the rectangle (in the $(q_2, \dot{q}_2)$ space) $P = [0.7 \times 0.9] \times [0.01, 0.02]$ at state s_3 and a goal orbit characterized by $F = [1.05, 1.3] \times [0.01, 0.02]$ at the same state. Starting from the inital set (s, P) we calculate, in a *breadth-first* manner, all its successors, i.e. continuous successors, and then, via intersection with the guards, the discrete successors. We continue until at some level k of the search tree, there is one or more paths having a leaf (s, Q) such that Q intersects F. The search graph of the first iteration is shown in Figure 3 and there are two intersections with the goal orbit after 4 transitions, along the paths s_3, s_2, s_3, s_2, s_3 and s_3, s_2, s_1, s_2, s_3. For every such path we do backward reachability analysis to find the predecessors of the goal orbit at every node and, in particular, the subset of P from which the goal can be reached by taking the k transitions that correspond to the path. This information is also used to derive the controller by restricting the guards. In our example we conclude that points satisfying $q_2 \in [0.7552, 0.9]$ can reach the goal orbit by following the sequence s_3, s_2, s_3, s_2, s_3 and those satisfying $q_2 \in [0.7152, 0.9]$ can do it following the sequence s_3, s_2, s_1, s_2, s_3. Note that from the interval $[0.7552, 0.9]$ both sequences can be taken.

If not all points in P are "covered" by the k-length sequences found in the first iteration, we restart the procedure from (s, P') where $P' \subseteq P$ is the subset of P

consisting of the points not covered yet. In our example P' consists of the points satisfying $q_2 \in [0.7, 0.7152]$. In the second iteration we find out that the goal orbit can be reached from any point in P' by either one of the three 6-transition sequences $s_3, s_2, s_3, s_2, s_3, s_2, s_3$, $\quad s_3, s_2, s_3, s_2, s_1, s_2, s_3$ and $s_3, s_2, s_1, s_2, s_1, s_2, s_3$, and this concludes the computation. The fact that $\dot{q}_2$ does not matter here is particular to this example — with other sets of parameters the partition of the initial set did involve conditions on $\dot{q}_2$. The reachable states which correspond to the discovery of the sequence $s_3, s_2, s_1, s_2, s_1, s_2, s_3$ in the second iteration are depicted in Figure 4 and 5.

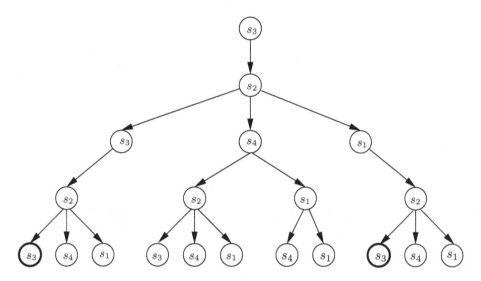

Fig. 3. The first iteration of the search tree. The goal orbits were first reached after 4 transitions along two paths of the tree.

5   Conclusion

We have investigated a new methodology for designing hybrid controllers which is partially-supported by our reachability analysis tool **d/dt**. Like [ABD+00] and [TLS00] this work explores the contribution of the hybrid automaton model to the alternative formulation and solution of problems in switching-based control. In this paper we have treated an interesting and open problem in robot control and provided a partial solution. To improve the performance of the algorithm, we plan to investigate other search procedures (backward computation and heuristic search) and validate our results via simulation.

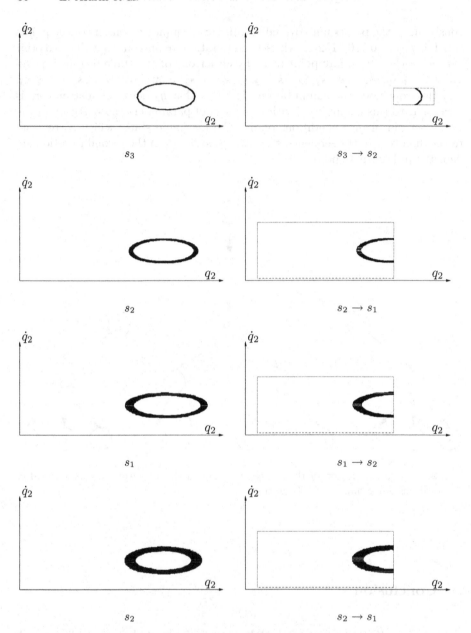

Fig. 4. Computation of reachable states for the sequence s_3, s_2, s_1, s_2. On the left we see the reachable set at mode s_i while at the right we show the intersecion with the guard from s_i to s_j.

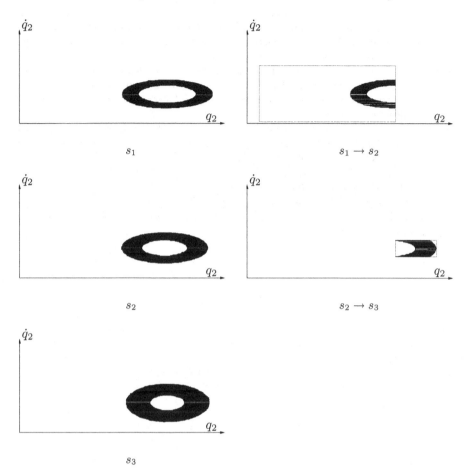

Fig. 5. Computation of reachable states for the sequence $s_3, s_2, s_1, s_2, s_1, s_2, s_3$ continued from Figure 4.

References

AD94. R. Alur and D.L. Dill, A Theory of Timed Automata, *Theoretical Computer Science* 126, 183–235, 1994.

ACH$^+$95. R. Alur, C. Courcoubetis, N. Halbwachs, T.A. Henzinger, P.-H. Ho, X. Nicollin, A. Olivero, J. Sifakis and S. Yovine, The Algorithmic Analysis of Hybrid Systems, *Theoretical Computer Science* 138, 3–34, 1995.

ABDM99. E. Asarin, O. Bournez, T. Dang and O. Maler, Reachability Analysis of Piecewise-Linear Dynamical Systems, in B. Krogh and N. Lynch (Eds.), *Hybrid Systems: Computation and Control*, 20-31 LNCS 1790, Springer, 2000.

ABD$^+$00. E. Asarin, O. Bournez, T. Dang, O. Maler and A. Pnueli, Effective Synthesis of Switching Controllers for Linear Systems, *Proceedings of the IEEE* 88, 1011-1025, 2000.

AMP95.   E. Asarin, O. Maler and A. Pnueli, Reachability Analysis of Dynamical Systems having Piecewise-Constant Derivatives, *Theoretical Computer Science* 138, 35-66, 1995.

EGP99.   B. Espiau, I. Guigues, R. Pissard-Gibollet, Can an Underactuated Leg with a Passive Joint at the Knee Achieve a Ballistic Step?, *Proceedings of the International Symposium on Experimental Robotics* Sydney, Australia, 26-28 march 1999

D00.   T. Dang, *Verification and Synthesis of Hybrid Systems*, Ph.D. Thesis, INPG Grenoble, 2000, `ftp://ftp.imag.fr/pub/Mediatheque.IMAG/theses/2000/Dang.Thi-Xuan-Thao/these.dir`

HHW97.   T.A. Henzinger, P.-H. Ho, and H. Wong-Toi, HyTech: A Model Checker for Hybrid Systems, *Software Tools for Technology Transfer* 1, 110-122, 1997.

TLS00.   C. Tomlin, J. Lygeros and S. Sastry, A Game-Theoretic Approach to Controller Design for Hybrid Systems, in *Proceedings of the IEEE* 88, 949-970, 2000.

On the Decidability of the Reachability Problem for Planar Differential Inclusions*

Eugene Asarin **, Gerardo Schneider ***, and Sergio Yovine

VERIMAG
2, Ave de Vignate
38610 - Gières, France
{Eugene.Asarin, Gerardo.Schneider, Sergio.Yovine}@imag.fr

Abstract. In this paper we develop an algorithm for solving the reachability problem of two-dimensional piece-wise rectangular differential inclusions. Our procedure is not based on the computation of the reach-set but rather on the computation of the limit of individual trajectories. A key idea is the use of one-dimensional affine Poincaré maps for which we can easily compute the fixpoints. As a first step, we show that between any two points linked by an arbitrary trajectory there always exists a trajectory without self-crossings. Thus, solving the reachability problem requires considering only those. We prove that, indeed, there are only finitely many "qualitative types" of those trajectories. The last step consists in giving a decision procedure for each of them. These procedures are essentially based on the analysis of the limits of extreme trajectories. We illustrate our algorithm on a simple model of a swimmer spinning around a whirlpool.

1 Introduction

One of the main research areas in hybrid systems is reachability analysis. It comprises two (closely related) issues, namely, the study of decidability and the development of algorithms. Most of the proved decidability results are based on the existence of a finite and computable partition of the state space into classes of states which are equivalent with respect to reachability. This is the case for timed automata [2], and classes of rectangular automata [12] and hybrid automata with linear vector fields [15]. Except for timed automata, these results rely on stringent hypothesis such as the resetting of variables along transitions.

Although analysis techniques based on the construction of a finite partition have been proposed [7], mainly all implemented computational procedures resort to (forward or backward) propagation of constraints, typically (unions of convex) polyhedra or ellipsoids [1,3,6,9,11,14]. In general, these techniques provide semi-decision procedures, that is, if the given final set of states is reachable, they will

---

* This work was partially supported by Projet IMAG MASH "Modélisation et Analyse de Systèmes Hybrides".
** Partially supported by the NATO under grant CRG-961115.
*** Supported by ESPRIT-LTR Project 26270 VHS "Verification of Hybrid Systems".

M.D. Di Benedetto, A. Sangiovanni-Vincentelli (Eds.): HSCC 2001, LNCS 2034, pp. 89–104, 2001.
© Springer-Verlag Berlin Heidelberg 2001

terminate, otherwise they may fail to. This is a property of the techniques, not of the problem, that is, it does not imply that the reachability problem itself is undecidable, but only that they do not implement a decision procedure for it. In other words, these algorithms may be unsuccessful (i.e., not terminate) for certain classes of systems for which the reachability problem is indeed decidable (by other means). Nevertheless, they provide tools for computing (approximations of) the reach-set for large classes of hybrid systems with linear and non-linear vector fields.

Maybe the major drawback of set-propagation, reach-set approximation procedures is that they pay little attention to the geometric properties of the specific (class of) systems under analysis. To our knowledge, in the context of hybrid systems there are two lines of work in the direction of developing more "geometric" approaches. One is based on the existence of (enough) integrals and the ability to compute them all [7,10]. These methods, however, do not necessarily result in decision procedures (they are actually not meant to). The other, applicable to two-dimensional dynamical systems, relies on the topological properties of the plane, and explicitly focuses on decidability issues. This approach has been proposed in [16]. There, it is shown that the reachability problem for two-dimensional systems with piece-wise constant derivatives (PCD) is decidable. This result has been extended in [8] for planar piece-wise Hamiltonian systems. In [4] it has been shown that the reachability problem for PCD is undecidable for dimensions higher than two.

In this paper we develop an algorithm for solving the reachability problem of two-dimensional piece-wise rectangular differential inclusions. As in [16], our procedure is not based on the computation of the reach-set but rather on the computation of the limit of individual trajectories. A key idea is the use of one-dimensional affine Poincaré maps for which we can easily compute the fixpoints. The decidability result of [16] fundamentally relies on the determinism of PCD which implies that planar trajectories do not intersect themselves. This property is no longer true for differential inclusions. As a first step, we show that between any two points linked by an arbitrary trajectory there always exists a trajectory without self-crossings. Thus, solving the reachability problem requires considering only those. We prove that, indeed, there are only finitely many "qualitative types" of those trajectories. The last step consists in giving a decision procedure for each of them. These procedures are essentially based on the analysis of the limits of extreme trajectories (which do not cut themselves).

2   Simple Planar Differential Inclusions

A *simple planar differential inclusion system* (SPDI) consists of a partition of the plane into convex polygonal regions, together with a differential inclusion associated with each region. As an example consider the problem of a swimmer trying to escape from a whirlpool in a river.

Example. The dynamics $\dot{x}$ of the swimmer around the whirlpool is approximated by the piece-wise differential inclusion defined as follows. The zone of the river nearby the whirlpool is divided into 8 regions $R_1, \ldots, R_8$. To each region R_i we associate a pair of vectors $(\mathbf{a}_i, \mathbf{b}_i)$ meaning that $\dot{\mathbf{x}}$ belongs to their positive hull: $\mathbf{a}_1 = \mathbf{b}_1 = (1, 5)$, $\mathbf{a}_2 = \mathbf{b}_2 = (-1, \frac{1}{2})$, $\mathbf{a}_3 = (-1, \frac{11}{60})$ and $\mathbf{b}_3 = (-1, -\frac{1}{4})$, $\mathbf{a}_4 = \mathbf{b}_4 = (-1, -1)$, $\mathbf{a}_5 = \mathbf{b}_5 = (0, -1)$, $\mathbf{a}_6 = \mathbf{b}_6 = (1, -1)$, $\mathbf{a}_7 = \mathbf{b}_7 = (1, 0)$, $\mathbf{a}_8 = \mathbf{b}_8 = (1, 1)$. The corresponding SPDI is illustrated in Fig. 1. □

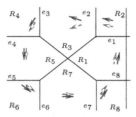

Fig. 1. The SPDI of the swimmer.

More formally, a SPDI is a pair $\mathcal{H} = (\mathcal{P}, \phi)$, where $\mathcal{P}$ is a finite partition of the plane into convex polyhedral sets, and for each $P \in \mathcal{P}$, $\phi(P)$, also denoted by $\angle_{\mathbf{a}_P}^{\mathbf{b}_P}$, is the set of all linear combinations $\mathbf{x} = \alpha\,\mathbf{a}_P + \beta\,\mathbf{b}_P$, with $\alpha, \beta \geq 0$, and $\alpha + \beta > 0$, of two vectors $\mathbf{a}_P$ and $\mathbf{b}_P$, such that $\hat{\mathbf{a}}_P \cdot \mathbf{b}_P < 0$, where $\cdot$ is the scalar product and $\hat{\mathbf{a}}_P = (a_2, -a_1)$ is the clockwise rotation of $\mathbf{a}_P$ by the angle $\frac{\pi}{2}$ (notice that $\hat{\mathbf{a}}_P \cdot \mathbf{a}_P = 0$).

Let $E(P)$ be the set of edges of P, that is, the set of open segments forming the boundary of P, and $V(P)$ be the set of vertices in the boundary of P. We say that e is an *entry* of P if for all $\mathbf{x} \in e$ and for all $\mathbf{c} \in \phi(P)$, $\mathbf{x} + c\epsilon \in P$ for some $\epsilon > 0$. We say that e is an *exit* of P if the same condition holds for some $\epsilon < 0$. We denote by $in(P) \subseteq E(P)$ the set of all entries of P and by $out(P) \subseteq E(P)$ the set of all exits of P. In general, $E(P) \neq in(P) \cup out(P)$. We say that P is a *good* region iff all the edges in $E(P)$ are entries or exits, that is, $E(P) = in(P) \cup out(P)$. Notice that, if P is a good region, then for all $e \in E(P)$, the director vector of e does not belongs to $\phi(P)$ (Fig. 2). Hereinafter, we assume that all regions are good regions. Let $\mathbf{x} \in V(P)$ be a common vertex of two edges e and e'. $\mathbf{x}$ is an *entry point* to P if both e and e' are entry edges; it is an exit point if both e and e' are exit edges. In fact, vertices can be seen as a particular kind of edges, with exactly one point. In what follows the term *edge* will be understood as belonging to the set $EV(P) = E(P) \cup V(P)$. If needed, the difference between edge and vertex will be explicitly specified.

A *trajectory* in some interval $[0, T] \subseteq \mathbb{R}$, with initial condition $\mathbf{x} = \mathbf{x}_0$, is a continuous and almost-everywhere (everywhere except on finitely many points) derivable function $\xi(\cdot)$ such that $\xi(0) = \mathbf{x}_0$ and for all $t \in (0, T)$, if $\xi(t) \in P \setminus EV(P)$, then $\dot{\xi}(t)$ is defined and $\dot{\xi}(t) \in \phi(P)$.

The point-to-point reachability problem for $\mathcal{H}$, is the following: Given $\mathbf{x}, \mathbf{x}' \in \mathbb{R}^2$, is there a trajectory ξ and $t \geq 0$ such that $\xi(0) = \mathbf{x}$ and $\xi(t) = \mathbf{x}'$?. If the

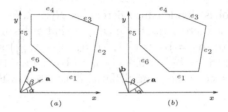

Fig. 2. a) A good region. b) A bad region ($e_5 \notin in(P) \cup out(P)$).

answer is yes, we say that $\mathbf{x}'$ is *reachable* from $\mathbf{x}$. The edge-to-edge reachability problem is the following: Given two edges e and e' of $\mathcal{H}$, is there $\mathbf{x} \in e$ and $\mathbf{x}' \in e'$ such that $\mathbf{x}'$ is reachable from $\mathbf{x}$? The region-to-region reachability problem is defined similarly.

3   Properties of Trajectories

W.l.o.g. we will consider in what follows that $\xi(0) \in e$ for some edge e. The *trace* of a trajectory ξ is the sequence $\tau(\xi) = \mathbf{x}_0 \mathbf{x}_1 \ldots$ of the intersection points of ξ with the set of edges, that is, $\mathbf{x}_i \in \xi \cap \bigcup EV(P)$ for all $P \in \mathcal{P}$. The *edge signature* of ξ is the sequence $\sigma(\xi) = e_0 e_1 \ldots$ of traversed edges, that is, $\mathbf{x}_i \in e_i$. The *region signature* of ξ is the sequence $\rho(\xi) = P_0 P_1 \ldots$ of traversed regions, that is, $e_i \in in(P_i)$.

Let ξ be a trajectory whose trace is $\tau(\xi) = \mathbf{x}_0 \ldots \mathbf{x}_k$. Let $0 = t_0 < t_1 < \ldots < t_k$ be such that $\xi(t_i) = \mathbf{x}_i$. Since ξ is continuous and derivable in the interval (t_i, t_{i+1}), there exists a unique trajectory ξ' with $\xi'(t_i) = \xi(t_i)$ for all $i \in [0, k-1]$, such that the derivative $\dot{\xi}'$ is constant in the interval (t_i, t_{i+1}). That is,

Proposition 1. *For every trajectory ξ there exists a trajectory ξ' with the same initial and final points, and edge and region signatures, such that for each P_i in the region signature, there exists $\mathbf{c}_i \in \phi(P_i)$, such that $\dot{\xi}'(t) = \mathbf{c}_i$ for all $t \in (t_i, t_{i+1})$.*

Hence, in order to solve the reachability problem it is enough to consider trajectories having piecewise constant slopes. Notice that, however, such slopes need not be the same for each occurrence of the same region in the region signature. Hereinafter, we use the word "trajectory" to mean trajectories whose derivatives are piecewise constant.

Consider a region P and let $\mathbf{c} \in \phi(P)$. The mapping $\Omega : \mathbb{R}^2 \to \mathbb{R}$, defined as $\Omega(\mathbf{x}) = \mathbf{x} \cdot \hat{\mathbf{c}}$, assigns to every $\mathbf{x} \in \mathbb{R}^2$ a value proportional to the length of the projection of the vector $\mathbf{x}$ on the right rotation of $\mathbf{c}$ (see [4]). Indeed, the ordering is given by the direction of $\hat{\mathbf{c}}$ and one can easily see that the relation $\preceq$, defined as $\mathbf{x}_1 \preceq \mathbf{x}_2$ if $\Omega(\mathbf{x}_1) \leq \Omega(\mathbf{x}_2)$, is a dense linear order on $in(P)$ and $out(P)$ (Fig. 3). We use $\prec$ to denote the strict variant of $\preceq$ and say that $e_1 \prec e_2$

iff $e_1 \neq e_2$ and $\mathbf{x}_1 \preceq \mathbf{x}_2$ for every $\mathbf{x}_1 \in e_1, \mathbf{x}_2 \in e_2$. For example, in Fig. 3 we have $e_1 \prec e_2 \prec e_3$. Notice that the order does not depend on the choice of $\mathbf{c}$.

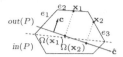

Fig. 3. Ordering: $\mathbf{x}_1 \preceq \mathbf{x}_2$.

We say that a trajectory ξ crosses itself if there exist $t \neq t'$ such that $\xi(t) = \xi(t')$. If a trajectory does not cross itself, the sequence of consecutive intersection points with $in(P)$ or $out(P)$ is monotone with respect to $\preceq$. That is, for every three points $\mathbf{x}_1$, $\mathbf{x}_2$ and $\mathbf{x}_3$ (visited in this order), if $\mathbf{x}_1 \prec \mathbf{x}_2 \prec \mathbf{x}_3$ the trajectory is a "counterclockwise expanding spiral"(Fig. 4(a)) or a "clockwise contracting spiral" (Fig. 4(b)) and if $\mathbf{x}_3 \prec \mathbf{x}_2 \prec \mathbf{x}_1$, the trajectory is a "counterclockwise contracting spiral" (Fig. 4(c)) or a "clockwise expanding spiral" (Fig. 4(d)). On the other hand, if the sequence of intersections points with $in(P)$ or $out(P)$ is monotone (both increasing or both decreasing), the trajectory does not cross itself.

Lemma 1. *For every trajectory ξ, if ξ does not cross itself, then for every edge e, the sequence $\tau(\xi) \cap e$ is monotone (with respect to $\prec$).*

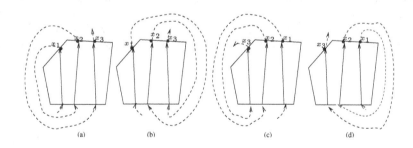

Fig. 4. Spirals.

Now suppose that the trajectory ξ with trace $\tau(\xi) = \mathbf{x}_0 \ldots \mathbf{x}_f$ crosses itself *once* inside the region P. Let $e_1, e_2 \in in(P)$ be the input edges and $e_1', e_2' \in out(P)$ be the output ones. Let $\mathbf{x} = \mathbf{x}_i \in e_1$ and $\mathbf{y} = \mathbf{x}_j \in e_2$, with $i < j$, be the points in $\tau(\xi)$ the first and the second times ξ enters P, and let $\mathbf{x}' = \mathbf{x}_{i+1} \in e_2'$ and $\mathbf{y}' = \mathbf{x}_{j+1} \in e_1'$ be the corresponding output points. Let $\mathbf{c}_x, \mathbf{c}_y \in \phi(P) = \angle_\mathbf{a}^\mathbf{b}$ be the derivatives of ξ in the time intervals (t_i, t_{i+1}) and (t_j, t_{j+1}), respectively. Indeed,

c_x and c_y are the director vectors of the segments $\overline{\mathbf{xx'}}$ and $\overline{\mathbf{yy'}}$, respectively (Fig. 5(a)).

Consider now the segment $\overline{\mathbf{xy'}}$. Notice that the director vector c'_x of this segment can be obtained as a positive combination of the vectors c_x and c_y. Thus, $c'_x \in \phi(P)$. Hence, there exists a trajectory ξ' that does not cross itself in P having a trace $\tau(\xi') = \mathbf{x}_0 \dots \mathbf{xy'} \dots \mathbf{x}_f$ (Fig. 5(b)). Notice that the result also works for the *degenerate* case when the trajectory crosses itself at an edge (or vertex).

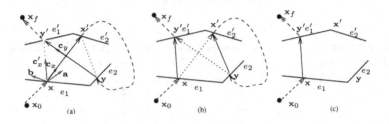

Fig. 5. Obtaining a non-crossing trajectory

If the trajectory ξ crosses itself more than once in region P, then the number of times the trajectory ξ', obtained by cutting away the loop (Fig. 5(c)), crosses itself in P is strictly smaller than the number of times ξ does it (see Fig. 6). After replacing $\overline{\mathbf{xx'}}$ and $\overline{\mathbf{yy'}}$ by $\overline{\mathbf{xy'}}$, the intersection q of $\overline{\mathbf{xx'}}$ and $\overline{\mathbf{yy'}}$ disappears. If the new segment of line $\overline{\mathbf{xy'}}$ crosses another segment $\overline{\mathbf{zz'}}$ (say at a point t), then $\overline{\mathbf{zz'}}$ necessarily crosses either $\overline{\mathbf{xx'}}$ (at r) or $\overline{\mathbf{yy'}}$ (at s) -or both-, before the transformation. The above is due to the fact that if $\overline{\mathbf{zz'}}$ crosses one side of the triangle $\mathbf{xy'}q$ then it must also cross one of the other sides of the triangle, say at r. Thus, no new crossing can appear and the number of crossings in the new configuration is always less than in the old one.

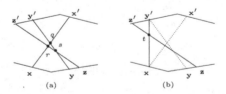

Fig. 6. The number of crossings decreases: (a) Before (3 crossings); (b) After (1 crossing).

Lemma 2. *For every trajectory ξ that crosses itself at least once, there exists a trajectory ξ' with the same initial and final points of ξ having a number of self-crossings strictly smaller.*

The above result follows from a straightforward inductive reasoning, as well as the following one.

Proposition 2. *If there exists an arbitrary trajectory from points $\mathbf{x}_0 \in e_0$ to $\mathbf{x}_f \in e_f$ then there always exists a non-crossing trajectory between them.*

Hence, in order to solve the reachability problem we only need to consider non-crossing trajectories with piecewise constant derivatives. In what follows, we only deal with trajectories of this kind.

4   Properties of Edge Signatures

Let ξ be a trajectory with trace $\tau(\xi) = \mathbf{x}_0 \ldots \mathbf{x}_p$, edge signature $\sigma(\xi) = e_0 \ldots e_p$, and region signature $\rho(\xi) = P_0 \ldots P_p$. An edge e is said to be *abandoned* by ξ after position i, if $e_i = e$ and for some j, k, $i \leq j < k$, $P_j \ldots P_k$ forms a region cycle and $e \notin \{e_{i+1}, \ldots, e_k\}$. Since trajectories are *finite* we should add the trivial case when $e \neq e_j$ for all $j > i$.

Lemma 3 (Claim 2 in [4]). *For every trajectory ξ and edge e, if e is abandoned by ξ after position i, e will not appear in $\sigma(\xi)$ at any position $j > i$.*

Given a sequence s, we use notations $first(s)$ and $last(s)$ for the first and last elements of the sequence respectively. ε denotes the empty sequence An edge signature $\sigma(\xi)$ can be canonically expressed as a sequence of edges and cycles of the form $\sigma_c(\xi) = r_1 s_1^{k_1} r_2 s_2^{k_2} \ldots r_n s_n^{k_n} r_{n+1}$, where

1. For all $i \in [1, n+1]$, r_i is a sequence of pairwise different edges;
2. For all $i \in [1, n]$, s_i is a simple cycle (i.e., without repetition of edges) repeated k_i times;
3. For all $i \in [1, n-1]$, $first(r_{i+1}) \neq first(s_i)$ if $r_{i+1} \neq \varepsilon$, otherwise $first(s_{i+1}) \neq first(s_i)$;
4. For all $i \in [1, n]$, if $r_i \neq \varepsilon$ then $last(r_i) = last(s_i)$;
5. $r_{n+1} \neq \varepsilon$. Moreover, $r_{n+1} = first(s_n)$ if $\sigma(\xi)$ ends in a loop and $first(r_{n+1}) \neq first(s_n)$ otherwise.

This canonical representation can be obtained as follows. Let $\sigma(\xi) = e_1 \ldots e_{p-1} e_p$ be an edge signature. Starting from e_{p-1} and traversing backwards, take the first edge that occurs the second time. If there is no such edge, then trivially the signature can be expressed in a canonical way and we are done. Otherwise, suppose that the edge e_j occurs again at position i (i.e. $e_i = e_j$ with $i < j$), thus $\sigma_c(\xi) = wsr$, where w, s and r are obtained as follows, depending on the repeated edge:

$$w = e_0 \ldots e_i$$
$$s = e_{i+1} \ldots e_j$$
$$r = e_{j+1} \ldots e_{p-1}$$

Clearly r is not a cycle and s is a simple cycle with no repeated edges. We continue the analysis with w. Let $k_m = max\{l \mid s^l$ is a suffix of $w\}$. Thus, $\sigma_c(\xi) = w's^k r$ with $w' = e_0 \ldots e_h$ (a prefix of w) and $k = k_m + 1$. We repeat recursively the procedure above with w'. Adding the edge e_p to the last r (at the end) we obtain $\sigma_c(\xi) = r_1 s_1^{k_1} \ldots r_n s_n^{k_n} r_{n+1}$ that is a canonical representation of signature σ.

Let us define the *type of a signature* σ as $type(\sigma(\xi)) = r_1, s_1, \ldots, r_n, s_n, r_{n+1}$. Notice that the "preprocessing" (taking away the last edge e_p) is done in order to differentiate edges signatures that end with a cycle from those that do not. There exists many other (maybe easier) ways of decomposing a signature σ in a canonical form (in particular, traversing forward instead of backwards), but the one chosen here permits a clearer and simpler presentation of the reachability algorithm. In fact in this canonical form, the last visited edge in a cycle $e_1 \ldots e_k$ is always the last one (e_k).

Example. Let us consider the following examples. Suppose that $\sigma = abcdbcefg$ $efgefgefhi$. Then, after applying once the above procedure we obtain that $\sigma_c = w(s_2)^3 r_1$, with $w = abcdbcef$; $s_2 = gef$; $r_1 = h$. Applying the procedure once more to w we obtain $w = w'(s_3)^1 r_2$ with $w' = r_3 = abc$; $s_3 = dbc$; $r_2 = ef$. Putting all together and adding the last edge (i) gives $\sigma_c = abc(dbc)^1 ef(gef)^3 hi$ with type $type(\sigma) = abc, dbc, ef, gef, hi$. Suppose now, that the signature ends with a cycle: $\sigma = abcdbcefgefgefgef$. In this case we apply the preprocessing obtaining $\sigma_c = w(s_2)^4 r_1$ with $w = abcdbce$; $s_2 = fge$; $r_1 = \varepsilon$. Applying the procedure to w we finally obtain $w = w'(s_3)^1 r_2$ with $w' = r_3 = abc$; $s_3 = dbc$; $r_2 = e$ and that gives $\sigma_c = abc(dbc)^1 e(fge)^4 f$ (adding f to the end). □

Lemma 4. *The type of a signature* σ, $type(\sigma)$, *has the following properties:*

1. *For every* $1 \le i \ne j \le n+1$, r_i *and* r_j *are disjoint;*
2. *For every* $1 \le i \ne j \le n$, s_i *and* s_j *are different;*
3. *If* v *is a vertex appearing in* $type(\sigma)$, *then it can only occur exactly once in* r_i *for some* $1 \le i \le n+1$ *in* σ. *Moreover,* $v \notin last(r_i)$ *unless* $i = n+1$.

Proposition 3. *The set of types of edge signatures is finite.*

Thus, to solve the reachability problem we can proceed by examining one by one the types of signatures.

5   Affine Operators

Before getting into the problem of analyzing types of edge signatures, we need to introduce some useful notions.

An *affine function* $f : \mathbb{R} \to \mathbb{R}$ is defined by a formula $f(x) = ax + b$ with $a > 0$. An *affine multivalued operator* $F : \mathbb{R} \to 2^{\mathbb{R}}$ is determined by two affine functions $f_l(x)$ and $f_u(x)$ and maps x to the interval $\langle f_l(x), f_u(x) \rangle$, where $\langle a, b \rangle$

means (a, b), $[a, b]$, $(a, b]$ or $[a, b)$: $F(x) = \langle f_l(x), f_u(x) \rangle$. We use the notation $F = \langle f_l, f_u \rangle$. Such an operator can be naturally extended to subsets of $\mathbb{R}$: $F(S) = \bigcup_{x \in S} F(x)$. In particular, if $S = \langle l, u \rangle$: $F(\langle l, u \rangle) = \langle f_l(l), f_u(u) \rangle$. A *truncated affine multi-valued operator* $G : \mathbb{R} \to 2^{\mathbb{R}}$ is determined by an affine multi-valued operator F and an interval $\langle L, U \rangle$ as follows: $G(x) = F(x) \cap \langle L, U \rangle$. Such operators can be also extended to sets. We use notations $G = F \cap \langle L, U \rangle$ and $F = \widetilde{G}$.

Lemma 5 (composition of affine operations). *Affine functions, affine multi-valued operators, and truncated affine multi-valued operators are closed under composition.*

Example. Let $\widetilde{G}_1(x) = (2x + 3, \, 3x + 5]$ and $\widetilde{G}_2(x) = [5x + 2, \, 7x + 6]$ be two (non-truncated) affine multi-valued functions, $G_1 = \widetilde{G}_1 \cap (1, \, 6]$, and $G_2 = \widetilde{G}_2 \cap [6, \, 10)$ their truncated versions. The truncated affine multi-valued operator $G_2 \circ G_1(x)$ is obtained as follows:

$$G_2 \circ G_1(x) = \widetilde{G}_2 \circ \widetilde{G}_1(x) \cap \widetilde{G}_2((1, \, 6]) \cap [6, \, 10)$$
$$= (5(2x + 3) + 2, \, 7(3x + 5) + 6] \cap (5 \cdot 1 + 2, \, 7 \cdot 6 + 6] \cap [6, \, 10)$$
$$= (10x + 17, \, 21x + 41] \cap (7, \, 48] \cap [6, \, 10)$$
$$= (10x + 17, \, 21x + 41] \cap (7, \, 10).$$

Notice also that for any interval $\langle l, u \rangle$ its image is $G_2 \circ G_1(\langle l, u \rangle) = \langle 10l + 17, \, 21u + 41 \rangle \cap (7, \, 10)$. □

Let f be an affine function, x_0 be any initial point and $x_n = f^n(x)$. Clearly, the sequence x_n is monotonous, and it converges to a limit x^* (finite or infinite). Indeed, x^* can be effectively computed knowing a, b and x_0, as follows. If $a < 1$, x^* is the unique fixpoint of f, that is, $ax^* + b = x^*$, which yields $x^* = b/(1 - a)$. If $a = 1$, $x^* = -\infty$ if $b < 0$, $x^* = \infty$ if $b > 0$, and $x^* = x_0$, if $b = 0$. If $a > 1$, let $x_* = b/(1 - a)$, then $x^* = -\infty$ if $x_0 < x_*$, $x^* = \infty$ if $x_0 > x_*$, $x^* = x_0 = x_*$, otherwise. This result can be extended to multi-valued affine functions.

Lemma 6. *Let $\langle l_0, u_0 \rangle$ be any initial interval and $\langle l_n, u_n \rangle = \widetilde{F}^n(\langle l_0, u_0 \rangle)$. Then*

1. *The sequences l_n and u_n are monotonous;*
2. *They converge to limits l^* and u^* (finite or infinite), which can be effectively computed.*

Proposition 4. *Let F be truncated affine and $I \subseteq \langle L, U \rangle$. Then $F^n(I) = \widetilde{F}^n(I) \cap \langle L, U \rangle$.*

6   Computing the Successor Function

To solve the reachability problem for SPDI, the next step is to provide a procedure for computing the successors of a point (and an interval), which requires having an effective representation of (rational) points and intervals on edges.

Let us first introduce a one-dimensional coordinate system on each edge. For each edge e we chose (1) a point on it (the origin) with radius-vector $\mathbf{v}$, and (2) a director vector $\mathbf{e}$ going in the positive direction in the sense of the order $\prec$. Now to characterize e we need the coordinates of its extreme points, namely, $e^l, e^u \in \mathbb{Q} \cup \{-\infty, \infty\}$ such that $e = \{\mathbf{x} = \mathbf{v} + x\mathbf{e} \mid e^l < x < e^u\}$. That is, an edge $e \in E$ can be represented by a triplet $(\mathbf{v}, \mathbf{e}, (e^l, e^u))$. If the edge is a vertex, the representation is simply $(\mathbf{v}, [0,0])$. Now, every point $\mathbf{x} = \mathbf{v} + x\mathbf{e} \in e$ is represented by the pair (e, x) (Fig.7(a)), and every interval $\langle \mathbf{x}_1, \mathbf{x}_2 \rangle \subseteq e$ is represented as $(e, \langle x_1, x_2 \rangle)$, where $\mathbf{x}_1 = (e, x_1)$ and $\mathbf{x}_2 = (e, x_2)$ (Fig.7(b)). Now, having fixed

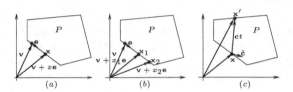

Fig. 7. (a) Representation of edges; (b) Representation of an interval; (c) One-step successor.

a one-dimensional coordinate system to represent points, the question now is to take advantage of it to compute the successor of a point or an interval.

Let $e = \langle e^l, e^u \rangle \in in(P)$ and $e' = \langle e'^l, e'^u \rangle \in out(P)$. For $\mathbf{x} = (e, x)$ and $\mathbf{c} \in \phi(P)$, we denote by $\mathrm{Succ}^{\mathbf{c}}_{e,e'}(x)$ the unique $\mathbf{x}' = (e', x')$ such that $\mathbf{x}' = \mathbf{x} + \mathbf{c}t$ for some $t > 0$. The point (e', x') is the successor of (e, x) in the direction $\mathbf{c}$ (see Fig.7(c)). Expanding, $\mathbf{v}' + x'\mathbf{e}' = \mathbf{v} + x\mathbf{e} + t\mathbf{c}$. Multiplying both expressions by $\hat{\mathbf{c}}$ we obtain that $(\mathbf{v}' + x'\mathbf{e}')\hat{\mathbf{c}} = \mathbf{v} \cdot \hat{\mathbf{c}} + x\mathbf{e}\hat{\mathbf{c}}$, i.e. $x'(\mathbf{e}' \cdot \hat{\mathbf{c}}) = x(\mathbf{e} \cdot \hat{\mathbf{c}}) + (\mathbf{v} - \mathbf{v}') \cdot \hat{\mathbf{c}}$. Thus, $x' = \mathrm{Succ}^{\mathbf{c}}_{e,e'}(x) = \frac{\mathbf{e} \cdot \hat{\mathbf{c}}}{\mathbf{e}' \cdot \hat{\mathbf{c}}} x + \frac{\mathbf{v} - \mathbf{v}'}{\mathbf{e}' \cdot \hat{\mathbf{c}}} \cdot \hat{\mathbf{c}}$ and $x' \in \langle e'^l, e'^u \rangle$. Indeed, putting $\alpha(\mathbf{c}) = \frac{\mathbf{e}\hat{\mathbf{c}}}{\mathbf{e}'\hat{\mathbf{c}}}$, and $\beta(\mathbf{c}) = \frac{\mathbf{v} - \mathbf{v}'}{\mathbf{e}' \cdot \hat{\mathbf{c}}} \cdot \hat{\mathbf{c}}$ we have the following result.

Lemma 7. *The function* $\mathrm{Succ}^{\mathbf{c}}_{e,e'}(x) = \alpha(\mathbf{c})x + \beta(\mathbf{c}) \cap \langle e'^l, e'^u \rangle$ *is truncated affine.*

$\widetilde{\mathrm{Succ}}_{e,e'}(x)$ will denote the *non-truncated* function $\alpha(\mathbf{c})x + \beta(\mathbf{c})$. The notion of *successor* can be extended on all possible directions $\mathbf{c} \in \phi(P)$ and it can be applied to any subset $S \subseteq \langle e^l, e^u \rangle$ and in particular to intervals $\langle l, u \rangle$:

Lemma 8. *Let* $\phi(P) = \angle^{\mathbf{b}}_{\mathbf{a}}$, $\mathbf{x} = (e, x)$ *and* $\langle l, u \rangle \subseteq \langle e^l, e^u \rangle$. *Then:*

1. $\mathrm{Succ}_{e,e'}(x) = \bigcup_{\mathbf{c} \in \phi(P)} \mathrm{Succ}^{\mathbf{c}}_{e,e'}(x) = \langle \widetilde{\mathrm{Succ}}^{\mathbf{b}}_{e,e'}(x), \widetilde{\mathrm{Succ}}^{\mathbf{a}}_{e,e'}(x) \rangle \cap \langle e'^l, e'^u \rangle$;
2. $\mathrm{Succ}_{e,e'}(\langle l, u \rangle) = \langle \widetilde{\mathrm{Succ}}^{\mathbf{b}}_{e,e'}(l), \widetilde{\mathrm{Succ}}^{\mathbf{a}}_{e,e'}(u) \rangle \cap \langle e'^l, e'^u \rangle$.

The successor operator will be used as a building block in the reachability algorithm. It can be naturally extended on edge signatures: for $w = e_1, e_2, \ldots, e_n$ let

$$\mathrm{Succ}_w(I) = \mathrm{Succ}_{e_{n-1}, e_n} \circ \ldots \circ \mathrm{Succ}_{e_2, e_3} \circ \mathrm{Succ}_{e_1, e_2}(I)$$

that by Lemma 5 is truncated affine. Notice that since we use edge signatures the semi-group property takes the following form.

Lemma 9. *For any edge signatures w and v and an edge e, $\mathsf{Succ}_{ew} \circ \mathsf{Succ}_{ve} = \mathsf{Succ}_{vew}$.*

Example. Let us come back to the example of the swimmer trying to escape from a whirlpool in a river (see Fig. 1). Suppose that the swimmer is following a trajectory with edge signature $(e_1 \ldots e_8)^*$. It is not difficult to find a representation of the edges such that for each edge e_i, $(e_i^l, e_i^u) = (0, 1)$. Besides, the truncated affine successor functions are:

$$\mathsf{Succ}_{e_1 e_2}(x) = \left[\frac{x}{2}, \frac{x}{2}\right] \cap (0, 1) \qquad\qquad \mathsf{Succ}_{e_2 e_3}(x) = \left[x - \frac{3}{10}, x + \frac{2}{15}\right] \cap (0, 1)$$

$$\mathsf{Succ}_{e_i e_{i+1}}(x) = [x, x] \cap (0, 1), \text{ for all } i \in [3, 7] \quad \mathsf{Succ}_{e_8 e_1}(x) = \left[x + \frac{1}{5}, x + \frac{1}{5}\right] \cap (0, 1)$$

The successor function for the loop $s = e_1 \ldots e_8$ is obtained by composition of the above functions as follows. Let us first compute

$$\begin{aligned}
\mathsf{Succ}_{e_1 e_2 e_3}(l, u) &= \mathsf{Succ}_{e_2 e_3} \circ \mathsf{Succ}_{e_1 e_2}(l, u)\\
&= [\tfrac{l}{2} - \tfrac{3}{10}, \tfrac{u}{2} + \tfrac{2}{15}] \cap (0 - \tfrac{3}{10}, 1 + \tfrac{2}{15}) \cap (0, 1)\\
&= [\tfrac{l}{2} - \tfrac{3}{10}, \tfrac{u}{2} + \tfrac{2}{15}] \cap (0, 1)
\end{aligned}$$

Since $\widetilde{\mathsf{Succ}}_{e_i e_{i+1}}$ for $i \in [3, 7]$ are the identity functions, we have that

$$\begin{aligned}
\mathsf{Succ}_{e_1 \ldots e_8}(l, u) &= \mathsf{Succ}_{e_8 e_1} \circ \mathsf{Succ}_{e_1 e_2 e_3}(l, u)\\
&= [\tfrac{l}{2} - \tfrac{3}{10} + \tfrac{1}{5}, \tfrac{u}{2} + \tfrac{2}{15} + \tfrac{1}{5}] \cap (\tfrac{0}{2} + \tfrac{1}{5}, \tfrac{1}{2} + \tfrac{1}{5}) \cap (0, 1)\\
&= [\tfrac{l}{2} - \tfrac{1}{10}, \tfrac{u}{2} + \tfrac{1}{3}] \cap (\tfrac{1}{5}, 1)
\end{aligned}$$

By Lemma 6 we have that $l^* = \frac{-\frac{1}{10}}{1 - \frac{1}{2}} = -\frac{1}{5}$, and $u^* = \frac{\frac{1}{3}}{1 - \frac{1}{2}} = \frac{2}{3}$. □

7   Reachability Analysis

The algorithm for solving the reachability problem between two points $\mathbf{x}_0 = (e_0, x_0)$ and $\mathbf{x}_f = (e_f, x_f)$ is depicted in Fig. 8. The proofs of soundness and termination are given in the extended version ([5]). It works as follows.

Reach. From the section above we know that there exists a finite number of type signatures of the form $r_1, s_1, \ldots, r_n, s_n, r_{n+1}$. Moreover, the type signatures are restricted to those with $e_0 = first(r_1)$ and $e_f = last(r_{n+1})$. Given such a set of type signatures $type(e_0, e_f)$, the algorithm $Reach(\cdot)$ is guaranteed to terminate, answering YES if $\mathbf{x}_f$ is reachable from $\mathbf{x}_0$ or NO otherwise. Reachability from $\mathbf{x}_0$ to $\mathbf{x}_f$ with fixed signature w is tested by the function $Reach_{type}(x_0, x_f, w)$.

Reach_type. Let the type w have the form $w = r_1, s_1, \ldots, r_n, s_n, r_{n+1}$. Put $f_i = first(s_i)$ and $ex_i = first(r_{i+1})$ if r_{i+1} is non-empty and f_{i+1} otherwise (i.e. ex_i is the edge to which the trajectory exits from the loop s_i). Let us say that a type signature w has a loop_end property if $r_{n+1} = first(s_n)$, i.e. signatures of type w terminate by several repetitions of the last loop. This algorithm uses two functions: $Test(S, s, x)$ that answers whether x is reachable from a set S (represented as a finite union of intervals) in the loop s (formally, whether $x \in \mathsf{Succ}_{s+first(s)}(I)$); and the function $Exit(S, s, e)$ that for an initial set S, a loop s, and an edge e (not in this loop) finds all the points on e reachable by making s several times and then exiting to e (formally, it computes $\mathsf{Succ}_{s+e}(I)$, which is always a finite union of intervals). Since we know how to calculate the successor of a given interval in one and in several steps ($\mathsf{Succ}_{ee'}(\cdot)$ and $\mathsf{Succ}_r(\cdot)$), in order to implement $Test(\cdot)$ and $Exit(\cdot)$ it remains to show how to analyze the (simple) cycles s_i and eventually their continuation. Both algorithms $Test(\cdot)$ and $Exit(\cdot)$ start by qualitative analysis of the cycle implemented in the function $Analyze(I, s)$. This analysis proceeds as follows.

Analyze. The function $Analyze(I, s)$ returns the kind of qualitative behavior of the interval $I = \langle l, u \rangle$ under the loop s. Let s be a simple cycle, $f = first(s)$ its first edge, and $I = \langle l, u \rangle \subset f$ an initial interval and $\mathsf{Succ}_{s,f}(x) = \widetilde{\mathsf{Succ}}_{s,f}(x) \cap \langle L, U \rangle$. The first thing to do is to determine the qualitative behavior of the leftmost and rightmost trajectories of the interval endpoints in the cycle. This can be done without iterating Succ_{sf}. Indeed, by Lemma 6, we can compute the limits $(l_1^*, u_1^*) = \lim_{n \to \infty} \widetilde{\mathsf{Succ}}_{s,f}^n(\langle l, u \rangle)$ (notice that those limits only for the *non-truncated operator* $\widetilde{\mathsf{Succ}}$), not taking into account that the edges are possible bounded (we use Lemma 4) and compare these limit points corresponding to unrestricted dynamics with L and U. There are five possibilities:

1. **STAY** The cycle is not abandoned by any of the two trajectories: $L \leq l^* \leq u^* \leq U$.

function $Reach(x_0, x_f)$ $R = \text{false}$ **for each** $w \in type(e_0, e_f)$ $\quad R = R \vee Reach_{type}(x_0, x_f, w)$ $\longleftarrow R$	**function** $Reach_{type}(x_0, x_f, w):$ $S = \mathsf{Succ}_{r_1 f_1}(x_0)$ **for** $i = 1$ **to** $n - 1$ $\quad S = \mathsf{Succ}_{r_{i+1} f_{i+1}}(Exit(S, s_i, ex_i))$ **if** loop_end(w) **then** $\longleftarrow Test(S, s_n, x_f)$ **else** $\longleftarrow x_f \in \mathsf{Succ}_{r_{n+1}}(Exit(S, s_n, ex_n))$?
function $Exit(S, s, ex)$ $E = \emptyset$ **for each** $I \in S$ such that $\mathsf{Succ}_{s,f}(I) \neq \emptyset$ $\quad E = E \cup Exit_{Analyze}(\mathsf{Succ}_{s,f}(I), s, ex)$ $\longleftarrow E$	**function** $Test(S, s, x)$ $R = \text{false}$ **for each** $I \in S$ such that $\mathsf{Succ}_{s,f}(I) \neq \emptyset$ $\quad R = R \vee Test_{Analyze}(\mathsf{Succ}_{s,f}(I), s, x)$ $\longleftarrow R$

Fig. 8. Main algorithm.

2. **DIE** The right trajectory exits the cycle through the left (consequently the left one also exits) or the left trajectory exits the cycle through the right (consequently the right one also exits). In symbols, $u^* < L \vee l^* > U$.

3. **EXIT-BOTH** Both trajectories exit the cycle (the left one through the left and the right one through the right): $l^* < L \wedge u^* > U$.

4. **EXIT-LEFT** The leftmost trajectory exits the cycle but not the other: $l^* < L \le u^* \le U$.

5. **EXIT-RIGHT** The rightmost trajectory exits the cycle but not the other: $L \le l^* \le U < u^*$.

Exit. The function $Exit(S, s, ex)$ should return $\mathsf{Succ}_{s+ex}(S)$. Both the argument S and the result are finite collections of intervals. The exploration is made for each initial interval separately. Notice that the call $\mathsf{Succ}_{s,f}(I)$ ensures that $I \subseteq \langle L, U \rangle$. All the work for each initial interval I is done by the function $Exit_{Analyze}(I, s, ex)$ which launches the $Analyze(\cdot)$ procedure described above and last, according to the result of this analysis launches one of five specialized procedures $Exit_{STAY}$, $Exit_{LEFT}$, $Exit_{RIGHT}$, $Exit_{BOTH}$, $Exit_{DIE}$ which calculates the exit set (Fig. 10).

	function $Found(I, x)$
	cases
function $Search(I, x)$	
while $Found(I, x) = \text{NOTYET}$	$x \in I :$ ⟵ YES
$I = \mathsf{Succ}_{s,f}(I)$	$I = \emptyset :$ ⟵ NO
⟵ $Found(I, x)$	$x < I \wedge l \uparrow :$ ⟵ NO
	$x > I \wedge u \downarrow :$ ⟵ NO
	else : ⟵ NOTYET

Fig. 9. *Search and Found.*

Test. The upper-level structure is the same as for EXIT: each initial interval is treated separately by $Test_{Analyze}$, which makes one turn of the loop, calls *Analyze* and delegates all the remaining to one of the five specialized functions $Test_{STAY}$, $Test_{LEFT}$, $Test_{RIGHT}$, $Test_{BOTH}$, $Test_{DIE}$ (Fig. 10). The five specialized *Test* functions use the following two procedures (Fig. 9). The function $Found(I, x)$ determines if the current interval I contains x (YES), does not contain x and moves in the opposite direction (NO), or none of both these cases (NOTYET). $Found(I, x)$ uses the fact that the sequences l_n and u_n are increasing or decreasing (which can be easily determined at the stage of the preliminary analysis of the loop): $l \uparrow$ means that the sequence $l, l_1, l_2, \ldots$ of successive successors of l is increasing whereas $l \downarrow$ means that the sequence is decreasing, and similarly for $u \uparrow$ and $u \downarrow$. The function $Search(I, x)$ iterates the loop s until the previous function $Found$ gives a definite answer YES or NO (Fig. 9). It is used only when its convergence is guaranteed.

	Exit	Test
STAY	**function** $Exit_{STAY}(I, s, ex)$ $\longleftarrow \emptyset$	**function** $Test_{STAY}(I, s, x)$ **cases** $\quad l^* < x < u^* : \longleftarrow$ YES $\quad x \leq l^* \wedge l \downarrow : \longleftarrow$ NO $\quad x \geq u^* \wedge u \uparrow : \longleftarrow$ NO $\quad$ **else** : $\qquad \longleftarrow Search(I, x)$
DIE	**function** $Exit_{DIE}(I, s, ex)$ $\quad f = first(s)$ $\quad S = \emptyset$ $\quad$ **repeat** $\qquad I = \mathsf{Succ}_{sf}(I)$ $\qquad S = S \bigcup \mathsf{Succ}_{s,ex}(I)$ $\quad$ **until** $I = \emptyset$ $\quad \longleftarrow$ S	**function** $Test_{DIE}(I, s, x)$ $\quad \longleftarrow Search(I, x)$
BOTH	**function** $Exit_{BOTH}(I, s, ex)$ $\quad \longleftarrow \mathsf{Succ}_{s,ex}(\langle L, U \rangle)$	**function** $Test_{BOTH}(I, s, x)$ $\quad \longleftarrow x \in \langle L, U \rangle ?$
LEFT	**function** $Exit_{LEFT}(I, s, ex)$ $\quad \longleftarrow \mathsf{Succ}_{s,ex}(\langle L, u \rangle)$	**function** $Test_{LEFT}(I, s, x)$ **cases** $\quad x \in \langle L, u^* \rangle : \qquad \longleftarrow$ YES $\quad x < \langle L, u^* \rangle : \qquad \longleftarrow$ NO $\quad \langle L, u^* \rangle < x \wedge u \uparrow : \longleftarrow$ NO $\quad$ **else** : $\qquad \longleftarrow Search(I, x)$
RIGHT	Similar to the previous case.	Similar to the previous case.

Fig. 10. *Exit* and *Test*.

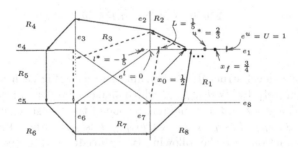

Fig. 11. Example: $\mathbf{x}_f = (e_1, \frac{3}{4})$ is not reachable from $\mathbf{x}_0 = (e_1, \frac{1}{2})$ $(u^* < \frac{3}{4})$.

Example. Consider again the swimmer. Let $\mathbf{x}_0 = (e_1, \frac{1}{2})$ be her initial position. We want to decide whether she is able to escape from the whirlpool and reach the final position $\mathbf{x}_f = (e_1, \frac{3}{4})$. Recall that $l^* = \frac{-\frac{1}{10}}{1-\frac{1}{2}} = -\frac{1}{5}$ and $u^* = \frac{\frac{1}{3}}{1-\frac{1}{2}} = \frac{2}{3}$. Thus, by the *Analyze* function we know that the cycle behaves as an Exit-LEFT and applying the function $Test_{LEFT}$ we obtain that $\mathbf{x}_f = (e_1, \frac{3}{4})$ is not reachable from $\mathbf{x}_0 = (e_1, \frac{1}{2})$ because we have that $u \uparrow$ and $u^* < x_f$ ($\frac{2}{3} < \frac{3}{4}$) (Fig. 11). $\quad\square$

From all the results above we have the following theorem.

Theorem 1 (Point–to–Point Reachability). *The point-to-point, edge-to-edge and region-to-region reachability problems for SPDI systems are decidable.*

$\square$

8 Concluding Remarks

We have presented an algorithm for solving the reachability problem for simple planar differential inclusions. The novelty of the approach for the domain of Hybrid System is the combination of two techniques, namely, the representation of the two-dimensional continuous dynamics as a one-dimensional discrete system (due to Poincaré), and the characterization of the set of qualitative behaviors of the latter as a finite set of types of signatures.

One possible direction of future work is to try to apply the same method for solving the *parameter synthesis problem* for SPDI's, that is, for any two points, $\mathbf{x}_0$ and $\mathbf{x}_f$, assign a constant slope $\mathbf{c}_P \in \phi(P)$ to every region P such that $\mathbf{x}_f$ is reachable from $\mathbf{x}_0$, or conclude that such an assignment does not exist. Clearly, the decidability of the reachability problem does not imply the decidability of the parameter synthesis one.

Another question that naturally arises is decidability of the reachability problem for hybrid automata whose locations are equipped with SPDI's. We can certainly find (stringent) conditions, such as planarity of the automaton, "memoryless" resets, etc., under which decidability follows almost straightforwardly from the decidability of SPDI's. On the other hand, it is not difficult to see that this problem, without such conditions, is equivalent to deciding whether given a piece-wise linear map f on the unit interval and a point x in this interval, the sequence of iterates x, $f(x)$, $f(f(x))$, and so on, reaches some point y. This last question is still open [13]. And last but not the least, another interesting issue is the complexity analysis of the algorithm. It should be based on counting all "feasible" types of signatures. Our finiteness argument of lemma 4 gives a doubly exponential estimation, which can certainly be improved.

References

1. R. Alur, C. Courcoubetis, N. Halbwachs, T. Henzinger, P. Ho, X. Nicollin, A. Olivero, J. Sifakis, and S. Yovine. The algorithmic analysis of hybrid systems. TCS **138** (1995) 3–34.
2. R. Alur and D.L. Dill. A theory of timed automata. TCS **126** (1994) 183–235.
3. E. Asarin, O. Bournez, T. Dang, and O. Maler. Reachability analysis of piecewise-linear dynamical systems. In *HSCC'00*, 20–31. LNCS 1790, Springer Verlag, 2000.
4. E. Asarin, O. Maler, and A. Pnueli. On the analysis of dynamical systems having piecewise-constant derivatives. TCS, **138** (1995) 35–65.

5. E. Asarin, G. Schneider and S. Yovine. On the Decidability of the Reachability Problem for Planar Differential Inclusions. VERIMAG Technical Report. 2001. http://www-verimag.imag.fr/~gerardo.

6. O. Botchkarev and S. Tripakis. Verification of hybrid systems with linear differential inclusions using ellipsoidal approximations. In *HSCC'00*. LNCS 1790, Springer Verlag, 2000.

7. M. Broucke. A geometric approach to bisimulation and verification of hybrid systems. In *HSCC'99*. LNCS 1569, Springer Verlag, 1999.

8. K. Čerāns and J. Vīksna. Deciding reachability for planar multi-polynomial systems. In *Hybrid Systems III*. LNCS 1066, Springer Verlag, 1996.

9. T. Dang and O. Maler. Reachability analysis via face lifting. In *HSCC'98*, 96–109. LNCS 1386, Springer Verlag, 1998.

10. J. Della Dora and S. Yovine. Looking for a methodology for analyzing hybrid systems. Submitted to ECC 2001, 2000.

11. M. R. Greenstreet and I. Mitchell. Reachability analysis using polygonal projections. In *HSCC'99*. LNCS 1569, 103–116. Springer Verlag, 1999.

12. T.A. Henzinger, P.W. Kopke, A. Puri, and P. Varaiya. What's decidable about hybrid automata? In *27th Annual Symposium on Theory of Computing*, 373–382. ACM Press, 1995.

13. P. Koiran. My favourite problems. http://www.ens-lyon.fr/~koiran/problems.html.

14. A.B. Kurzhanski and P. Varaiya. Ellipsoidal techniques for reachability analysis. In *HSCC'00*. LNCS 1790, Springer Verlag, 2000.

15. G. Lafferriere, G. J. Pappas, and S. Yovine. A new class of decidable hybrid systems. In *HSCC'99*. LNCS 1569, 137–151. Springer Verlag, 1999.

16. O. Maler and A. Pnueli. Reachability analysis of planar multi-linear systems. In *CAV'93*. LNCS 697, 194–209. Springer Verlag, 1993.

The Substratum of Impulse and Hybrid Control Systems

Jean-Pierre Aubin

Université Paris-Dauphine, Centre de Recherche Viabilité,
Jeux, Contrôle, F-75775, Paris cx (16),
Tel. [33] (0)1-46-33-71-21, Fax. [33] (0)1-44-05-49-11
aubin@viab.dauphine.fr, http://viab.dauphine.fr

Abstract. The behavior of the run of an impulse differential inclusion, and, in particular, of a hybrid control system, is "summarized" by the " initialization map" associating with each initial condition the set of new initialized conditions and more generally, by its "substratum", that is a set-valued map associating with a cadence and a state the next reinitialized state. These maps are characterized in several ways, and in particular, as "set-valued" solutions of a system of Hamilton-Jacobi partial differential inclusions, that play the same role than usual Hamilton-Jacobi-Bellman equations in optimal control.

Keywords: hybrid control, impulse control, differential inclusion, viability, run, execution, periodic, cadenced run, equilibrium, Kakutani Theorem, contingent cone, Marchaud map.

1 Introduction

Impulse differential inclusions, and in particular, hybrid control systems, are defined by a differential inclusion (or a control system) and a reset map. A run of an impulse differential inclusion is defined by a sequence of cadences, of reinitialized states and of motives describing the evolution along a given cadence between two distinct consecutive impulse times, the value of a motive at the end of a cadence being reset as the next reinitialized state of the next cadence.

A first advantage of introducing impulse differential inclusions is to summarize the usually protracted description of an hybrid system[1] by only two set-valued maps F — the right-hand side of the differential inclusion governing the continuous evolution of a hybrid system — and R, describing the reset map reinitializing the system when required and a constrained set K inside which the evolution of the "run" or "execution" must remain. Hence, for instance, the existence of a run of an hybrid system for every initial set becomes a viability problem of an adequate auxiliary subset under an impulse differential inclusion, that can be characterized elegantly end efficaciously.

---

[1] See for instance among many papers and books [13, Branicky, Borkar & Mitter], [12, Bensoussan & Menaldi], [17,18, Matveev & Savkin] and [20, Shaft & Schumacher].

M.D. Di Benedetto, A. Sangiovanni-Vincentelli (Eds.): HSCC 2001, LNCS 2034, pp. 105–118, 2001.
© Springer-Verlag Berlin Heidelberg 2001

The behavior of the run is "summarized" by the " initialization map" $U :=$ $U_{(F,R)}$ associating with each initial condition $x_0 \in K$ the set of new initialized conditions $x_1 \in R(x(^-t_1))$ when $x(\cdot)$ ranges over the set of solutions to the differential inclusion $x' \in F(x)$ viable in K until they reach $R^{-1}(K)$ at time $t_1 \geq 0$ at $x(^-t_1) \in R^{-1}(K)$.

Indeed, the sequence of successive initial conditions x_n of a viable run $x(\cdot)$ of the impulse differential inclusion (F, R) — constituting the "discrete component of the run" — is governed by the discrete system $x_n \in U_{(F,R)}(x_{n-1}) \cap K$ starting at x_0. The knowledge of the sequence of initialized states x_n allows us to reconstitute the "continuous component" of the run by solving the differential inclusion $x' \in F(x)$ starting at each reinitialized state x_n and satisfying the end-point condition $x_{n+1} \in R(x(^-t_{n+1}))$, which exists thanks to the definition of the map $U^K_{(F,R)}$.

Assume for a while that the impulse differential inclusion is actually an impulse differential equation (f, r) where the maps f and r are single-valued and that the initialization map is single-valued and differentiable. Then we shall prove that the initialization map is a solution to the system of first-order partial differential inclusions

$$\forall\, i = 1, \ldots n, \quad \sum_{j=1}^{n} \frac{\partial u_i(x)}{\partial x_j} f_j(x) \;=\; 0$$

or, in a more compact form, $0 \;=\; \dfrac{\partial u}{\partial x} f(x)$, satisfying the "condition"

$$\forall\, x \in K \cap r^{-1}(K), \quad r(x) \;=\; u(x)$$

Actually, we shall extend this result to general impulse differential inclusions by characterizing the initialization map $U_{(F,R)}$ as a generalized (set-valued) solution — a Frankowska solution — to the system of first-order partial differential inclusions

$$0 \;\in\; \frac{\partial u}{\partial x} F(x)$$

satisfying the "condition"

$$\forall\, x \in K \cap R^{-1}(K), \quad R(x) \subset U(x)$$

These are indeed really Dirichlet boundary condition whenever the reset map R is defined only on the boundary ∂K of a closed subset K and maps ∂K into the interior of K. In this case, resetting initial conditions happens only when the continuous evolution of the state governed by the differential inclusion or the control system is about to leave the domain K. Hence the reset map assigns new initialized states in the interior of K.

We shall introduce more generally another set-valued map summarizing the behavior of an impulse differential inclusion, called the **substratum**, that is the topic of this paper.

Outline: We begin by giving our definition of impulse differential inclusions. We then recall the characterization of viable subsets under an impulse differential inclusion an derive from it a necessary and sufficient condition for the existence of solutions to hybrid differential inclusions. Then, we devote the next section to the graphical properties of the initialization map U and we derive its properties from the general properties of viable-capture basins of a target by a differential inclusion.

In the last section, we translate the Frankowska characterization of viable-capture basins in terms of kinds of systems of first-order Hamilton-Jacobi partial differential equations characterizing the substratum the solutions of which are the initialization maps and the substratum.

2   Impulse Differential Inclusions

"Hybrid control systems", as they are called by engineers, or "multiple-phase dynamical economies", as they are called by economists (see for instance [16, Day]), or "Integrate and Fire" models in neurobiology (see for instance [14, Brette]) — may be regarded as impulse differential inclusions.

Here, $X := \mathbf{R}^n$ and $Y := \mathbf{R}^m$ denote finite dimensional vector spaces. Let $f : X \times Y \mapsto X$ be a single-valued map describing the dynamics of a control system and $P : X \rightsquigarrow Y$ the set-valued map describing the state-dependent constraints on the controls.

First, any solution to a control system with state-dependent constraints on the controls

$$\begin{cases} i) & x'(t) = f(x(t), u(t)) \\ ii) & u(t) \in P(x(t)) \end{cases}$$

can be regarded as a solution to the differential inclusion $x'(t) \in F(x(t))$ where the right hand side is defined by $F(x) := f(x, P(x)) := \{f(x, u)\}_{u \in P(x)}$.

Therefore, from now on, as long as we do not need to implicate explicitly the controls in our study, we shall replace control problems by differential inclusions.

We shall say that K *is locally viable under F* if from every $x \in K$ starts a solution $x(\cdot)$ to the differential inclusion $x' \in F(x)$ viable in K on the nonempty interval $[0, T_x[$ in the sense

$$\forall t \in [0, T_x[, \quad x(t) \in K$$

and that K is viable if we can take $T_x = +\infty$. It is *locally backward invariant under F* if for every $t_0 \in]0, +\infty[$, $x \in K$, for all solutions $x(\cdot)$ to the differential inclusion $x' \in F(x)$ arriving at x at time t_0, there exists $s \in [0, t_0[$ such that $x(\cdot)$ is viable in K on the interval $[s, t_0]$, and backward invariant if we can take $s = 0$.

We denote by

$$\mathrm{Graph}(F) := \{(x, y) \in X \in Y \mid y \in F(x)\}$$

the graph of a set-valued map $F : X \rightsquigarrow Y$ and $\mathrm{Dom}(F) := \{x \in X \mid F(x) \neq \emptyset\}$ its domain.

Let us set $x(^-t) := \lim_{\tau \mapsto t-} x(\tau)$ when $x(\cdot)$ is defined on some interval $[t-\eta, t[$ where $\eta > 0$, and, for consistency purposes, $x(s) = x(^-t)$ if $s = t$. An impulse differential inclusion (and in particular, an impulse control system) is described by a pair (F, R), where the set-valued map $F : X \rightsquigarrow X$ mapping the state space $X := \mathbf{R}^n$ to itself governs the continuous evolution of the system in K and where R, the reset map, governs the discrete switches to new "initial conditions" when the continuous evolution is doomed to leave K.

Such a hybrid evolution, mixing continuous evolution "punctuated" by discontinuous impulses at impulse times is called in the "hybrid system" literature a "run" or an "execution".

Definition 21 *Let us consider a finite dimensional vector space X, a closed subset $K \subset X$, a set-valued map $F : X \rightsquigarrow X$ and a set-valued map $R : X \rightsquigarrow X$, regarded as a* reset map. *We regard the pair (F, R) as the dynamics of an* impulse differential inclusion.

A run *of the impulse differential inclusion is a map $x(\cdot)$ from $[0, T]$ to X if $T < +\infty$ or from $[0, +\infty[$ to X if $T = +\infty$ which is associated with a non decreasing sequence $\mathcal{T}(x(\cdot)) := \{t_n\}_{n \geq 0}$ of impulse or switching times $t_0 := 0 \leq t_1 \leq \cdots \leq t_n \leq \cdots \leq T$ (depending on the run $x(\cdot)$) such that*

1. *$x(t_{n+1}) \in R(x(t_n))$ if $t_{n+1} = t_n$,*
2. *or else, on the interval $[t_n, t_{n+1}[$, $x(\cdot)$ is a solution to the differential inclusion $x' \in F(x)$ starting at $x(t_n)$ at time t_n until time t_{n+1} at which we take $x(t_{n+1}) \in R(x(^-t_{n+1}))$.*

We denote by $\tau_n := t_n - t_{n-1}$ the nth cadence *of the run and by $x_n(\cdot) := x(\cdot + t_n)$ the nth* motive *of the run, a solution to the differential inclusion $x' \in F(x)$ starting at $x(t_n)$ on the interval $[0, \tau_n]$ and satisfying the end-point condition $x_n(\tau_n) \in R^{-1}(x_{n+1})$. The sequence of states $x(t_n)$ is called the sequence of* initialized states.

We say that a run $x(\cdot)$ is viable in K *if for any $t \geq 0$, $x(t) \in K$.*

At this stage, a run $x(\cdot)$ can just be a (discrete) sequence of states $x_{n+1} \in R(x_n)$ at a fixed time, or just a (continuous) solution $x(\cdot)$ to the differential inclusion $x' \in F(x)$, or an hybrid of these two modes, the discrete and the continuous.

Hybrid systems can be regarded as instances of viable impulse differential inclusions: we refer to [2, Aubin] or [11, Aubin, Lygeros, Quincampoix, Sastry & Seube] for more details on that topic.

3   The Substratum and the Initialization and Impulse Maps

We denote by $\mathcal{S}(x) \subset \mathcal{C}(0, \infty; X)$ the set of absolutely continuous functions $t \mapsto x(t) \in X$ satisfying

$$\text{for almost all } t \geq 0, \quad x'(t) \in F(x(t))$$

starting at time 0 at x: $x(0) = x$ and by $\mathcal{S}^K : K \rightsquigarrow \mathcal{C}(0, \infty, K)$ the viable solution map mapping an initial state $x \in K$ to the set $\mathcal{S}^K(x)$ of solutions to the differential inclusion $x' \in F(x)$ starting at $x \in K$ and viable in K.

The set-valued map $\mathcal{S} : X \rightsquigarrow \mathcal{C}(0, \infty; X)$ is called the solution map associated with F.

We next denote by

$$\vartheta^K(t, x) := \bigcup_{x(\cdot) \in \mathcal{S}^K(x)} \{x(t)\} \quad \& \quad \vartheta^K(t, C) := \bigcup_{x \in C} \vartheta^K(t, x)$$

the K-viable reachable maps (or set-valued flow) of $x \in K$ and $C \subset K$ respectively. We set $\vartheta := \vartheta^X$ when viability constraints are absent.

Definition 31 *We associate with the dynamics (F, R) of the impulse differential inclusion its substratum $\Gamma^K := \Gamma^K_{(F,R)} : \mathbf{R}_+ \times K \rightsquigarrow K$, that is the set-valued map associating with any $(t, x) \in \mathbf{R}_+ \times K$ the subset*

$$\Gamma^K_{(F,R)}(t, x) := R(\vartheta^K(t, x)) \cap K$$

of the elements $y \in R(c)$ where $c \in C := K \cap R^{-1}(K)$ through which the solutions to the differential inclusion $x' \in F(x)$ starting at x and viable in K until they reach $R^{-1}(K)$ at time t.

Knowing the substratum $\Gamma^K_{(F,R)}$, we introduce

1. *the* impulse map

$$\mathbf{T}^K_{(F,R)}(x) := \{t \geq 0 \quad \text{such that} \quad \Gamma^K_{(F,R)}(t, x) \neq \emptyset\}$$

2. *and the* initialization map $U^K_{(F,R)} : K \rightsquigarrow X$

$$U^K_{(F,R)}(x) = \bigcup_{t \in \mathbf{T}^K_{(F,R)}(x)} \Gamma^K_{(F,R)}(t, x)$$

First, we single out the following property:

Proposition 32 *Let (F, R) be an impulse differential inclusion defined on a subset K. Knowing the substratum $\Gamma^K_{(F,R)}$ of (K, F, R), and thus the impulse map $\mathbf{T}^K_{(F,R)}$ and the initialization map $U^K_{(F,R)}$, we can reconstruct a viable run of the impulse differential inclusion (F, R) through the following algorithm: Given the cadence τ_n and the initial state x_n, we take*

$$\begin{cases} i) & \text{the next cadence } \tau_{n+1} \in \mathbf{T}^K_{(F,R)}(x_n), \\ ii) & \text{the next reinitialized state } x_{n+1} \in \Gamma^K_{(F,R)}(\tau_{n+1}, x_n) \subset U^K_{(F,R)}(x_n), \\ iii) & \text{the next motive } x_n(\cdot) := x(\cdot + t_n), \text{ a solution to } x' \in F(x) \text{ satisfying} \\ & \quad x_n(0) = x_n \ \& \ x_n(\tau_{n+1}) \in R^{-1}(x_{n+1}) \end{cases}$$

$$(1)$$

In other words, in terms of impulse times, given the impulse time t_n and the initial state x_n, we take

$$
\begin{cases}
i) & \text{the next impulse time } t_{n+1} \in t_n + \mathbf{T}^K_{(F,R)}(x_n), \\
ii) & \text{the next reinitialized state } x_{n+1} \in \Gamma^K_{(F,R)}(t_{n+1} - t_n, x_n) \subset U^K_{(F,R)}(x_n) \\
iii) & \forall\, t \in [t_n, t_{n+1}], \text{ a solution } x(\cdot) \text{ to the differential inclusion } x' \in F(x) \\
& \text{starting from } x_n \text{ at time } t_n \text{ viable in } K \text{ until it reaches } R^{-1}(x_{n+1}) \\
& \text{at time } t_{n+1}.
\end{cases}
$$

$$(2)$$

Proof —   Take any run $x(\cdot)$ associated with a sequence $\mathcal{T}(x(\cdot)) := \{t_n\}$ of impulse times starting at $x_0 \in K$ and viable in K. Then the sequence $\boldsymbol{x}$: $n \to x(t_n)$ is a solution of the discrete dynamical system $\Gamma^K_{(F,R)}(t_{n+1} - t_n, x_n)$, obviously viable in K.

Conversely, assume that the substratum $\Gamma^K_{(F,R)}$ is known. The above algorithm (2) starting at time 0 and state $x_0 \in K$ provides a run $x(\cdot)$ associated with the sequence $\mathcal{T}(x(\cdot)) := \{t_n\}$ of impulse times of the impulse differential inclusion (F, R) viable in K.   □

Actually, if we are interested only in the sequence of reinitialized states and not necessarily in knowledge of the sequence of impulse times, the knowledge of the initialization map $U^K_{(F,R)}$ is sufficient:

Proposition 33 *A subset K is viable under the impulse differential inclusion (F, R) if and only if the domain of the initialization map $U^K_{(F,R)}$ is equal to K.*

Proof —   Assume that K is viable under (F, R) and prove that for every $x \in K$, $U^K_{(F,R)}(x) \neq \emptyset$. Take any $x_0 \in K$. By definition, there exists a run $x(\cdot)$ associated with a sequence $\mathcal{T}(x(\cdot)) := \{t_n\}$ of impulse times viable in K. Then the sequence $\boldsymbol{x} : n \to x(t_n)$ is a solution of the discrete dynamical system $U^K_{(F,R)}$, obviously viable in K.

Conversely, assume that K is viable under the discrete system $U_{(F,R)}$, i.e., that for every $x \in K$, $U^K_{(F,R)}(x) \neq \emptyset$. We shall prove that K is viable under the impulse differential inclusion (F, R). Let x_0 given in K and a solution $\boldsymbol{x} : n \to x_n \in U^K_{(F,R)}(x_{n-1}) \cap K$ to the discrete dynamical system $U^K_{(F,R)}$. By definition of the initialization map $U^K_{(F,R)}$, we can associate with

$$
x_n \in U^K_{(F,R)}(x_{n-1}) := \bigcup_{t \in \mathbf{T}^K_{(F,R)}(x_{n-1})} \Gamma^K_{(F,R)}(t, x_{n-1})
$$

some $\tau_{n-1} \in \mathbf{T}^K_{(F,R)}(x_{n-1})$ such that

$$
x_n := x_n(\tau_{n-1}) \in R(\vartheta^K(\tau_{n-1}, x_{n-1}))
$$

where $x_n(\cdot)$ is a solution to the differential inclusion $x' \in F(x)$ starting at time 0 from x_{n-1}. Setting $t_n := t_{n-1} + \tau_{n-1}$ and $x(t) := x_n(t + t_{n-1})$ if $t \in [t_{n-1}, t_n]$, we have checked that $x(\cdot)$ is a run to the impulse differential inclusion (F, R) associated with the sequence $\{t_n\}_{n \geq 0}$ of impulse times t_n starting from x_0 and viable in K. $\qquad\square$

4   Some Prerequisite from Viability Theory

Most of the results of viability theory are true whenever we assume that the dynamics is Marchaud:

Definition 41 (Marchaud Map) *We shall say that F is a* Marchaud map *if*

$$\begin{cases} i) & \text{the graph of } F \text{ is closed} \\ ii) & \text{the values } F(x) \text{ of } F \text{ are convex} \\ iii) & \text{the growth of } F \text{ is linear: } \exists\, c > 0 \mid \forall\, x \in X, \\ & \quad \|F(x)\| := \sup_{v \in F(x)} \|v\| \leq c(\|x\| + 1) \end{cases}$$

This covers the case of Marchaud control systems where $(x, u) \mapsto f(x, u)$ is continuous, affine with respect to the controls u and with linear growth and when P is Marchaud.

We recall the following version of the important Theorem 3.5.2 of **Viability Theory**, [1, Aubin]:

Theorem 42 *Assume that $F : X \rightsquigarrow X$ is Marchaud. Then the solution map $\mathcal{S}$ is upper semicompact with nonempty values: This means that whenever $x_n \in X$ converge to x in X and $x_n(\cdot) \in \mathcal{S}(x_n)$ is a solution to the differential inclusion $x' \in F(x)$ starting at x_n, there exists a subsequence (again denoted by) $x_n(\cdot)$ converging to a solution $x(\cdot) \in \mathcal{S}(x)$ uniformly on compact intervals.*

Our purpose is to characterize the viability of a subset K under an impulse differential inclusion:

Definition 43 *We shall say that a subset K is viable under an impulse differential inclusion (F, R) if from any initial state x of K starts at least one run viable in K.*

The Viability Theorem[2] and its consequences imply the following

Theorem 44 *Let (F, R) be an impulse differential inclusion and $K \subset X$ be a closed subset. Assume that F is Marchaud and that $R^{-1}(K)$ is closed. Then the following statements are equivalent*

1. *K is viable under (F, R),*
2. *The subset[3] $K \backslash R^{-1}(K)$ is locally viable under F,*

---

[2] See for instance Theorems 3.2.4, 3.3.2 and 3.5.2 of [1, Aubin].

[3] The subset $K \backslash C$ denotes the intersection of K and the complement of C, i.e., is the set of elements of K which do not belong to C.

3. K, F and R are linked through the tangential condition[4]

$$\forall\, x \in K \backslash R^{-1}(K), \ \ F(x) \cap T_K(x) \neq \emptyset$$

(see [2, Aubin] or [11, Aubin, Lygeros, Quincampoix, Sastry & Seube] for a proof.)

We shall also need some other prerequisites from Viability Theory:

Definition 45 *Let $C \subset K \subset X$ be two subsets, C being regarded as a target, K as a constrained set. The subset $\text{Capt}^K(C)$ of initial states $x_0 \in K$ such that C is reached in finite time before possibly leaving K by at least one solution $x(\cdot) \in S(x_0)$ starting at x_0 is called the viable-capture basin of C in K. A subset K is a repeller under F if all solutions starting from K leave K in finite time. A subset D is locally backward invariant relatively to K if all backward solutions starting from D viable in K are actually viable in K.*

We shall use the following characterization of capture basin (see [6, Aubin]):

Theorem 46 *Let us assume that F is Marchaud and that the subsets $C \subset K$ and K are closed. If $K \backslash C$ is a repeller (this is the case when K itself is a repeller), then the viable-capture basin $\text{Capt}^K(C)$ of the target C under S is the* **unique** *closed subset satisfying $C \subset D \subset K$ and*

$$\begin{cases} i) & D \backslash C \text{ is locally viable under } S \\ ii) & D \text{ is locally backward invariant relatively to } K \end{cases} \tag{3}$$

5   The Graph of the Substratum

We begin by characterizing the graph of the substratum $\Gamma^K_{(F,R)}$:

Theorem 51 *Let us assume that F is Marchaud, that $C \subset R$ is closed and that the graph of $R : C \rightsquigarrow X$ is closed.*

Then the substratum $\Gamma^K_{(F,R)} : K \rightsquigarrow K$ is the **unique** *set-valued map with closed graph satisfying*

$$\forall\, x \in K, \ \ \Gamma^K_{(F,R)}(0,x) := R(x) \cap K$$

and, for any $T > 0$

1. for any $y \in \Gamma^K_{(F,R)}(T,x)$, there exists a solution $x(\cdot)$ to the differential inclusion $x' \in F(x)$ viable in K on $[0,T]$ such that

$$\forall\, t \in [0,T], \ \ y \in \Gamma^K_{(F,R)}(T - t, x(t)) \tag{4}$$

---

[4] The contingent cone $T_L(x)$ to $L \subset X$ at $x \in L$ is the set of directions $v \in X$ such that there exist sequences $h_n > 0$ converging to 0 and v_n converging to v satisfying $x + h_n v_n \in K$ for every n (see for instance [8, Aubin & Frankowska]) or [19, Rockafellar & Wets] for more details).

2. *for any* $y \in K \backslash \Gamma^K_{(F,R)}(T, x)$, *for every solution* $x(\cdot)$ *to the differential inclusion* $x' \in F(x)$ *viable in* K *on* $[0, T]$, *then*

$$\forall\, t \in [0, T], \quad y \in K \backslash \Gamma^K_{(F,R)}(T - t, x(t))$$

As a consequence[5], *for any* $T > 0$ *and for any* $y \in \partial_K \Gamma^K_{(F,R)}(T, x)$, *for every solution* $x(\cdot)$ *to the differential inclusion* $x' \in F(x)$ *satisfying* (4), *then*

$$\forall\, t \in [0, T], \quad y \in \partial_K \Gamma^K_{(F,R)}(T - t, x(t))$$

For proving Theorem 51, we shall first observe that the graph of the substratum of (K, F, R) is a viable-capture basin and next, deduce the above results from the characterization of viable-capture basins. Let us recall that we denoted by $R^{|K}_{|K}$ the graphical restriction of R to $K \times K$ defined by

$$R^{|K}_{|K}(x) := \begin{cases} R(x) \cap K & \text{if } x \in K \\ \emptyset & \text{if } x \notin K \end{cases}$$

We observe that $C := \mathrm{Dom}(R^{|K}_{|K}) = K \cap R^{-1}(K)$, that $\mathrm{Im}(R^{|K}_{|K})$ and that $\mathrm{Graph}(R^{|K}_{|K}) = \mathrm{Graph}(R) \cap (K \times K)$.

Lemma 52 *The graph of the substratum* $\Gamma^K_{(F,R)}$ *of* (K, F, R) *is the viable-capture basin of* $\{0\} \times \mathrm{Graph}(R^{|K}_{|K})$ *under the set-valued map* $\{-1\} \times F \times \{0\}$:

$$\mathrm{Graph}(\Gamma^K_{(F,R)}) = \mathrm{Capt}^{\mathbf{R}_+ \times K \times K}_{\{-1\} \times F \times \{0\}} \left(\{0\} \times \mathrm{Graph}(R^{|K}_{|K}) \right)$$

and $\forall\, x \in C := K \cap R^{-1}(K)$, $\Gamma^K_{(F,R)}(0, x) = R(x) \cap K$.

Proof — Indeed, to say (T, x, y) belongs to the viable-capture basin

$$\mathrm{Capt}^{\mathbf{R}_+ \times K \times K}_{\{-1\} \times F \times \{0\}} \left(\{0\} \times \mathrm{Graph}(R^{|K}_{|K}) \right)$$

means that there exists a solution $x(\cdot) \in \mathcal{S}(x)$ and $\bar{t} \in [0, T]$ such that

$$\begin{cases} i) \ \forall\, t \in [0, \bar{t}], \ (T - t, x(t), y) \in \mathrm{Capt}^{\mathbf{R}_+ \times K \times K}_{\{-1\} \times F \times \{0\}}(\{0\} \times \mathrm{Graph}(R^{|K}_{|K})) \\ ii) \ (T - \bar{t}, y, x(\bar{t})) \in \{0\} \times \mathrm{Graph}(R^{|K}_{|K}) \end{cases}$$

i.e., if and only if $\bar{t} = T$ and

$$\begin{cases} i) \ \forall\, t \in [0, T[, \ x(t) \in K \\ ii) \ y \in R(x(T)) \cap K \end{cases}$$

This is equivalent to say that $y \in \Gamma^K_{(F,R)}(T, x) \cap K$.

---

[5] The relative boundary $\partial_K D$ to K of a subset $D \subset K$ is equal to $\overline{D} \cap \overline{K \backslash X}$.

Consequently, to say that y belongs to $\Gamma^K_{(F,R)}(0,x)$ means that $y \in R(x) \cap K$. $\square$

Proof of Theorem 51 — We observe first that the map $\{-1\} \times F \times \{0\}$: $\mathbf{R} \times X \times X \rightsquigarrow \mathbf{R} \times X \times X$ is Marchaud and that $\mathbf{R}_+ \times K \times K$ is a repeller under this map since any solution $(T-t, x(t), y)$ starting at (T, x, y) leaves $\mathbf{R}_+ \times K \times K$ at time T. Theorem 46 states that the viable-capture basin

$$\mathrm{Graph}(\Gamma^K_{(F,R)}) = \mathrm{Capt}^{\mathbf{R}_+ \times K \times K}_{\{-1\} \times F \times \{0\}}\left(\{0\} \times \mathrm{Graph}(R^{|K}_{|K})\right)$$

is the unique closed subset $\mathcal{V} \subset \mathbf{R} \times K \times K$ containing $\{0\} \times \mathrm{Graph}(R^{|K}_{|K})$ satisfying

1. $\mathcal{V} \setminus (\{0\} \times \mathrm{Graph}(R^{|K}_{|K}))$ is locally viable under $\{-1\} \times F \times \{0\}$
2. and
$$\mathrm{Capt}^{\mathbf{R}_+ \times K \times K}_{\{-1\} \times F \times \{0\}}(\mathcal{V}) = \mathcal{V}$$

This states that whenever $(T, x, y) \in (\mathbf{R}_+ \times K \times K) \setminus \mathcal{V}$, all solutions to the differential inclusion $(t', x', y') \in \{-1\} \times F(x) \times \{0\}$ leave $(\mathbf{R}_+ \times K \times K)$ before possibly reaching the target $\{0\} \times \mathrm{Graph}(R^{|K}_{|K})$.

The first statement means that whenever (T, x, y) belongs to $\mathcal{V}$, there exists a solution $x(\cdot)$ to the differential inclusion $x' \in F(x)$ such that $(T-t, x(t), y)$ belongs to $\mathcal{V}$ until it reaches $\{0\} \times \mathrm{Graph}(R^{|K}_{|K})$. This is equivalent to saying that

$$\forall\, t \in [0, T], \quad y \in \Gamma^K_{(F,R)}(T-t, x(t))$$

The second statement means that whenever (T, x, y) does not belong to $\mathcal{V}$, all solutions $x(\cdot)$ to the differential inclusion $x' \in F(x)$ are such that $(T-t, x(t), y)$ do not belong to $\mathcal{V}$ whenever $(T-t, x(t), y) \in \mathbf{R}_+ \times K \times K$, i.e., whenever $x(\cdot)$ is viable in K on the interval $[0, T]$. This is equivalent to saying that for all solutions to $x' \in F(x)$ viable in K on the interval $[0, T]$,

$$\forall\, t \in [0, T], \quad y \in K \setminus \Gamma^K_{(F,R)}(T-t, x(t))$$

Let us consider now $y \in \partial \Gamma^K_{(F,R)}(T, x)$ where $T > 0$. This means that there exists a sequence $y_n \in K$ such that $y_n \in K \setminus \Gamma^K_{(F,R)}(T, x)$. Hence (T, x, y_n) does not belong to the capture basin of $\{0\} \times \mathrm{Graph}(R^{|K}_{|K})$ viable in $\mathbf{R}_+ \times K \times K$. Therefore we know that for any solution $x(\cdot) \in \mathcal{S}(x)$ viable in K on $[0, T]$, for any $t \in [0, T]$, $y_n \in K \setminus \Gamma^K_{(F,R)}(T-t, x(t))$ and, in particular, that $y_n \in K \setminus \Gamma^K_{(F,R)}(0, x(T)) = R(x(T))$. Taking any solution $x(\cdot) \in \mathcal{S}(x)$ satisfying (4) and the limit when $n \to +\infty$, we infer that

$$\forall\, t \in [0, T], \quad y \in \partial_K \Gamma^K_{(F,R)}(T-t, x(t))$$

and that

$$y \in \partial_K R(x(T))$$

6   Hamilton-Jacobi Characterization of the Substratum

Before stating the general result characterizing the substratum as a solution to a system of first-order partial differential inclusions, let us consider the following particular case:

Proposition 61 *Let us assume that $f : X \mapsto X$ is Lipschitz, $r : X \mapsto X$ is single-valued and continuous, that $\varpi^{\flat}_{(K,C)}$ is continuous, that K is viable under (f, r) and $\Gamma^K_{(f,r)}$ is differentiable. Then it is the **unique** solution to the system of first-order partial differential equations*

$$\forall\, x \in K\backslash C,\ \forall\, j = 1, \ldots, n, \quad -\frac{\partial u_j(t,x)}{\partial t} + \sum_{i=1}^{n} \frac{\partial u_j(t,x)}{\partial x_i} f_i(x) \;=\; 0$$

or, in a more compact form,

$$\forall\, x \in K\backslash C, \quad -\frac{\partial u(t,x)}{\partial t} + \frac{\partial u(t,x)}{\partial x} f(x) \;=\; 0$$

satisfying the condition

$$\forall\, x \in C, \quad u(0,x) \;=\; r(x)$$

We shall deduce from Theorem 63 below. Indeed, thanks to the concepts of contingent derivative, we shall show that the substratum $\Gamma^K_{(F,R)}$ is the unique (set-valued) solution in the "Frankowska sense" to the "Hamilton-Jacobi inclusion"

$$0 \,\in\, -\frac{\partial V(t,x)}{\partial t} + \frac{\partial V(t,x)}{\partial x} \cdot F(x) \tag{5}$$

satisfying the condition

$$\forall\, x \in C, \quad V(0,x) \;=\; R(x) \cap K$$

We refer to [5,7, Aubin], [9, Aubin & Frankowska] and their references for set-valued solutions to systems of Hamilton-Jacobi inclusions. For that purpose, we recall that the (graphical contingent) derivative of a set-valued map $V :$ $\mathbf{R}_+ \times K \rightsquigarrow K$ may be defined by the relation

$$\mathrm{Graph}(DV(T,x,y)) \;:=\; T_{\mathrm{Graph}(V)}(T,x,y)$$

Definition 62 *We shall say that a set-valued map $V : \mathbf{R}_+ \times K \rightsquigarrow K$ is a* Frankowska solution *to the Hamilton-Jacobi system of first-order partial differential inclusions (5) satisfying the initial condition $V(0,x) = R(x)$ if its graph is closed, if*

$$\forall\, t > 0,\ \forall\, y \in V(t,x),\ \exists\, v \in F(x) \quad \text{such that } 0 \in DV(t,x,y)(-1,v)$$

and if for every $v \in F(x)$

$$\forall\, t \geq 0,\ \forall\, y \in V(t,x),\quad 0 \in DV(t,x,y)(1,-v)$$

or

$$\begin{cases} i)\ -v \in T_{X\setminus K}(x)\ \text{if}\ x \in \partial K \\ ii)\ -v \in T_K(x)\ \text{if}\ y \in \partial K \end{cases}$$

Theorem 63 *Let us assume that F is Marchaud, that $C := K \cap R^{-1}(K)$ is closed and that the graph of $R : C \rightsquigarrow K$ is closed.*

1. *The substratum $\Gamma^K_{(F,R)} : K \rightsquigarrow K$ is the **largest** set-valued map $V : \mathbf{R}_+ \times K \rightsquigarrow K$ with closed graph contained in $K \times K$ satisfying*

$$\forall\, t > 0,\ y \in V(t,x),\ \exists\, v \in F(x)\quad \text{such that}\ 0 \in DV(t,x,y)(-1,v)$$

and the condition $V(0,x) = R(x) \cap K$,

2. *If furthermore, F is assumed to be Lipschitz, the substratum $\Gamma^K_{(F,R)} : K \rightsquigarrow K$ is the **unique** Frankowska solution $V : \mathbf{R}_+ \times K \rightsquigarrow K$ to the Hamilton-Jacobi system of first-order differential inclusions (5) satisfying the initial condition $V(0,x) = R(x)$.*

Proof —   When F is Marchaud, to say that $\mathrm{Graph}(V)\setminus(\{0\} \times \mathrm{Graph}\left(R^{|K}_{|K}\right))$ is locally viable under $\{-1\} \times F \times \{0\}$ means that

$$\forall\, (t,x,y) \in \mathrm{Graph}(V)\setminus(\{0\} \times \mathrm{Graph}\left(R^{|K}_{|K}\right)),$$

$$\{-1\} \times F(x) \times \{0\} \cap T_{\mathrm{Graph}(V)}(t,x,y) \neq \emptyset$$

We observe that $(t,x,y) \in \mathrm{Graph}(V)\setminus(\{0\} \times \mathrm{Graph}(R^{|K}_{|K}))$ whenever $t > 0$ and we recall that

$$T_{\mathrm{Graph}(V)}(t,x,y) = \mathrm{Graph}(DV(t,x,y))$$

so that the above condition reads

$$\forall\, t > 0, \forall\, y \in \Gamma^K_{(F,R)}(t,x),\ \exists\, v \in F(x)\quad \text{such that}\ 0 \in DV(t,x,y)(-1,v)$$

When F is assumed to be Lipschitz, to say that

$$\mathrm{Capt}^{\mathbf{R}_+ \times K \times K}_{\{-1\} \times F \times \{0\}}(\mathrm{Graph}(V)) = \mathrm{Graph}(V)$$

means that

1. for any $(t,x,y) \in \mathrm{Graph}(V)) \cap \mathrm{Int}(\mathbf{R}_+ \times K \times K)$,

$$(\{1\} \times -F(x) \times \{0\}) \subset T_{\mathrm{Graph}(V)}(t,x,y) = \mathrm{Graph}(DV(t,x,y))$$

This is equivalent to say that for every $v \in F(x)$,

$$\forall\, t > 0,\ x \in \mathrm{Int}(K),\ y \in V(t,x) \cap \mathrm{Int}(K),\ 0 \in DV(t,x,y)(1,-v) \quad (6)$$

2. and otherwise, for any $(t, x, y) \in \text{Graph}(V)) \cap \partial(\mathbf{R}_+ \times K \times K)$,

$$(\{1\} \times -F(x) \times \{0\}) \subset T_{\text{Graph}(V)}(t, x, y) \cup T_{(\mathbf{R} \times X \times X) \setminus (\mathbf{R}_+ \times K \times K)}(t, x, y)$$

This means that for every $v \in F(x)$,

$$\begin{cases} i) & 0 \in DV(t, x, y)(1, -v) \text{ if } t = 0, y \in R(x) \\ ii) & 0 \in D(t, x, y)(1, -v) \text{ or } -v \in T_{X \setminus K} \text{ if } t \geq 0, x \in \partial K, y \in R(x) \\ iii) & 0 \in D(t, x, y)(1, -v) \text{ or } -v \in T_K \text{ if } t \geq 0, y \in R(x) \cap \partial K \end{cases}$$

Indeed,

$$\overline{(\mathbf{R} \times X \times X) \setminus (\mathbf{R}_+ \times K \times K)} =$$

$$(\mathbf{R}_- \times K \times K) \cup (\mathbf{R}_+ \times (X \setminus K) \times K) \cup (\mathbf{R}_+ \times K \times (X \setminus K))$$

Therefore, condition $(1, -v, 0)$ belongs to the contingent cone to $\mathbf{R}_- \times K \times K$ at $(0, x, y)$ is impossible, condition $(1, -v, 0)$ belongs to the contingent cone to $\mathbf{R}_- \times (X \setminus K) \times K$ at (t, x, y) when $x \in \partial K$ means that $-v$ belongs to $T_{X \setminus K}(x)$ and condition $(1, -v, 0)$ belongs to the contingent cone to $\mathbf{R}_- \times K \times (X \setminus K)$ at (t, x, y) when $y \in \partial K$ means that $-v$ belongs to $T_K(x)$. $\quad\square$

For the initialization map, we obtain the following Hamilton-Jacobi inclusion :

Theorem 64 *Let us assume that F is Marchaud, that $C := K \cap R^{-1}(K)$ is closed and that the graph of $R : C \rightsquigarrow K$ is closed.*

1. *The initialization map $U^K_{(F,R)} : K \rightsquigarrow K$ is the **largest** set-valued map $V : \mathbf{R}_+ \times K \rightsquigarrow K$ with closed graph contained in $K \times K$ satisfying*

$$\forall y \in V(x), \ \exists v \in F(x) \quad \text{such that} \quad 0 \in DV(x, y)(v)$$

2. *If furthermore, F is assumed to be Lipschitz, the initialization map $U^K_{(F,R)} : K \rightsquigarrow K$ is the **unique** Frankowska solution $V : \mathbf{R}_+ \times K \rightsquigarrow K$ to the Hamilton-Jacobi system of first-order differential inclusions (5) satisfying the condition $\forall x \in C, V(x) = R(x)$.*

References

1. AUBIN J.-P. (1991) **Viability Theory** Birkhäuser, Boston, Basel, Berlin
2. AUBIN J.-P. (1999) **Impulse Differential Inclusions and Hybrid Systems: A Viability Approach**, Lecture Notes, University of California at Berkeley
3. AUBIN J.-P. (2000) *Lyapunov Functions for Impulse and Hybrid Control Systems*, Proceedings of the CDC 2000 Conference
4. AUBIN J.-P. (2000) *Optimal Impulse Control Problems and Quasi-Variational Inequalities Thirty Years Later: a Viability Approach*, in **Contrôle optimal et EDP: Innovations et Applications**, IOS Press
5. AUBIN J.-P. (2000) *Boundary-Value Problems for Systems of First-Order Partial Differential Inclusions*, NoDEA, 7, 61-84

6. AUBIN J.-P. (to appear) *Viability Kernels and Capture Basins of Sets under Differential Inclusions*, SIAM J. Control

7. AUBIN J.-P. (submitted) *Boundary-Value Problems for Systems of Hamilton-Jacobi-Bellman Inclusions with Constraints*, SIAM J. Control

8. AUBIN J.-P. & FRANKOWSKA H. (1990) **Set-Valued Analysis**, Birkhäuser, Boston, Basel, Berlin

9. AUBIN J.-P. & FRANKOWSKA H. (1992) *Hyperbolic systems of partial differential inclusions*, Annali Scuola Normale di Pisa, 18, 541-562

10. AUBIN J.-P. & HADDAD G. (to appear) *Cadenced runs of impulse and hybrid control systems*, International Journal Robust and Nonlinear Control

11. AUBIN J.-P., LYGEROS J., QUINCAMPOIX. M., SASTRY S. & SEUBE N. (to appear) *Impulse Differential Inclusions: A Viability Approach to Hybrid Systems*,

12. BENSOUSSAN A. & MENALDI (1997) *Hybrid Control and Dynamic Programming*, Dynamics of Continuous, Discrete and Impulse Systems, 3, 395-442

13. BRANICKY M.S., BORKAR V.S. & MITTER S. (1998) *A unified framework for hybrid control: Background, model and theory*, IEEE Trans. Autom. Control, 43, 31-45

14. BRETTE R. (2000) *Rotation numbers of orientation preserving circle maps*, submitted to Nonlinearity

15. CARDALIAGUET P., QUINCAMPOIX M. & SAINT-PIERRE P. (1994) *Temps optimaux pour des problèmes avec contraintes et sans contrôlabilité locale* Comptes-Rendus de l'Académie des Sciences, Série 1, Paris, 318, 607-612

16. DAY R.H. (1995) *Multiple-phase economic dynamics*, in **Multiple-phase economic dynamics**, T. Maruyama & W. Takahashi, Eds., Springer-Verlag, 25-45

17. MATVEEV A.S. , SAVKIN A.V. (2000) **Qualitative Theory of Hybrid Dynamical Systems**, Birkhäuser

18. MATVEEV A.S. , SAVKIN A.V. (2001) **Hybrid dynamical systems: Controller and sensor switching problems**, Birkhäuser

19. ROCKAFELLAR R.T. & WETS R. (1997) **Variational Analysis**, Springer-Verlag

20. SHAFT (van der) A. & SCHUMACHER H. (1999) **An introduction to hybrid dynamical systems**, Springer-Verlag, Lecture Notes in Control, 251

21. TAVERNI L. (1987) *Differential autamata and their discrete simulators*, Nonlinear Analysis, TMA, 11, 665-683

Path-Dependent Impulse and Hybrid Systems

Jean-Pierre Aubin[1] and George Haddad[2]

[1] Université Paris-Dauphine, Centre de Recherche Viabilité,
Jeux, Contrôle, F-75775, Paris cx (16)
Tel. [33] (0)1-46-33-71-21, Fax. [33] (0)1-44-05-49-11
aubin@viab.dauphine.fr, http://viab.dauphine.fr
[2] Université Panthéon-Sorbonne, Président Honoraire,
Sorbonne, 47, rue des Ecoles, F-75005, Paris
Tel. [33] (0)1-40-46-28-02, Fax. [33] (0)1-46-34-20-56

Abstract. Path-dependent impulse differential inclusions, and in particular, path-dependent hybrid control systems, are defined by a path-dependent differential inclusion (or path-dependent control system, or differential inclusion and control systems with memory) and a path-dependent reset map.

In this paper, we characterize the viability property of a closed subset of paths under an impulse path-dependent differential inclusion using the Viability Theorems for path-dependent differential inclusions.

Actually, one of the characterizations of the Characterization Theorem is valid for any general impulse evolutionary system that we shall defined in this paper.

Keywords: hybrid control, impulse control, path-dependent differential inclusion, differential inclusion with memory, functional differential inclusions, viability, run, execution, Kakutani Theorem, contingent cone, Marchaud map.

Introduction

In this paper, we characterize the viability property of a closed subset of paths under an impulse path-dependent differential inclusion using the method of [2, Aubin] or [8, Aubin, Lygeros, Quincampoix, Sastry & Seube], the Path-Dependent Viability Theorems of [12,13,14, Haddad].

Actually, one of the characterizations of the Characterization Theorem is true for any general impulse evolutionary system that we shall define in this paper, which is based on recent results of [5, Aubin].

We recall that hybrid control systems[1] can be embedded in the framework of impulse differential inclusions; in the same way, path-dependent hybrid systems can be regarded as instances of viable path-dependent impulse differential inclusions, and enjoy the same properties.

---

[1] See for instance among many papers and books [10, Branicky, Borkar & Mitter], [9, Bensoussan & Menaldi], [15,16, Matveev & Savkin] and [18, Shaft & Schumacher].

M.D. Di Benedetto, A. Sangiovanni-Vincentelli (Eds.): HSCC 2001, LNCS 2034, pp. 119–132, 2001.

1 Impulse Path-Dependent Differential Inclusions

Let $X := \mathbf{R}^n$ be a finite dimensional vector space.

1.1 History Spaces

We denote by

$$\mathcal{H}(X) := \mathcal{C}(-\infty, 0; X)$$

the history (or memory, path) space .

It is supplied with the compact convergence topology. We denote by $\mathcal{H}_\lambda(X)$ the subset of Lipschitz functions with Lipschitz constant λ.

If $\mathbf{K} \subset \mathcal{H}(X)$, we set

$$\forall \tau \in]-\infty, 0], \ \ \mathbf{K}(\tau) := \{\varphi(\tau)\}_{\varphi \in \mathbf{K}}$$

Observe that Ascoli's Theorem states that a *closed subset* $\mathbf{K} \subset \mathcal{H}_\lambda(X)$ *is compact if and only if* $\mathbf{K}(0) := \{\varphi(0)\}_{\varphi \in \mathbf{K}}$ *is bounded,* since it is closed and equicontinuous (by assumption) and pointwise bounded because, for all $\psi \in \mathbf{K}$ and $\tau \leq 0$,

$$\|\psi(\tau)\| \leq \|\psi(\tau) - \psi(0)\| + \|\psi(0)\| \leq \lambda|\tau| + \|\mathbf{K}(0)\|$$

Our study invlves a constrained subset $\mathbf{K} \subset \mathcal{H}(X)$ made of paths or histories and of a target $\mathbf{C} \subset \mathbf{K}$.

A first example of constrained subset of paths or histories and targets associated with subsets $C \subset K \subset X$ of the vector space are given by

$$\mathbf{C} := \{\, \varphi \in \mathcal{H}(X) \mid \varphi(0) \in C \,\} \subset \mathbf{K} := \{\, \varphi \in \mathcal{H}(X) \mid \varphi(0) \in K \,\}$$

where the constraints bear only on the present.

Another class is given by Volterra sets defined through a "kernel" $k :\,]-\infty, 0] \times X \mapsto Y$ and a set-valued map $M : Y \rightsquigarrow X$ by

$$\mathbf{K} := \left\{ \varphi \in \mathcal{H}(X) \mid \varphi(0) \in M \left(\int_{-\infty}^{0} k(-s, \varphi(s)) d\mu(s) \right) \right\}$$

where the constraints involve cumulated consequences of the history.

In the discrete case,

$$\mathbf{K} := \left\{ \varphi \in \mathcal{H}(X) \mid \varphi(0) \in M \left(\sum_{j=-\infty}^{0} k(-j, \varphi(\beta_j)) \right) \right\}$$

involves discrete cumulated consequences of the history (delays).

Associated targets can be asociated with set-valued maps $P \subset M$ in the same fashion.

1.2   Histories or Paths

We associate with any continuous function $x(\cdot) \in \mathbf{C}(-\infty, +\infty; X)$ its *history (or path)*[2] $T(t)x$ *up to time t* defined by:

$$\forall \, \tau \in]-\infty, 0], \;\; T(t)x(\tau) := x(t + \tau)$$

Then $T(t)$ maps $\mathcal{C}(-\infty, +\infty; X)$ to $\mathcal{H}(X)$ and satisfies the semi-group property

$$T(t + s)x = T(s)T(t)x$$

We then observe that for any function $x(\cdot) \in \mathcal{C}(-\infty, +\infty; X)$, we have $x(t) = (T(t)x)(0)$.

In this continuous framework, we define the constraints of the history of the evolution through a closed subset $\mathbf{K} \subset \mathcal{H}(X)$. Viable evolutions $x(\cdot)$ with memory are the ones that satisfy

$$\forall \, t \geq 0, \;\; T(t)x \in \mathbf{K} \tag{1}$$

and an evolution $x(\cdot)$ reach a target $\mathbf{C}$ at time s if $T(s)x \in \mathbf{C}$.

For instance, an evolution is viable in $\mathbf{K} := \{\varphi \in \mathcal{H}(X) \mid \varphi(0) \in K\}$ if and only if for every $t \in]-\infty, 0], \; x(t) \in K$. If

$$\mathbf{K} := \left\{\varphi \in \mathcal{H}(X) \mid \varphi(0) \in M\left(\int_{-\infty}^{0} k(-s, \varphi(s))d\mu(s)\right)\right\}$$

then $x(\cdot)$ is viable in $\mathbf{K}$ if and only if

$$\forall \, t \geq 0, \;\; x(t) \in M\left(\int_{-\infty}^{t} k(t - s, \varphi(s))d\mu(s)\right)$$

1.3   Path-Dependent Differential Inclusions

Let us consider a set-valued map $F : \mathcal{H}(X) \mapsto X$ governing the continuous evolution of the state $x(t)$ through the path-dependent differential inclusion

$$\text{for almost all } t \geq 0, \;\; x'(t) \in F(T(t)x)$$

starting at a given $\varphi \in \mathcal{H}(X)$ in the sense that

$$T(0)x = \varphi$$

i.e., for every $\tau \in]-\infty, 0], \; x(\tau) = \varphi(\tau)$.

We denote by $\mathcal{R}_F : \mathcal{H}(X) \rightsquigarrow \mathcal{C}(0, \infty; X)$ the map associating with any initial path $\varphi \in \mathcal{H}(X)$ the set $\mathcal{R}_F(\varphi)$ of solutions $t \mapsto x(t)$ to the path-dependent differential inclusion $x'(t) \in F(T(t)x)$ starting at the initial path φ in the sense that $T(0)x = \varphi$.

---

[2] often denoted by $x_t := T(t)x$

Actually, we shall need the properties of the associated set-valued map $\mathcal{S}_F$: $\mathcal{H}(X) \rightsquigarrow \mathcal{C}(0, \infty; \mathcal{H}(X))$ defined by

$$\mathcal{S}_F(\varphi) := \{t \mapsto \varphi(t) := T(t)x\}_{x(\cdot) \in \mathcal{R}_F(\varphi)}$$

Definition 11 *We shall say that this set-valued map* $\mathcal{S}_F : \mathcal{H}(X) \rightsquigarrow \mathcal{C}(0, +\infty$; $\mathcal{H}(X))$ *is the* solution map *of* F.

The solution map $\mathcal{S}_F$ has the advantage of mapping the set $\mathcal{H}(X)$ into time-dependent functions $t \mapsto \varphi(t) := T(t)x$ that belong to the same histoy space $\mathcal{H}(X)$, even though the traditional view is to call a solution a function $t \mapsto x(t)$, taking its values in X.

This choice of $\mathcal{S}_F$ instead of $\mathcal{R}_F$ is justified by its following properties:

1. the translation property: Let $\varphi(\cdot) \in \mathcal{S}(\varphi)$. Then for all $s \geq 0$, the function $\psi(\cdot)$ defined by $\psi(t) := \varphi(t + s)$ is the history $\psi(\cdot) := T(\cdot)y \in \mathcal{S}(T(s)x)$ of the solution $y(\cdot)$ to the path-dependent differential inclusion starting at $T(s)x$,
2. the concatenation property: Let $\varphi(\cdot) \in \mathcal{S}_F(\varphi)$ be the history of a solution to the path-dependent differential inclusion starting at the path φ and $s \geq 0$. Then for every history $\psi(\cdot) \in \mathcal{S}_F(T(s)x)$ of a solution $y(\cdot)$ to the path-dependent differential inclusion starting at the initial path $T(s)x$, the function $\xi(\cdot)$ defined by

$$\xi(t) := \begin{cases} \varphi(t) := T(t)x & \text{if } t \in [0, s] \\ \psi(t - s) := T(t - s)y & \text{if } t \geq s \end{cases}$$

is the history of the solution $z(\cdot)$ defined by

$$z(t) := \begin{cases} x(t) & \text{if } t \in [0, s] \\ y(t - T) & \text{if } t \geq s \end{cases}$$

to the path-dependent differential inclusion starting at the initial path φ, and thus, belongs to $\mathcal{S}_F(\varphi)$.

These two properties to which we add the upper compactness of the solution map are enough to obtain relevant (and interesting) properties of path-dependent impulse differential inclusions, common to other dynamical systems.

1.4   Runs of Impulse Path-Dependent Differential Inclusions

We now introduce a constrained functional set $\mathbf{K} \subset \mathcal{H}(X)$, a functional target $\mathbf{C} \subset \mathbf{K}$ and a path-dependent reset map $R : \mathbf{C} \rightsquigarrow \mathbf{K}$ with nonempty values $R(\varphi)$.

The pair (F, R) governs the evolution of impulse systems in the following sense.

Definition 12 *Let us consider a finite dimensional vector space X, the space $\mathcal{H}(X)$ of histories, a subset $\mathbf{K} \subset \mathcal{H}(X)$, a target $\mathbf{C} \subset \mathbf{K}$, a set-valued map $F : \mathcal{H}(X) \rightsquigarrow X$ and a set-valued map $R : \mathbf{C} \rightsquigarrow \mathcal{H}$ with nonempty values, regarded as a* path-dependent reset *map. We regard the pair (F, R) as the dynamics of a* path-dependent impulse differential inclusion.

A run *of the path-dependent impulse differential inclusion (F, R) is defined by*

1. *a finite or infinite sequence $\tau(x(\cdot)) := \{\tau_n\}_n$ of nonnegative* cadences $\tau_n \in [0, \infty[$,
2. *a sequence of reinitialized paths $\varphi_n \in \mathcal{H}(X)$,*
3. *a sequence of motives $\varphi_n(\cdot) := T(\cdot)x_n \in \mathcal{S}_F(\varphi_n)$ where $\varphi_n \in \mathcal{H}(X)$ is the history of a solution $x_n(\cdot)$ to the path-dependent differential inclusion $x'(t) \in F(T(t)x)$ starting at the initial path φ_n and satisfying the end-point condition $T(\tau_n)x_n \in R^{-1}(\varphi_{n+1})$*

by

$$\begin{cases} i) & \text{defining the sequence of impulse times } t_{n+1} := t_n + \tau_n, \\ ii) & \forall\, t \in [t_n, t_{n+1}[, \quad x(t) := x_n(t - t_n) \end{cases} \tag{2}$$

If the sequence of cadences is finite[3] and stops at τ_N, we agree that the Nth motive is defined on $[0, +\infty[$, i.e., that we take $\tau_{N+1} = +\infty$.

We say that a run $x(\cdot)$ is viable in $\mathbf{K}$ if for any $t \geq 0$, $T(t)x \in \mathbf{K}$ and that $\mathbf{K}$ is locally viable *under (F, R) if for any $\varphi \in \mathbf{K}$, there exists* at least *one run of the impulse path-dependent differential inclusion viable on a nonempty time interval and (globally) viable if it is viable on $[0, +\infty[$.*

At this stage, a run $x(\cdot)$ can just be a (discrete) sequence of paths $\varphi_{n+1} \in R(\varphi_n)$ at the initial time (case when for all $n \geq 0$, the cadences $\tau_n = 0$), or just a (continuous) solution $x(\cdot)$ to the path-dependent differential inclusion $x'(t) \in F(T(t)x)$ (case when $\tau_1 = +\infty$), or an hybrid of these two path-dependent modes, the discrete and the continuous.

Path-dependent hybrid systems can be regarded as instances of viable path-dependent impulse differential inclusions as in the case of usual hybrid systems: we refer to [2, Aubin] or [8, Aubin, Lygeros, Quincampoix, Sastry & Seube] for more details on this topic.

2 Statement of the Impulse Path-Dependent Viability Theorem

2.1 Marchaud Maps

The Viability Theorems hold true whenever we assume that the dynamics governing the path-dependent evolution is Marchaud:

---

[3] We shall see that we can eliminate this situation by assuming that $R(\mathbf{C}) \cap \mathrm{Viab}_F(\mathbf{K}) = \emptyset$.

Definition 21 (Marchaud Map) *We shall say that* $F : \mathcal{H}(X) \rightsquigarrow X$ *is a Marchaud map if*

$$\begin{cases} i) & F \text{ is upper semicontinuous} \\ ii) & \text{the values } F(\varphi) \text{ of } F \text{ are convex} \\ iii) & \text{the growth of } F \text{ is linear: } \exists\, c > 0 \mid \forall\, \varphi \in \mathcal{H}(X), \\ & \|F(\varphi)\| := \sup_{v \in F(\varphi)} \|v\| \leq c(\|\varphi(0)\| + 1) \end{cases}$$

This covers the case of Marchaud control systems where $(\varphi, u) \mapsto f(\varphi, u)$ is continuous, affine with respect to the controls u and with linear growth and when $P : \mathcal{H}(X) \rightsquigarrow Z$ is Marchaud.

We recall the following version of the important Haddad Theorem 12.4.1 of [1, Aubin]:

Theorem 22 *Assume that* $F : \mathcal{H}(X) \rightsquigarrow X$ *is Marchaud. Then its solution map* S_F *is upper semicompact with nonempty values: This means that whenever* $\varphi_n \in \mathcal{H}(X)$ *converge uniformly on compact intervals to* φ *in* $\mathcal{H}(X)$ *and any history* $\varphi_n(\cdot) := T(\cdot)x_n \in S_F(\varphi_n)$ *associated to a solution* $x_n(\cdot)$ *to the path-dependent differential inclusion* $x'(t) \in F(T(t)x)$ *starting at* φ_n, *there exists a subsequence (again denoted by)* $\varphi_n(\cdot)$ *converging uniformly on compact intervals to the history* $\varphi(\cdot) := T(\cdot)x$ *of a solution* $x(\cdot)$ *to the path-dependent differential inclusion starting at* φ.

2.2   Contingent Directions

In the case of path-dependent impulse differential inclusions, we shall characterize the viability of a functional constrained set **K** in terms of contingent directions to a **K** $\subset \mathcal{H}(X)$ be a subset of histories at a path $\varphi \in \mathcal{H}$. Let

$$\mathcal{A}(X) := \{x(\cdot) \in \mathcal{C}(0, +\infty; X) \quad \text{such that } x(0) = 0\}$$

denote the "future space". We embed the state space X into $\mathcal{A}(X)$ by identifying a vector x with the function $\psi_x(t) := tx$. The image of the ball λB_X of radius λ under this embedding is contained in $\mathcal{A}_\lambda(X)$ of λ-Lipschitz functions.

Definition 23 *Let* $h > 0$ *be given. The* h-concatenation *(or* concatenation *when there are no ambiguities)* $\varphi \Diamond_h \psi$ *is the bilinear form from* $\mathcal{H}(X) \times \mathcal{A}(X) \mapsto \mathcal{H}(X)$ *defined by*

$$(\varphi \Diamond_h \psi)(\tau) := \begin{cases} \varphi(\tau + h) & \text{if } \tau \in\,] - \infty, -h] \\ \varphi(0) + \psi(\tau + h) & \text{if } \tau \in [-h, 0] \end{cases}$$

As an example, the concatenation of $\varphi \in \mathcal{H}(X)$ and $x \in X$ is defined by

$$(\varphi \Diamond_h x)(\tau) = \begin{cases} \varphi(\tau + h) & \text{if } \tau \in\,] - \infty, h] \\ \varphi(0) + (\tau + h)x & \text{if } \tau \in [-h, 0] \end{cases}$$

We attach to a function $\varphi \in \mathcal{H}(X)$ and a sequence $v_1, \ldots, v_n$ the Euler concatenation defined by

$$\varphi \Diamond_h v_1 \Diamond_h v_2 \Diamond_h \cdots \Diamond_h v_n$$

which is piecewise linear function on the interval $[-nh, 0]$.

Lemma 24 *For any Lipschitz constant $\lambda > 0$, the h-concatenation maps $\mathcal{H}_\lambda(X) \times \mathcal{A}_\lambda(X)$ to $\mathcal{H}_\lambda(X)$*

Definition 25 *We denote by $\mathcal{D}_{\mathbf{K}}(\varphi)$ the set of vectors $v \in X$ such that there exist a sequence $h_n > 0$ converging to 0 and a sequence $v_n \in X$ converging to v satisfying*

$$\forall\, n \geq 0, \ \ \varphi \Diamond_{h_n} v_n \in \mathbf{K}$$

2.3   The Impulse Path-Dependent Viability Theorem

Theorem 26 *Let (F, R) be a path-dependent impulse differential inclusion and $\mathbf{K} \subset \mathcal{H}(X)$ be a closed subset. Assume that F is Marchaud and that $\mathbf{C} \subset \mathbf{K}$ is closed. Then the following statements are equivalent*

1. *$\mathbf{K}$ is viable under (F, R),*
2. *The subset $\mathbf{K}\backslash\mathbf{C}$ is locally viable under the path-dependent differential inclusion governed by F,*
3. *$\mathbf{K}$, $\mathbf{C}$, F and R are linked through the tangential condition*

$$\forall\, \varphi \in \mathbf{K}\backslash\mathbf{C}, \ \ F(\varphi) \cap \mathcal{D}_{\mathbf{K}}(\varphi) \neq \emptyset$$

Actually, both impulse differential inclusions and path-dependent impulse differential inclusions[4] share the same properties at a higher abstraction level, the level of impulse evolutionary systems we are about to define. It is at this level that the two first statements are equivalent.

The equivalence between the second and third statement is specific, and provided in our case by the Path-Dependent Viability Theorems of [12,13,14, Haddad].

2.4   Examples

Take any path-dependent differential inclusion $x'(t) \in F(T(t)x)$ associated with a Marchaud right-hand side F.

We refer to Chapter 12 of [1, Aubin] for examples of tangential conditions when the constrained set $\mathbf{K}$ and the constrained targets $\mathbf{C} \subset \mathbf{K}$ are Volterra sets defined by kernels, by lack of space. Consider only the simple case when

---

[4] as well as parabolic (or reaction-diffusion type) partial differential inclusions and mutational equations governing the evolution of subset.

the constrained subset of paths or histories and the target are associated with subsets $C \subset K \subset X$ of the vector space X by

$$\mathbf{C} := \{\,\varphi \in \mathcal{H}(X) \mid \varphi(0) \in C\,\} \subset \mathbf{K} := \{\,\varphi \in \mathcal{H}(X) \mid \varphi(0) \in K\,\}$$

Assume that the reset map R is associated with an usual reset map $R_0 : C \rightsquigarrow K$, where $C \subset K$ by the formula

$$\forall\,\varphi \in \mathcal{H}(X),\ \forall\,\tau \in]-\infty, 0],\ (R(\varphi))(\tau) := R_0(\varphi(\tau))$$

In this case, a run of the path-dependent impulse differential inclusion (F, R_0) is defined by

1. a finite or infinite sequence $\tau(x(\cdot)) := \{\tau_n\}_n$ of nonnegative cadences $\tau_n \in [0, \infty[$,
2. a sequence of reinitialized states $x_n \in K$,
3. a sequence of motives $x_n(\cdot)$ that are solutions to the path-dependent differential inclusion $x'(t) \in F(T(t)x)$ starting at the initial state x_n and satisfying the end-point condition $x_{n+1} \in R(x_n(\tau_n))$

by

$$\begin{cases} i)\ \ \text{defining the sequence of impulse times } t_{n+1} := t_n + \tau_n, \\ ii)\ \forall\, t \in [t_n, t_{n+1}[,\ \ x(t) := x_n(t - t_n) \end{cases} \tag{3}$$

Theorem 27 *Let F be a path-dependent Marchaud set-valued map, K and $C \subset K$ and $R_0 : C \rightsquigarrow K$ be a reset map. Then K is viable under (F, R_0) if and only if the tangential condition*

$$\forall\,\varphi \in \mathcal{H}(X)\ \ \text{such that}\ \ \varphi(0) \in K\backslash C,\ \ F(\varphi) \cap T_K(\varphi(0)) \neq \emptyset$$

2.5   Path-Dependent Hybrid Systems

Definition 28 *An path-dependent hybrid differential inclusion (K, F, R_0) is defined by*

1. *a finite dimensional vector space E of states e called locations,*
2. *a set-valued map $K : E \rightsquigarrow X$ associating with any location e a (possibly empty) subset $K(e) \subset X$ and a set-valued map $C : E \rightsquigarrow X$ associating with any location e a (possibly empty) subset $C(e) \subset K(e)$,*
3. *a set-valued map $F : E \times \mathcal{H}(X) \rightsquigarrow X$ with which we associate the path-dependent differential inclusion $x'(t) \in F(e, T(t)x)$,*
4. *a set-valued map (reset map) $R_0 : \mathrm{Graph}(C) \rightsquigarrow \mathrm{Graph}(K)$.*

A run of the path-dependent hybrid system is defined by

1. *a finite or infinite sequence $\tau(e, x(\cdot)) := \{\tau_n\}_n$ of nonnegative cadences $\tau_n \in [0, \infty[$,*
2. *a sequence of locations e_n and of reinitialized states $x_n \in K(e_n)$,*

3. *a sequence of motives $x_n(\cdot)$ that are solutions to the path-dependent differential inclusion $x'(t) \in F(e_n, T(t)x)$ starting at the initial state x_n and satisfying the end-point condition $x_{n+1} \in R_0(e_n, x_n(\tau_n))$*

by (3).

We observe right away that a map $(e, x(\cdot))$ is a run of the hybrid differential inclusions if and only if $(e(\cdot), x(\cdot))$ is a run of

$$\begin{cases} i) & e'(t) = 0 \\ ii) & x'(t) \in F(e(t), T(t)x) \end{cases}$$

"viable" in $\text{Graph}(K)$ until it reaches the graph of the map C. Indeed the locations remain constant in the intervals $[t_n, t_{n+1}[$ since their velocities are equal to 0.

Since the existence of solutions to path-dependent hybrid differential inclusions amounts to the viability of the graph of the set-valued map K under an associated auxiliary path-dependent impulse differential inclusion, we obtain a necessary and condition for the existence of solutions to hybrid differential inclusions thanks to Theorem 27. For that purpose, we need the definition of the contingent derivative $DK(e, x) : E \rightsquigarrow X$ of a set-valued map $K : E \rightsquigarrow X$ at a point (e, x) of its graph: It can be defined by

$$\text{Graph}(DK(e, x)) := T_{\text{Graph}(K)}(e, x)$$

Theorem 29 *Let (K, F, R_0) be a path-dependent hybrid differential inclusion. Assume that F is Marchaud. Then the path-dependent hybrid differential inclusion has a solution for every initial state if and only if*

$$\forall \, e \in E, \forall \, \varphi \in \mathcal{H}(X) \quad \text{such that}$$

$$\varphi(0) \in K(e) \backslash K(e) \backslash C(e), \quad F(e, \varphi) \cap DK(e, \varphi(0))(0) \neq \emptyset$$

3   Impulse Evolutionary Systems

Therefore, it costs nothing to prove the equivalence between the two first statements in the general case of impulse evolutionary systems:

3.1   Impulse Evolutionary Systems

Definition 31 *An evolutionary system is a set-valued map $\mathcal{S} : X \rightsquigarrow \mathcal{C}(0, \infty; X)$ satisfying*

1. *the translation property: Let $x(\cdot) \in \mathcal{S}(x)$. Then for all $T \geq 0$, the function $y(\cdot)$ defined by $y(t) := x(t+T)$ is a solution $y(\cdot) \in \mathcal{S}(x(T))$ starting at $x(T)$,*

2. *the* concatenation *property: Let* $x(\cdot) \in \mathcal{S}(x)$ *and* $T \geq 0$. *Then for every* $y(\cdot) \in \mathcal{S}(x(T))$, *the function* $z(\cdot)$ *defined by*

$$z(t) := \begin{cases} x(t) & \text{if } t \in [0, T] \\ y(t - T) & \text{if } t \geq T \end{cases}$$

belongs to $\mathcal{S}(x)$.

We can define impulse evolutionary systems in the following way:

Definition 32 *Let* $K \subset X$, $C \subset K$ *be two nonempty subsets and* $R : C \rightsquigarrow K$ *a set-valued map[5] with nonempty values, regarded as a reset map, and* $\mathcal{S} : X \rightsquigarrow \mathcal{C}(0, \infty; X)$ *be an evolutionary system. Then the pair* $(\mathcal{S}, R)$ *governs a run* $x(\cdot)$ *of an impulse evolutionary system defined by*

1. *a finite or infinite sequence* $\tau(x(\cdot)) := \{\tau_n\}_n$ *of nonnegative* cadences $\tau_n \in [0, +\infty[$,
2. *a sequence of reinitialized states* x_n,
3. *a sequence of motives* $x_n(\cdot) \in \mathcal{S}(x_n)$ *satisfying the end-point condition* $x_n(\tau_n) \in R^{-1}(x_{n+1})$

by

$$\begin{cases} i) & \text{defining the sequence of impulse times } t_{n+1} := t_n + \tau_n, \\ ii) & \forall\, t \in [t_n, t_{n+1}[,\ x(t) := x_n(t - t_n) \end{cases} \qquad (4)$$

If the sequence of cadences is finite[6] and stops at τ_N, *we agree that the* N*th motive* $x_N(\cdot) \in \mathcal{S}(x_N)$ *is taken on* $[0, +\infty[$, *i.e., and we agree to set* $\tau_{N+1} = +\infty$.

We say that a run $x(\cdot)$ is viable in K if for any $t \geq 0$, $x(t) \in K$ and that a closed subset K is viable under an impulse evolutionary system $(\mathcal{S}, R)$ if from any $x \in K$ starts at least one run viable in K.

In order to characterize the viability of K under an evolutionary system, we also need the following definitions:

Definition 33 *Let* $\mathcal{S} : X \rightsquigarrow \mathcal{C}(0, +\infty; X)$ *be a set-valued evolutionary system and* $K \subset X$ *be a subset regarded as a constrained set.*

The subset K *is said* locally viable *under* $\mathcal{S}$ *if from any initial state* $x \in K$ *starts at least one solution viable in* K *on a nonempty interval and* viable *if this solution is viable on* $[0, +\infty[$.

The viability kernel $\mathrm{Viab}(K)$ *is the subset of initial states* $x_0 \in K$ *such that one solution* $x(\cdot) \in \mathcal{S}(x_0)$ *starting at* x_0 *is viable in* K *for all* $t \geq 0$. *A subset* K *is a repeller under* $\mathcal{S}$ *if its viability kernel is empty.*

---

[5] When $R : X \rightsquigarrow X$ is defined on X, we associate with it its "graphical restriction" to $K \times K$ (again denoted by) R where $C := K \cap R^{-1}(K)$ and $R(x)$ is replaced by $R(x) \cap K$.

[6] We shall see that we can eliminate this situation by assuming that $R(C) \cap \mathrm{Viab}_{\mathcal{S}}(K) = \emptyset$.

3.2   Characterization of Impulse Evolutionary Systems Viability

We can adapt the proof of [2, Aubin] or [8, Aubin, Lygeros, Quincampoix, Sastry & Seube] for characterizing the viability of a closed subset under an impulse evolutionary system:

Theorem 34 *Let $(\mathcal{S}, R)$ be an impulse evolutionary system and $K \subset X$ and $C \subset K$ be closed subsets. Assume that $\mathcal{S}$ is upper semicompact. Then the following statements are equivalent*

1. *K is viable under $(\mathcal{S}, R)$,*
2. *The subset $K \backslash C$ is locally viable under $\mathcal{S}$,*

3.3   Prerequisites of Viability Theory

For proving this characterization theorem, we need some results of viability theory.

Definition 35 *Let $K \subset X$ be a subset. The functional $\tau_K : \mathcal{C}(0, \infty; X) \mapsto \mathbf{R}_+ \cup \{+\infty\}$ associating with $x(\cdot)$ its* exit time *$\tau_K(x(\cdot))$ defined by*

$$\tau_K(x(\cdot)) := \inf\{t \in [0, \infty[\mid x(t) \notin K\} := \varpi_{X \backslash K}(x(\cdot))$$

is called the exit functional.

Let $C \subset K$ be a target. We introduce the (constrained) hitting functional *$\varpi_{(K,C)}$ defined by*

$$\varpi_{(K,C)}(x(\cdot)) := \inf\{t \geq 0 \mid x(t) \in C \ \& \ \forall s \in [0, t], \ x(s) \in K \}$$

associating with $x(\cdot)$ its hitting time, *introduced in [11, Cardaliaguet, Quincampoix & Saint-Pierre]).*

Consider an evolutionary system $\mathcal{S} : X \rightsquigarrow \mathcal{C}(0, +\infty; X)$. Let $C \subset K$ and K be two subsets.

The function $\tau_K^\sharp : K \mapsto \mathbf{R}_+ \cup \{+\infty\}$ defined by

$$\tau_K^\sharp(x) := \sup_{x(\cdot) \in \mathcal{S}(x)} \tau_K(x(\cdot))$$

is called the upper exit function.

The function $\varpi_{(K,C)}^\flat : K \mapsto \mathbf{R}_+ \cup \{+\infty\}$ defined by

$$\varpi_{(K,C)}^\flat(x) := \inf_{x(\cdot) \in \mathcal{S}(x)} \varpi_{(K,C)}(x(\cdot))$$

is called the lower constrained hitting function.

We shall need the following

Theorem 36 *Let* $S : X \rightsquigarrow \mathcal{C}(0, +\infty; X)$ *be a strict upper semicompact map and* C *and* K *be two closed subsets such that* $C \subset K$. *Then the hitting function* $\varpi^\flat_{(K,C)}$ *is lower semicontinuous and the exit function* $\tau^\sharp_K$ *is upper semicontinuous. Furthermore, for any* $x \in \mathrm{Dom}(\varpi^\flat_{(K,C)})$, *there exists at least one solution* $x^\flat(\cdot) \in S(x)$ *which hits* C *as soon as possible before possibly leaving* K

$$\varpi^\flat_{(K,C)}(x) \; = \; \varpi_{(K,C)}(x^\flat(\cdot))$$

and for any $x \in \mathrm{Dom}(\tau^\sharp_K)$, *there exists at least one solution* $x^\sharp(\cdot) \in S(x)$ *which remains viable in* K *as long as possible:*

$$\tau^\sharp_K(x) \; = \; \tau_K(x^\sharp(\cdot))$$

(See [5, Aubin] for a proof and more details on evolutionary systems).

3.4   Proof of the Characterization of Impulse Evolutionary Systems Viability

Indeed, if K is viable under (S, R), then from any $x_0 \in K \backslash C$ starts at least a solution $x(\cdot) \in S(x)$ viable in K

1. either forever if x_0 belongs to the viability kernel $\mathrm{Viab}(K)$ of K
2. or until it reaches at some time $t_1 > 0$ a state $x(^-t_1)$ in C.

This shows that $K \backslash C$ is locally viable.

Conversely, let us assume that $K \backslash C$ is locally viable and take an initial state $x_0 \in K$. If x_0 belongs to C, we may take $\tau_0 = 0$ and $x_1 \in R(x_0)$. Consider now the case when $x_0 \in K \backslash C$.

If x_0 belongs to $\mathrm{Viab}(K)$, then at least one solution starting from x_0 is viable in K, and thus, defines a run viable in K: We may take the cadence $\tau_0 = +\infty$ and for motive a solution $x_0(\cdot) \in S(x_0)$.

If x_0 does not belong to $\mathrm{Viab}(K)$, all solutions leave K in finite time before (possibly) reaching the viability kernel. It is then enough to prove that at least one of them reaches C before leaving K. This is the case of a solution $x^\sharp(\cdot) \in S(x)$ which maximizes $\tau_K(x(\cdot))$, i.e., which satisfies

$$\tau^\sharp_K(x) \; := \; \sup_{x(\cdot) \in S(x)} \tau_K(x(\cdot)) \; = \; \tau_K(x^\sharp(x))$$

leaves $K \backslash (\mathrm{Viab}(K) \cup C)$ through C. This solution exists by Theorem 36 since K is closed and S is upper semicompact. Next, we claim that $x^\sharp := x^\sharp(\tau^\sharp_K(x)) \in K \backslash \mathrm{Viab}(K)$. Otherwise, if $x^\sharp$ would belong to the viability kernel, it could be concatenated with a solution viable in K for ever, so that the initial state x_0 would belong the viability kernel, which is not the case.

Furthermore, $x^\sharp$ belongs to C. If not, $x^\sharp$ would belong to $K \backslash C$ which is assumed to be locally viable. Then one could associate with $x^\sharp \in K \backslash (\mathrm{Viab}(K) \cup C)$ a solution $y(\cdot) \in S(x^\sharp)$ and $T > 0$ such that $y(\tau) \in K \backslash (\mathrm{Viab}(K) \cup C)$ for all $\tau \in [0, T]$. Concatenating this solution to $x^\sharp(\cdot)$, we obtain a solution viable in K on an interval $[0, \tau^\sharp_K(x) + T]$, which contradicts the definition of $x^\sharp(\cdot)$.

Therefore $x^\sharp$ belongs to $K \cap C$ so that there exists $x^\sharp_1 \in K \cap R(x^\sharp)$.   □

4   The Path-Dependent Viability Theorem

Since the solution map of a Marchaud map $F : \mathcal{H}(X) \rightsquigarrow X$ is upper semicompact by Theorem 22, the equivalence between the first and second statements of Theorem 34 holds true.

The equivalence between the second and the third statement follow from the following Haddad's Path-Dependent Viability Theorem:

Theorem 41 *Assume that F is Marchaud and take $\lambda > 0$. The two following statements hold true:*

1. *If $\mathbf{K} \subset \mathcal{H}_\lambda(X)$ is closed, then $\mathbf{K}$ is (globally) viable under F if and only if*

$$\forall\, \varphi \in \mathbf{K}, \quad F(\varphi) \cap \mathcal{D}_{\mathbf{K}}(\varphi) \neq \emptyset$$

2. *If $\mathbf{C} \subset \mathbf{K}$ is closed, then $\mathbf{K}\backslash\mathbf{C}$ is locally viable under F if and only if*

$$\forall\, \varphi \in \mathbf{K}\backslash\mathbf{C}, \quad F(\varphi) \cap \mathcal{D}_{\mathbf{K}}(\varphi) \neq \emptyset$$

References

1. AUBIN J.-P. (1991) **Viability Theory** Birkhäuser, Boston, Basel, Berlin
2. AUBIN J.-P. (1999) **Impulse Differential Inclusions and Hybrid Systems: A Viability Approach**, Lecture Notes, University of California at Berkeley
3. AUBIN J.-P. (2000) *Lyapunov Functions for Impulse and Hybrid Control Systems*, Proceedings of the CDC 2000 Conference
4. AUBIN J.-P. (2000) *Optimal Impulse Control Problems and Quasi-Variational Inequalities Thirty Years Later: a Viability Approach*, in **Contrôle optimal et EDP: Innovations et Applications**, IOS Press
5. AUBIN J.-P. (to appear) *Viability Kernels and Capture Basins of Sets under Differential Inclusions*, SIAM J. Control
6. AUBIN J.-P. & FRANKOWSKA H. (1990) **Set-Valued Analysis**, Birkhäuser, Boston, Basel, Berlin
7. AUBIN J.-P. & HADDAD G. (to appear) *Cadenced runs of impulse and hybrid control systems*, International Journal Robust and Nonlinear Control
8. AUBIN J.-P., LYGEROS J., QUINCAMPOIX. M., SASTRY S. & SEUBE N. (to appear) *Impulse Differential Inclusions: A Viability Approach to Hybrid Systems*,
9. BENSOUSSAN A. & MENALDI (1997) *Hybrid Control and Dynamic Programming*, Dynamics of Continuous, Discrete and Impulse Systems, 3, 395-442
10. BRANICKY M.S., BORKAR V.S. & MITTER S. (1998) *A unified framework for hybrid control: Background, model and theory*, IEEE Trans. Autom. Control, 43, 31-45
11. CARDALIAGUET P., QUINCAMPOIX M. & SAINT-PIERRE P. (1994) *Temps optimaux pour des problèmes avec contraintes et sans contrôlabilité locale* Comptes-Rendus de l'Académie des Sciences, Série 1, Paris, 318, 607-612
12. HADDAD G. (1981) *Monotone trajectories of differential inclusions with memory*, Isr. J. Math., 39, 83-100
13. HADDAD G. (1981) *Monotone viable trajectories for functional differential inclusions*, J. Diff. Eq., 42, 1-24

14. HADDAD G. (1981) *Topological properties of the set of solutions for functional differential differential inclusions*, Nonlinear Anal. Theory, Meth. Appl., 5, 1349-1366

15. MATVEEV A.S. , SAVKIN A.V. (2000) QUALITATIVE THEORY OF HYBRID DYNAMICAL SYSTEMS, Birkhäuser

16. MATVEEV A.S. , SAVKIN A.V. (2001) HYBRID DYNAMICAL SYSTEMS: CONTROLLER AND SENSOR SWITCHING PROBLEMS, Birkhäuser

17. ROCKAFELLAR R.T. & WETS R. (1997) **Variational Analysis**, Springer-Verlag

18. SHAFT (van der) A. & SCHUMACHER H. (1999) **An introduction to hybrid dynamical systems**, Springer-Verlag, Lecture Notes in Control, 251

Hybrid Feedback Control for Path Tracking by a Bounded–Curvature Vehicle[*]

Andrea Balluchi[1], Philippe Souères[2], and Antonio Bicchi[3]

[1] PARADES, Via di S.Pantaleo, 66, 00186 Roma, Italy.
balluchi@parades.rm.cnr.it
[2] Laboratoire d'Analyse et d'Architecture des Systèmes – LAAS,
CNRS, 7, Avenue du Colonel Roche, 31077 Toulouse, France.
soueres@laas.fr
[3] Centro Interdipartimentale di Ricerca "Enrico Piaggio",
Università di Pisa, 56100 Pisa, Italy,
bicchi@ing.unipi.it

Abstract. In this paper, we consider the problem of stabilizing the kinematic model of a car to a general path in the plane, subject to very mild restrictions. The car model, although rather simplified, contains some of the most relevant limitations that make application of existing results in the literature impossible: namely, the car can only move forward, and turn with a bounded steering radius; also, only limited sensory information is available.

The approach we follow to stabilization is to adapt to the present general case an optimal synthesis approach successfully applied in our previous work to tracking rectilinear paths. Due to both the nature of the problem, and the solution technique used, the analysis of the controlled system involves a rather complex switching logic. Hybrid formalism and verification techniques prove extremely useful in this context to formally proof stability of the resulting system, and are described in detail in the paper.

1 Introduction

In this paper we consider the design of a control law for path tracking by a so–called Dubins' model of a car. Dubins' cars are kinematic models of wheeled (nonholonomic) vehicles that move only forward in a plane, and possess a lower–bounded turning radius. The model is relevant to the kinematics of road vehicles as well as aircraft cruising at constant altitude, or sea vessels.

Although the design of control techniques for nonholonomic vehicles has been the subject of extensive research recently (see e.g. [10,12,6]), the additional constraint that the steering radius of the vehicle is lower bounded has not been explicitly considered. However, such a restriction appears to be crucial in making a kinematic model of a car relevant to real–world vehicles encountered in

[*] The work has been conducted with partial support of PARADES, a Cadence, Magneti-Marelli and ST-microelectronics E.E.I.G, by CNR PF–MADESSII SP3.1.2.

M.D. Di Benedetto, A. Sangiovanni-Vincentelli (Eds.): HSCC 2001, LNCS 2034, pp. 133–146, 2001.

most applications. Another important assumption often used in the literature is that the full state of the system is available for measurement, and that the path to be tracked is entirely known in advance. Instead, we consider in this paper the more realistic and less demanding case that the vehicle can only measure its current distance and heading angle error with respect to the closest point on the reference path in the plane, where only the sign of the path curvature is detected.

The approach we follow to stabilization of Dubins' cars is to adapt to the present general case an optimal synthesis approach successfully applied in our previous work to tracking rectilinear paths [11]. Due to both the nature of the problem, the type of sensors, and the solution technique used, the analysis of the controlled system involves a rather complex switching logic. Hybrid formalism (see [5,14,2]) and verification techniques (see [8,7,1]) prove extremely useful in this context to formally proof stability of the resulting system, and are described in detail in the paper, which is organized as follows.

In Section 2, a hybrid automaton that describes the motion of the vehicle with respect to the path is introduced, while in Section 3 the path–tracking controller is developed. Such controller, described in detail in Section 3.2, is obtained by considering a local approximation of the desired path with the tangent line, and by using a feedback controller designed for stabilization on straight paths (reported in Section 3.1). The advantages of the novel hybrid path–tracking formalization are exploited in Section 4, where the stability properties of the proposed controller are investigated. By a reachability analysis in the continuous state space, a finite state abstract representation of the hybrid closed–loop automaton is obtained. Though this representation is not a bisimulation, but rather a simulation, of the hybrid automaton ([5]), it suffices to prove the stability properties of the proposed control. It is shown that the proposed hybrid feedback controller achieves stabilization of the Dubins' car on a generic reference path and sufficient conditions for global attractivity are derived.

2   Hybrid Path Tracking Modeling Using Switching Frenet's Frames

We consider the kinematic model of a car moving forward on a plane, which was introduced by Dubins in [4]. A configuration of the vehicle is defined by an ordered pair $(M(x, y), \theta) \in \mathbb{R}^2 \times S^1$, where (x, y) are the coordinates of a reference point M in the plane and θ is the angle made by the direction of the car with respect to the x-axis. The kinematics of the car are described by

$$\begin{cases} \dot{x} = V \cos \theta \\ \dot{y} = V \sin \theta \\ \dot{\theta} = \omega \end{cases} \quad \text{with} \quad |\omega| < \frac{V}{R}, \tag{1}$$

where V is the constant forward velocity, ω the is turning speed and the input constraint models a lower bound $R > 0$ on the turning radius of the Dubins' car.

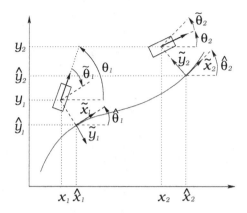

Fig. 1. Reference path and transformed coordinates.

The problem we are concerned with is that of steering the vehicle to a given *feasible* path Γ, defined in the arclength parametrization by

$$\Gamma = \left\{ (\hat{x}, \hat{y}) \in \mathbb{R}^2 \mid (\hat{x}, \hat{y}) = \hat{g}(\beta) \text{ for } \beta \in \mathbb{R} \right\}, \tag{2}$$

with the following conditions:

A) $\hat{g}(\cdot)$ is a class C^1 mapping from $\mathbb{R}$ to $\mathbb{R}^2$ and the orientation of Γ is that induced by increasing. β;

B) Let $\kappa(\beta)$ denote the extension by continuity from the left[1] of the curvature of Γ, expressed as a function of the arclength β. There exists a positive real R_Γ such that the normalized curvature $\hat{\kappa}(s) \equiv R\kappa(s)$ satisfies

$$|\hat{\kappa}(\beta)| = R|\kappa(\beta)| \leq \frac{R}{R_\Gamma} \equiv C < 1. \tag{3}$$

C) Considering the open neighborhood of the path

$$\mathcal{T}_\Gamma = \left\{ \mathbf{x} \in \mathbb{R}^2 : \exists \beta \in \mathbb{R}, \|\mathbf{x} - \hat{g}(\beta)\| < R_\Gamma \right\} \subset \mathbb{R}^2, \tag{4}$$

for all $\mathbf{x} \in \mathcal{T}_\Gamma$ there exists a unique nearest point on Γ.

In order to describe the motion of the vehicle with respect to the reference path Γ a mobile Frenet's frame associated to the curve Γ is considered. Given a vehicle position $M(x, y) \in \mathcal{T}_\Gamma$, the Frenet's frame $\mathcal{S}_T(s)|_{s=\bar{\beta}}$ is defined by the tangent, the principal normal and the binormal axes of the curve at the point $(\hat{x}(\bar{\beta}), \hat{y}(\bar{\beta}))$ of Γ, located at the minimum distance[2] from $M(x, y)$ (see Figure 1). As the vehicle moves with velocity V, the Frenet's frame $\mathcal{S}_T(s)$ follows its motion so

---

[1] By definition, $\kappa(\beta) = \lim_{s \to \beta^-} \kappa(s)$, at points $(x(\beta), y(\beta))$ where the curvature of Γ is not defined.

[2] Note that, by $A)$, $B)$ and $C)$ the Frenet's frame is well-defined along Γ.

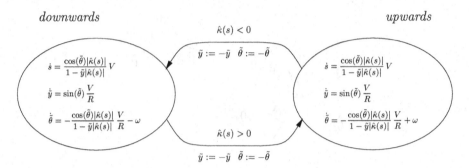

Fig. 2. Hybrid automaton $PTHA_3$ modeling the car in the transformed state space.

as to keep it on the principal normal axis. The arclength abscissa s locates the current Frenet's frame. The tangent and the principal normal axes of $\mathcal{S}_T(s)$ remain within the plane containing the curve, while the binormal axis points either upwards, if the local curvature of Γ is counterclockwise (i.e. $\kappa(s) > 0$), or downwards, if the local curvature is clockwise (i.e. $\kappa(s) < 0$). Introduce the transformated coordinates $(s, \tilde{y}, \tilde{\theta})$, where:

- abscissa s defines the position of the Frenet's frame along the curve;
- $\tilde{y}$ denotes the position of the car along the principal normal of $\mathcal{S}_T(s)$ (lateral distance) normalized with respect to the minimum turning radius R;
- $\tilde{\theta}$ denotes its orientation with respect to the tangent axis of $\mathcal{S}_T(s)$ (heading angle error), with sign taken according to the local direction of the binormal axis (see Figure 1).

It can be noticed that this coordinate system is similar to the one used by Samson [9], except for the switchings of the Frenet's frame. In fact, a change of curvature along the path produces a jump of the variables $\tilde{y}$ and $\tilde{\theta}$ to the symmetric point with respect to the origin in the $(\tilde{y}, \tilde{\theta})$–plane. The reason for introducing such discontinuity in the model is related to the different behaviors that a vehicle with bounded curvature has when it approaches a reference path. Indeed, the approach is apparently easier if the vehicle and the center of curvature of the path lie on the opposite sides of the curve[3]. This formulation will turn out to be useful in the verification of the proposed path tracking controller.

The motion of the car in the transformed state $(s, \tilde{y}, \tilde{\theta})^T$ can be described by using the formalism of hybrid automata (see [5,3]). The discrete nature of the model arises from the fact that the Frenet's frame $\mathcal{S}_T(s)$ changes its orientation during the motion, depending on the sign of the curvature $\hat{\kappa}(s)$. The discrete state, referred to as *bin* , models the two possible orientations of the binormal axis of $\mathcal{S}_T(s(t))$ at time t and assumes either the value *upwards* or the value

---

[3] For instance, if the vehicle is required to approach a circle with curvature $1/R$, then it can approach it only from outside.

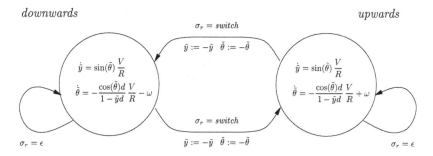

Fig. 3. Hybrid automaton $PTHA_2$ of the vehicle in the reduced state space.

downwards. Its initial value is: *upwards*, if $\hat{\kappa}(s(0)) > 0$; *downwards*, if $\hat{\kappa}(s(0)) < 0$; and any of those, otherwise. The dynamics the continuous states are subject to are obtained by geometric arguments. The complete Path–Tracking Hybrid Automaton, referred to as $PTHA_3$, is depicted in Figure 2.

The specification for the design of a path tracking controller for the Dubins' car can be formulated using the hybrid automaton $PTHA_3$, which captures the different behaviors of the bounded–curvature vehicle in approaching the path. For such hybrid model, the problem reduces to that one of steering $(\tilde{y}, \tilde{\theta})$ to $(0, 0)$.

Assuming that only the sign of $\hat{\kappa}(s)$ is available but not its amplitude, a reduced hybrid automaton can be considered for the path tracking problem. The local curvature $|\hat{\kappa}(s)|$ is replaced by an unknown input disturbance $d(t)$ the path tracking controller has to be robust to. By (3), disturbance $d(t)$ satisfies

$$0 \le d(t) \le C < 1. \tag{5}$$

The path tracking problem is described in the reduced continuous state space $(\tilde{y}, \tilde{\theta})$. Curvature sign switching conditions $\hat{\kappa}(s) > 0$ and $\hat{\kappa}(s) < 0$ are modeled by a discrete uncontrollable input σ_r, assuming either the value *switch* (when a change of curvature sign occurs) or the *silent move* ϵ (otherwise). The reduced hybrid automaton, referred to as $PTHA_2$, is reported in Figure 3.

In this case the path tracking problem is formulated as follows:

Problem 1. Let Γ as in (2) be a feasible reference path. Given the hybrid automaton $PTHA_2$, find a feedback control law $\omega(bin, (\tilde{y}, \tilde{\theta}))$ satisfying curvature constraint (1) such that, from any initial state $(bin_0, (\tilde{y}_0, \tilde{\theta}_0))$ the trajectory $(\tilde{y}(t), \tilde{\theta}(t))$ converges to the origin under the action of any unknown disturbance $d(t)$, bounded as in (5), and any sequence of uncontrollable events σ_r.

Table 1. Partition of domain $\mathcal{D}_{(\tilde{y},\tilde{\theta})}$ used to define the shortest path synthesis.

$\mathbf{O} = \{(0,0)\}$	$\mathbf{r}^{(1)} = \{(\tilde{y},\tilde{\theta})\mid \tilde{\theta} \in (0, \frac{\pi}{2}), \sigma_R(\tilde{y},\tilde{\theta}) = 0\}$
	$\mathbf{l}^{(1)} = \{(\tilde{y},\tilde{\theta})\mid \tilde{\theta} \in (-\frac{\pi}{2}, 0), \sigma_L(\tilde{y},\tilde{\theta}) = 0\}$
$\varOmega^0 = \mathbf{sr} \cup \mathbf{sl} \cup \mathbf{O}$	$\mathbf{r}^{(2)} = \{(\tilde{y},\tilde{\theta})\mid \tilde{\theta} \in [\frac{\pi}{2}, \pi), \sigma_R(\tilde{y},\tilde{\theta}) = 0\}$
$\varOmega^- = \mathbf{r} \cup \mathbf{rsr} \cup \mathbf{rsl} \cup \mathbf{rl}^{(1)} \cup \mathbf{rl}^{(2)}$	$\mathbf{l}^{(2)} = \{(\tilde{y},\tilde{\theta})\mid \tilde{\theta} \in (-\pi, -\frac{\pi}{2}], \sigma_L(\tilde{y},\tilde{\theta}) = 0\}$
$\varOmega^+ = \mathbf{l} \cup \mathbf{lsr} \cup \mathbf{lsl} \cup \mathbf{lr}^{(1)} \cup \mathbf{lr}^{(2)}$	$\mathbf{r}^{(3)} = \{(\tilde{y},\tilde{\theta})\mid \tilde{\theta} \in [\pi, \frac{3}{2}\pi), \sigma_R(\tilde{y},\tilde{\theta}) = 0\} \cup \{(0,\pi)\}$
	$\mathbf{l}^{(3)} = \{(\tilde{y},\tilde{\theta})\mid \tilde{\theta} \in (-\frac{3}{2}\pi, -\pi], \sigma_L(\tilde{y},\tilde{\theta}) = 0\}$
	$\mathbf{lr}^{(1.1)} = \{(\tilde{y},\tilde{\theta})\mid \tilde{\theta} \in (0, \frac{\pi}{2}), \sigma_N(\tilde{y},\tilde{\theta}) \geq 0, \sigma_L(\tilde{y},\tilde{\theta}) < 0\}$
	$\mathbf{rl}^{(1.1)} = \{(\tilde{y},\tilde{\theta})\mid \tilde{\theta} \in (-\frac{\pi}{2}, 0), \sigma_L(\tilde{y},\tilde{\theta}) > 0, \sigma_P(\tilde{y},\tilde{\theta}) \leq 0\}$
$\mathbf{r} = \mathbf{r}^{(1)} \cup \mathbf{r}^{(2)} \cup \mathbf{r}^{(3)}$	$\mathbf{lr}^{(1.2)} = \{(\tilde{y},\tilde{\theta})\mid \tilde{\theta} \in (-\frac{\pi}{2}, 0], \sigma_N(\tilde{y},\tilde{\theta}) \geq 0, \sigma_R(\tilde{y},\tilde{\theta}) < 0\}$
$\mathbf{lr}^{(1)} = \mathbf{lr}^{(1.1)} \cup \mathbf{lr}^{(1.2)} \cup \mathbf{lr}^{(1.3)}$	$\mathbf{rl}^{(1.2)} = \{(\tilde{y},\tilde{\theta})\mid \tilde{\theta} \in [0, \frac{\pi}{2}), \sigma_R(\tilde{y},\tilde{\theta}) > 0, \sigma_P(\tilde{y},\tilde{\theta}) \leq 0\}$
$\mathbf{lsr} = \mathbf{lsr}^{(1)} \cup \mathbf{lsr}^{(2)}$	$\mathbf{lr}^{(1.3)} = \{(\tilde{y},\tilde{\theta})\mid \tilde{\theta} \in (-\pi, -\frac{\pi}{2}], \sigma_N(\tilde{y},\tilde{\theta}) \geq 0, \sigma_R(\tilde{y},\tilde{\theta}) < 0\}$
$\mathbf{rsr} = \mathbf{rsr}^{(1)} \cup \mathbf{rsr}^{(2)}$	$\mathbf{rl}^{(1.3)} = \{(\tilde{y},\tilde{\theta})\mid \tilde{\theta} \in [\frac{\pi}{2}, \pi), \sigma_R(\tilde{y},\tilde{\theta}) > 0, \sigma_P(\tilde{y},\tilde{\theta}) \leq 0\}$
$\mathbf{l} = \mathbf{l}^{(1)} \cup \mathbf{l}^{(2)} \cup \mathbf{l}^{(3)}$	$\mathbf{lr}^{(2)} = \{(\tilde{y},\tilde{\theta})\mid \tilde{\theta} \in [\pi, \frac{3}{2}\pi), \sigma_R(\tilde{y},\tilde{\theta}) > 0, \sigma_N(\tilde{y},\tilde{\theta}) < 0\}$
$\mathbf{rl}^{(1)} = \mathbf{rl}^{(1.1)} \cup \mathbf{rl}^{(1.2)} \cup \mathbf{rl}^{(1.3)}$	$\mathbf{rl}^{(2)} = \{(\tilde{y},\tilde{\theta})\mid \tilde{\theta} \in (-\frac{3}{2}\pi, -\pi], \sigma_P(\tilde{y},\tilde{\theta}) > 0, \sigma_L(\tilde{y},\tilde{\theta}) < 0\}$
$\mathbf{rsl} = \mathbf{rsl}^{(1)} \cup \mathbf{rsl}^{(2)}$	$\mathbf{sr} = \{(\tilde{y},\tilde{\theta})\mid \tilde{y} < -1, \tilde{\theta} = \frac{\pi}{2}\}$
$\mathbf{lsl} = \mathbf{lsl}^{(1)} \cup \mathbf{lsl}^{(2)}$	$\mathbf{sl} = \{(\tilde{y},\tilde{\theta})\mid \tilde{y} > +1, \tilde{\theta} = -\frac{\pi}{2}\}$
	$\mathbf{lsr}^{(1)} = \{(\tilde{y},\tilde{\theta})\mid \tilde{\theta} \in [0, \frac{\pi}{2}), \sigma_N(\tilde{y},\tilde{\theta}) < 0\}$
	$\mathbf{rsl}^{(1)} = \{(\tilde{y},\tilde{\theta})\mid \tilde{\theta} \in (-\frac{\pi}{2}, 0], \sigma_P(\tilde{y},\tilde{\theta}) > 0\}$
	$\mathbf{lsr}^{(2)} = \{(\tilde{y},\tilde{\theta})\mid \tilde{\theta} \in [-\frac{\pi}{2}, 0), \sigma_N(\tilde{y},\tilde{\theta}) < 0\}$
$\sigma_N(\tilde{y},\tilde{\theta}) = \tilde{y} + 1 + \cos(\tilde{\theta})$	$\mathbf{rsl}^{(2)} = \{(\tilde{y},\tilde{\theta})\mid \tilde{\theta} \in (0, \frac{\pi}{2}], \sigma_P(\tilde{y},\tilde{\theta}) > 0\}$
$\sigma_P(\tilde{y},\tilde{\theta}) = \tilde{y} - 1 - \cos(\tilde{\theta})$	$\mathbf{rsr}^{(1)} = \{(\tilde{y},\tilde{\theta})\mid \tilde{\theta} \in (\frac{\pi}{2}, \pi), \sigma_R(\tilde{y},\tilde{\theta}) < 0\}$
$\sigma_R(\tilde{y},\tilde{\theta}) = \tilde{y} + 1 - \cos(\tilde{\theta})$	$\mathbf{lsl}^{(1)} = \{(\tilde{y},\tilde{\theta})\mid \tilde{\theta} \in (-\pi, -\frac{\pi}{2}), \sigma_L(\tilde{y},\tilde{\theta}) > 0\}$
$\sigma_L(\tilde{y},\tilde{\theta}) = \tilde{y} - 1 + \cos(\tilde{\theta})$	$\mathbf{rsr}^{(2)} = \{(\tilde{y},\tilde{\theta})\mid \tilde{\theta} \in [\pi, \frac{3}{2}\pi), \sigma_R(\tilde{y},\tilde{\theta}) < 0\}$
	$\mathbf{lsl}^{(2)} = \{(\tilde{y},\tilde{\theta})\mid \tilde{\theta} \in (-\frac{3}{2}\pi, -\pi], \sigma_L(\tilde{y},\tilde{\theta}) > 0\}$

3   Hybrid Path–Tracking Feedback Controller

3.1   Optimal Feedback Control for Line Tracking

In [11], the problem of driving the Dubins' car to a straight path has been considered. An optimal feedback control that minimizes the length travelled by the vehicle to reach the specified path was deviced. Define $\sigma_N(\tilde{y}, \tilde{\theta}) = \tilde{y} + 1 + \cos(\tilde{\theta})$ and $\sigma_P(\tilde{y}, \tilde{\theta}) = \tilde{y} - 1 - \cos(\tilde{\theta})$. The optimal feedback control presented in [11] is defined inside the region

$$\mathcal{D}_{(\tilde{y},\tilde{\theta})} = \begin{cases} \sigma_N(\tilde{y}, \tilde{\theta}) < 0 \ \wedge \ \tilde{\theta} \in [\pi, \frac{3}{2}\pi) \ \vee \\ \sigma_P(\tilde{y}, \tilde{\theta}) \leq 0 \ \wedge \ \tilde{\theta} \in (\frac{\pi}{2}, \pi) \ \vee \\ \tilde{\theta} \in [-\frac{\pi}{2}, \frac{\pi}{2}] \ \vee \\ \sigma_N(\tilde{y}, \tilde{\theta}) \geq 0 \ \wedge \ \tilde{\theta} \in [-\pi, -\frac{\pi}{2}) \ \vee \\ \sigma_P(\tilde{y}, \tilde{\theta}) > 0 \ \wedge \ \tilde{\theta} \in (-\frac{3}{2}\pi, -\pi) \end{cases} \tag{6}$$

in the state space $(\tilde{y}, \tilde{\theta})$, which, modulo 2π angles on $\tilde{\theta}$, corresponds to the whole space (see Figure 5). The optimal controller is described by three modes,

- *go_straight*, where $\omega = 0$
- *turn_right*, where $\omega = -\frac{V}{R}$ (7)
- *turn_left*, where $\omega = +\frac{V}{R}$,

which are chosen as follows

$$[go\_straight, \text{if } (\tilde{y}, \tilde{\theta}) \in \Omega^0] \wedge [turn\_right, \text{if } (\tilde{y}, \tilde{\theta}) \in \Omega^-] \wedge [turn\_left, \text{if } (\tilde{y}, \tilde{\theta}) \in \Omega^+]$$
(8)

where the partition $\Omega^0 \cup \Omega^- \cup \Omega^+$ of domain $\mathcal{D}_{(\tilde{y}, \tilde{\theta})}$ is defined as in Table 1. In Figure 5 the boundaries between the subsets of the partition $\Omega^0 \cup \Omega^- \cup \Omega^+$ are represented by dotted lines, and the direction of motion, when the reference path is a straight line i.e. $d = 0$, is represented by directed curves.

3.2   Feedback Tracking Control for Generic Path

In this section a hybrid feedback controller that solves Problem 1 is derived from the one reported in the previous section. The hybrid model of the vehicle $PTHA_2$ is characterized by the two modes: *upwards* and *downwards*. In mode *downwards* input ω appears with opposite sign with respect to mode *upwards*. Since the controller modes in (8) has been set assuming an upwards binormal axis then, the controller modes *turn_right* and *turn_left* have to be switched when the vehicle is in mode *downwards*. Hence, for a generic feasible path Γ, the full–state feedback controller is defined in $\{upwards, downwards\} \times \mathcal{D}_{(\tilde{y}, \tilde{\theta})}$ by setting the controller modes as follows

- *go_straight*, if $(bin, (\tilde{y}, \tilde{\theta})) \in \{upwards, downwards\} \times \Omega^0$
- *turn_right*, if $(bin, (\tilde{y}, \tilde{\theta})) \in (upwards \times \Omega^-) \vee (bin, (\tilde{y}, \tilde{\theta})) \in (downwards \times \Omega^+)$
- *turn_left*, if $(bin, (\tilde{y}, \tilde{\theta})) \in (upwards \times \Omega^+) \vee (bin, (\tilde{y}, \tilde{\theta})) \in (downwards \times \Omega^-)$
(9)

where Ω^0, Ω^- and Ω^+ are as in Table 1. The closed–loop hybrid automaton $CLHA$ obtained by applying the feedback (7),(9) to the vehicle hybrid automaton $PTHA_2$ is depicted in Figure 4. According to (9) and (8), $CLHA$ has a discrete state *mode* that assumes values in the set $\mathcal{O} = \{zero, negative, positive\}$, as follows

- $mode = zero$ if $(\tilde{y}, \tilde{\theta}) \in \Omega^0$
- $mode = negative$ if $(\tilde{y}, \tilde{\theta}) \in \Omega^-$ (10)
- $mode = positive$ if $(\tilde{y}, \tilde{\theta}) \in \Omega^+$.

The initial state $(mode_0, (\tilde{y}_0, \tilde{\theta}_0))$ of the hybrid automaton $CLHA$ has to satisfy (10).

The coordinate transformation $(x, y, \theta) \rightarrow (s, \tilde{y}, \tilde{\theta})$ becomes singular when the vehicle lies on the center of the local osculating circle to the path Γ. That is if, at some time $\bar{t}$, $\tilde{y}(\bar{t})|\hat{\kappa}(s(\bar{t}))| = 1$, or equivalently $\tilde{y}(\bar{t}) d(\bar{t}) = 1$. For any initial configuration $(M(x_0, y_0), \theta_0)$, with $M(x_0, y_0) \in \mathcal{T}_\Gamma$ as in (4), the corresponding state $(\tilde{y}_0, \tilde{\theta}_0)$ satisfies $\tilde{y}_0 < C^{-1}$. Further, since by (5) $d \leq C$, then $\tilde{y}_0 d < 1$ at the given initial condition. However, to ensure that

$$\tilde{y} d < 1 \quad \text{i.e.} \quad 1 - \tilde{y} d > 0$$
(11)

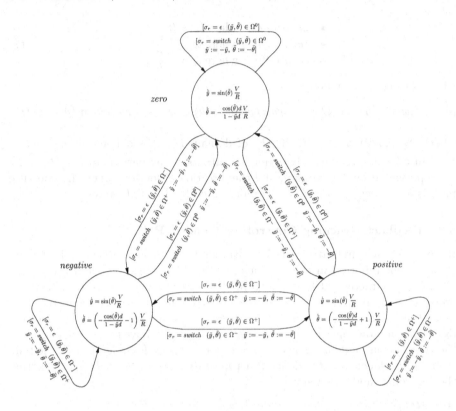

Fig. 4. Hybrid model of the closed-loop system $CLHA$.

will hold along all the trajectories of $CLHA$, we need to further restrict the admissible initial vehicle configurations, in terms of its initial orientation θ_0.

Proposition 1. *Let the continuous disturbance d be bounded to belong to the interval $[0, C]$, with*

$$C < 0.5 . \tag{12}$$

Then, (11) is satisfied along all trajectories of CLHA provided that the initial configuration $(mode_0, (\tilde{y}_0, \tilde{\theta}_0))$ is such that

$$(\tilde{y}_0, \tilde{\theta}_0) \in \mathcal{I}_{(\tilde{y}, \tilde{\theta})} = \left\{ (\tilde{y}, \tilde{\theta}) \in \mathcal{D}_{(\tilde{y}, \tilde{\theta})} \mid |\tilde{y}| < C^{-1} - 1 + |\cos(\tilde{\theta})| \right\} . \tag{13}$$

The proof of the above proposition is not reported due to space limitation.

Note that, for initial configurations satisfying (13) we have $M(x_0, y_0) \in \mathcal{T}_\Gamma$ as in (4). By Proposition 1, if a reference path Γ has minimum radius of curvature R_Γ greater than twice the minimum turning radius R of the vehicle, then for any initial configuration $(M(x_0, y_0), \theta_0)$, with lateral position and orientation errors bounded to belong to $\mathcal{I}_{(\tilde{y}, \tilde{\theta})}$ as in (13), condition (11) is ensured.

4   Verification of the Hybrid Path–Tracking Controller

In this section the behavior of the hybrid automaton $CLHA$ is analyzed by introducing an equivalence relation $\sim$ in the hybrid state space $\mathcal{O} \times \mathcal{D}_{(\tilde{y},\tilde{\theta})}$ and by computing the corresponding quotient system (see [5]).

Consider the partition $\Pi_{(\tilde{y},\tilde{\theta})}$ of the domain $\mathcal{D}_{(\tilde{y},\tilde{\theta})}$ in (6) given by the 24 subsets $\left\{ \mathbf{r}^{(1)}, \cdots, \mathbf{rl}^{(2)}\mathbf{l}^{(3)}, \cdots, \mathbf{lsl}^{(2)}, \mathbf{O} \right\}$, defined in Table 1, with $\mathbf{rl}^{(2)}$ and $\mathbf{l}^{(3)}$ replaced by $\mathbf{rl}^{(2)}\mathbf{l}^{(3)}$. We say that $(mode_1, (\tilde{y}_1, \tilde{\theta}_1))$, $(mode_2, (\tilde{y}_2, \tilde{\theta}_2))$ are equivalent, i.e. $(mode_1, (\tilde{y}_1, \tilde{\theta}_1)) \sim (mode_2, (\tilde{y}_2, \tilde{\theta}_2))$, iff $(\tilde{y}_1, \tilde{\theta}_1) \in \mathbf{p}$, for some $\mathbf{p} \in \Pi_{(\tilde{y},\tilde{\theta})}$, implies $(\tilde{y}_2, \tilde{\theta}_2) \in \mathbf{p}$. We associate to the corresponding quotient space $Q^\sim = \left\{ \mathcal{O} \times \mathbf{r}^{(1)}, \cdots, \mathcal{O} \times \mathbf{O} \right\}$ a nondeterministic finite state machine, referred to as FSM_{PTC} , with states corresponding to the equivalence classes in $Q^\sim$ (labeled, with a slight abuse of notation, $\mathbf{r}^{(1)}, \cdots, \mathbf{O}$). The next–state function of FSM_{PTC} is defined as follows: for any $Q_1, Q_2 \in Q^\sim$, a transition from Q_1 to Q_2 occurs iff there exists an arc of trajectory of the hybrid automoton $CLHA$ from some $(mode_1, (\tilde{y}_1, \tilde{\theta}_1)) \in Q_1$ to some $(mode_2, (\tilde{y}_2, \tilde{\theta}_2)) \in Q_2$, for some discrete disturbance σ_r and some continuous disturbance d.

Proposition 2. *Given the hybrid system CLHA , if the discrete disturbance σ_r takes always the value ϵ, then, for any initial hybrid state $(mode, (\tilde{y}_0, \tilde{\theta}_0)) \in \mathcal{O} \times \mathcal{I}_{(\tilde{y},\tilde{\theta})}$ as in (13), under the action of any disturbance d bounded as in (5) with C as in (12), we have:*

- *the quotient system obtained from the equivalence relation $\sim$ is the finite state machine FSM_{PTC} depicted in Figure 5;*
- *an upper bound for the space travelled by the origin of the Frenet's frame along the path Γ, when the hybrid state is in a given equivalence class is represented by the weight associated to exiting arc;*
- *the quotient system FSM_{PTC} remains in each equivalence class a bounded amount of time, except for the equivalent class $\mathbf{O}$ where $(\tilde{y}, \tilde{\theta}) = (0, 0)$.*

The proof of the above proposition, which is based on reachability analysis, is not reported due to space limitation.

If the reference path Γ has curvature always of the same sign, the convergence of the Dubins' car to the path is guaranteed by:

Corollary 1. *If the reference path Γ has curvature always of the same sign and amplitude lower than $\frac{1}{2R}$, the hybrid feedback control (7) and (9), ensures the tracking of Γ for any initial vehicle configuration in the domain $\mathcal{I}_{(\tilde{y},\tilde{\theta})}$ as in (13). The origin of the Frenet's frame covers at most a distance of*

$$\begin{cases} 1 + \frac{9}{2}\pi + \frac{\pi}{C} & \text{if } C \in [0, \frac{\pi}{6+5\pi}) \\ 4 + 7\pi + \frac{\pi}{2C} & \text{if } C \in [\frac{\pi}{6+5\pi}, \frac{1}{2}) \end{cases} \tag{14}$$

along the reference path Γ before the vehicle approaches it with correct orientation.

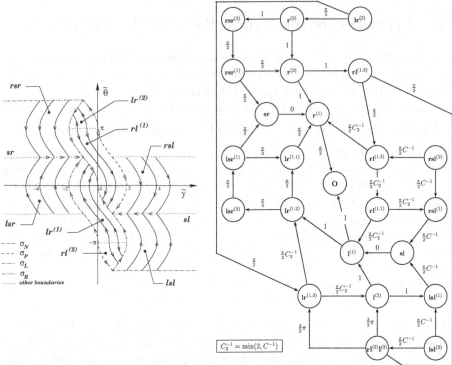

Fig. 5. On the left: shortest paths synthesis when $d = 0$. On the right: quotient system FSM_{PTC} representing the behavior of the closed–loop hybrid system $CLHA$, when $\sigma_r = \epsilon$.

The proof of the above corollary is obtained by computing the longest path to the node **O**.

By Proposition 2, if Γ is a straight line then the closed–loop system enforces *sliding* motions (see [13] for a tutorial) in the space $(\tilde{y}, \tilde{\theta})$ on the lines **sr**, **sl** and the arcs $\mathbf{r}^{(1)}$, $\mathbf{l}^{(1)}$, $\mathbf{r}^{(3)}$, $\mathbf{l}^{(3)}$ until the origin is reached. If the reference path Γ is not a straight line, sliding motions are enforced only on the lines **sr**, **sl**, on the arcs $\mathbf{r}^{(1)}$, $\mathbf{r}^{(3)}$ and on a piece of the arc $\mathbf{l}^{(3)}$. Under ideal sliding motion, around the origin the control ω switches at infinite frequency between $\frac{V}{R}, 0$ and $-\frac{V}{R}$. The mean value of such control (i.e. the *equivalent control*) is the signal κV that makes the car follows the reference path Γ with velocity V. In the real implementation smoothing techniques are applied to avoid the chattering of the control signal between the three values $\frac{V}{R}, 0$ and $-\frac{V}{R}$.

The behavior of the closed–loop system $CLHA$ under the action of the discrete disturbance σ_r is characterized by the following propositions.

Proposition 3. *Given an initial condition $(\tilde{y}_0, \tilde{\theta}_0)$ in the open neighborhood of the origin*

$$\mathcal{N}_{(\tilde{y}, \tilde{\theta})} = \left\{ (\tilde{y}, \tilde{\theta}) : |\tilde{y}| < 1, -\arccos\left(\frac{1}{2} - \frac{\tilde{y}}{2}\right) < \tilde{\theta} < \arccos\left(\frac{1}{2} + \frac{\tilde{y}}{2}\right) \right\} \quad (15)$$

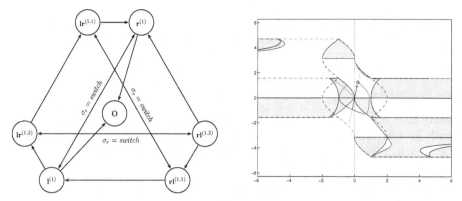

Fig. 6. On the left:quotient system FSM^D_{PTC} representing the behavior of the closed–loop hybrid system $CLHA$, when the intial state belongs to $\mathcal{O} \times \mathcal{N}_{(\tilde{y},\tilde{\theta})}$. On the right: regions in the domain $\mathcal{D}_{(\tilde{y},\tilde{\theta})}$ where $\dot{W} > 0$.

(see Figure 6), the hybrid closed–loop system CLHA keeps the continuous–time trajectory $(\tilde{y}(t), \tilde{\theta}(t))$ inside $\mathcal{N}_{(\tilde{y},\tilde{\theta})}$, under any disturbance $d(t)$ bounded as in (5) and any sequence of events σ_r.

Due to space limitation, the proof of the above proposition is not reported.

Proposition 4. *If the reference path Γ is such that changes in the curvature sign are at distance greater than $(5 + \frac{\pi}{2})R$ along it, then the hybrid feedback control (7), with modes chosen according to (9) stabilizes the Dubins' car along the reference path Γ.*

Proof. The set $\mathcal{N}_{(\tilde{y},\tilde{\theta})}$ defined in (15) is such that

$$\mathcal{N}_{(\tilde{y},\tilde{\theta})} \subset \mathbf{O} \cup \mathbf{r}^{(1)} \cup \mathbf{l}^{(1)} \cup \mathbf{lr}^{(1.1)} \cup \mathbf{lr}^{(1.2)} \cup \mathbf{rl}^{(1.1)} \cup \mathbf{rl}^{(1.2)} .$$

Since, by Proposition 3, $\mathcal{N}_{(\tilde{y},\tilde{\theta})}$ is a robust invariant set for the closed–loop hybrid system $CLHA$, then, if we restrict our attention to the domain $\mathcal{N}_{(\tilde{y},\tilde{\theta})}$, the transitions from $\mathbf{lr}^{(1.2)}$ to $\mathbf{lsr}^{(2)}$ and from $\mathbf{rl}^{(1.1)}$ to $\mathbf{rsl}^{(1)}$ in the quotient system FSM_{PTC} should be removed. Furthermore, notice that, under the action of the discrete disturbance $\sigma_r = switch$, the reset $\tilde{y} := -\tilde{y}$ and $\tilde{\theta} := -\tilde{\theta}$ introduces the mutual transitions $\mathbf{r}^{(1)} \leftrightarrows \mathbf{l}^{(1)}$, $\mathbf{lr}^{(1.1)} \leftrightarrows \mathbf{rl}^{(1.1)}$, and $\mathbf{lr}^{(1.2)} \leftrightarrows \mathbf{rl}^{(1.2)}$. Hence, in the presence of the discrete disturbance σ_r and for any disturbance d as in (5), when the initial state belongs to $\mathcal{O} \times \mathcal{N}_{(\tilde{y},\tilde{\theta})}$, the quotient system FSM^D_{PTC} obtained from the equivalent relation $\sim$ is as in Figure 6.

To analyse the convergence of the trajectories to $\mathbf{O}$, introduce the function

$$W(\tilde{y}, \tilde{\theta}) = \frac{1}{2}(\tilde{y}^2 + \tilde{\theta}^2). \tag{16}$$

$W(\tilde{y}, \tilde{\theta})$ has the property that if, at time $t = \bar{t}$, $\sigma_r = switch$ then $W(\tilde{y}(\bar{t}), \tilde{\theta}(\bar{t})) = W(\tilde{y}(\bar{t}^-), \tilde{\theta}(\bar{t}^-))$. The derivative with respect to time of W evaluates to

$$\dot{W}(\tilde{y}, \tilde{\theta}) = \left[\tilde{y} \sin(\tilde{\theta}) - \tilde{\theta} \frac{\cos(\tilde{\theta})d}{1 - \tilde{y}d} - \tilde{\theta} \varpi \right] \frac{V}{R}, \tag{17}$$

where $\varpi = 0, -1$, and 1 in mode *zero*, *negative*, and *positive*, respectively. The study of the sign of $\dot{W}(\tilde{y}, \tilde{\theta})$ is extended to the entire domain $\mathcal{D}_{(\tilde{y}, \tilde{\theta})}$. Under assumption (11), multiplying (17) by $\frac{R}{V}(1 - \tilde{y}d)$, we have

$$\dot{W} > 0 \iff \mu(\tilde{y}, \tilde{\theta}) = d \left[-\tilde{y}^2 \sin(\tilde{\theta}) - \tilde{\theta} \cos(\tilde{\theta}) + \varpi \tilde{y} \tilde{\theta} \right] + \left[\tilde{y} \sin(\tilde{\theta}) - \varpi \tilde{\theta} \right] > 0,$$

for some disturbance d bounded as in (5). Hence, for any $(\tilde{y}, \tilde{\theta})$ such that

$$\eta_1(\tilde{y}, \tilde{\theta}) = \tilde{y} \sin(\tilde{\theta}) - \varpi \tilde{\theta} > 0,$$

there exists d as in (5) such that $\mu(\tilde{y}, \tilde{\theta}) > 0$ and $\dot{W} > 0$. Otherwise, if $(\tilde{y}, \tilde{\theta})$ is such that $\eta_1(\tilde{y}, \tilde{\theta}) < 0$, then there exists d as in (5) such that $\dot{W} > 0$ if and only if $\mu(\tilde{y}, \tilde{\theta})$ is positive for $d = 1$. That is, if

$$\eta_2(\tilde{y}, \tilde{\theta}) = -\sin(\tilde{\theta})\tilde{y}^2 + \left[\sin(\tilde{\theta}) + \varpi \tilde{\theta} \right] \tilde{y} - \left[\tilde{\theta} \cos(\tilde{\theta}) + \varpi \tilde{\theta} \right] > 0.$$

The regions in the domain $\mathcal{D}_{(\tilde{y}, \tilde{\theta})}$ where function (16) locally increases are reported in Figure 6. Such regions are delimited by the curves $\eta_1(\tilde{y}, \tilde{\theta}) = 0$ and $\eta_2(\tilde{y}, \tilde{\theta}) = 0$. By (17), the continuous disturbance d that maximizes $\dot{W}(t)$ is

$$d^* = \begin{cases} 1 & \text{if } \tilde{\theta} \cos(\tilde{\theta}) < 0 \quad \text{i.e. } \tilde{\theta} \in (-\frac{\pi}{2}, 0) \cup (\frac{\pi}{2}, \frac{3}{2}\pi) \\ 0 & \text{if } \tilde{\theta} \cos(\tilde{\theta}) > 0 \quad \text{i.e. } \tilde{\theta} \in (-\frac{3}{2}\pi, -\frac{\pi}{2}) \cup (0, \frac{\pi}{2}) \end{cases}. \tag{18}$$

Consider an initial condition $(\tilde{y}_0, \tilde{\theta}_0)$ in a neighborhood of the origin contained in $\mathcal{N}_{(\tilde{y}, \tilde{\theta})} \cap \mathbf{rl}^{(1.2)}$. At the initial time, the hybrid model *CLHA* is in mode *negative*. Let us assume that $\sigma_r = \epsilon$, for the moment, and let us analyse the evolution of the hybrid model *CLHA* (see Figure 6). Under the action of the worst disturbance (18), the trajectory $(\tilde{y}(t), \tilde{\theta}(t))$ originating from $(\tilde{y}_0, \tilde{\theta}_0)$ reaches the curves $\mathbf{r}^{(1)}$. First $W(t)$ decreases (in $\mathbf{rl}^{(1.2)}$), then it increases (in $\mathbf{rl}^{(1.1)}$). Hence, *mode* switches to *positive*. $W(t)$ decreases (in the first part of $\mathbf{lr}^{(1.2)}$), and it increases again later on (in $\mathbf{lr}^{(1.2)}$ and $\mathbf{lr}^{(1.1)}$) until $(\tilde{y}(t), \tilde{\theta}(t))$ reaches $\mathbf{r}^{(1)}$. Finally, following a sliding motion along the curve $\mathbf{r}^{(1)}$, $(\tilde{y}(t), \tilde{\theta}(t))$ reaches the origin.

Along this trajectory $W(t)$ assume two local maxima, which correspond to the intersections of $\mathbf{l}^{(1)}$ and $\mathbf{r}^{(1)}$, and two local minima: the first on the line $\tilde{\theta} = 0$ when $\tilde{y} > 0$, and the second inside region $\mathbf{rl}^{(1.2)}$. Let $\delta = \|(\tilde{y}_0, \tilde{\theta}_0)\|$. Since the trajectory $(\tilde{y}(t), \tilde{\theta}(t))$ is continuous with respect to the initial condition $(\tilde{y}_0, \tilde{\theta}_0)$, then there exist two continuous functions $\zeta_{\max}, \zeta_{\min} : \mathbb{R} \to \mathbb{R}$ such that

$$\max_d \max_t \|(\tilde{y}(t), \tilde{\theta}(t))\| = \zeta_{\max}(\delta), \quad \min_d \min_t \|(\tilde{y}(t), \tilde{\theta}(t))\| = \zeta_{\min}(\delta). \tag{19}$$

Further, since the local maximum and minimum points tend to the origin as $\|(\tilde{y}_0, \tilde{\theta}_0)\|$ tends to zero, then $\lim_{\delta \to 0} \zeta_{\max}(\delta) = 0$ and $\lim_{\delta \to 0} \zeta_{\min}(\delta) = 0$.

Suppose now that a discrete disturbance $\sigma_r = switch$ occurs at the precise time $\bar{t}$ at which $(\tilde{y}(\bar{t}^-), \tilde{\theta}(\bar{t}^-))$ is opposite to $(\tilde{y}_0, \tilde{\theta}_0)$ with respect to the origin. Then, the state $(\tilde{y}(\bar{t}^-), \tilde{\theta}(\bar{t}^-))$ is reset to $(\tilde{y}(\bar{t}), \tilde{\theta}(\bar{t})) = (-\tilde{y}(\bar{t}^-), -\tilde{\theta}(\bar{t}^-)) \in \mathcal{N}_{(\tilde{y}, \tilde{\theta})}$, which lies on the same line to the origin of $(\tilde{y}_0, \tilde{\theta}_0)$. If $W(\tilde{y}_0, \tilde{\theta}_0) > W(\tilde{y}(\bar{t}), \tilde{\theta}(\bar{t})) = W(-\tilde{y}(\bar{t}^-), -\tilde{\theta}(\bar{t}^-))$ then the convergence is preserved. But, if $W(\tilde{y}_0, \tilde{\theta}_0) < W(\tilde{y}(\bar{t}), \tilde{\theta}(\bar{t})) = W(-\tilde{y}(\bar{t}^-), -\tilde{\theta}(\bar{t}^-))$ then, under the action of the discrete disturbance $\sigma_r = switch$, the state $(\tilde{y}, \tilde{\theta})$ is reset to a point farther away from the origin than the initial state $(\tilde{y}_0, \tilde{\theta}_0)$ and convergence can be lost.

However, if the reference path Γ is such that changes in the curvature sign are at a distance greater than $(5 + \frac{\pi}{2})R$ along it, between to successive actions of the discrete disturbance σ_r, the state $(\tilde{y}, \tilde{\theta})$ has enough time to reach the origin. In fact, assuming that, in the worst case, $(\tilde{y}(\bar{t}), \tilde{\theta}(\bar{t})) \in \mathcal{N}_{(\tilde{y}, \tilde{\theta})} \cap \mathbf{rl}^{(1.2)}$, an upper bound on the length the arc of Γ spanned by the origin of the Frenet's frame as $(\tilde{y}(t), \tilde{\theta}(t))$ converges to the origin, is given by $L(\mathbf{rl}^{(1.2)}) + L(\mathbf{rl}^{(1.1)}) + L(\mathbf{l}^{(1)}) + L(\mathbf{lr}^{(1.2)}) + L(\mathbf{lr}^{(1.1)}) + L(\mathbf{r}^{(1)})$ that, according to the weights reported on the quotient system FSM_{PTC} depicted in Figure 5, evaluates to $(5 + \frac{\pi}{2})R$.

To prove the robust stabilization of the car along the reference path Γ we have to show that for any $\epsilon > 0$, there exists $\delta > 0$ such that any trajectory $(\tilde{y}(t), \tilde{\theta}(t))$ of the hybrid system $CLHA$, originating from any $(\tilde{y}_0, \tilde{\theta}_0)$ with $\|(\tilde{y}_0, \tilde{\theta}_0)\| < \delta$, we have $\|(\tilde{y}(t), \tilde{\theta}(t))\| < \epsilon$. Given any $\epsilon > 0$, consider any initial condition $(\tilde{y}_0, \tilde{\theta}_0)$ with

$$\|(\tilde{y}_0, \tilde{\theta}_0)\| \leq \delta = \zeta_{\max}^{-1}(\zeta_{\min}^{-1}(\zeta_{\max}^{-1}(\epsilon))). \tag{20}$$

The trajectory $(\tilde{y}(t), \tilde{\theta}(t))$ evolves inside a ball of radius $\zeta_{\min}^{-1}(\zeta_{\max}^{-1}(\epsilon))$. If a disturbance $\sigma_r = switch$ occurs at some time $\bar{t}$, then the state is reset to $(\tilde{y}(\bar{t}), \tilde{\theta}(\bar{t})) = (-\tilde{y}(\bar{t}^-), -\tilde{\theta}(\bar{t}^-)) \in \mathcal{N}_{(\tilde{y}, \tilde{\theta})}$. In the evolution for $t > \bar{t}$ the trajectory reaches the origin before a further discrete disturbance will show up. Morever, since $\|(\tilde{y}(\bar{t}), \tilde{\theta}(\bar{t}))\| \leq \zeta_{\min}^{-1}(\zeta_{\max}^{-1}(\epsilon))$ then, the trajectory $(\tilde{y}(t), \tilde{\theta}(t))$ for $t > \bar{t}$ does not exit a ball of radius $\zeta_{\max}(\zeta_{\max}^{-1}(\epsilon)) = \epsilon$. Then, the hybrid feedback control (7), with modes chosen according to (9) robustly stabilizes the car along the reference path Γ.

5   Conclusions

In this paper, we have used modern techniques developed for hybrid systems simulation and verification to solve and prove stability of a control technique for an interesting problem, that is route tracking by nonholonomic vehicles with bounds on the curvature and limited sensory information. The proposed controller is reminiscent of a synthesis proposed elsewhere for an optimal control problem to track straight routes, whose generalization to generic routes turned out to be difficult to analyze otherwise. We believe that this case study, besides its intrinsic interest in applications, also has a value in showing the potential of hybrid systems analysis techniques as applied to complex control problems.

References

1. E. Asarin, T. Dang, O. Maler, and O. Bournez. Approximate reachability analysis of piecewise–linear dynamical systems. In Nancy Lynch and Bruce H. Krogh, editors, *Third International Workshop, HSCC2000, Hybrid Systems: Computation and Control*, volume 1790 of *Lecture Notes in Computer Science*, pages 20–31. Springer-Verlag, New York, U.S.A., 2000.
2. A. Balluchi, L. Benvenuti, M. D. Di Benedetto, C. Pinello, and A. L. Sangiovanni-Vincentelli. Automotive engine control and hybrid systems: Challenges and opportunities. *Proceedings of the IEEE*, 88, "Special Issue on Hybrid Systems" (invited paper)(7):888–912, July 2000.
3. A. Balluchi, L. Benvenuti, H. Wong-Toi, T. Villa, and A. L. Sangiovanni-Vincentelli. Controller synthesis for hybrid systems with lower bounds on event separation. In *Proc. 38th IEEE Conference on Decision and Control*, pages 3984–3989, Phoenix, Arizona, USA, December 1999.
4. L. E. Dubins. On curves of minimal length with a constraint on average curvature and with prescribed initial and terminal positions and tangents. *American Journal of Mathematics*, 79:497–516, 1957.
5. Thomas A. Henzinger. Hybrid automata with finite bisimulations. In Z. Fülöp and F. Gécseg, editors, *ICALP'95: Automata, Languages, and Programming*, pages 324–335. Springer–Verlag, 1995.
6. J.P. Laumond, S. Sekhavat, and F. Lamiraux. *Robot motion planning and control*. Springer-Verlag, Berlin, Germany, 1998.
7. J. Lygeros, C. Tomlin, and S. Sastry. Controllers for reachability specifications for hybrid systems. *Automatica*, 35(3), March 1999.
8. A. Olivero, J. Sifakis, and S. Yovine. Using abstractions for the verification of linear hybrid systems. In *Proceedings of Sixth International Conference on Computer-Aided Verification (CAV-94)*, pages 81–94. Springer-Verlag, 1994. Lecture Notes in Computer Science 818.
9. C. Samson. Control of chained systems application to path following and time–varying point–stabilization of mobile robots. *IEEE Transaction on Automatic Control*, 40(1):64–77, January 1995.
10. O.J. Sordalen and C. Canudas de Wit. Exponential control law for a mobile robot: Extension to path following. *IEEE Transactions on Robotics and Automation*, 9(6):837–842,, 1993.
11. P. Souères, A. Balluchi, and A. Bicchi. Optimal feedback control for line tracking with a bounded–curvature vehicle. to appear in International Journal of Control, 2000.
12. D. Tilbury, O.J. Sordalen, L. Bushnell, and S.S. Sastry. A multi-steering trailer system: conversion into chained form using dynamic feedback. *IEEE Transactions on Robotics and Automation*, 11(6):807–18, December 1995.
13. V.I. Utkin. Variable structure systems with sliding modes: a survey. *IEEE Transations on Automatic Control*, 22:212–222, 1977.
14. J. Zhang, K. H. Johansson, J. Lygeros, and S. Sastry. Dynamical systems revisited: Hybrid systems with zeno executions. In Nancy Lynch and Bruce H. Krogh, editors, *Third International Workshop, HSCC2000, Hybrid Systems: Computation and Control*, volume 1790 of *Lecture Notes in Computer Science*, pages 451–464. Springer-Verlag, New York, U.S.A., 2000.

Minimum-Cost Reachability for Priced Timed Automata*

Gerd Behrmann[1], Ansgar Fehnker[3]**, Thomas Hune[2], Kim Larsen[1],
Paul Pettersson[4]***, Judi Romijn[3], and Frits Vaandrager[3]

[1] Basic Research in Computer Science, Aalborg University,
{behrmann,kgl}@cs.auc.dk.
[2] Basic Research in Computer Science, Aarhus University,
baris@brics.dk.
[3] Computing Science Institute, University of Nijmegen,
{ansgar,judi,fvaan}@cs.kun.nl.
[4] Department of Computer Systems, Information Technology,
Uppsala University, paupet@docs.uu.se.

Abstract. This paper introduces the model of *linearly priced timed automata* as an extension of timed automata, with prices on both transitions and locations. For this model we consider the minimum-cost reachability problem: i.e. given a linearly priced timed automaton and a target state, determine the minimum cost of executions from the initial state to the target state. This problem generalizes the minimum-time reachability problem for ordinary timed automata. We prove decidability of this problem by offering an algorithmic solution, which is based on a combination of branch-and-bound techniques and a new notion of priced regions. The latter allows symbolic representation and manipulation of reachable states together with the cost of reaching them.

Keywords: Timed Automata, Verification, Data Structures, Algorithms, Optimization.

1 Introduction

Recently, real-time verification tools such as UPPAAL [14], KRONOS [7] and HyTech [11], have been applied to synthesize feasible solutions to static job-shop scheduling problems [9,13,18]. The basic common idea of these works is to reformulate the static scheduling problem as a reachability problem that can be solved by the verification tools. In this approach, the timed automata [3] based modeling languages of the verification tools serve as the basic input language in which the scheduling problem is described. These modeling languages have

* This work is partially supported by the European Community Esprit-LTR Project 26270 VHS (Verification of Hybrid Systems).
** Research supported by Netherlands Organization for Scientific Research (NWO) under contract SION 612-14-004.
*** Research partly sponsored by the AIT-WOODDES Project No IST-1999-10069.

M.D. Di Benedetto, A. Sangiovanni-Vincentelli (Eds.): HSCC 2001, LNCS 2034, pp. 147–161, 2001.

proven particularly well-suited in this respect, as they allow for easy and flexible modeling of systems, consisting of several parallel components that interact in a time-critical manner and constrain each other's behavior in a multitude of ways.

In this paper we introduce the model of *linearly priced timed automata* and offer an algorithmic solution to the problem of determining the minimum cost of reaching a designated set of target states. This result generalizes previous results on computation of minimum-time reachability and accumulated delays in timed automata, and should be viewed as laying a theoretical foundation for algorithmic treatments of more general optimization problems as encountered in static scheduling problems.

As an example consider the very simple static scheduling problem represented by the timed automaton in Fig. 1 from [17], which contains 5 'tasks' $\{A, B, C, D, E\}$. All tasks are to be performed precisely once, except task C, which should be performed *at least* once. The order of the tasks is given by the timed automaton, e.g. task B must not commence before task A has finished. In addition, the timed automaton specifies three timing requirements to be satisfied: the delay between the start of the first execution of task C and the start of the execution of E should be at least 3 time units; the delay between the start of the last execution of C and the start of D should be no more than 1 time unit; and, the delay between the start of B and the start of D should be at least 2 time units, each of these requirements are represented by a clock in the model. Using a standard timed model checker we are able to verify that location E of

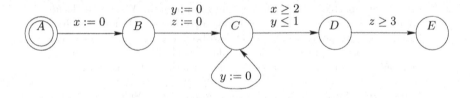

Fig. 1. Timed automata model of scheduling example.

the timed automaton is reachable. This can be demonstrated by a trace leading to the location[1]:

$$(A, 0, 0, 0) \xrightarrow{\tau} \xrightarrow{\epsilon(1)} (B, 1, 1, 1) \xrightarrow{\tau} \xrightarrow{\epsilon(1)} (C, 2, 1, 1) \xrightarrow{\tau} \xrightarrow{\epsilon(2)} (D, 4, 3, 3) \xrightarrow{\tau} (E, 4, 3, 3) \quad (1)$$

The above trace may be viewed as a feasible solution to the original static scheduling problem. However, given an optimization problem, one is often not satisfied with an arbitrary feasible solution but insist on solutions which are *optimal* in some sense. When modeling a problem like this one using timed automata an obvious notion of optimality is that of minimum accumulated time. For the

---

[1] Here a quadruple (X, v_x, v_y, v_z) denotes the state of the automaton in which the control location is X and where v_x, v_y and v_z give the values of the three clocks x, y and z. The transitions labelled τ are actual transitions in the model, and the transitions labelled $\epsilon(d)$ represents a delay of d time units.

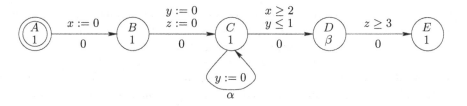

Fig. 2. A linearly priced timed automaton.

timed automaton of Fig. 1 the trace of (1) has an accumulated time-duration of
4. This, however, is not optimal as witnessed by the following alternative trace,
which by exploiting the looping transition on C reaches E within a total of 3
time-units[2]:

$$(A,0,0,0) \xrightarrow{\tau} \xrightarrow{\tau} \xrightarrow{\epsilon(2)} (C,2,2,2) \xrightarrow{\tau} (C,2,0,2) \xrightarrow{\tau} \xrightarrow{\epsilon(1)} (D,3,1,3) \xrightarrow{\tau} (E,3,1,3) \quad (2)$$

In [4] algorithmic solutions to the minimum-time reachability problem and the
more general problem of controller synthesis has been given using a backward
fix-point computation. In [17] an alternative solution based on forward reachability analysis is given, and in [5] an algorithmic solution is offered, which applies
branch-and-bound techniques to prune parts of the symbolic state-space which
are guaranteed not to contain optimal solutions. In particular, by introducing
an additional clock for accumulating time-elapses, the minimum-time reachability problem may be dealt with using the existing efficient data structures (e.g.
DBMs [8], CDDs [15] and DDDs [16]) already used in the real-time verification
tools UPPAAL and KRONOS for reachability. The results of the present paper
also extends the work in [2] which provides an algorithm for computing the
accumulated delay in a timed automata.

In this paper, we provide the basis for dealing with more general optimization problems. In particular, we introduce the model of *linearly priced timed
automata*, as an extension of timed automata with *prices* on both transitions
and locations: the price of a transition gives the cost for taking it and the price
on a location specifies the cost *per time-unit* for staying in that location. This
model can capture not only the passage of time, but also the way that e.g. tasks
with different prices for use per time unit, contributes to the total cost. Figure 2
gives a linearly priced extension of the timed automaton from Fig. 1. Here, the
price of location D is set to β and the price on all other locations is set to 1 (thus
simply accumulating time). The price of the looping transition on C is set to α,
whereas all other transitions are free of cost (price 0). Now for $(\alpha, \beta) = (1, 3)$
the costs of the traces (1) and (2) are 8 and 6, respectively (thus it is cheaper
to actually exploit the looping transition). For $(\alpha, \beta) = (2, 2)$ the costs of the
two traces are both 6, thus in this case it is immaterial whether the looping
transition is taken or not. In fact, the optimal cost of reaching E will in general

---

[2] In fact, 3 is the minimum time for reaching E.

be the minimum of $2 + 2 * \beta$ and $3 + \alpha$, and the optimal trace will include the looping transition on C depending on the particular values of α and β.

In this paper we deal with the problem of determining the minimum cost of reaching a given location for linearly priced timed automata. In particular, we offer an algorithmic solution to this problem[3]. In contrast to minimum-time reachability for timed automata, the minimum-cost reachability problem for linearly priced timed automata requires the development of new data structures for symbolic representation and the manipulation of reachable *sets* of states *together with* the cost of reaching them. In this paper we put forward one such data structure, namely a priced extension of the fundamental notion of *clock regions* for timed automata [3].

The remainder of the paper is structured as follows: Section 2 formally introduces the model of linearly priced timed automata together with its semantics. Section 3 develops the notion of priced clock regions, together with a number of useful operations on these. The priced clock regions are then used in Section 4 to give a symbolic semantics capturing (sufficiently) precisely the cost of executions and used as a basis for an algorithm solution to the minimum-cost problem. Finally, in Section 5 we give some concluding remarks. We refer the read to [6] for the proofs not included in this paper.

2   Linearly Priced Timed Automata

In this section, we introduce the model of linearly priced timed automata, which is an extension of timed automata [3] with prices on both locations and transitions. Dually, linearly priced timed automata may be seen as a special type of linear hybrid automata [10] or multirectangular automata [10] in which the accumulation of prices (i.e. the cost) is represented by a single continuous variable. However, in contrast to known undecidability results for these classes, minimum-cost reachability is computable for linearly priced timed automata[4].

Let C be a finite set of clocks. Then $\mathcal{B}(C)$ is the set of formulas obtained as conjunctions of atomic constraints of the form $x \bowtie n$ where $x \in C$, n is natural number, and $\bowtie \in \{<, \leq, =, \geq, >\}$. Elements of $\mathcal{B}(C)$ are called *clock constraints* over C. Note that for each timed automaton that has constraints of the form $x - y \bowtie c$, there exists a strongly bisimilar timed automaton with only constraints of the form $x \bowtie c$. Therefore, the results in this paper are applicable to automata having constraints of the type $x - y \bowtie c$ as well.

Definition 1 (Linearly Priced Timed Automaton). *A Linearly Priced Timed Automaton (LPTA) over clocks C and actions Act is a tuple (L, l_0, E, I, P) where L is a finite set of locations, l_0 is the initial location, $E \subseteq L \times \mathcal{B}(C) \times Act \times \mathcal{P}(C) \times L$ is the set of edges, $I : L \rightarrow \mathcal{B}(C)$ assigns*

---

[3] Thus settling an open problem given in [4].

[4] An intuitive explanation for this is that the additional (cost) variable does not influence the behavior of the automata.

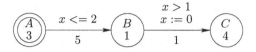

Fig. 3. An example LPTA.

invariants to locations, and $P : (L \cup E) \rightarrow \mathbb{N}$ assigns prices to both locations and edges. In the case of $(l, g, a, r, l') \in E$, we write $l \xrightarrow{g,a,r} l'$.

Formally, clock values are represented as functions called *clock assignments* from C to the non-negative reals $\mathbb{R}_{\geq 0}$. We denote by $\mathbb{R}^C$ the set of clock assignments for C ranged over by u, u' etc. We define the operation $u' = [r \mapsto 0]u$ to be the assignment such that $u'(x) = 0$ if $x \in r$ and $u(x)$ otherwise, and the operation $u' = u + d$ to be the assignment such that $u'(x) = u(x) + d$. Also, a clock valuation u satisfies a clock constraint g, $u \in g$, if $u(x) \bowtie n$ for any atomic constraint $x \bowtie n$ in g. Notice that the set of clock valuations satisfying a guard is always a convex set.

The semantics of a LPTA A is defined as a transition system with the state-space $L \times \mathbb{R}^C$, with initial state (l_0, u_0) (where u_0 assigns zero to all clocks in C), and with the following transition relation:

- $(l, u) \xrightarrow{\epsilon(d),p} (l, u + d)$ if $u + d \in I(l)$, and $p = P(l) * d$.
- $(l, u) \xrightarrow{a,p} (l', u')$ if there exists g, r such that $l \xrightarrow{g,a,r} l'$, $u \in g$, $u' = [r \mapsto 0]u$, $u' \in I(l')$ and $p = P((l, g, a, r, l'))$.

Note that the transitions are decorated with two labels: a delay-quantity or an action, together with the cost of the particular transition. For determining the cost, the price of a location gives the cost rate of staying in that location (per time unit), and the price of a transition gives the cost of taking that transition. In the remainder, states and executions of the transition system for LPTA A will be referred to as states and executions of A.

Definition 2 (Cost). Let $\alpha = (l_0, u_0) \xrightarrow{a_1,p_1} (l_1, u_1) \ldots \xrightarrow{a_n,p_n} (l_n, u_n)$ be a finite execution of LPTA A. The cost of α, $\mathsf{cost}(\alpha)$, is the sum $\Sigma_{i \in \{1,\ldots,n\}} p_i$.

For a given state (l, u), the minimal cost of reaching (l, u), $\mathsf{mincost}((l, u))$, is the infimum of the costs of finite executions ending in (l, u). Similarly, the minimal cost of reaching a location l, $\mathsf{mincost}(l)$, is the infimum of the costs of finite executions ending in a state of the form (l, u).

Example 1. Consider the LPTA of Fig. 3. The LPTA has a single clock x, and the locations and transitions are decorated with prices. A sample execution of this LPTA is for instance:

$$(A, 0) \xrightarrow{\epsilon(1.5),4.5} (A, 1.5) \xrightarrow{\tau,5} (B, 1.5) \xrightarrow{\tau,1} (C, 1.5)$$

The cost of this execution is 10.5. In fact, there are executions with cost arbitrarily close to the value 7, obtainable by avoiding delay in location A, and delaying just long enough in location B. Due to the infimum definition of mincost, it follows that $\text{mincost}(C) = 7$. However, note that because of the strict comparison in the guard of the second transition, no execution actually achieves this cost. $\square$

3   Priced Clock Regions

For ordinary timed automata, the key to decidability results has been the valuable notion of *region* [3]. In particular, regions provide a finite partitioning of the uncountable set of clock valuations, which is also stable with respect to the various operations needed for exploration of the behavior of timed automata (in particular the operations of delay and reset).

In the setting of linearly priced timed automata, we put forward a new extended notion of *priced region*. Besides providing a finite partitioning of the set of clock-valuations (as in the case of ordinary regions), priced regions also associate costs to each individual clock-valuation within the region. However, as we shall see in the following, priced regions may be presented and manipulated in a symbolic manner and are thus suitable as an algorithmic basis.

Definition 3 (Priced Regions). *Given set S, let $Seq(S)$ be the set of finite sequences of elements of S. A priced clock region over a finite set of clocks C*

$$R = (h, [r_0, \ldots , r_k], [c_0, \ldots , c_l])$$

is an element of $(C \to \mathbb{N}) \times Seq(2^C) \times Seq(\mathbb{N})$, with $k = l$, $C = \cup_{i \in \{0, \ldots , k\}} r_i$, $r_i \cap r_j = \emptyset$ when $i \neq j$, and $i > 0$ implies that $r_i \neq \emptyset$.

Given a clock valuation $u \in \mathbb{R}^C$, and region $R = (h, [r_0, \ldots , r_k], [c_0, \ldots , c_k])$, $u \in R$ iff

1. *h and u agree on the integer part of each clock in C,*
2. *$x \in r_0$ iff $\text{frac}(u(x)) = 0$,*
3. *$x, y \in r_i \Rightarrow \text{frac}(u(x)) = \text{frac}(u(y))$, and*
4. *$x \in r_i, y \in r_j$ and $i < j \Rightarrow \text{frac}(u(x)) < \text{frac}(u(y))$.*

For a priced region $R = (h, [r_0, \ldots , r_k], [c_0, \ldots , c_k])$ the first two components of the triple constitute an ordinary (unpriced) region $\hat{R} = (h, [r_0, \ldots , r_k])$. The naturals $c_0, \ldots , c_k$ are the costs, which are associated with the vertices of the closure of the (unpriced) region, as follows. We start in the left-most lower vertex of the exterior of the region and associate cost c_0 with it, then move one time unit in the direction of set r_k to the next vertex of the exterior, and associate cost c_1 with that vertex, then move one unit in the direction of r_{k-1}, etc. In this way, the costs $c_0, \ldots , c_k$, span a linear cost plane on the k-dimensional unpriced region.

The closure of the unpriced region R is the convex hull of the vertices. Each clock valuation $u \in R$ is a (unique) convex combination[5] of the vertices. Therefore the cost of u can be defined as the same convex combination of the cost in the vertices. This gives the following definition:

Definition 4 (Cost inside Regions). *Given priced region* $R = (h, [r_0, \ldots, r_k], [c_0, \ldots, c_k])$ *and clock valuation* $u \in R$, *the cost of* u *in* R *is defined as:*

$$\text{cost}(u, R) = c_0 + \sum_{i=0}^{k-1} \text{frac}(u(x_{k-i})) * (c_{i+1} - c_i)$$

where x_j *is some clock in* r_j. *The minimal cost associated with* R *is* $\text{mincost}(R) = \min(\{c_0, \ldots, c_k\})$.

In the symbolic state-space, constructed with the priced regions, the costs will be computed such that for each concrete state in a symbolic state, the cost associated with it is the minimal cost for reaching that state by the symbolic path that was followed. In this way, we always have the minimal cost of all concrete paths represented by that symbolic path, but there may be more symbolic paths leading to a symbolic state in which the costs are different. Note that the cost of a clock valuation in the region is computed by adding fractions of costs for equivalence sets of clocks, rather than for each clock.

To prepare for the symbolic semantics, we define in the following a number of operations on priced regions. These operations are also the ones used in the algorithm for finding the optimal cost of reaching a location.

The delay operation computes the time successor, which works exactly as in the classical (unpriced) regions. The changing dimensions of the regions cause the addition or deletion of vertices and thus of the associated cost. The price

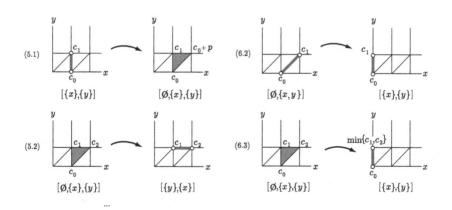

Fig. 4. Delay and reset operations for two-dimensional priced regions.

---

[5] A linear expression $\sum a_i v_i$ where $\sum a_i = 1$, and $a_i \geq 0$.

argument will be instantiated to the price of the location in which time is passing; this is needed only when a vertex is added. The two cases in the operation are illustrated in Fig. 4 to the left (5.1) and (5.2).

Definition 5 (Delay). *Given a priced region* $R = (h, [r_0, \ldots, r_k], [c_0, \ldots, c_k])$ *and a price* p, *the function* delay *is defined as follows:*

1. *If* r_0 *is not empty, then*

$$\mathsf{delay}(R, p) = (h, [\emptyset, r_0, \ldots, r_k], [c_0, \ldots, c_k, c_0 + p])$$

2. *If* r_0 *is empty, then*

$$\mathsf{delay}(R, p) = (h', [r_k, r_1, \ldots, r_{k-1}], [c_1, \ldots, c_k])$$
$$\text{where } h' = h \text{ incremented for all clocks in } r_k$$

When resetting a clock, a priced region may lose a dimension. If so, the two costs, associated with the vertices that are collapsed, are compared and the minimum is taken for the new vertex. Two of the three cases in the operation is illustrated in Fig. 4 to the right (6.2) and (6.3).

Definition 6 (Reset). *Given a priced region* $R = (h, [r_0, \ldots, r_k], [c_0, \ldots, c_k])$ *and a clock* $x \in r_i$, *the function* reset *is defined as follows:*

1. *If* $i = 0$ *then* $\mathsf{reset}(x, R) = (h', [r_0, \ldots, r_k], [c_0, \ldots, c_k])$, *where* $h' = h$ *with* x set to zero
2. *If* $i > 0$ *and* $r_i \neq \{x\}$, *then*

$$\mathsf{reset}(x, R) = (h', [r_0 \cup \{x\}, \ldots, r_i \setminus \{x\}, \ldots, r_k], [c_0, \ldots, c_k])$$
$$\text{where } h' = h \text{ with } x \text{ set to zero}$$

3. *If* $i > 0$ *and* $r_i = \{x\}$, *then*

$$\mathsf{reset}(x, R) = (h', [r_0 \cup \{x\}, \ldots, r_{i-1}, r_{i+1}, \ldots, r_k],$$
$$[c_0, \ldots, c_{k-i-1}, c', c_{k-i+2}, \ldots, c_k])$$
$$\text{where } c' = \min(c_{k-i}, c_{k-i+1})$$
$$h' = h \text{ with } x \text{ set to zero}$$

The reset operation on a set of clocks: $\mathsf{reset}(C \cup \{x\}, R) = \mathsf{reset}(C, \mathsf{reset}(x, R))$, *and* $\mathsf{reset}(\emptyset, R) = R$.

The price argument in the increment operation will be instantiated to the price of the particular transition taken; all costs are updated accordingly.

Definition 7 (Increment). *Given a priced region* $R = (h, [r_0, \ldots, r_k], [c_0, \ldots, c_k])$ *and a price* p, *the increment of* R *with respect to* p *is the priced region* $R \oplus p = (h, [r_0, \ldots, r_k], [c_0', \ldots, c_k'])$ *where* $c_i' = c_i + p$.

If in region R, no clock has fractional part 0, then time may pass in R, that is, each clock valuation in R has a time successor and predecessor in R. When changing location with R, we must choose for each clock valuation u in R between delaying in the previous location until u is reached, followed by the change of location, or changing location immediately and delaying to u in the new location. This depends on the price of either location. For this the following operation self is useful.

Definition 8 (Self). *Given a priced region* $R = (h, [r_0, \ldots, r_k], [c_0, \ldots, c_k])$ *and a price* p, *the function* self *is defined as follows:*

1. *If* r_0 *is not empty, then* $\mathsf{self}(R, p) = R$.
2. *If* r_0 *is empty, then*

$$\mathsf{self}(R, p) = (h, [r_0, \ldots, r_k], [c_0, \ldots, c_{k-1}, c'])$$
$$\textit{where } c' = \min(c_k, c_0 + p)$$

Definition 9 (Comparison). *Two priced regions may be compared only if their unpriced versions are equal:* $(h, [r_0, \ldots, r_k], [c_0, \ldots, c_k]) \leq (h', [r'_0, \ldots, r'_{k'}],$ $[c'_0, \ldots, c'_{k'}])$ *iff* $h = h'$, $k = k'$, *and for* $0 \leq i \leq k$: $r_i = r'_i$ *and* $c_i \leq c'_i$.

The operations delay and self satisfy the following useful properties:

Proposition 1 (Interaction Properties).

1. $\mathsf{self}(R, p) \leq R$,
2. $\mathsf{self}(\mathsf{self}(R, p), p) = \mathsf{self}(R, p)$,
3. $\mathsf{delay}(\mathsf{self}(R, p), p) \leq \mathsf{delay}(R, p)$,
4. $\mathsf{self}(\mathsf{delay}(R, p), p) = \mathsf{delay}(R, p)$,
5. $\mathsf{self}(R \oplus q, p) = \mathsf{self}(R, p) \oplus q$,
6. $\mathsf{delay}(R \oplus q, p) = \mathsf{delay}(R, p) \oplus q$,
7. For $g \in \mathcal{B}(C)$, whenever $R \in g$ then $\mathsf{self}(R, p) \in g$.

Stated in terms of the cost, $\mathsf{cost}(u, R)$, of an individual clock valuation, u, of a priced region, R, the symbolic operations behave as follows:

Proposition 2 (Cost Relations).

1. Let $R = (h, [r_0, \ldots, r_k], [c_0, \ldots, c_k])$. If $u \in R$ and $u + d \in R$ then $\mathsf{cost}(u + d, R) = \mathsf{cost}(u, R) + d * (c_k - c_0)$.
2. If $R = \mathsf{self}(R, p)$, $u \in R$ and $u + d \in \mathsf{delay}(R, p)$ then $\mathsf{cost}(u + d, \mathsf{delay}(R, p)) = \mathsf{cost}(u, R) + d * p$.
3. $\mathsf{cost}(u, \mathsf{reset}(x, R)) = \inf\{ \mathsf{cost}(v, R) \mid [x \mapsto 0]v = u \}$.

4   Symbolic Semantics and Algorithm

In this section, we provide a symbolic semantics for linearly priced timed automata based on the notion of priced regions and the associated operations presented in the previous section. As a main result we shown that the cost of an execution of the underlying automaton is captured sufficiently accurately. Finally, we present an algorithm based on priced regions. We refer the reader to the full version of this paper for the proofs not given here.

Definition 10 (Symbolic Semantics). *The symbolic semantics of a LPTA A is defined as a transition system with the state-space $L \times ((C \to \mathbb{N}) \times Seq(2^C) \times Seq(\mathbb{N}))$, with initial state $(l_0, (h_0, [C], [0]))$ (where h_0 assigns zero to the integer part of all clocks in C), and with the following transition relation:*

- $(l, R) \to (l, \mathsf{delay}(R, P(l)))$ *if* $\mathsf{delay}(R, P(l)) \in I(l)$.
- $(l, R) \to (l', R')$ *if there exists g, r such that $l \xrightarrow{g,a,r} l'$, $R \in g$, $R' = \mathsf{reset}(R, r) \oplus P((l, g, a, r, l'))$ and $R' \in I(l')$.*
- $(l, R) \to (l, \mathsf{self}(R, P(l)))$

In the remainder, states and executions of the symbolic transition system for LPTA A will be referred to as the symbolic states and executions of A.

Lemma 1. *Given LPTA A, for each execution α of A that ends in state (l, u), there is a symbolic execution β of A, that ends in symbolic state (l, R), such that $u \in R$, and $\mathsf{cost}(u, R) \le \mathsf{cost}(\alpha)$.*

Lemma 2. *Whenever (l, R) is a reachable symbolic state and $u \in R$, then $\mathsf{mincost}((l, u)) \le \mathsf{cost}(u, R)$.*

Combining the two lemmas we obtain as a main theorem that the symbolic semantics captures (sufficiently) accurately the cost of reaching states and locations:

Theorem 1. *Let l be a location of a LPTA A. Then*

$$\mathsf{mincost}(l) = \min(\{\, \mathsf{mincost}(R) \mid (l, R) \text{ is reachable} \,\})$$

Example 2. We now return to the linearly priced timed automaton in Fig. 2 where the value of both α and β is two, and look at its symbolic state-space. The shaded area in Fig. 5(i) including the lines in and around the shaded area represents some of the reachable priced regions in location B after time has passed (a number of delay actions have been taken). Only priced regions with integer values up to 3 are shown. The numbers are the cost of the vertices. The shaded area in Fig. 5(ii) represents in a similar way some of the reachable priced regions in location C after time has passed.   □

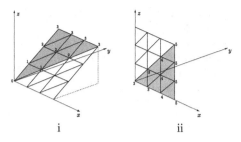

Fig. 5. Two reachable sets of priced regions.

The introduction of priced regions provides a first step towards an algorithmic solution for the minimum-cost reachability problem. However, in the present form both the integral part as well as the cost of vertices of priced regions may grow beyond any given bound during symbolic exploration. In the unpriced case, the growth of integral parts is often dealt with by suitable abstractions of (unpriced) regions, taking the maximal constant of the given timed automaton into account. Here we have chosen a very similar approach exploiting the fact, that any LPTA A may be transformed into an equivalent *"bounded"* LPTA $\tilde{A}$ in the sense that A and $\tilde{A}$ reaches the same locations with the exact same cost.

Theorem 2. *Let $A = (L, l_0, E, I, P)$ be a LPTA with maximal constant* max. *Then there exists a bounded time equivalent of A, $\tilde{A} = (L, l_0, E', I', P')$, satisfying the following:*

1. *Whenever (l, u) is reachable in $\tilde{A}$, then for all $x \in C$, $u(x) \leq$ max $+2$.*
2. *For any location $l \in L$, l is reachable with cost c in A if and only if l is reachable with cost c in $\tilde{A}$*

Now, we suggest in Fig. 6 a branch-and-bound algorithm for determining the minimum-cost of reaching a given target location l_g from the initial state of a LPTA. All encountered states are stored in the two data structures PASSED and WAITING, divided into explored and unexplored states, respectively. The global variable COST stores the lowest cost for reaching the target location found so far. In each iteration, a state is taken from WAITING. If it matches the target location l_g and has a lower cost than the previously lowest cost COST, then COST is updated. Then, only if the state has not been previously explored with a lower cost do we add it to PASSED and add the successors to WAITING. This bounding of the search in line 6 of Fig. 6 may be optimized even further by adding the constraint mincost$(R) <$ COST; i.e. we only need to continue exploration if the minimum cost of the current region is below the optimal cost computed so far. Due to Theorem 1, the algorithm of Fig. 6 does indeed yield the correct minimum-cost value.

Theorem 3. *When the algorithm in Fig. 6 terminates, the value of* COST *equals* mincost(l_g).

COST := ∞, PASSED := ∅, WAITING := $\{(l_0, R_0)\}$
while WAITING $\neq \emptyset$ **do**
    select (l, R) from WAITING
    if $l = l_g$ **and** mincost(R) < COST **then**
        COST := mincost(R)
    if for all (l, R') in PASSED: $R' \not\leq R$ **then**
        add (l, R) to PASSED
        for all (l', R') such that $(l, R) \to (l', R')$: add (l', R') to WAITING
return COST

Fig. 6. Branch-and-bound state-space exploration algorithm.

Proof. First, notice that if (l_1, R_1) can reach (l_2, R_2), then a state (l_1, R_1'), where $R_1' \leq R_1$, can reach a state (l_2, R_2'), such that $R_2' \leq R_2$. We prove that COST equals min{mincost(R) | (l_g, R) is reachable}. Assume that this does not hold. Then there exists a reachable state (l_g, R) where mincost(R) < COST. Thus the algorithm must at some point have discarded a state (l', R') on the path to (l_g, R). This can only happen in line 6, but then there must exist a state $(l', R'') \in$ PASSED, where $R'' \leq R'$, encountered in a prior iteration of the loop. Then, there must be a state (l_g, R''') reachable from (l', R''), and COST $\leq$ mincost$(R''') \leq$ mincost(R), contradicting the assumption. The theorem now follows from Theorem 1. □

For bounded LPTA, application of Higman's Lemma [12] ensures termination. In short, Higman's Lemma says that under certain conditions the embedding order on strings is a well quasi-order.

Theorem 4. *The algorithm in Fig. 6 terminates for any bounded LPTA.*

Proof. Even if A is bounded (and hence yields only finitely many unpriced regions), there are still infinitely many priced regions, due to the unboundedness of cost of vertices. However, since all costs are positive application of Higman's lemma ensures that one cannot have an infinite sequence $\langle (c_1^i, \ldots, c_m^i) :$ $0 \leq i < \infty \rangle$ of cost-vectors (for any fixed length m) without $c_l^j \leq c_l^k$ for all $l = 1, \ldots, m$ for some $j < k$. Consequently, due to the finiteness of the sets of locations and unpriced regions, it follows that one cannot have an infinite sequence $\langle (l_i, R_i) : 0 \leq i < \infty \rangle$ of symbolic states without $l_j = l_k$ and $R_j \leq R_k$ for some $j < k$, thus ensuring termination of the algorithm. □

Finally, combining Theorem 3 and 4, it follows, due to Theorem 2, that the minimum-cost reachability problem is decidable.

Theorem 5. *The minimum-cost problem for LPTA is decidable.*

5   Conclusion

In this paper, we have successfully extended the work on regions and their operations to a setting of timed automata with linear prices on both transitions and locations. We have given the principle basis of a branch-and-bound algorithm for the minimum-cost reachability problem, which is based on an accurate symbolic semantics of timed automata with linear prices, and thus showing the minimum-cost reachability problem to be decidable.

The algorithm is guaranteed to be rather inefficient and highly sensitive to the size of constants used in the guards of the automata — a characteristic inherited from the time regions used in the basic data-structure of the algorithm. An obvious continuation of this work is therefore to investigate if other more (in practice) efficient data structures can be found. Possible candidates include data structures used in reachability algorithms of timed automata, such as DBMs, extended with costs on the vertices of the represented zones (i.e. convex sets of clock assignments). In contrast to the priced extension of regions, operations on such a notion of priced zones[6] can not be obtained as direct extensions of the corresponding operations on zones with suitable manipulation of cost of vertices.

The need for infimum in the definition of minimum cost executions arises from linearly priced timed automata with strict bounds in the guards, such as the one shown in Fig. 3 and discussed in Example 1. Due to the use of infimum, a linearly priced timed automaton is not always able to realize an execution with the exact minimum cost of the automata, but will be able to realize one with a cost (infinitesimally) close to the minimum value. If all guards include only non-strict bounds, the minimum cost trace can always be realized by the automaton. This fact can be shown by defining the minimum-cost problem for executions covered by a given symbolic trace as a linear programming problem.

In this paper we have presented an algorithm for computing minimum-costs for reachability of linearly priced timed automata, where prices are given as constants (natural numbers). However, a slight modification of our algorithm provides an extension to a parameterized setting, in which (some) prices may be parameters. In this setting, costs within priced regions will be finite collections, C, of linear expressions over the given parameters rather than simple natural numbers. Intuitively, C denotes for any given instantiation of the parameters the minimum of the concrete values denoted by the linear expressions within C. Now, two cost-expressions may be compared simply by comparing the sizes of corresponding parameters, and two collections C and D (both denoting minimums) are related if for any element of D there is a smaller element in C. In the modified version of algorithm Fig. 6, COST will similarly be a collection of (linear) cost-expressions with which the goal-location has been reached (so far). From recent results in [1] (generalizing Higman's lemma) it follows that the ordering on (parameterized) symbolic states is again a well-quasi ordering, hence guaranteeing termination of our algorithm. Also, we are currently working on extending the algorithmic solution offered here to synthesis of minimum-cost controllers in the sense of [4]. In this extension, a priced region will be given by a conventional unpriced region together with a min-max expression over cost vectors for the vertices of the region. In both the parametric and the controller synthesis case, it follows from recent results in [1] (generalizing Higman's lemma) that the

---

[6] In particular, the reset-operation.

orderings on symbolic states are again well-quasi orderings, hence guaranteeing termination of our algorithms.

Acknowledgements. The authors would like to thank Lone Juul Hansen for her great, creative effort in making the figures of this paper. Also, the authors would like to thank Parosh Abdulla for sharing with us some of his expertise and knowledge on the world beyond well-quasi orderings.

References

1. Parosh Aziz Abdulla and Aletta Nylén. Better is better than well: On efficient verification of infinite-state systems. In *Proc. of the 14th IEEE Symp. on Logic in Computer Science*. IEEE, 2000.
2. R. Alur, C. Courcoubetis, and T. A. Henzinger. Computing accumulated delays in real-time systems. In *Proc. of the 5th Int. Conf. on Computer Aided Verification*, number 697 in Lecture Notes in Computer Science, pages 181–193, 1993.
3. R. Alur and D. Dill. Automata for Modelling Real-Time Systems. *Theoretical Computer Science*, 126(2):183–236, April 1994.
4. E. Asarin and O. Maler. As soon as possible: Time optimal control for timed automata. In *Hybrid Systems: Computation and Control*, number 1569 in Lecture Notes in Computer Science, pages 19–30. Springer–Verlag, March 1999.
5. Gerd Behrmann, Ansgar Fehnker, Thomas Hune, Kim Larsen, Paul Pettersson, and Judi Romijn. Efficient guiding towards cost-optimality in UPPAAL. Accepted for TACAS 2001.
6. Gerd Behrmann, Ansgar Fehnker, Thomas Hune, Kim Larsen, Paul Pettersson, Judi Romijn, and Frits Vaandrager. Minimum-cost reachability for priced timed automata. Technical Report RS-01-03, BRICS, January 2001.
7. Marius Bozga, Conrado Daws, Oded Maler, Alfredo Olivero, Stavros Tripakis, and Sergio Yovine. Kronos: A Model-Checking Tool for Real-Time Systems. In *Proc. of the 10th Int. Conf. on Computer Aided Verification*, number 1427 in Lecture Notes in Computer Science, pages 546–550. Springer–Verlag, 1998.
8. David Dill. Timing Assumptions and Verification of Finite-State Concurrent Systems. In J. Sifakis, editor, *Proc. of Automatic Verification Methods for Finite State Systems*, number 407 in Lecture Notes in Computer Science, pages 197–212. Springer–Verlag, 1989.
9. Ansgar Fehnker. Scheduling a steel plant with timed automata. In *Proceedings of the 6th International Conference on Real-Time Computing Systems and Applications (RTCSA99)*, pages 280–286. IEEE Computer Society, 1999.
10. T. A. Henzinger. The theory of hybrid automata. In *Proc. of 11th Annual Symp. on Logic in Computer Science (LICS 96)*, pages 278–292. IEEE Computer Society Press, 1996.
11. Thomas A. Henzinger, Pei-Hsin Ho, and Howard Wong-Toi. HyTech: A Model Checker for Hybird Systems. In Orna Grumberg, editor, *Proc. of the 9th Int. Conf. on Computer Aided Verification*, number 1254 in Lecture Notes in Computer Science, pages 460–463. Springer–Verlag, 1997.
12. G. Higman. Ordering by divisibility in abstract algebras. *Proc. of the London Math. Soc.*, 2:326–336, 1952.

13. Thomas Hune, Kim G. Larsen, and Paul Pettersson. Guided Synthesis of Control Programs Using UPPAAL. In Ten H. Lai, editor, *Proc. of the IEEE ICDCS International Workshop on Distributed Systems Verification and Validation*, pages E15–E22. IEEE Computer Society Press, April 2000.
14. Kim G. Larsen, Paul Pettersson, and Wang Yi. UPPAAL in a Nutshell. *Int. Journal on Software Tools for Technology Transfer*, 1(1–2):134–152, October 1997.
15. Kim G. Larsen, Carsten Weise, Wang Yi, and Justin Pearson. Clock difference diagrams. *Nordic Journal of Computing*, 6(3):271–298, 1999.
16. J. Møller, J. Lichtenberg, H. R. Andersen, and H. Hulgaard. Difference decision diagrams. Technical Report IT-TR-1999-023, Department of Information Technology, Technical University of Denmark, February 1999.
17. Peter Niebert, Stavros Tripakis, and Sergio Yovine. Minimum-time reachability for timed automata. In *IEEE Mediteranean Control Conference*, 2000.
18. Peter Niebert and Sergio Yovine. Computing optimal operation schemes for multi batch operation of chemical plants. VHS deliverable, May 1999. Draft.

A Hybrid Approach to Traction Control

Francesco Borrelli[1], Alberto Bemporad[1,3], Michael Fodor[2], and Davor Hrovat[2]

[1] Automatic Control Laboratory, ETH, CH-8092 Zurich, Switzerland
Phone: +41 1 632-4158, Fax: +41 1 632-1211
{borrelli,bemporad}@aut.ee.ethz.ch
[2] Ford Research Laboratories,
Dearborn, MI 48124
Phone: +1 313 594-2958, Fax: +1 313 322-5562
{mfodor1,dhrovat}@ford.com
[3] Dip. Ingegneria dell'Informazione, Università di Siena
Phone: +39 0577 234-631, Fax: +39 0577 234-632
bemporad@dii.unisi.it

Abstract. In this paper we describe a hybrid model and an optimization-based control strategy for solving a traction control problem currently under investigation at Ford Research Laboratories. We show through simulations on a model and a realistic set of parameters that good and robust performance is achieved. Furthermore, the resulting optimal controller is a piecewise linear function of the measurements that can be implemented on low cost control hardware.

1 Introduction

For more than a decade advanced mechatronic systems controlling some aspects of vehicle dynamics have been investigated and implemented in production [13]. Among them, the class of traction control problems is one of the most studied. Traction controllers are used to improve a driver's ability to control a vehicle under adverse external conditions such as wet or icy roads. By maximizing the tractive force between the vehicle's tire and the road, a traction controller prevents the wheel from slipping and at the same time improves vehicle stability and steerability. In most control schemes the wheel slip, i.e., the difference between the normalized vehicle speed and the speed of the wheel is chosen as the controlled variable. The objective of the controller is to maximize the tractive torque while preserving the stability of the system. The relation between the tractive force and the wheel slip is nonlinear and is a function of the road condition [2]. Therefore, the overall control scheme is composed of two parts: a device that estimates the road surface condition, and a traction controller that regulates the wheel slip at any desired value. Regarding the second part, several control strategies have been proposed in the literature mainly based on sliding-mode controllers, fuzzy logic and adaptive schemes [5, 14, 4, 19, 20, 17, 2, 18]. Such control schemes are motivated by the fact that the system is nonlinear and uncertain.

The presence of nonlinearities and constraints on one hand, and the simplicity needed for real-time implementation on the other, have discouraged the

M.D. Di Benedetto, A. Sangiovanni-Vincentelli (Eds.): HSCC 2001, LNCS 2034, pp. 162–174, 2001.

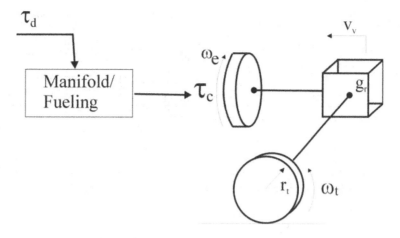

Fig. 1. Simple vehicle model

design of optimal control strategies for this kind of problem. Recently we proposed a new framework for modeling hybrid systems [8] and an algorithm to synthesize piecewise linear optimal controllers for such systems [6]. In this paper we describe how the hybrid framework [8] and the optimization-based control strategy [6] can be successfully applied for solving the traction control problem in a systematic way. We show, through simulations on a simplified model and for a set of parameters provided by Ford Research Laboratories, that good and robust performance can be achieved. Furthermore, the resulting optimal controller consists of a piecewise linear function of the measurements, that can be easily implemented.

A mathematical model of the vehicle/tire system is introduced in Section 2. The hybrid modeling and the optimal control strategy are discussed in Sections 2.1 and 3, respectively. In Section 4 we derive the piecewise affine optimal control law for traction control and present some simulation results.

2   Vehicle Model

The model of the vehicle used for the design of the traction controller is depicted in Figure 1, and consists of the equations

$$\begin{pmatrix} \dot{\omega}_e \\ \dot{v}_v \end{pmatrix} = \begin{pmatrix} -\frac{b_e}{J_e'} & 0 \\ 0 & 0 \end{pmatrix} \begin{pmatrix} \omega_e \\ v_v \end{pmatrix} + \begin{pmatrix} \frac{1}{J_e'} \\ 0 \end{pmatrix} \tau_c + \begin{pmatrix} -\frac{1}{J_e' g_r} \\ -\frac{1}{m_v r_t} \end{pmatrix} \tau_t \qquad (1)$$

with

$$\dot{\tau}_c(t) = -k_i \tau_c(t) + k_i \tau_d(t - \tau_f) \qquad (2)$$

where the involved physical quantities and parameters are described in Table 1.

Table 1. Physical quantities and parameters of the vehicle model

ω_e	Engine speed	r_t	Tire radius
v_v	Vehicle speed	τ_c	Actual combustion torque
J'_e	Combined engine/wheel inertia	τ_d	Desired combustion torque
b_e	Engine damping	τ_t	Frictional torque on the tire
g_r	Total driveline gear ratio between ω_e and v_v	μ	Road coefficient of friction
m_v	Vehicle mass	τ_f	Fueling to combustion pure delay period
$\Delta\omega$	Wheel slip		

The frictional torque τ_t is approximated as a piecewise linear function of the slip $\Delta\omega$ and of the road coefficient of friction μ

$$\tau_t(\Delta\omega, \mu) = \begin{cases} k_1^i \Delta\omega & \text{if } \Delta\omega \le \Delta\omega_b^i \\ k_2^i \Delta\omega & \text{if } \Delta\omega > \Delta\omega_b^i \end{cases} \text{ for } \mu_i \le \mu \le \mu_{i+1} \quad i = 0, \ldots, N \quad (3)$$

as depicted in Figure 2(a).

Model (1) contains two states for the mechanical system downstream of the manifold/fueling dynamics. The first equation represents the wheel dynamics under the effect of the combustion torque and of the traction torque, while the second one describes the longitudinal motion dynamics of the vehicle. In addition to the mechanical equations (1) the air intake and fueling model (2) also contributes to the dynamic behaviour of the overall system. For simplicity, the intake manifold dynamics is modeled as a first order filter and the fueling combustion delay is modeled as a pure delay.

2.1   Discrete-Time Hybrid Model

Hybrid systems provide a unified framework for describing processes evolving according to continuous dynamics, discrete dynamics, and logic rules [1, 16, 10, 3]. The interest in hybrid systems is mainly motivated by the large variety of practical situations, for instance real-time systems, where physical processes interact with digital controllers. Several modeling formalisms have been developed to describe hybrid systems [12,15], among them the class of Mixed Logical Dynamical (MLD) systems introduced by Bemporad and Morari [8]. Examples of real-world applications that can be naturally modeled within the MLD framework are reported in [7, 8, 9]. The language HYSDEL (HYbrid Systems DEscription Language) was developed in [21] to obtain MLD models from of a high level textual description of the hybrid dynamics.

The model obtained in Section 2 is transformed into an equivalent discrete-time MLD model through the following steps:

1. Discretize the model (1)–(3) with sampling time $T_s = 20$ ms;
2. Introduce an auxiliary logic variable δ^i for each interval $[\mu_i, \mu_{i+1}]$ whose value can be 1 or 0 depending on the value of the slip $\Delta\omega$, as shown in Figure 2(b).

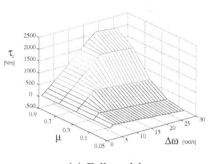

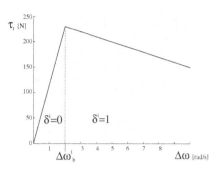

(a) Full model

(b) Piecewise linear model of the tire torque τ_t with $\mu \in (\mu_i, \mu_{i+1})$

Fig. 2. Model of the tire torque τ_t as a function of the slip $\Delta\omega$ and road coefficient adhesion μ

Remark 1. In the sequel we will use a simplified model where the slopes $k_1^1 = k_1^2 = \ldots = k_1^N$ and $k_2^1 = k_2^2 = \ldots = k_2^N$, while the breakpoints ω_b^i in (3) are allowed to be different. In this case the number of auxiliary logic variables δ^i reduces from $\log_2 N$ to 1, at the price of a "rougher" model of the nonlinearity. The resultant MLD system is the following[1]:

$$x(t+1) = Ax(t) + B_1 u(t) + B_2 \delta(t) + B_3 z(t) \tag{4a}$$

$$y(t) = Cx(t) + D_1 u(t) + D_2 \delta(t) + D_3 z(t) \tag{4b}$$

$$E_2 \delta(t) + E_3 z(t) \leq E_1 u(t) + E_4 x(t) + E_5 \tag{4c}$$

where $x \in \mathbb{R}^5$, $(x_1 = \Delta\omega_d,\ x_2 = \omega_e,\ x_3 = v_v,\ x_4 = \tau_t,\ x_5 = \tau_c)$, $u \in \mathbb{R}$, $(u = \tau_d)$, $y \in \mathbb{R}$ $(y = \Delta\omega)$, $\delta \in \{0, 1\}$ and $z \in \mathbb{R}^3$. The variables δ and z are auxiliary variables whose value is determined uniquely by the inequalities (4c) once $x(t)$ and $u(t)$ are fixed [8].

In Figure 4 we compare the evolution of the discrete-time MLD model (4) with the evolution of the continuous time model (1)–(3), depicted in Figure 3, when $\mu = .1$, $\Delta\omega_b = 2$ rad/s and a pulse torque $\tau_d = 50$ Nm is applied to the system. The MLD model (4) captures in discrete time the hybrid behavior of the system satisfactorily.

3   Optimal Control

It is clear from Figure 2(b) that if the slip increases beyond Δw_b, the driving force on the tire decreases considerably and the vehicle cannot speed up as desired. By

---

[1] The numerical values of the matrices in (4) are reported in the Appendix.

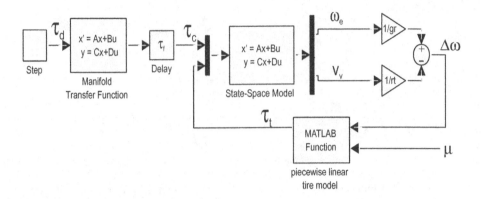

Fig. 3. Simulink scheme of the vehicle model

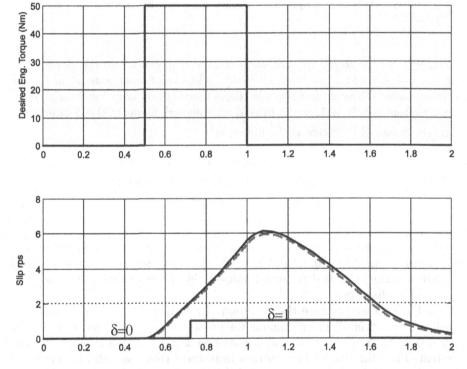

Fig. 4. Continuous time simulation of the Matlab-Simulink block in Figure 3 (solid line), discrete-time simulation of the MLD model (dashed line)

maximizing the tractive force between the vehicle's tire and the road, a traction controller prevents the wheel from slipping and at the same time improves vehicle stability and steerability. The overall control scheme is composed of two parts: a device that estimates the road surface condition, and a traction controller that regulates the wheel slip at any desired value. In this paper we will focus only on the second part, as the first one is available at Ford Research Laboratories.

Once the road coefficient of adhesion μ has been estimated, a desired wheel sleep Δw_d^k is chosen corresponding to the breakpoints Δw_b^k in model (3), $\mu \in [\mu_{k-1}, \mu_k]$, where the frictional torque $\tau_t(\Delta w)$ on the tire is maximized. Alternatively, to increase the safety of the controller [18] we could avoid operating in the region where the slope of the curve $\tau_t(\Delta w)$ is negative, see Figure 2(b), by simply choosing $\Delta w_d^k(\mu) < \Delta w_b^k$ ($\mu \in [\mu_{k-1}, \mu_k]$). The control system takes the desired wheel slip Δw_d^k and measured wheel speed as input and generates the desired engine torque. The following constraints on the torque and its variation need to be satisfied:

$$-20 \text{ Nm} \leq \tau_d \leq 176 \text{ Nm} \tag{5}$$

$$\dot{\tau}_d(t) \leq 2000 \text{ Nm/s} \tag{6}$$

In the sequel we describe how a Model Predictive Controller (MPC) can be designed for the posed traction control problem described. The main idea of MPC is to use the *model* of the plant to *predict* the future evolution of the system. Based on this prediction, at each time step t a certain performance index is optimized under operating constraints with respect to a sequence of future input moves. The first of such optimal moves is the *control* action applied to the plant at time t. At time $t + 1$, a new optimization is solved over a shifted prediction horizon. For the traction control problem, at each time step t the following finite horizon optimal control problem is solved:

$$\min_{\{\Delta u_0^{T-1}\}} \sum_{k=0}^{T-1} |\Delta\omega(t+k|t) - \Delta\omega_d(t)| \tag{7}$$

$$\text{subj. to } \begin{cases} \text{MLD dynamics (4)} \\ \tau_{min} \leq u(t+k) \leq \tau_{max}, \quad k = 0, 1, \ldots, T-1 \\ \Delta\tau_{min} \leq \delta u(t+k) \leq \Delta\tau_{max}, \quad k = 0, 1, \ldots, T-1 \\ x_{min} \leq x(t+k|t) \leq x_{max}, \quad k = 1, \ldots, T-1 \end{cases} \tag{8}$$

where $\Delta u_0^{T-1} = \{\delta u(t), \ldots, \delta u(t+T-1)\}$, and "$(t+k|t)$" denotes the predicted value at time $t + k$ based on the state information available at time t. Note that the optimization variables are not the future inputs u_{t+k}, but the variation $\delta u(t + k) = u(t + k) - u(t + k - 1)$, which makes it necessary to increase the dimension of the state vector by one to include the previous torque $\tau_d(t-1)$ as a an additional state $x_6(t) = \tau_d(t-1)$.

Problem (7)-(8) can be translated into a mixed integer linear program (MILP) (the minimization of a linear cost function subject to linear constraints where variables can be binary and/or continuous) of the form:

$$\min_{z=\{z_c, z_d\}} f_c^T z_c + f_d^T z_d$$

$$\tag{9}$$

$$\text{subj. to } G_c z_c + G_c z_d \leq S + Fx(t)$$

where $z_c \in \mathbb{R}^l$ and $z_d \in \{0, 1\}^m$.

Given the measurement of the state $x(t)$, problem (9) is solved at each time step, but only the first optimal input $u^*(t) = \tau_d(t-1) + \delta u_0^*$ is implemented as the new command torque $\tau_d(t)$. At the next time step the procedure is repeated starting with the new measurement of the state.

The design of the controller is performed in two steps. First, the MPC controller (7)-(8) based on model (4) is tuned in simulation until the desired performance is achieved. The MPC controller is not directly implementable, as it would require the MILP (9) to be solved on-line, which is clearly prohibitive on standard automotive control hardware. Therefore, for implementation, in the second phase the explicit piecewise linear form of the MPC law (see Section 4.2) is computed off-line by using the multi-parametric mixed integer programming solver presented in [11]. Although the resulting piecewise linear control action is *identical* to the MPC designed in the first phase, the on-line complexity is reduced to the simple evaluation of a piecewise linear function.

4   Controller Design

The only parameter of the controller (7)-(8) to be tuned is the horizon length T. By increasing the prediction horizon the controller performance improves, but at the same time the number of constraints in (8) increases. As will be explained in Section 4.2 the complexity of the final piecewise linear controller increases with the number of constraints in (8). Therefore, tuning T amounts to finding the smallest T which leads to a satisfactory closed-loop behaviour.

4.1   Simulations

We simulate the closed-loop composed of the traction controller (7)-(8) and model (1)-(2), where the piecewise linear function modeling the frictional torque on the tire τ_t (3) is replaced by a more accurate nonlinear model provided by Ford, see Figure 5. The actual combustion torque τ_c is estimated from the two measurements ω_e and v_v by using an extended Kalman Filter designed for the PWA model.

The controlled system is simulated with an initial vehicle speed of zero. The intake manifold state τ_c is set to a large torque value, namely $\tau_c(0) = 100$ Nm, in order to approximate a wide-open throttle launch from a standstill. In Figure 6 we simulate a straight-ahead driving with a transition at time $t^* = 2$ s from a high coefficient of friction $\mu = 0.9$, and $\Delta\omega_d = 18$ rad/s (cement pavement) to a low one $\mu = 0.1$, $\Delta\omega_d = 2$ rad/s (dry ice). The simulations show the good performance of the controller despite the large mismatch between the nonlinear model of the frictional torque model and the piecewise linearized one.

The following controllers are simulated:

- Controller 1 (Figure 6(a)): T=3;
- Controller 2 (Figure 6(b)): T=9;

The Simulink control diagram used for simulation is shown in Figure 5.

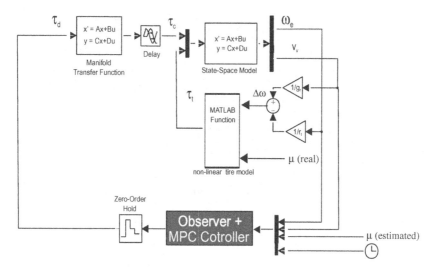

Fig. 5. Simulink diagram of the closed-loop control system

4.2   Explicit Controller

Once the controller has been tuned, the explicit piecewise linear form of the MPC law is computed off-line by using a multiparametric mixed integer linear programming (mp-MILP) solver, according to the approach of [6]. Rather than solving the MILP (9) *on-line* for the given current state $x(t)$, the idea is to use the mp-MILP solver to compute *off-line* the solution of the MILP (9) for all the states $x(t)$ within a given polyhedral set.

As shown in [6], the explicit solution $z^*(x(t))$ of (9) is a piecewise affine function of $x(t)$. Therefore, the model predictive controller is also available explicitly, as the optimal input $\delta u(t)$ consists simply of a component of $z^*(x(t))$. As a result, the state space is partitioned into polyhedral sets, where an affine control law is defined in each polyhedron.

We remark that for any given state $x(t)$ the on-line solution of MPC and the explicit off-line solution provide the same result. Therefore, a good design strategy consists of tuning the MPC controller using simulation and on-line optimization, and then to convert the controller to its piecewise affine explicit form. The explicit controller will behave in exactly the same way at much lower computation cost.

The result of the mp-MILP solver is a list of N records. The i-th record contains the constraints defining the i-th polyhedral region $H(i)x \leq K(i)$, $H(i) \in \mathbb{R}^{m_i \times n}$, and the corresponding i-th gain $\delta u = F(i)x + G(i)$. The control law can be implemented on-line in the following simple way: (1) determine the i-th region that contains the actual vector state $x(t)$ (measured and/or estimated); (2) compute $\delta u(t) = F(i)x(t) + G(i)$, according to the corresponding i-th control law.

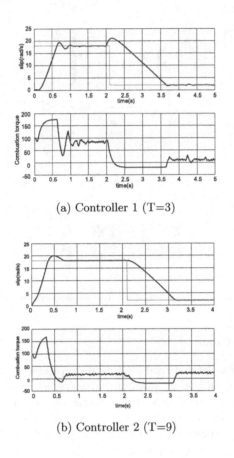

(a) Controller 1 (T=3)

(b) Controller 2 (T=9)

Fig. 6. Closed-loop simulation of Controller 1 and Controller 2. Straight-ahead driving with a transition at time $t^* = 2$ s from a high coefficient of friction $\mu = 0.9$, and $\Delta\omega_d = 18$ rad/s (cement pavement) to a low one $\mu = 0.1$, $\Delta\omega_d = 2$ rad/s (dry ice)

In Figure 6(a) we report the performance achieved with two explicit MPC controllers, obtained by solving the mp-MILP problem for the box $X_{min} \leq x(t) \leq X_{max}$, $X_{min} = [0, 0, 0, -20, -20, -40]$ and $X_{max} = [20, 150, 10, 100, 300, 40]$:

- Controller 1 : T=3, Number of regions $N = 76$, maximum number of constraints per region $M = \max_{i=1,\ldots,N} m_i = 13$;

- Controller 2: T=9, Number of regions $N = 243$, maximum number of constraints per region $M = 25$.

As an example, we report only the first and last region of Controller 1:

$$
\delta u = \begin{cases}
-40.0000 \\[4pt]
\text{if } \begin{bmatrix}
0.0 & 0.0 & -0.0 & 0.0 & 0.0 & -0.05 \\
0.0 & 0.01 & 0.0 & 0.0 & 0.0 & 0.0 \\
0.0 & 0.0 & 0.0 & 0.01 & 0.0 & 0.0 \\
0.0 & 0.0 & 0.0 & 0.0 & 0.0 & 0.02 \\
-1.0 & 0.0 & 0.0 & 0.0 & 0.0 & 0.0 \\
0.0 & -1.0 & 0.0 & 0.0 & 0.0 & 0.0 \\
0.0 & 0.0 & -1.0 & 0.0 & 0.0 & 0.0 \\
0.0 & 0.0 & 0.0 & -0.05 & 0.0 & 0.0 \\
-6.13 & 0.47 & -22.70 & -0.02 & 0.14 & 0.02 \\
0.0 & 0.0 & -0.0 & 0.0 & 0.0 & -0.05 \\
15.83 & -1.22 & 58.65 & 0.03 & -0.24 & -0.03 \\
-8.0 & 1.23 & -59.26 & -0.01 & 0.07 & 0.0 \\
-31.57 & 2.43 & -116.94 & -0.05 & 0.47 & 0.00 \\
12.25 & -0.94 & 45.38 & 0.03 & -0.26 & -0.02
\end{bmatrix} x \le \begin{bmatrix}
-1.0 \\ 1.0 \\ 1.0 \\ 1.0 \\ 1.0 \\ 0.0 \\ 0.0 \\ 1.0 \\ 1.0 \\ -1.0 \\ 1.0 \\ 0.0 \\ -1.0 \\ -1.0
\end{bmatrix} \\
\text{(Region \#1)} \\[4pt]
\vdots \\[4pt]
\begin{bmatrix} 368.11 \\ -28.34 \\ 1363.38 \\ 0.85 \\ -7.13 \\ -1.00 \end{bmatrix}^{T} x + 11.59 \\[4pt]
\text{if } \begin{bmatrix}
43.7456 & -3.3676 & 162.0209 & 0.1011 & -0.8468 & -0.0 \\
-7.8681 & 0.6057 & -29.1410 & -0.0153 & 0.1391 & 0.0178 \\
-6.1306 & 0.4719 & -22.7058 & -0.0180 & 0.1364 & 0.0215 \\
-8.0 & 1.2317 & -59.2593 & -0.0068 & 0.0697 & -0.0 \\
0.0 & 0.0067 & 0.0 & 0.0 & 0.0 & 0.0 \\
0.0 & 0.0 & 0.0 & 0.0100 & 0.0 & 0.0 \\
-1.0 & 0.0 & 0.0 & 0.0 & 0.0 & 0.0 \\
0.0 & -1.0 & 0.0 & 0.0 & 0.0 & 0.0 \\
0.0 & 0.0 & -1.0 & 0.0 & 0.0 & 0.0 \\
0.0 & 0.0 & 0.0 & -0.0500 & 0.0 & 0.0 \\
0.0 & 0.0 & 0.0 & 0.0 & 0.0 & -0.05
\end{bmatrix} x \le \begin{bmatrix}
1.0 \\ -1.0 \\ 1.0 \\ 0.0 \\ 1.0 \\ 1.0 \\ 1.0 \\ 0.0 \\ 0.0 \\ 1.0 \\ 1.0
\end{bmatrix} \\
\text{(Region \#76)}
\end{cases} \tag{10}
$$

In Figure 7 a zoomed section of the control law associated with Controller 1 is shown. The section is obtained by fixing the torque $\tau_c = 20$, the desired slip $\Delta\omega_d = 2$, the friction torque $\tau_t = 80$, and the previous input $\tau_d(t-1) = 20$. Note that the southeast corner is not feasible because it corresponds to a negative slip.

5 Conclusion

In this paper we described a hybrid model and an optimization-based control strategy for a traction control problem. We showed, through simulations on a model and a realistic set of parameters from Ford Research Laboratories, that good and robust performance is achieved. Furthermore, the resulting optimal controller is a piecewise linear function of the measurements that can be easily implemented on low cost hardware. In order to ease the implementation of the controller, the number of regions in the piecewise linear law should be reduced. One possible way is to exploit reachability analysis for hybrid systems in order to remove regions which are never entered, for all the operating conditions within a realistic set. At the same time, for complex piecewise linear partitions, we are developing efficient forms of implementation that greatly reduce the number of regions to be stored by exploiting properties of multiparametric linear programming.

Acknowledgments. We thank Manfred Morari for fruitful discussions and his helpful comments on the original manuscript.

6 Appendix

Below we report the numerical values of the matrices in (4) obtained by using the tool HYSDEL. See http://www.aut.ee.ethz.ch/~hybrid/FordExample.html

$$
A = \begin{bmatrix} 1 & 0 & 0 & 0 & 0 & 0 \\ 0 & 0 & 0 & 0 & 0 & 0 \\ 0 & 0 & 0 & 0 & 0 & 0 \\ 0 & 0 & 0 & 0 & 0 & 0 \\ 0 & 0 & 0 & 0 & 0.819 & 0.181 \\ 0 & 0 & 0 & 0 & 0 & 1 \end{bmatrix}, \ B_1 = \begin{bmatrix} 0 \\ 0 \\ 0 \\ 0 \\ 0.18127 \\ 1 \end{bmatrix}, \ B_2 = \begin{bmatrix} 0 \\ 0 \\ 0 \\ 0 \\ 0 \\ 0 \end{bmatrix}, \ B_3 = \begin{bmatrix} 0 & 0 & 0 \\ 1 & 0 & 0 \\ 0 & 1 & 0 \\ 0 & 0 & 1 \\ 0 & 0 & 0 \\ 0 & 0 & 0 \end{bmatrix}
$$

$$
C = \begin{bmatrix} 0 & 0 & 0 & 1 & 0 & 0 \end{bmatrix}, \ D_1 = \begin{bmatrix} 0 \end{bmatrix}, \ D_2 = \begin{bmatrix} 0 \end{bmatrix}, \ D_3 = \begin{bmatrix} 0 & 0 & 0 \end{bmatrix}
$$

$$
E_1 = \begin{bmatrix} 0 \\ 0 \\ 0 \\ 0 \\ 0 \\ 0 \\ 0 \\ 0 \\ 0 \\ 0 \\ 0 \\ 0 \end{bmatrix}, \ E_2 = \begin{bmatrix} 100 \\ -700 \\ 1400 \\ 200 \\ 6000 \\ 1400 \\ 200 \\ 6000 \\ -1400 \\ -200 \\ -6000 \\ -1400 \\ -200 \\ -6000 \end{bmatrix}, \ E_3 = \begin{bmatrix} 0 & 0 & 0 \\ 0 & 0 & 0 \\ -1 & 0 & 0 \\ 0 & -1 & 0 \\ 0 & 0 & -1 \\ 1 & 0 & 0 \\ 0 & 1 & 0 \\ 0 & 0 & 1 \\ -1 & 0 & 0 \\ 0 & -1 & 0 \\ 0 & 0 & -1 \\ 1 & 0 & 0 \\ 0 & 1 & 0 \\ 0 & 0 & 1 \end{bmatrix} \quad (11)
$$

$$
E_4 = \begin{bmatrix} -1 & 0 & -4 & 0 & 0 & 0 \\ 1 & 0 & 4 & 0 & 0 & 0 \\ 0 & -1 & 0 & 0 & 0 & 0 \\ 0 & 0 & -1 & 0 & 0 & 0 \\ 0 & 0 & 0 & -1 & 0 & 0 \\ 0 & 1 & 0 & 0 & 0 & 0 \\ 0 & 0 & 1 & 0 & 0 & 0 \\ 0 & 0 & 0 & 1 & 0 & 0 \\ 0 & -1 & 0 & 0 & 0 & 0 \\ 0 & 0 & -1 & 0 & 0 & 0 \\ 0 & 0 & 0 & -1 & -1 & 0 \\ 0 & 1 & 0 & 0 & 0 & 0 \\ 0 & 0 & 1 & 0 & 0 & 0 \\ 0 & 0 & 0 & 1 & 1 & 0 \end{bmatrix}, \ E_5 = \begin{bmatrix} 100 \\ -0.0001 \\ 1400 \\ 200 \\ 6000 \\ 200 \\ 6000 \\ 0 \\ 0 \\ 0 \\ 0 \\ 0 \\ 0 \end{bmatrix}
$$

References

1. P.J. Antsaklis. A brief introduction to the theory and applications of hybrid systems. *Proc. IEEE, Special Issue on Hybrid Systems: Theory and Applications*, 88(7):879–886, July 2000.
2. R. Balakrishna and A. Ghosal. Modeling of slip for wheeled mobile robots. *IEEE Trans. Robotics and automation*, 11(1):349–370, February 1995.
3. A. Balluchi, L. Benvenuti, M. Di Benedetto, C. Pinello, and A. Sangiovanni-Vincentelli. Automotive engine control and hybrid systems: Challenges and opportunities. *Proc. IEEE*, 88(7):888–912, 2000.

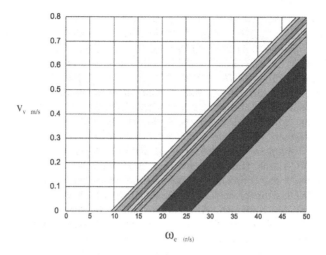

Fig. 7. Section of the explicit solution of Controller 1 for $x_1 = \Delta\omega_d = 2$, $x_4 = \tau_t = 70$, $x_5 = \tau_c = 70$, $x_6 = \tau_d(t-1) = 20$

4. M. Bauer and M. Tomizuka. Fuzzy logic traction controllers and their effect on longitudinal vehicle platoon. *Vehicle System Dynamics*, 25(4):277–303, April 1996.

5. A. Bellini, A. Bemporad, E. Franchi, N. Manaresi, R. Rovatti, and G. Torrini. Analog fuzzy implementation of a vehicle traction sliding-mode control. In *Proc. ISATA 29th International Symposium on Automotive Technology and Automation. Automotive Autom, Croydon, UK*, pages 275–282, 1996.

6. A. Bemporad, F. Borrelli, and M. Morari. Piecewise linear optimal controllers for hybrid systems. In *Proc. American Control Conf.*, Chicago, IL, 2000.

7. A. Bemporad, D. Mignone, and M. Morari. Moving horizon estimation for hybrid systems and fault detection. In *Proc. American Control Conf.*, 1999.

8. A. Bemporad and M. Morari. Control of systems integrating logic, dynamics, and constraints. *Automatica*, 35(3):407–427, March 1999.

9. A. Bemporad and M. Morari. Verification of hybrid systems via mathematical programming. In F.W. Vaandrager and J.H. van Schuppen, editors, *Hybrid Systems: Computation and Control*, volume 1569 of *Lecture Notes in Computer Science*, pages 31–45. Springer Verlag, 1999.

10. M.S. Branicky. *Studies in hybrid systems: modeling, analysis, and control*. PhD thesis, LIDS-TH 2304, Massachusetts Institute of Technology, Cambridge, MA, 1995.

11. V. Dua and E. N. Pistikopoulos. An algorithm for the solution of multiparametric mixed integer linear programming problems. *Annals of Operations Research*, to appear.

12. W.P.M.H. Heemels, B. De Schutter, and A. Bemporad. Equivalence of hybrid dynamical models. *Automatica*, to appear.

13. D. Hrovat. Automotive mechatronic systems. In Cornelius T. Leondes, editor, *Mechatronic Systems Techniques and Applications: Volume 2 - Transportation and Vehicular Systems*. Gordon and Breach Science Publishers, 2000.

14. P. Kachroo and M. Tomizuka. An adaptive sliding mode vehicle traction controller design. In *Proc. IEEE International Conference on Systems, Man and Cybernetics. Intelligent Systems for the 21st Century*, volume 1, pages 777–782, 1995.

15. G. Labinaz, M.M. Bayoumi, and K. Rudie. A survey of modeling and control of hybrid systems. In *13th IFAC World Congress 1996*, 1996.

16. J. Lygeros, C. Tomlin, and S. Sastry. Controllers for reachability specifications for hybrid systems. *Automatica*, 35(3):349–370, 1999.

17. G. F. Mauer. A fuzzy logic controller for an ABS braking system. *IEEE Transaction on Fuzzy Systems*, November 1995.

18. H. S. Tan. *Adaptive and Robust Controls with Application to Vehicle Traction Control.* PhD thesis, Univ. of California, Berkeley, 1988.

19. H. S. Tan and M. Tomizuka. Discrete time controller design for robust vehicle traction. *IEEE Control System Magazine*, 10(3):107–113, April 1990.

20. H.S. Tan and M. Tomizuka. An adaptive sliding mode vehicle traction controller design. In *Proc. American Control Conf.*, volume 2, pages 1856–1861, 1990.

21. F.D. Torrisi, A. Bemporad, and D. Mignone. HYSDEL - A language for describing hybrid systems. Technical Report AUT00-03, ETH Zurich, 2000. http://control.ethz.ch/~hybrid/hysdel.

Optimal Control Using Bisimulations: Implementation

Mireille Broucke[1], Maria Domenica Di Benedetto[1,2], Stefano Di Gennaro[2], and Alberto Sangiovanni-Vincentelli[1]

[1] Dept. of Electrical Engineering and Computer Sciences,
University of California at Berkeley, CA 94720, USA
Tel: +11 510 642-1792; Fax: +11 510 643-5052;
{mire,marika,alberto}@eecs.berkeley.edu
[2] Dip. di Ingegneria Elettrica, Università di L'Aquila, Poggio di Roio,
67040 L'Aquila, Italy.
digennar@dis.uniroma1.it

Abstract. We consider the synthesis of optimal controls for continuous feedback systems by recasting the problem to a hybrid optimal control problem which is to synthesize optimal enabling conditions for switching between locations in which the control is constant. We provide a single-pass algorithm to solve the dynamic programming problem that arises, with added constraints to ensure non-Zeno trajectories.

1 Introduction

In this paper we continue our investigation of the application of hybrid systems and bisimulation to optimal control problems. In the first paper [2] we developed a discrete method for solving an optimal control problem based on hybrid systems and bisimulation. We showed that the value function of the discrete problem converges to the value function of the continuous problem as a discretization parameter δ tends to zero. In this paper we focus on the pragmatic question of how the discretized problem can be efficiently solved.

Following the introduction of the concept of viscosity solution [10,4], Capuzzo-Dolcetta [3] introduced a method for obtaining approximations of viscosity solutions based on time discretization of the Hamilton-Jacobi-Bellman (HJB) equation. The approximations of the value function correspond to a discrete time optimal control problem, for which an optimal control can be synthesized that is piecewise constant. Finite difference approximations were also introduced in [5] and [13]. In general, the time discretized approximation of the HJB equation is solved by finite element methods. Gonzales and Rofman [9] introduced a discrete approximation by triangulating the domain of the finite horizon problem they considered, while the admissible control set is approximated by a finite set. Gonzales and Rofman's approach is adapted in several papers, including [7]. The approach of [14] uses the special structure of an optimal control problem to obtain a single-pass algorithm to solve the discrete

M.D. Di Benedetto, A. Sangiovanni-Vincentelli (Eds.): HSCC 2001, LNCS 2034, pp. 175–188, 2001.
© Springer-Verlag Berlin Heidelberg 2001

problem, thus bypassing the expensive iterations of a finite element method. The essential property needed to find a single pass algorithm is to obtain a partition of the domain so that the cost-to-go value from any equivalence class of the partition is determined from knowledge of the cost-to-go from those equivalence classes with strictly smaller cost-to-go values. In this paper we obtain a partition of the domain provided by a bisimulation partition. *The combination of the structure of the bisimulation partition and the requirement of non-Zeno trajectories enables us reproduce the essential property of [14], so that we obtain a Dijkstra-like algorithmic solution.* Our approach has complexity $O(N \log N)$ if suitable data structures are used, where N is the number of locations of the finite automaton.

While the objective is to solve a continuous optimal control problem, the method can be adapted to solve directly the problem of optimal synthesis of enabling conditions for hybrid systems. In that spirit, [11] investigates games on timed automata and obtains a dynamic programming formulation as well.

2   Optimal Control Problem

$cl(A)$ denotes the closure of set A. $\| \cdot \|$ denotes the Euclidean norm. $\mathcal{X}(\mathbb{R}^n)$ denotes the sets of smooth vector fields on $\mathbb{R}^n$. $\phi_t(x_0, \mu)$ denotes the trajectory of $\dot{x} = f(x, \mu)$ starting from x_0 and using control $\mu(\cdot)$.

Let U be a compact subset of $\mathbb{R}^m$, Ω an open, bounded, connected subset of $\mathbb{R}^n$, and Ω_f a compact subset of Ω. Define $\mathcal{U}_m$ to be the set of measurable functions mapping $[0, T]$ to U. We define the minimum hitting time $T : \mathbb{R}^n \times \mathcal{U}_m \to \mathbb{R}^+$ by

$$T(x, \mu) := \begin{cases} \infty & \text{if } \{t \mid \phi_t(x, \mu) \in \Omega_f\} = \emptyset \\ \min\{t \mid \phi_t(x, \mu) \in \Omega_f\} & \text{otherwise.} \end{cases} \tag{1}$$

A control $\mu \in \mathcal{U}_m$ specified on $[0, T]$ is *admissible* for $x \in \Omega$ if $\phi_t(x, \mu) \in \Omega$ for all $t \in [0, T]$. The set of admissible controls for x is denoted $\mathcal{U}_x$. Let $\mathcal{R} := \{ x \in \Omega \mid \exists \mu \in \mathcal{U}_x.\ T(x, \mu) < \infty \}$. We consider the following optimal control problem. Given $y \in \Omega$,

$$\text{minimize} \quad J(y, \mu) = \int_0^{T(y,\mu)} L(x(s), \mu(s))ds + h(x(T(y, \mu))) \tag{2}$$

$$\text{subject to} \quad \dot{x} = f(x, \mu), \qquad a.e.\ t \in [0, T(y, \mu)] \tag{3}$$

$$x(0) = y \tag{4}$$

among all admissible controls $\mu \in \mathcal{U}_y$. $J : \mathbb{R}^n \times \mathcal{U}_m \to \mathbb{R}$ is the *cost-to-go* function, $h : \mathbb{R}^n \to \mathbb{R}$ is the *terminal cost*, and $L : \mathbb{R}^n \times \mathbb{R}^m \to \mathbb{R}$ is the *instantaneous cost*. At $T(y, \mu)$ the terminal cost $h(x(T(y, \mu)))$ is incurred and the dynamics are stopped. The control objective is to reach Ω_f from $y \in \Omega$ with minimum cost.

The *value function* or optimal cost-to-go function $V : \mathbb{R}^n \to \mathbb{R}$ is given by

$$V(y) = \inf_{\mu \in \mathcal{U}_y} J(y, \mu)$$

for $y \in \Omega \setminus \Omega_f$, and by $V(y) = h(y)$ for $y \in \Omega_f$. V satisfies the *Hamilton-Jacobi-Bellman* equation

$$- \inf_{u \in U} \left\{ L(x, u) + \frac{\partial V}{\partial x} f(x, u) \right\} = 0 \tag{5}$$

at each point of $\mathcal{R}$ at which it is differentiable. The HJB equation is an infinitesimal version of the equivalent *Dynamic Programming Principle* (DPP) which says that

$$V(x) = \inf_{\mu \in \mathcal{U}_x} \left\{ \int_0^t L(\phi_s(x, \mu), \mu(s)) ds \; + \; V(\phi_t(x, \mu)) \right\}, \, x \in \Omega \setminus \Omega_f$$
$$V(x) = h(x) \qquad\qquad\qquad\qquad\qquad x \in \Omega_f.$$

Because the HJB equation may not have a C^1 solution it has not been possible to obtain a rigorous foundation for solutions in the usual sense. The correct concept for solutions is that of viscosity solutions [10,4], which provide the unique solution of (5) without differentiability. We showed in [2] that under assumptions of Lipschitz continuity of f,L, and h, and non-Zenoness and transversality with Ω_f of ϵ-optimal trajectories, that a particular discrete approximation $\hat{V}$ of the value function converges to the viscosity solution of HJB.

3   From Hybrid Automata to Finite Automata

In [2] we proposed a mapping from the continuous optimal control problem (2)-(4) to a hybrid optimal control problem. The first step is to restrict the class of controls over which the cost function is minimized to piecewise constant controls taking values in a set $\Sigma_\delta \subseteq U$. $\Sigma_\delta \subseteq U$ is a finite approximation of U having a mesh size $\delta := \sup_{u \in U} \min_{\sigma \in \Sigma_\delta} \|u - \sigma\|$. Next we restrict the continuous behavior to the set of vector fields $\{f(x, \sigma)\}_{\sigma \in \Sigma_\delta}$. If we associate each vector field to a location of a hybrid automaton and, additionally, define a location reserved for when the target is reached, we obtain a hybrid automaton

$$H := (\Sigma \times \mathbb{R}^n, \Sigma_\delta, D, E_h, G, R)$$

which has the following components:

State set $\Sigma \times \mathbb{R}^n$ is a finite set $\Sigma = \Sigma_\delta \cup \{\sigma_f\}$ of control locations and n continuous variables $x \in \mathbb{R}^n$. σ_f is a terminal location when the continuous dynamics are stopped (in the same sense that the dynamics are stopped in the continuous optimal control problem).
Events Σ_δ is a finite set of control event labels.
Vector fields $D : \Sigma \to \mathcal{X}(\mathbb{R}^n)$ is a function assigning an autonomous vector field to each location; namely $D(\sigma) = f(x, \sigma)$.
Control switches $E_h \subset \Sigma \times \Sigma$ is a set of control switches. $e = (\sigma, \sigma')$ is a directed edge between a source location σ and a target location σ'. If $E_h(\sigma)$ denotes the set of edges that can be enabled at $\sigma \in \Sigma$, then $E_h(\sigma) :=$

$\{(\sigma, \sigma') \mid \sigma' \in \Sigma \setminus \sigma\}$ for $\sigma \in \Sigma_\delta$ and $E_h(\sigma_f) = \emptyset$. Thus, from a source location not equal to σ_f, there is an edge to every other location (but not itself), while location σ_f has no outgoing edges.

Enabling conditions $G : E_h \to \{g_e\}_{e \in E_h}$ is a function assigning to each edge e an enabling (or guard) condition $g_e \subset \mathbb{R}^n$.

The enabling conditions are unknown and must be synthesized algorithmically. (See [2] for how the enabling conditions are extracted once the discrete problem is solved.) Trajectories of H evolve in σ-steps and t-steps. σ-steps occur when H changes locations (and the control changes value, since there are no self-loops) and t-steps occur when the continuous state evolves according to the dynamics of a location as time passes. The reader is referred to [2] for precise statements. A hybrid trajectory is *non-Zeno* if between every two non-zero duration t-steps there are a finite number of σ-steps and zero duration t-steps.

Let λ represent an arbitrary time interval. A *bisimulation* of H is an equivalence relation $\simeq \subset (\Sigma_\delta \times \mathbb{R}^n) \times (\Sigma_\delta \times \mathbb{R}^n)$ such that for all states $p_1, p_2 \in \Sigma_\delta \times \mathbb{R}^n$, if $p_1 \simeq p_2$ and $\sigma \in \Sigma_\delta \cup \{\lambda\}$, then if $p_1 \xrightarrow{\sigma} p_1'$, there exists p_2' such that $p_2 \xrightarrow{\sigma} p_2'$ and $p_1' \simeq p_2'$.

One sees that $\simeq$ encodes σ-steps and t-steps of H in a time abstract form by partitioning $\Sigma_\delta \times \mathbb{R}^n$. If $\simeq$ has a finite number of equivalence classes, then they form the states of a finite automaton A. If $q := [(\sigma, x)]$ and $q' := [(\sigma', x')]$ are two different equivalence classes of $\simeq$, then A has an edge $q \to q'$ if there exists $(\sigma, y) \in q$ and $(\sigma', y') \in q'$ such that $(\sigma, y) \to (\sigma', y')$ is a σ-step or t-step of H. We define the set of interesting equivalence classes of $\simeq$, denoted Q, as those that intersect $\Sigma_\delta \times cl(\Omega)$, and we identify a distinguished point $(\sigma, \xi) \in q$ for each $q \in Q$, denoted $q = [(\sigma, \xi)]$.

Consider the class of non-deterministic automata with cost structure represented by the tuple

$$A = (Q, \Sigma_\delta, E, obs, Q_f, \hat{L}, \hat{h}).$$

Q is the state set just defined, and Σ_δ is the set of control labels as before. $obs : E \to \Sigma_\delta$ is a map that assigns a control label to each edge and is given by $obs(e) = \sigma'$, where $e = (q, q')$, $q = [(\sigma, \xi)]$ and $q' = [(\sigma', \xi')]$. Q_f is an over (or under) approximation of Ω_f, $Q_f = \{q \in Q \mid \exists x \in \Omega_f . (\sigma, x) \in q\}$. $E \subseteq Q \times Q$ is the transition relation of A and is defined assuming that each enabling condition is initially the entire region Ω. The identity map is implemented in A by an over-approximation in terms of equivalence classes of $\simeq$. That is, for $\sigma \neq \sigma'$, $([\sigma, x)], [(\sigma', x')]) \in E$ if the projections to $\mathbb{R}^n$ of $[\sigma, x)]$ and $[(\sigma', x')]$ have non-empty intersection. This over-approximation introduces non-determinacy in A. Let

$$\tau_q = \sup_{(\sigma, x), (\sigma, y) \in q} \{t \mid y = \phi_t(x, \sigma)\}.$$

Let $e = (q, q')$ with $q = [(\sigma, \xi)]$ and $q' = [(\sigma', \xi')]$. $\hat{L} : E \to \mathbb{R}$ is the *discrete instantaneous cost* given by

$$\hat{L}(e) := \begin{cases} \tau_q L(\xi, \sigma) & \text{if } \sigma = \sigma' \\ 0 & \text{if } \sigma \neq \sigma'. \end{cases} \tag{6}$$

$\hat{h} : Q \to \mathbb{R}$ is the *discrete terminal cost* given by

$$\hat{h}(q) := h(\xi).$$

A transition or *step* of A from $q \in Q$ to $q' \in Q$ with observation $\sigma' \in \Sigma_\delta$ is denoted $q \xrightarrow{\sigma'} q'$. If $\sigma \neq \sigma'$ the transition is referred to as a *control switch*, and it is forced. $\sigma = \sigma'$ the transition is referred to as a *time step*. If $E(q)$ is the set of edges that can be enabled from $q \in Q$, then for $\sigma \in \Sigma_\delta$, $E_\sigma(q) = \{e \in E(q) \mid obs(e) = \sigma\}$. If $|E_\sigma(q)| > 1$, then we say that $e \in E_\sigma(q)$ is *unobservable* in the sense that when control event σ is issued, it is unknown which edge among $E_\sigma(q)$ is taken. (Note that unobservability of edges refers strictly to the discrete automaton A, whereas in H one may be able to reconstruct which edge was taken using continuous state information). If $\sigma = \sigma'$, then $|E_\sigma(q)| = 1$, by the uniqueness of solutions of ODE's and by the definition of bisimulation.

A *control policy* $c : Q \to \Sigma_\delta$ is a map assigning a control event to each state; $c(q) = \sigma$ is the control event issued when the state is at q. A *trajectory* π of A over c is a sequence $\pi = q_0 \xrightarrow{\sigma_1} q_1 \xrightarrow{\sigma_2} q_2 \xrightarrow{\sigma_3} \dots, q_i \in Q$. Let $\Pi_c(q)$ be the set of trajectories starting at q and applying control policy c, and let $\tilde{\Pi}_c(q)$ be the set of trajectories starting at q, applying control policy c, and eventually reaching Q_f. If for every $q \in Q$, $\pi \in \Pi_c(q)$ is non-Zeno then we say c is an *admissible control policy*. The set of all admissible control policies for A is denoted $\mathcal{C}$.

A control policy c is said to have a *loop* if A has a trajectory $q_0 \xrightarrow{c(q_0)} q_1 \xrightarrow{c(q_1)} \dots \xrightarrow{c(q_{m-1})} q_m = q_0$, $q_i \in Q$. A control policy has a *Zeno loop* if it has a loop made up of control switches and/or zero duration time steps (i.e. $\tau_q = 0$) only.

Lemma 1. *A control policy c for non-deterministic automaton A is admissible if and only if it has no Zeno loops.*

Proof. First we show that a non-deterministic automaton with non-Zeno trajectories has a control policy without Zeno loops. For suppose not. Then a trajectory starting on a state belonging to the loop can take infinitely many steps around the loop before taking a non-zero duration time step. This trajectory is not non-Zeno, a contradiction. Second, we show that a control policy without Zeno loops implies non-Zeno trajectories. Suppose not. Consider a Zeno trajectory that takes an infinite number of control switches and/or zero duration time steps between two non-zero duration time steps. Because there are a finite number of states in Q, by the Axiom of Choice, one of the states must be repeated in the sequence of states visited during the control switches and/or zero duration time steps. This implies the existence of a loop in the control policy. Either each step of the loop is a control switch, implying a Zeno loop; or the loop has one or more zero duration time steps. But the bisimulation partition permits zero duration time steps only if $\tau_q = 0$, which implies a Zeno loop.   □

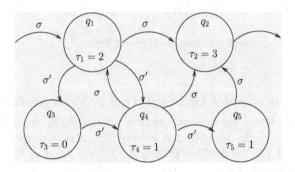

Fig. 1. Fragment of automaton with a zero duration time step.

Example 1. Consider the automaton in Figure 1. If we are at q_1 and the control $\sigma'\sigma'\sigma$ is issued, then three possible trajectories are $q_1 \xrightarrow{\sigma'} q_3 \xrightarrow{\sigma'} q_4 \xrightarrow{\sigma} q_2$, $q_1 \xrightarrow{\sigma'}$ $q_4 \xrightarrow{\sigma'} q_5 \xrightarrow{\sigma} q_2$, or $q_1 \xrightarrow{\sigma'} q_3 \xrightarrow{\sigma'} q_4 \xrightarrow{\sigma} q_1$. The first trajectory has a zero duration time step. The control is inadmissible since the last trajectory has a Zeno loop.

4   Dynamic Programming

In this section we formulate the dynamic programming problem on A. This involves defining a cost-to-go function and a value function that minimizes it over control policies suitable for non-deterministic automata.

Let $\pi = q_0 \xrightarrow{\sigma_1} q_1 \ldots q_{N-1} \xrightarrow{\sigma_N} q_N$, where $q_i = [(\sigma_i, \xi_i)]$ and π takes the sequence of edges $e_1 e_2 \ldots e_N$. We define a *discrete cost-to-go* $\hat{J} : Q \times C \to \mathbb{R}$ by

$$\hat{J}(q, c) = \begin{cases} \max_{\pi \in \tilde{\Pi}_c(q)} \left\{ \sum_{j=1}^{N_\pi} \hat{L}(e_j) + \hat{h}(q_{N_\pi}) \right\} & \text{if } \Pi_c(q) = \tilde{\Pi}_c(q) \\ \infty & \text{otherwise} \end{cases}$$

where $N_\pi = \min\{j \geq 0 \mid q_j \in Q_f\}$. We take the maximum over $\tilde{\Pi}_c(q)$ because of the non-determinacy of A: it is uncertain which among the (multiple) trajectories allowed by c will be taken so we must assume the worst-case situation. The *discrete value function* $\hat{V} : Q \to \mathbb{R}$ is

$$\hat{V}(q) = \min_{c \in C} \hat{J}(q, c)$$

for $q \in Q \setminus Q_f$ and $\hat{V}(q) = \hat{h}(q)$ for $q \in Q_f$. We showed in [2] that $\hat{V}$ satisfies a DPP that takes into account the non-determinacy of A and ensures that optimal control policies are admissible. Let $\mathcal{A}_q$ be the set of control assignments $c(q) \in \Sigma_\delta$ at q such that c is admissible.

Proposition 1. $\hat{V}$ *satisfies*

$$\hat{V}(q) = \min_{c(q) \in \mathcal{A}_q} \left\{ \max_{e=(q,q') \in E_{\sigma'}(q)} \{\hat{L}(e) + \hat{V}(q')\} \right\}, \quad q \in Q \setminus Q_f \tag{7}$$

$$\hat{V}(q) = \hat{h}(q), \qquad\qquad\qquad\qquad\qquad q \in Q_f. \tag{8}$$

5 Non-deterministic Dijkstra Algorithm

The dynamic programming solution (7)-(8) can be viewed as a shortest path problem on a non-deterministic graph subject to all optimal paths satisfying a non-Zeno condition. We propose an algorithm which is a modification of the Dijkstra algorithm for deterministic graphs [6]. First we define notation. F_n is the set of states that have been assigned a control and are deemed "finished" at iteration n, while U_n are the unfinished states. At each n, $Q = U_n \cup F_n$. $\Sigma_n(q) \subseteq \Sigma_\delta$ is the set of control events at iteration n that take state q to finished states exclusively. $\tilde{U}_n$ is the set of states for which there exists a control event that can take them to finished states exclusively. $\tilde{V}_n(q)$ is a tentative cost-to-go value at iteration n. B_n is the set of "best" states among $\tilde{U}_n$.

The non-deterministic Dijkstra (NDD) algorithm first determines $\tilde{U}_n$ by checking if any q in U_n can take a step to states belonging exclusively to F_n. For states belonging to $\tilde{U}_n$, an estimate of the value function $\tilde{V}$ following the prescription of (7) is obtained: among the set of control events constituting a step into states in F_n, select the event with the lowest worst-case cost. Next, the algorithm determines B_n, the states with the lowest $\tilde{V}$ among $\tilde{U}_n$, and these are added to F_{n+1}. The iteration counter is incremented until it reaches $N = |Q|$. It is assumed in the following description that initially $\hat{V}(q) = \infty$ and $c(q) = \emptyset$ for all $q \in Q$.

We prove that algorithm NDD is *optimal*; that is, it synthesizes a control policy so that each $q \in Q$ reaches Q_f with the best worst-case cost. We observe a few properties of the algorithm. First, if all states of Q can reach Q_f then $Q - Q_f = \cup_n B_n$. Second, as in the deterministic case, the algorithm computes $\hat{V}$ in order of level sets of $\hat{V}$. In particular, $\hat{V}(B_n) \le \hat{V}(B_{n+1})$. Finally, we need the following property.

Lemma 2. *For all $q \in Q$ and $\sigma' \in \Sigma_\delta$,*

$$\hat{V}(q) \le \max_{e=(q,q') \in E_{\sigma'}(q)} \{\hat{L}(e) + \hat{V}(q')\}.$$

Proof. Fix $q \in Q$ and $\sigma' \in \Sigma_\delta$. There are two cases.
Case 1.

$$\hat{V}(q) \le \max_{e=(q,q') \in E_{\sigma'}(q)} \{\hat{V}(q')\}.$$

In this case the result is obvious.
Case 2.

$$\hat{V}(q) > \max_{e=(q,q') \in E_{\sigma'}(q)} \{\hat{V}(q')\}. \tag{9}$$

Procedure NDD:

$F_1 = Q_f$; $U_1 = Q - Q_f$;
for each $q \in Q_f$, $\hat{V}(q) = \hat{h}(q)$;

for n = 1 to N, do
    for each $q \in U_n$,
        $\Sigma_n(q) = \{\sigma' \in \Sigma_\delta \mid \text{if } q \xrightarrow{\sigma'} q', \text{then } q' \in F_n\}$;
    $\tilde{U}_n = \{q \in U_n \mid \Sigma_n(q) \neq \emptyset\}$;
    for each $q \in \tilde{U}_n$,
        $\tilde{V}_n(q) = \min_{\sigma' \in \Sigma_n(q)}\{\max_{e=(q,q') \in E_{\sigma'}(q)}\{\hat{L}(e) + \hat{V}(q')\}\}$;
    $B_n = \mathrm{argmin}_{q \in \tilde{U}_n}\{\tilde{V}_n(q)\}$;
    for each $q \in B_n$,
        $\hat{V}(q) = \tilde{V}_n(q)$;
        $c(q) = \mathrm{argmin}_{\sigma' \in \Sigma_n(q)}\{\max_{e=(q,q') \in E_{\sigma'}(q)}\{\hat{L}(e) + \hat{V}(q')\}\}$;
    endfor
    $F_{n+1} = F_n \cup B_n$; $U_{n+1} = Q - F_{n+1}$;
endfor

We observed above that q belongs to some B_n. Suppose w.l.o.g. that $q \in B_j$. Together with (9) this implies $q' \in F_j$ for all q' such that $q \xrightarrow{\sigma'} q'$. This, in turn, means that $\sigma' \in \Sigma_j(q)$ and according to the algorithm

$$\hat{V}(q) = \tilde{V}_j(q) \leq \max_{e=(q,q') \in E_{\sigma'}(q)}\{\hat{L}(e) + \hat{V}(q')\}$$

which proves the result. $\qquad\qquad\qquad\qquad\qquad\qquad\qquad\qquad\qquad\qquad\qquad$ $\square$

Theorem 1. *Algorithm NDD is optimal and synthesizes a control policy with no Zeno loops.*

Proof. First we prove optimality. Let $V(q)$ be the optimal (best worst-case) cost-to-go for $q \in Q$ and $\overline{Q} = \{q \in Q \mid V(q) < \hat{V}(q)\}$. Let $l(\pi_q)$ be the number of edges taken by the shortest optimal (best worst-case) trajectory π_q from q. Define $\overline{q} = \arg\min_{q \in \overline{Q}}\{l(\pi_q)\}$. Suppose that the best worst-case trajectory starting at $\overline{q}$ is $\pi_{\overline{q}} = \overline{q} \xrightarrow{\sigma'} \overline{\overline{q}} \to \dots$. We showed in the previous lemma that

$$\hat{V}(\overline{q}) \leq \max_{e=(\overline{q},q') \in E_{\sigma'}(\overline{q})}\{\hat{L}(e) + \hat{V}(q')\} \leq \hat{L}(e) + \hat{V}(\overline{\overline{q}}).$$

Since $\pi_{\overline{q}}$ is the best worst-case trajectory from $\overline{q}$ and by the optimality of $V(\overline{q})$

$$V(\overline{q}) = \max_{e=(\overline{q},q') \in E_{\sigma'}(\overline{q})}\{\hat{L}(e) + V(q')\} = \hat{L}(e) + \hat{V}(\overline{\overline{q}}).$$

Since $\pi_{\overline{q}}$ is the shortest best worst-case trajectory, we know that $\overline{\overline{q}} \notin \overline{Q}$, so $V(\overline{\overline{q}}) = \hat{V}(\overline{\overline{q}})$. This implies $\hat{V}(\overline{q}) \leq \hat{L}(e) + V(\overline{\overline{q}}) = V(\overline{q})$, a contradiction.

To prove that the algorithm synthesizes a policy with no Zeno loops we argue by induction. The claim is obviously true for F_1. Suppose that the states of F_n have been assigned controls forming no Zeno loops. Consider F_{n+1}. Each state of B_n takes either a time step or a control switch to F_n so there cannot be a Zeno loop in B_n. The only possibility is for some $q \in B_n$ to close a Zeno loop with states in F_n. This implies there exists a control assignment that allows an edge from F_n to q to be taken; but this is not allowed by NDD. Thus, F_{n+1} has no Zeno loops.   □

Remarks:

1. It is intuitively reasonable that the algorithm cannot synthesize a controller with Zeno loops. This worst-case behavior would show up in the value function, forcing it to be infinite for states that can reach the loop.
2. When we say that the algorithm is optimal, we mean the algorithm determines the best worst-case cost to take each state to the target set. In fact, (see remark below) the hybrid system or continuous system using the synthesized controller may perform better than worst case.
3. The non-deterministic automaton predicts more trajectories than what either the continuous system or the hybrid system can exhibit. Indeed, the automaton may exhibit a trajectory that reaches the target set using only control switches, and thus accruing zero cost. This is not of concern. Such a trajectory is an artifact of the non-determinacy of the automaton, and is not used in the determination of the value function, which accounts only for worst-case behavior, nor is it exhibited in either the hybrid system or the continuous system when the control policy synthesized by Algorithm NDD is used.
4. Related to the previous remark is that the non-deterministic automaton may also predict worst-case behavior which is not exhibited by the continuous system. It would appear that a discrepancy will develop between the cost-to-go obtained by applying the synthesized controller to the continuous system and the cost-to-go predicted by the nondeterministic automaton. This error is incurred every time a control switch is taken and is effectively an error in predicting the state and has an upper bound of δ at each iteration. This error was accounted for in our proof of convergence of the method, and the convergence result essentially depends on the fact that only a finite number of control switches occur [2].

6   Example

We apply our method to the time optimal control problem of a double integrator

$$\dot{x}_1 = x_2$$
$$\dot{x}_2 = u.$$

Given the set of admissible controls $U = \{u \; : \; |u| \leq 1\}$, we select $\Omega = (-1,1) \times (-1,1)$ and $\Omega_f = \overline{B}_\epsilon(0)$, the closed epsilon ball centered at 0. The cost-to-go function is $J(x, \mu) = \int_0^{T(x,\mu)} dt$. The bang-bang solution obtained using Pontryagin's maximum principle is well known to involve a single switching curve. The continuous value function V is shown in Figure 2(a).

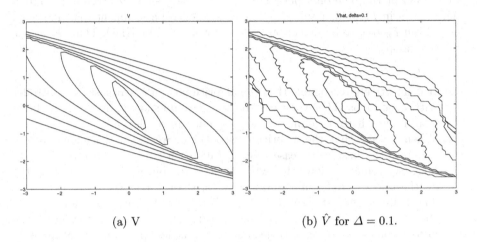

(a) V   (b) $\hat{V}$ for $\Delta = 0.1$.

Fig. 2. Continuous and discrete value functions for double integrator

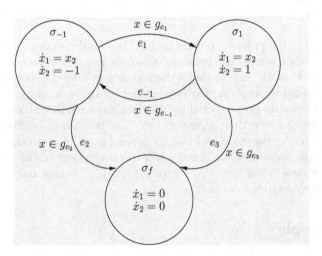

Fig. 3. Hybrid automaton for time optimal control of a double integrator system

To construct the hybrid automaton H we select $\Sigma_\delta = \{-1, 1\}$. H is show in Figure 3. The state space is $\{\sigma_{-1} = -1, \sigma_1 = 1, \sigma_f\} \times \mathbb{R}^n$. $g_{e_{-1}}$ and g_{e_1} are unknown and must be synthesized, while $g_{e_2} = g_{e_3} = \Omega_f$.

A first integral for vector field $\dot{x}_1 = x_2$, $\dot{x}_2 = 1$ is $x_1 - \frac{1}{2}x_2^2 = c_1$, $c_1 \in \mathbb{R}$. For $\dot{x}_1 = x_2$, $\dot{x}_2 = -1$ a first integral is $x_1 + \frac{1}{2}x_2^2 = c_2$, $c_2 \in \mathbb{R}$. We select a transverse foliation (see [1]) for each vector field, given by $x_2 = c_3$.

We define Q, Q_f, E, $\hat{L}$ and $\hat{h}$ for automaton A derived from H in Figure 3. Q can be visualized using Figure 4.

The states $q \in Q$ are of the form $(\sigma, [x])$ with $\sigma \in \{\sigma_{-1}, \sigma_1\}$. For the case $\sigma = \sigma_1$ with $c_1, c_2 \in \mathbb{R}$, $[x]$ is either an open subset of $\mathbb{R}^2$ bounded by the leaves $c_1 < x_1 - \frac{1}{2}x_2^2 < c_1 + \Delta$ and $c_2 < x_2 < c_2 + \Delta$; or an open interval in a horizontal leaf $x_1 - \frac{1}{2}x_2^2 = c_1$, $c_2 < x_2 < c_2 + \Delta$; or an open interval in a vertical leaf $c_1 < x_1 - \frac{1}{2}x_2^2 < c_1 + \Delta$, $x_2 = c_2$; or a point $x_1 - \frac{1}{2}x_2^2 = c_1$, $x_2 = c_2$. Analogous expressions can be written for $\sigma = \sigma_{-1}$. In Figure 4, $\Delta = 0.25$, $c_1 \in [-1, 1]$ and $c_2 \in [-1, 1]$. If we identify equivalence classes $(\sigma, [x])$ by their Euclidean coordinates (c_1, c_2) directly, then Q_f, shown in Figure 4 as the regions inside the dotted lines, includes states $(\sigma, [x])$, where $[x]$ satisfies $c_1, c_2 \in (-\Delta, \Delta)$.

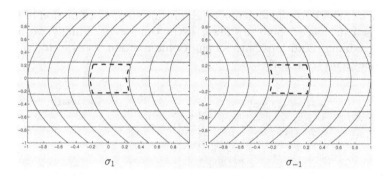

Fig. 4. Partitions for states σ_1 and σ_{-1} of the hybrid automaton of Figure 3

Let us consider the edges corresponding to control switches of A. $q = (\sigma_1, [x]) \in Q$ has an outgoing edge to $q' = (\sigma_{-1}, [y]) \in Q$ if $[x] \cap [y] \neq \emptyset$. For example, for $q = (\sigma_1, [x])$ and $[x]$ satisfying $c_1 \in (-.25, -.5)$ and $c_2 = .25$, there are three outgoing edges from q to $q'_i, i = 1, \ldots, 3$, with $[y]$ satisfying $c_2 = .25$ and $c_1 \in (-.5, -.25)$, $c_1 = -.25$, and $c_1 \in (-.25, 0)$, respectively. Similarly, for $q = (\sigma_1, [x])$ and $[x]$ satisfying $c_1 \in (-.5, -.25)$ and $c_2 \in (.75, 1)$, there are five outgoing edges from q to $q'_i, i = 1, \ldots, 5$, with $[y]$ satisfying $c_2 \in (.75, 1)$ and $c_1 \in (-.25, 0)$, $c_1 = 0$, $c_1 \in (0, .25)$, $c_1 = .25$ and $c_1 \in (.25, .5)$, respectively. Edges corresponding to time steps of A can be determined from visual inspection of Figure 4. For example, for $q = (\sigma_1, [x])$ with $[x]$ satisfying $c_1 \in (-.25, -.5)$ and $c_2 = .25$, there is an outgoing edge from q to $q' = (\sigma_1, [y])$ with $[y]$ satisfying $c_1 \in (-.25, -.5)$ and $c_2 \in (.25, .5)$.

The results of algorithm NDD are shown in Figure 2(b) and Figure 5. In Figure 5 the dashed line is the smooth switching curve for the continuous problem. The black dots identify equivalence classes where NDD assigns a control switch. Considering $g_{e_{-1}}$ we see that the boundary of the enabling condition in the upper left corner is a jagged approximation using equivalence classes of the smooth switching curve. Initial conditions in the upper left corner just inside the enabling condition must switch to a control of $u = -1$, otherwise the trajectory will increase in the x_2 direction and not reach the target. Initial conditions in the upper left corner just outside the enabling condition must allow time to pass until they reach the enabling condition, for if they switched to $u = -1$ they would be unable to reach the target. Hence the upper left boundary of the enabling condition is crisp. The lower right side of the enabling condition which has islands of time steps shows the effect of the non-determinacy of automaton A. These additional time steps occur because it can be less expensive to take a time step than to incur the cost of the *worst case* control switch. Indeed consider an initial condition in Figure 5(a) which lies in an equivalence class that takes a time step but should take a control switch according to the continuous optimal control. Such a point will move up and to the left before it takes a control switch. By moving slightly closer to the target, the worst-case cost-to-go incurred in a control switch is reduced. Notice that all such initial conditions eventually take a control switch. This phenomenon of extra time steps is a function of the mesh size δ: as δ decreases there are fewer extra time steps. Finally we note that the two enabling conditions have an empty intersection, as expected in order to ensure non-Zeno trajectories.

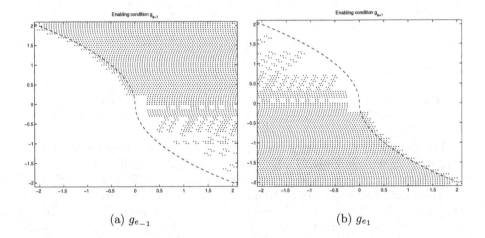

(a) $g_{e_{-1}}$ (b) g_{e_1}

Fig. 5. Enabling conditions

Figure 6 shows trajectories of the closed-loop system using the controller synthesized by NDD. The bold lines are the trajectories, the central hatched region is an enlarged target region, and the shaded areas are the equivalence classes visited during the simulation.

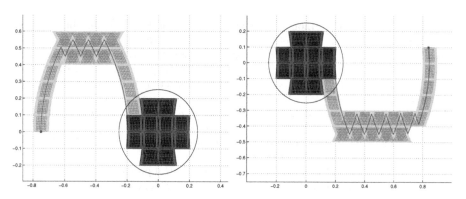

Fig. 6. Trajectories of the closed-loop system

7   Conclusion

In this paper we developed an efficient single-pass algorithm to solve a dynamic programming problem on a non-deterministic graph that arises in the solution of a continuous optimal control problem using hybrid systems and bisimulation. We have seen that the single-pass nature of the solution depends on the partitioning method. An area for future investigation is exploring other partition methods in relation to the efficiency of the algorithmic solution of the dynamic programming problem. This would include partitions that are not bisimulations, especially when analytical expressions for first integrals are difficult to obtain.

We have developed a prototype tool for the synthesis of hybrid optimal controls based on bisimulation. The algorithm has complexity $O(N \log N)$ where N is the number of states of the automaton. The number of states is exponential in the dimension of the continuous state space. In the "vanilla" version of our approach, the automaton is constructed before running the Djikstra-like algorithm. To improve the speed and the memory usage of the algorithm, we plan to build the automaton on the fly while algorithm NDD is executing. In addition, we plan to apply the approach to solving a number of optimal control problems arising in automotive engine control.

References

1. M. Broucke. A geometric approach to bisimulation and verification of hybrid systems. In *Hybrid Systems: Computation and Control*, F. Vaandrager and J. van Schuppen, eds., LNCS 1569, Springer-Verlag, pp. 61-75, 1999.
2. M. Broucke, M.D. Di Benedetto, S. Di Gennaro, A. Sangiovanni-Vincentelli. Theory of optimal control using bisimulations. In *Hybrid Systems: Computation and Control*, N. Lynch and B. Krogh, eds., LNCS 1790, Springer-Verlag, pp. 89-102, 2000.
3. I. Capuzzo Dolcetta. On a discrete approximation of the Hamilton-Jacobi equation for dynamic programming. *Applied Math. Optim.*, vol. 10, pp. 367-377, 1983.

4. M.G. Crandall, P.L. Lions. Viscosity solutions of Hamilton-Jacobi equations. *Trans. Amer. Math. Soc.*, vol. 277, no. 1, pp. 1-42, 1983.
5. M.G. Crandall, P.L. Lions. Two approximations of solutions of Hamilton-Jacobi equations. *Mathematics of Computation*, vol. 43, no. 176, pp. 1-19, July 1984.
6. E.W. Dijkstra. A note on two problems in connection with graphs. *Numerische Mathematik* 1, p. 269-271, 1959.
7. M. Falcone. A numerical approach to the infinite horizon problem of deterministic control theory. *Applied Mathematics and Optimization*, 15, pp. 1-13, 1987.
8. W.H. Fleming, R.W. Rishel. *Deterministic and stochastic optimal control.* Springer-Verlag, New York, 1975.
9. R. Gonzales and E. Rofman. On deterministic control problems: an approximation procedure for the optimal cost. I: the stationary problem. *SIAM J. Contr. Optim.*, vol. 23, no. 2, pp. 242-266, 1985.
10. P.L. Lions. *Generalized solutions of Hamilton-Jacobi equations.* Pitman, Boston, 1982.
11. E. Asarin and O. Maler. As soon as possible: time optimal control for timed automata. In *Hybrid Systems: Computation and Control*, F. Vaandrager and J. van Schuppen, eds., LNCS 1569, Springer-Verlag, pp. 19-30, 1999.
12. L. Polymenakos, D. Bertsekas, and J. Tsitsiklis. Implementation of efficient algorithms for globally optimal trajectories. *IEEE Trans. AC*, vol.43, no.2, pp. 278-83, Feb. 1998.
13. P.E. Souganidis. Approximation schemes for viscosity solutions of Hamilton-Jacobi equations. *Journal of Differential Equations*, vol. 59, no. 1, p. 1-43, August 1985.
14. J.N. Tsitsiklis. Efficient algorithms for globally optimal trajectories. *IEEE Transactions on Automatic Control*, vol. 40, no. 9, pp. 1528-1538, September 1995.

A Generalized Approach for Analysis and Control of Discrete-Time Piecewise Affine and Hybrid Systems

Francesco Alessandro Cuzzola* and Manfred Morari

Institut für Automatik, ETH - Swiss Federal Institute of Technology, ETHZ - ETL,
CH 8092 Zurich, Switzerland
{cuzzola, morari}@aut.ee.ethz.ch

Abstract. In this paper we investigate some analysis and control problems for discrete-time hybrid systems in the piece-wise affine form. By using arguments from the dissipativity theory for nonlinear systems, we show that H_∞ analysis and synthesis problems can be formulated and solved via *Linear Matrix Inequalities* by taking into account the switching structure of the considered system. In this paper we address the generalized problem of controlling hybrid systems whose switching structure does not depend only on the state but also on the control input.

1 Introduction

Piece-Wise Affine (PWA) systems have been receiving increasing attention by the control community because they provide a useful modeling framework for hybrid systems. In fact, discrete-time PWA systems are equivalent to interconnections of linear systems and finite automata [17], to complementarity systems [9] and also hybrid systems in the *Mixed Logic Dynamical* (MLD) form [1]. In particular, the MLD form is capable to model a large class of hybrid systems including linear hybrid dynamical systems, hybrid automata, some classes of discrete-event systems, and systems with qualitative inputs/outputs [1,3]. The algorithm to obtain the discrete-time PWA representation of an MLD system and vice-versa is reported in [3]. In order to stress the importance of PWA systems it is worth recalling that in [2] the explicit form of Model Predictive Control (MPC) for linear constrained systems was derived and, besides providing an algorithm for its computation, it was shown that the closed-loop system has a PWA structure. Also in this case the closed-loop system turns out to be a PWA model.

An important feature of a PWA model is that the state-update map can be discontinuous along the boundary of the regions. For instance, when considering PWA systems stemming from hybrid systems in the MLD form, discontinuities can arise from the representation of logic conditions.

The control synthesis problem for MLD systems and consequently PWA systems

---

* This research has been supported by the Swiss National Science Foundation.

M.D. Di Benedetto, A. Sangiovanni-Vincentelli (Eds.): HSCC 2001, LNCS 2034, pp. 189–203, 2001.
© Springer-Verlag Berlin Heidelberg 2001

is computationally difficult: in [1] a *Mixed Integer Quadratic Programming* (MIQP) approach is proposed in order to solve the control problem of MLD systems by means of MPC techniques. Needless to say, the computational complexity of this approach may increase exponentially with the prediction horizon considered. The use of *Linear Matrix Inequalities* (LMI) techniques, for which computationally advantageous and numerically reliable algorithms as well as toolboxes are available (see [8]) would seem to be a promising alternative.

Concerning the stability analysis of PWA systems, the authors presented various algorithms with different degrees of conservativeness in [15]. Similarly to [12, 13], where a particular class of continuous-time PWA systems was considered, such procedures exploit Piece-Wise Quadratic (PWQ) Lyapunov functions that can be computed as the solution of a set of LMIs. For the sake of completeness, the main stability test of [15] is reported in Section 2 in a suitable form.

In this work, we consider both analysis and synthesis problems for the general class of PWA models whose switching sequence depends on both state and input trajectories. As pointed out in [3] the dependence of the switching sequence on the input can be met by translating an MLD system into a PWA form. Moreover, the dependence of the switching sequence on the input signal is common in real systems: for example, it could be caused by saturation effects or limitations on the control signal.

It is worthwhile emphasizing that this type of PWA models is more general than that considered in [12,13] and [15]: indeed, in these works the switching structure depended on the state only. Furthermore, we generalize the results of [15] by considering analysis and synthesis problems with performance for PWA systems.

We focus on the H_∞ norm showing that the H_∞-analysis and the H_∞-synthesis of a piecewise linear state-feedback can be addressed by resorting to LMI-based algorithms. The rationale of our derivation hinges on the use of passivity theory for nonlinear systems [14]. We point out that a significant application of the H_∞ analysis test is the possibility of checking *a posteriori* the performance of MPC for both linear and MLD systems. As mentioned before this can be done by exploiting the explicit PWA form of the closed-loop system.

The results are presented in Sections 3 and 4. An illustrative example is provided in Section 5.

Notation: The symbol $*$ will be used in some matrix expressions to induce a symmetric structure. For example, if L and R are symmetric matrices, then

$$\begin{bmatrix} L + M + * & * \\ N & R \end{bmatrix} := \begin{bmatrix} L + M + M^T & N^T \\ N & R \end{bmatrix}. \tag{1}$$

Moreover, we define

$$\|x_k\|_{l_2(0,N)} := \sum_{k=0}^{N} \{x_k^T x_k\}^{\frac{1}{2}}. \tag{2}$$

2   Stability and State-Feedback Stabilization of PWA Systems

A linear discrete-time piecewise affine system is defined by the state-space equation

$$x_{k+1} = A_i x_k + B_i u_k + a_i, \text{ for } \begin{bmatrix} x_k \\ u_k \end{bmatrix} \in \chi_i \tag{3}$$

where $x_k \in \mathbb{R}^n$ is the state and $u_k \in \mathbb{R}^m$ is the control input. The set $\mathbb{X} \subseteq \mathbb{R}^{n+m}$ of every possible vector $\begin{bmatrix} x_k^T & u_k^T \end{bmatrix}^T$ is either $\mathbb{R}^{n+m}$ or a polyhedron containing the origin, $\{\chi_i\}_{i=1}^s$ is a polyhedral partition [1] of $\mathbb{X}$ and $a_i \in \mathbb{R}^n$, are constant vectors. We refer to each χ_i as a *cell*. Moreover, in order to simplify the exposition, we assume that our cells are polyhedra defined by matrices F_i^x, F_i^u, f_i^x and f_i^u as follows

$$\chi_i := \left\{ \begin{bmatrix} x^T & u^T \end{bmatrix}^T \text{ such that } F_i^x x \geq f_i^x \text{ and } F_i^u u \geq f_i^u \right\}. \tag{4}$$

The results presented in this paper can be extended to systems whose cells χ_i have a more complicate structure.

Moreover, it is worth introducing the following notation:

$$\bar{\chi}_i := \{x \text{ such that } F_i^x x \geq f_i^x\} \tag{5}$$

and

$$\mathcal{S}_j := \left\{ i \text{ such that } \exists x, u \text{ with } x \in \bar{\chi}_j, \begin{bmatrix} x^T & u^T \end{bmatrix}^T \in \chi_i \right\}. \tag{6}$$

In a nutshell, $\mathcal{S}_j$ is the set of all indices i such that χ_i is a cell containing a vector $\begin{bmatrix} x^T & u^T \end{bmatrix}^T$ for which the condition $x \in \bar{\chi}_j$ is satisfied. We denote with $\mathcal{I} = \{1, \dots, s\}$ the set of indices of the cells χ_i whereas the symbol $\mathcal{J} = \{1, \dots, t\}$ will be used to denote the set of indices of the cells $\bar{\chi}_j$. It is important to observe that:

$$\bigcup_{j=1}^t \mathcal{S}_j = \mathcal{I}. \tag{7}$$

Furthermore, if cells χ_i have the structure pointed out in eq. (4) then the sets $\mathcal{S}_j$ are disjoint whereas if cells χ_i have a more complicate structure (for instance when mixed state-input constraints are used to define each cell χ_i) then the sets $\mathcal{S}_j$ could be overlapping. In the latter case the results we are going to present could become more conservative.

When we focus on the stability of the origin, we consider *autonomous*

---

[1] Each set χ_i is a (not necessarily closed) convex polyhedron s.t. $\chi_i \cap \chi_j = \emptyset$, $\forall i \neq j$, $\bigcup_{i=1}^s \chi_i = \mathbb{X}$.

PWA systems and we assume that $x = 0$ is an equilibrium point. To begin with it is necessary to observe that an autonomous system can be obtained from system (3) by applying a suitable control law. In the following we consider a piecewise linear state feedback with the structure

$$u_k = K_i x_k, \text{ for } \begin{bmatrix} x_k \\ u_k \end{bmatrix} \in \chi_i. \tag{8}$$

By applying the controller (8) to the system (3) we achieve the following closed-loop dynamic system

$$x_{k+1} = \mathcal{A}_i x_k + a_i, \text{ for } \begin{bmatrix} x_k \\ u_k \end{bmatrix} \in \chi_i \tag{9}$$

where $\mathcal{A}_i = A_i + B_i K_i$ and $u_k = K_i x_k$. We note that the the evolution of closed-loop system (9) depends on the "hidden" variable u_k since it influences the index i of the current cell χ_i.

As customary for constrained systems, we assume that the state trajectories $\begin{bmatrix} x_k^T & u_k^T \end{bmatrix}^T$ generated by the control law (8) satisfy $\begin{bmatrix} x_k^T & u_k^T \end{bmatrix}^T \in \mathbb{X}, \forall k \in \mathbb{N}$.

In [15] the stability of the origin of PWA system was characterized by using Piece-Wise Quadratic (PWQ) Lyapunov functions. In the following theorem we report the main result of [15] valid for the case $a_i = 0, \forall i \in \mathcal{I}$ and adapted to the closed loop system (9).

Theorem 1. *Consider the system (9). If there exist matrices $P_i = P_i^T > 0$, $\forall i \in \mathcal{I}$ such that the positive-definite function $V(x, u) = x^T P_i x, \forall \begin{bmatrix} x_k^T & u_k^T \end{bmatrix}^T \in \chi_i$ satisfies $V(x_{k+1}, u_{k+1}) - V(x_k, u_k) < 0$, then the origin of the PWA systems (9) is exponentially stable and $\lim_{k \to +\infty} \|x_k\| = 0$ for all system trajectories fulfilling $\begin{bmatrix} x_k^T & u_k^T \end{bmatrix}^T \in \mathbb{X}, \forall k \in \mathbb{N}$.* □

The Lyapunov function appearing in Theorem 1 can be computed by solving the LMIs

$$\mathcal{A}_j^T P_i \mathcal{A}_j - P_j < 0, \quad \forall (i, j) \in \mathcal{S} \tag{10}$$

$$P_i = P_i^T > 0, \quad \forall i \in \mathcal{I} \tag{11}$$

where

$$\mathcal{S} := \left\{ (i, j) : i, j \in \mathcal{I} \text{ and } \exists k \in \mathbb{N}_0, \exists \begin{bmatrix} x_k \\ u_k \end{bmatrix}, \begin{bmatrix} x_{k+1} \\ u_{k+1} \end{bmatrix} \in \mathbb{X} \right.$$

$$\left. \text{such that } \begin{bmatrix} x_k \\ u_k \end{bmatrix} \in \chi_j \text{ and } \begin{bmatrix} x_{k+1} \\ u_{k+1} \end{bmatrix} \in \chi_i \right\}. \tag{12}$$

In other words, the set $\mathcal{S}$ contains all the ordered pairs of indices denoting the possible switches from cell j to cell i and it can be computed via *reachability analysis for MLD systems* [4]. Then, the inequalities (10) take into account all the admissible switches between different regions and guarantee that the Lyapunov function is decreasing along all possible state trajectories. When there exist matrices P_i such that the LMIs (10) and (11) are satisfied, the PWA system and the corresponding controller (eq. (8)) are termed *PWQ-stable* and *PWQ-stabilizing* respectively. We refer the interested reader to [15] for further details.

Remark 1. Conservativeness.
The conservativeness of the LMIs conditions for stability analysis can be reduced by exploiting the so-called S-Procedure [20] in order to avoid imposing $x^T P_i x > 0$ for $\begin{bmatrix} x^T & u^T \end{bmatrix}^T \in \chi_j$, $j \neq i$ [15]. This modification was proposed in [12] for continuous-time PWA systems and can be easily generalized to the discrete-time case. We point out that similar modifications can be applied to all the analysis LMIs we derive in the following.
It is important to highlight that with respect to the continuous-time case (see [12]) in the discrete-time case there is no need to guarantee the continuity of the Lyapunov function over the whole state-space. This fact can determine a reduced degree of conservativeness of the results that we are going to present with respect to those presented in [12].
Finally, following the lead given in [11], the authors proposed in [7] discrete-time performance analysis results with a notably reduced degree of conservativeness.

□

Remark 2. Extension of Theorem 1.
Theorem 1 can be extended to the case $a_i \neq 0$ as done in [12,13] by introducing the extended state $\bar{x}_k = \begin{bmatrix} x_k^T & 1 \end{bmatrix}^T$ and rewriting the system (3) as follows:

$$\bar{x}_{k+1} = \bar{A}_i \bar{x}_k + \bar{B}_i u_k \text{ for } \begin{bmatrix} x_k \\ u_k \end{bmatrix} \in \chi_i \qquad (13)$$

where

$$\bar{A}_i = \begin{bmatrix} A_i & a_i \\ 0 & 1 \end{bmatrix} \quad \bar{B}_i = \begin{bmatrix} B_i \\ 0 \end{bmatrix}. \qquad (14)$$

□

When designing the controller *i.e.* when the controller gains K_i appearing in the inequalities (10) are unknown, the set of all possible switches is generally not known in advance, and it could be necessary to consider all the pairs of indices in

$$\mathcal{S}_{all} := \mathcal{I} \times \mathcal{I}$$

instead of $\mathcal{S}$.

Furthermore, we note that the design of a controller of type (8) could be a very hard task because, at each time instant, the vector u_k has to be calculated by means of a control gain $K_{\bar{i}}$ whose index $\bar{i}$ is found on the basis of the admissibility condition

$$\begin{bmatrix} x_k \\ u_k \end{bmatrix} \in \chi_{\bar{i}}. \tag{15}$$

This implies that in general it is not possible to calculate u_k since the index $\bar{i}$ for which the condition (15) is satisfied, is difficult to know in advance. Therefore, we turn our problem into one of designing a controller with the following structure

$$u_k = K_j x_k, \quad x_k \in \bar{\chi}_j. \tag{16}$$

Thus we consider a different control gain not for all the cells χ_i with $i \in \mathcal{I}$ but for all cells $\bar{\chi}_j$ with $j \in \mathcal{J}$. Despite this restricted controller structure, in order to design a control law of type (16) one must exploit a different Lyapunov matrix P_i for each cell χ_i with $i \in \mathcal{I}$ (see the corresponding analysis result of Theorem 1) to reduce the conservativeness.

3   Synthesis of a Stabilizing State Feedback

In this section we consider the problem of finding a state feedback control law of type (16) for the system (3). For this purpose we start from the analysis condition (10) rewritten for the closed-loop system:

$$x_{k+1} = \mathcal{A}_{ij} x_k, \text{ for } \begin{bmatrix} x_k \\ u_k \end{bmatrix} \in \chi_i, x_k \in \bar{\chi}_j \tag{17}$$

where $\mathcal{A}_{ij} = A_i + B_i K_j$ and $u_k = K_j x_k$. More precisely, eq. (10) rewritten for the closed loop system (17) assumes the following form

$$\mathcal{A}_{ij}^T P_l \mathcal{A}_{ij} - P_i < 0 \quad \forall j \in \mathcal{J}, \forall i \in \mathcal{S}_j, \forall l \text{ such that } (l, i) \in \mathcal{S}_{all}, \tag{18}$$

$$P_i = P_i^T > 0, \quad \forall i \in \mathcal{I}. \tag{19}$$

Inequalities (18)-(19) represent a closed-loop stability condition. For each cell $\bar{\chi}_j$ (with $j \in \mathcal{J}$) we want to calculate a state feedback control law represented by the gain matrix K_j. The control gain K_j is used when $\begin{bmatrix} x_k^T & u_k^T \end{bmatrix}$ belongs to any cell χ_i such that $i \in \mathcal{S}_j$ or, equivalently, if $x_k \in \bar{\chi}_j$. Furthermore, this controller is applied independently of the subcell χ_l in which $\begin{bmatrix} x_{k+1}^T & u_{k+1}^T \end{bmatrix}^T$ is contained (obviously, the pair (l, i) has to belong to the set of all possible switches i.e. $\mathcal{S}_{all}$). Clearly, in view of eq. (7) these inequalities are exhaustive stability conditions since they cover all possible transitions of the set $\mathcal{S}_{all}$.

Because each matrix P_i is positive definite we can rewrite (18) by resorting to the Schur lemma as follows:

$$\begin{bmatrix} -Q_i & Q_i \mathcal{A}_{ij}^T \\ \mathcal{A}_{ij} Q_i & -Q_l \end{bmatrix} < 0, \quad \forall j \in \mathcal{J}, \forall i \in \mathcal{S}_j, \forall l \text{ such that } (l, i) \in \mathcal{S}_{all} \tag{20}$$

where $Q_i := P_i^{-1}$. We will show that (20) is guaranteed if there exist matrices G_j with $j \in \mathcal{J}$ of suitable dimensions such that the following alternative inequalities are satisfied

$$\begin{bmatrix} Q_i - G_j - G_j^T & G_j^T \mathcal{A}_{ij}^T \\ \mathcal{A}_{ij} G_j & -Q_l \end{bmatrix} < 0, \quad \forall j \in \mathcal{J}, \forall i \in \mathcal{S}_j, \forall l \text{ such that } (l,i) \in \mathcal{S}_{all} \quad (21)$$

where G_j, $j \in \mathcal{J}$ are matrices of suitable dimensions. In order to demonstrate that (21) implies inequalities (20) we first observe that matrices G_j are nonsingular since we have assumed $Q_i > 0$ $\forall i \in \mathcal{I}$ whereas the element $\{1,1\}$ of (21) implies that $G_j + G_j^T > Q_i$. Secondly, if $Q_i > 0$ the matrix $(G_j^T - Q_i)Q_i^{-1}(G_j - Q_i)$ is nonnegative definite and consequently:

$$0 < G_j + G_j^T - Q_i \leq G_j^T Q_i^{-1} G_j. \quad (22)$$

Moreover, because of (22) inequalities (21) imply

$$\begin{bmatrix} -G_j^T Q_i^{-1} G_j & G_j^T \mathcal{A}_{ij}^T \\ \mathcal{A}_{ij} G_j & -Q_l \end{bmatrix} < 0, \quad \forall j \in \mathcal{J}, \forall i \in \mathcal{S}_j, \forall l \text{ such that } (l,i) \in \mathcal{S}_{all}. \quad (23)$$

Finally, recalling that the matrices G_j are nonsingular we can obtain (20) from (23) by multiplying (23) from the right by $diag\{Q_i G_j^{-T}, I\}$ and from the left by $diag\{G_j^{-1} Q_i, I\}$.

These considerations lead to the following algorithm to calculate a stabilizing state-feedback control law. Indeed, in the following theorem we propose calculating a state-feedback controller of type (16) by exploiting a Piece-Wise Quadratic (PWQ) Lyapunov function defined by s matrices P_i with $i \in \mathcal{I}$:

Theorem 2. *Consider the PWA system (3). There exists a state feedback control law of type (16) guaranteeing PWQ stability if there exist matrices $Q_i = Q_i^T > 0$ with $i \in \mathcal{I}$ and matrices G_j, Y_j with $j \in \mathcal{J}$, such that $\forall j \in \mathcal{J}, \forall i \in \mathcal{S}_j$ and $\forall l$ with $(l,i) \in \mathcal{S}_{all}$*

$$\begin{bmatrix} Q_i - G_j - G_j^T & G_j^T A_i^T + Y_j^T B_i^T \\ A_i G_j + B_i Y_j & -Q_l \end{bmatrix} < 0. \quad (24)$$

The feedback gains K_j are given by:

$$K_j := Y_j G_j^{-1}, j \in \mathcal{J}. \quad (25)$$

$\square$

4 H_∞ Performance of Piecewise Affine Systems

Consider the PWA system

$$\begin{aligned} x_{k+1} &= A_i x_k + B_i u_k + B_i^w w_k + a_i \\ z_k &= C_i x_k + D_i u_k + D_i^w w_k, \end{aligned} \quad \begin{bmatrix} x_k \\ u_k \end{bmatrix} \in \chi_i, x_k \in \bar{\chi}_j \quad (26)$$

where $w_k \in \mathbb{R}^r$ is a disturbance signal and $z_k \in \mathbb{R}^s$ is a performance output that can model, for instance, tracking errors or the cost of the input. First, to simplify the exposition we consider the case $a_i = 0, \forall i \in \mathcal{I}$ (Subsection 4.1). Then, we extend our results to the case $a_i \neq 0$ (Subsection 4.2). In any case, we assume that the system (26) admits $x = 0$ as an equilibrium point.

As customary in control of nonlinear systems [14] we consider performance indices defined over a finite time horizon. In this section we focus on the disturbance attenuation problem in an H_∞ framework: given a real number $\gamma > 0$, the exogenous signal w is attenuated by γ if, assuming $x_0 = 0$, for each integer $N \geq 0$ and for every $w \in l_2([0, N], \mathbb{R}^r)$

$$\sum_{k=0}^{N} \|z_k\|^2 < \gamma^2 \sum_{k=0}^{N} \|w_k\|^2. \tag{27}$$

The control problem of discrete-time nonlinear systems can be very difficult due to the lack of geometric properties [14]. We will show that for PWA systems this task turns out to be less impervious provided the use of some fundamental LMI techniques [16,6].

To begin with, we present some analysis results for the following closed-loop system obtained by applying a feedback control law of type (16) to system (26):

$$\begin{aligned} x_{k+1} &= \mathcal{A}_{ij} x_k + B_i^w w_k \\ z_k &= \mathcal{C}_{ij} x_k + D_i^w w_k, \end{aligned} \quad \begin{bmatrix} x_k \\ u_k \end{bmatrix} \in \chi_i, x_k \in \bar{\chi}_j \tag{28}$$

where $\mathcal{A}_{ij} = A_i + B_i K_j, \mathcal{C}_{ij} = C_i + D_i K_j$ and $u_k = K_j x_k$. We observe again that the evolution of the closed-loop system (28) depends on the "hidden" variable u_k since it influences the index i of the cell χ_i.

A discrete-time nonlinear system (as the PWA system (28)) is *strictly dissipative* with *supply rate* $W : \mathbb{R}^s \times \mathbb{R}^r \rightarrow \mathbb{R}$ if there exists a non-negative function $V : \mathbb{R}^n \times \mathbb{R}^m \rightarrow \mathbb{R}$ termed *storage function* such that

$$\forall w \in \mathbb{R}^r, \forall k \geq 0, \quad V(x_{k+1}, u_{k+1}) - V(x_k, u_k) < W(z_k, w_k) \tag{29}$$

and $V(0, u) = 0, \forall u$ [5]. Condition (29), is the so-called *dissipation inequality* that can be equivalently represented through the condition [14,19]

$$\forall w_k, \forall N \geq 0, \forall x_0, \quad V(x_{N+1}, u_{N+1}) - V(x_0, u_0) < \sum_{k=0}^{N} W(z_k, w_k). \tag{30}$$

Hereafter we concentrate on finite gain dissipative PWA systems with the following supply rate

$$W_\infty(z, w) = (\gamma^2 \|w\|^2 - \|z\|^2), \gamma > 0. \tag{31}$$

As will be shown, the supply rate $W_\infty(z, w)$ is related to the H_∞ performance of the PWA system.

4.1 H_∞ Analysis and Synthesis for PWA Systems without Displacement Terms

The rationale presented in this section hinges on the assumption that the pair $(A_i, B_i), i \in \mathcal{I}$ is PWQ *stabilizable*: that is, we assume that there exists $K_j, j \in \mathcal{J}$ and $P_i = P_i^T > 0$ with $i \in \mathcal{I}$ such that $\forall j \in \mathcal{J}, \forall i \in \mathcal{S}_j, \forall l$ with $(l, i) \in \mathcal{S}_{all}$

$$\mathcal{A}_{ij}^T P_l \mathcal{A}_{ij} - P_i < 0 \tag{32}$$

where $\mathcal{A}_{ij} = A_i + B_i K_j$ if $i \in \mathcal{S}_j$ and $\mathcal{S}_{all}$ is the set of all possible switches. The next Lemma, which is a generalization of the classical Bounded Real Lemma [18,14] to PWA systems, allows to analyze the H_∞ performance.

Lemma 1. *Consider the system (28) with zero initial condition $x_0 = 0$. If there exists a function $V(x, u) = x^T P_i x$ for $\begin{bmatrix} x^T u^T \end{bmatrix}^T \in \chi_i$ with $P_i = P_i^T > 0$ satisfying the dissipativity inequality (29) with supply rate (31), i.e.*

$$\forall k, V(x_{k+1}, u_{k+1}) - V(x_k, u_k) < (\gamma^2 \|w_k\|^2 - \|z_k\|^2), \tag{33}$$

then, the H_∞ performance condition (27) is satisfied.
Furthermore, condition (33) is fulfilled if the following matrix inequalities are satisfied

$$\forall j \in \mathcal{J}, \forall i \in \mathcal{S}_j, \forall l \text{ with } (l, i) \in \mathcal{S}, M_{l,ij} < 0. \tag{34}$$

where

$$M_{l,ij} := \begin{bmatrix} \mathcal{A}_{ij}^T P_l \mathcal{A}_{ij} - P_i + \mathcal{C}_{ij}^T \mathcal{C}_{ij} & * \\ D_i^T \mathcal{C}_{ij} + B_i^T P_l \mathcal{A}_{ij} & B_i^T P_l B_i + D_i^T D_i - \gamma^2 I \end{bmatrix}. \tag{35}$$

In this last case the system (28) is PWQ stable.

Proof. By recalling that $x_0 = 0$, from (33) it follows that, $\forall N \geq 0$

$$V(x_{N+1}, u_{N+1}) < \sum_{k=0}^{N} \left(\gamma^2 \|w_k\|^2 - \|z_k\|^2 \right). \tag{36}$$

Since $V(x_{N+1}, u_{N+1})$ is well defined and positive it follows that condition (27) is met.
Moreover, if we assume $\begin{bmatrix} x_k^T u_k^T \end{bmatrix}^T \in \chi_i$ and $\begin{bmatrix} x_{k+1}^T u_{k+1}^T \end{bmatrix}^T \in \chi_l$ we can write inequality (33) as:

$$\forall w_k, \begin{bmatrix} x_k^T w_k^T \end{bmatrix} M_{l,ij} \begin{bmatrix} x_k^T w_k^T \end{bmatrix}^T < 0. \tag{37}$$

Obviously, inequality (37) is satisfied if condition (34) is met. On the other hand, it holds that $\mathcal{C}_{ij}^T \mathcal{C}_{ij} \geq 0$. Consequently by considering the element (1,1) of (34) we can state that

$$\forall j \in \mathcal{J}, \forall i \in \mathcal{S}_j, \forall l \text{ with } (l, i) \in \mathcal{S}, \mathcal{A}_{ij}^T P_l \mathcal{A}_{ij} - P_i < 0. \tag{38}$$

This implies that the system (28) is PWQ stable.   □

Next we focus on finding a state-feedback control law of the type (16) for the system (26) satisfying a suitable H_∞ requirement. The main result is summarized in the following theorem.

Theorem 3. *Consider the PWA system (26). There exists a state feedback control law of type (16) guaranteeing PWQ Lyapunov stability and fulfilling the dissipativity constraint (29) with supply rate (31) if there exist matrices $Q_i = Q_i^T > 0$ with $i \in \mathcal{I}$ and matrices G_j, Y_j with $j \in \mathcal{J}$, such that $\forall j \in \mathcal{J}, \forall i \in \mathcal{S}_j, \forall l$ with $(l, i) \in \mathcal{S}_{all}$*

$$
\begin{bmatrix}
Q_i - G_j - G_j^T & * & * & * \\
A_i G_j + B_i Y_j & -Q_l & * & * \\
C_i G_j + D_i Y_j & 0 & -I & * \\
0 & B_i^{wT} & D_i^{wT} & -\gamma^2 I
\end{bmatrix} < 0.
\tag{39}
$$

The feedback gains K_j with $j \in \mathcal{J}$ are given by:

$$
K_j := Y_j G_j^{-1}.
\tag{40}
$$

□

The proof of this theorem can be achieved form the results reported in Lemma 1 by applying the same line of reasoning used to demonstrate Theorem 2.

4.2   Extension to PWA Systems with Displacement Terms

Some analysis results have been extended to the case $a_i \neq 0$ by considering an extended state space (see eq. (13)) [12,13]. Unfortunately, this approach is very restrictive for synthesis problems because the extended dynamic matrix $\bar{A}_i$ is never a stability matrix ($\bar{A}_i$ contains an unreachable eigenvalue at 1) and consequently it is never possible to find $P = P^T > 0$ satisfying the Lyapunov stability condition

$$
\bar{A}_i^T P \bar{A}_i - P < 0.
\tag{41}
$$

On the other hand, the set $\mathcal{S}_{all}$ of all possible transitions contains also the transitions of type (i, i) *i.e.* from region i to the same region. This implies that the synthesis approach proposed in the previous part of this section can never be applied to a system obtained by extending the state vector as proposed in [12,13].

Therefore we consider a different approach based on the extension of the input signal w_k as follows:

$$
\tilde{w}_k := \begin{bmatrix} w_k \\ a_i \end{bmatrix}.
\tag{42}
$$

Thus, the system (26) can be rewritten as:

$$\begin{aligned} x_{k+1} &= A_i x_k + B_i u_k + \tilde{B}_i^w \tilde{w}_k \\ z_k &= C_i x_k + D_i u_k + \tilde{D}_i^w \tilde{w}_k, \end{aligned} \quad \begin{bmatrix} x_k \\ u_k \end{bmatrix} \in \chi_i, x_k \in \bar{\chi}_j \tag{43}$$

where

$$\tilde{B}_i^w = \begin{bmatrix} B_i^w & I \end{bmatrix} \; \tilde{D}_i^w = \begin{bmatrix} D_i^w & 0 \end{bmatrix}. \tag{44}$$

The H_∞ framework considered here, is based on a finite horizon definition of the l_2 gain and, consequently, the proposed extension of the disturbance input is sensible.

Clearly, it is possible to apply the control approach proposed in Theorem 3 directly to the extended system (43). This can be conservative because a_i is not an unknown disturbance but a known term. Unfortunately, in general, a_i is known only when the control signal u_k has already been calculated. Notwithstanding this, under the standard assumption

$$a_i = \bar{a}_j, \forall i \in \mathcal{S}_j, \forall j \in \mathcal{J}, \tag{45}$$

an alternative control strategy can be proposed. More precisely, the control is assumed to have the following structure:

$$u_k = \begin{bmatrix} K_j^1 & K_j^2 \end{bmatrix} \begin{bmatrix} x_k \\ \bar{a}_j \end{bmatrix}, \quad x_k \in \bar{\chi}_j. \tag{46}$$

In this way the controller can take into account also the displacement term $a_i = D\tilde{w}_k$ where

$$D := \begin{bmatrix} 0 & I \end{bmatrix}.$$

By applying the control law (46) to the PWA system (43) we obtain the closed-loop PWA system:

$$\begin{aligned} x_{k+1} &= \mathcal{A}_{ij} x_k + \tilde{\mathcal{B}}_{ij}^w \tilde{w}_k \\ z_k &= \mathcal{C}_{ij} x_k + \tilde{\mathcal{D}}_{ij}^w \tilde{w}_k, \end{aligned} \quad \begin{bmatrix} x_k \\ u_k \end{bmatrix} \in \chi_i, x_k \in \bar{\chi}_j \tag{47}$$

where

$$\begin{aligned} \mathcal{A}_{ij} &= A_i + B_i K_j^1 \; \tilde{\mathcal{B}}_{ij}^w = \tilde{B}_i^w + B_i K_j^2 D \\ \mathcal{C}_{ij} &= C_i + D_i K_j^1 \; \tilde{\mathcal{D}}_{ij}^w = \tilde{D}_i^w + D_i K_j^2 D. \end{aligned} \tag{48}$$

Now, we can apply the H_∞ result of Lemma 1 to the closed-loop PWA system (47) to arrive at the synthesis procedure summarized in the subsequent theorem. In this case, the controller gain is composed of two different parts, K_j^1 and K_j^2, that constitute two unknowns of a suitable LMI problem:

Theorem 4. *Consider the PWA system (26). There exists a state feedback control law of type (46) guaranteeing PWQ Lyapunov stability and fulfilling the dissipativity constraint (29) with supply rate*

$$\tilde{W}_\infty(z_k, w_k) = (\gamma^2 \| \left[w_k^T \ a_i^T \right]^T \|^2 - \|z_k\|^2) = \tag{49}$$

$$= (\gamma^2 \left(\|w_k\|^2 + \|a_i\|^2 \right) - \|z_k\|^2), \gamma > 0, \begin{bmatrix} x_k \\ u_k \end{bmatrix} \in \chi_i \tag{50}$$

if there exist matrices $Q_i = Q_i^T > 0$ *with* $i \in \mathcal{I}$ *and matrices* G_j, Y_j, K_j^2 *with* $j \in \mathcal{J}$, *such that* $\forall j \in \mathcal{J}, \forall i \in \mathcal{S}_j, \forall l$ *with* $(l, i) \in \mathcal{S}_{all}$

$$\begin{bmatrix} Q_i - G_j - G_j^T & * & * & * \\ A_i G_j + B_i Y_j & -Q_l & * & * \\ C_i G_j + D_i Y_j & 0 & -I & * \\ 0 & \left(\tilde{B}_i^w + B_i K_j^2 D \right)^T & \left(\tilde{D}_i^w + D_i K_j^2 D \right)^T & -\gamma^2 I \end{bmatrix} < 0. \tag{51}$$

The feedback gain matrices K_j^1 *with* $j \in \mathcal{J}$ *are given by:*

$$K_j^1 := Y_j G_j^{-1}. \tag{52}$$

□

5   Numerical Example: The Tank Case

The example we consider here is inspired by the three-tank benchmark described in [10] that will be the subject of future investigation. It consists of a single tank with cross section section A. It is filled by means of a pump whose mass flow

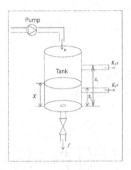

Fig. 1. Tank configuration

rate is given by the control variable u (see Figure 1). Obviously, we suppose that $0 \le u \le u_{max}$. The tank level is denoted by x. At the heights $\bar{x}_1$ and $\bar{x}_2$ we assume there are two pipes through which we have the output mass flow rates

$K_1 x$ and $K_2 x$ respectively. Finally, at the bottom we have a constant output mass flow rate f. In our case we have chosen the following numerical values with suitable dimensions:

$$A = 1, \quad K_1 = 0.2, \, K_2 = 0.1,$$
$$\bar{x}_1 = 0.3, \, \bar{x}_2 = 0.6, \, f = 0.01, \, u_{max} = 0.019. \tag{53}$$

In order to introduce the tank model we adopt the following notation. Let b be a boolean expression, then we denote with $|\cdot|$ the function

$$|b| = \begin{cases} 1 & \text{if } b = TRUE \\ 0 & \text{if } b = FALSE \end{cases} \tag{54}$$

Then, a possible continuous-time model for the tank of Figure 1 is given as follows:

$$A\dot{x} = u|(u \geq 0) \wedge (u \leq u_{max})| + u_{max}|u > u_{max}| +$$
$$- f - K_1 x|x \geq \bar{x}_1| - K_2 x|x \geq \bar{x}_2|. \tag{55}$$

In this model we have neglected the obvious physical condition $x \geq 0$. Moreover, it is very simple to obtain from (55) the following PWA continuous-time model:

$$A\dot{x} = \begin{cases} -f & \text{if} & u < 0, & x < \bar{x}_1 \\ u - f & \text{if } 0 \leq u \leq u_{max}, & x < \bar{x}_1 \\ u_{max} - f & \text{if} & u > u_{max}, & x < \bar{x}_1 \\ -f - K_1 x & \text{if} & u < 0, & \bar{x}_1 \leq x < \bar{x}_2 \\ u - f - K_1 x & \text{if } 0 \leq u \leq u_{max}, & \bar{x}_1 \leq x < \bar{x}_2 \\ u_{max} - f - K_1 x & \text{if} & u > u_{max}, & \bar{x}_1 \leq x < \bar{x}_2 \\ -f - (K_1 + K_2)x & \text{if} & u < 0, & x \geq \bar{x}_2 \\ u - f - (K_1 + K_2)x & \text{if } 0 \leq u \leq u_{max}, & x \geq \bar{x}_2 \\ u_{max} - f - (K_1 + K_2)x & \text{if} & u > u_{max}, & x \geq \bar{x}_2. \end{cases} \tag{56}$$

This model can be reduced to a discrete-time PWA system of type (26) by discretization (employing the implicit Euler's rule with a discretization time equal to 0.5 $sec.$). Finally, the PWA discrete-time model has 9 cells χ_i and 3 cells $\bar{\chi}_j$. Furthermore, we do not consider any disturbance inputs of type w and we consider the problem of regulating the level $z := x$ around 0.1. For this

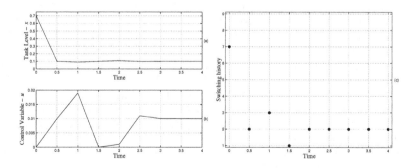

Fig. 2. Closed Loop simulation - (a) State, (b) Control Input, (c) Switching history

purpose we have applied to the discretized model an H_∞ regulator obtained by means of the synthesis procedure of Theorems 3 and 4. In Figures 2.(a)-2.(b) we report the time-histories of the state variable and of the control input (the initial state considered is $x_0 = 0.7$). Finally, in Figure 2.(c) we show the corresponding switching history (we recall that we have 9 cells of type χ_i and in this picture we report the index of the cell χ_i in which the vector $\begin{bmatrix} x_k^T & u_k^T \end{bmatrix}^T$ is contained).

6   Conclusions

In this paper we derived LMIs-based procedures to solve H_∞ analysis and synthesis problems for PWA systems whose switching sequence depends on the state and on the control input. These PWA systems can be found by translating an MLD system into PWA form. The analysis tests can be applied to assess the performance of MPC control schemes applied both to linear and hybrid systems. Moreover, the state-feedback design methodologies provide an alternative way to synthesize controllers with a prescribed degree of performance. All the proposed synthesis procedures are clearly only *sufficient* i.e. nothing can be said if the LMIs are infeasible. A thorough analysis of their conservativeness will be subject of further investigations.

References

1. Bemporad, A., Morari, M.: Control of Systems Integrating Logic, Dynamics, and Constraints. *Automatica*, **35(3)**, (1999), 407-427.
2. Bemporad, A., Morari, M., Dua, V., Pistikopoulos, E. N.: The Explicit Linear Quadratic Regulator for Constrained Systems. *American Control Conference*, Chicago, IL, (2000).
3. Bemporad, A., Ferrari-Trecate, G., Morari, M.: Observability and Controllability of Piecewise Affine and Hybrid Systems. *IEEE Transactions on Automatic Control*, **45(10)**, (2000), 1864–1876.
4. Bemporad, A., Torrisi, F.D., Morari, M.: Optimization-Based Verification and Stability Characterization of Piecewise Affine and Hybrid Systems. *Proceedings 3rd International Workshop on Hybrid Systems*, Lecture Notes in Computer Science, Springer-Verlag, Pittsburgh, USA (2000).
5. Byrnes, C. I., Lin, W.: Passivity and absolute stabilization of a class of discrete-time nonlinear systems. *Automatica*, **31(2)**, (1995), 263–268.
6. de Oliveira, M. C., Bernussou, J., Geromel, J. C.: A new discrete-time robust stability condition. *System & Control Letters*, **37**, (1999), 261–265.
7. Ferrari-Trecate, G., Cuzzola, F. A., Mignone, D., Morari, M.: Analysis of Discrete-Time Piecewise Affine and Hybrid Systems. *Submitted for publication*.
8. Gahinet, P., Nemirowski, A., Laub, A. J., Chilali, M.: *LMI Control Toolbox*, The MathWorks Inc., (1994).
9. Heemels, W.P.M.H., De Schutter, B.: On the Equivalence of Classes of Hybrid Systems: Mixed Logical Dynamical and Complementarity Systems. *T.R. 00 I/04*, Technische Universiteit Eindhoven, (2000).

10. Heiming, B., Lunze, J.: Definition of the Three-Tank Benchmark Problem for Controller Reconfiguration, *European Control Conference*, Karlshrue, Germany, (1999).
11. Johansen, T. A.: Computation of Lyapunov functions for smooth nonlinear systems using convex optimisation. *Automatica*, **36**, (2000), 1617–1626.
12. Johansson, M., Rantzer, A.: Computation of Piecewise Quadratic Lyapunov Functions for Hybrid Systems. *IEEE Transactions on Automatic Control*, **43(4)**, (2000), 555–559.
13. Johansson, M., Rantzer, A.: Piecewise Linear Quadratic Optimal Control. *IEEE Transactions on Automatic Control*, **43(4)**, (2000), 629–637.
14. Lin, W., Byrnes, C. I.: H_∞ Control of Discrete-Time Nonlinear Systems. *IEEE Transactions on Automatic Control*, **41(4)**, (1996), 494–510.
15. Mignone, D., Ferrari-Trecate, G., Morari, M.: Stability and Stabilization of Piecewise Affine and Hybrid Systems: An LMI Approach, *IEEE Conference on Decision and Control*, Sydney, Australia, (2000).
16. Scherer, C. W., Gahinet, P., Chilali, M.: Multi-Objective Output-Feedback Control via LMI Optimization. *IEEE Transactions on Automatic Control*, **42(7)**, (1997), 896–911.
17. Sontag, E.D.: Interconnected automata and linear systems: A theoretical framework in discrete-time. *Hybrid Systems III - Verification and Control*, R. Alur, T.A. Henzinger and E.D. Sontag eds., 1066, Lecture Notes in Computer Science. Springer-Verlag, Pittsburgh, USA, (1996), 436–448.
18. Van der Schaft, A. J.: L_2-gain analysis of nonlinear systems and nonlinear H_∞ control, *IEEE Transactions on Automatic Control*, **37**, (1992), 770–784.
19. Willems, J. C.: Dissipative dynamic systems, *Arch. Rational Mechanics Analysis*, **45**, (1972), 321–393.
20. Yakubovich, V. A.: S-Procedure in nonlinear control theory. *Vestnik Leninggradskogo Universiteta*, Ser. Matematika, (1971), 62–77.

Accurate Event Detection
for Simulating Hybrid Systems

Joel M. Esposito[1], Vijay Kumar[1], and George J. Pappas[2]

[1] MEAM Department, University of Pennsylvania, Philadelphia, PA 19104,
[2] EE Department, University of Pennsylvania, Philadelphia, PA 19104
{jme,kumar,pappasg}@grip.cis.upenn.edu

Abstract. It has been observed that there are a variety of situations in which the most popular hybrid simulation methods can fail to properly detect the occurrence of discrete events. In this paper, we present a method for detecting discrete which, using techniques borrowed from control theory, selects integration step sizes in such a way that the simulation slows down as the state approaches a set which triggers an event (a guard set). Our method guarantees that the state will approach the boundary of this set exponentially; and in the case of linear or polynomial guard descriptions, terminating on it, without entering it. Given that any system with a nonlinear guard description can be transformed to an equivalent system with a linear guard description, this technique is applicable to a broad class of systems. Even in situations where nonlinear guards have not been transformed to the canonical form, the method is still increases the chances of detecting and event in practice. We show how to extend the method to guard sets which are constructed from many simple sets using boolean operators (*e.g.* polyhedral or semi-algebraic sets) . The technique is easily used in combination with existing numerical integration methods and does not adversely affect the underlying accuracy or stability of the algorithms.

1 Motivation and Previous Work

Numerical simulation is an important tool for designing and analyzing hybrid systems. In addition to simulation, numerical approximation techniques are increasingly being used in approximate reachability computations, verification and other forms of automated analysis [5], [6], [13]. It is well known that when simulating hybrid systems failure to detect an event can have disastrous results on the global solution due to the discontinuous nature of the problem. Several documents detailing requirements for hybrid simulators list accurate event detection as one primary concern [14], [11].

Figure 1a illustrates graphically the behavior of a generic hybrid system model. At the initial time t_0, the mode q_1 is active and the continuous system flows according to the differential equation $\dot{x} = f_1(x)$ with initial condition $x_0 = x(t_0)$. Once the condition *Guard* is true the transition from q_1 to q_2 is enabled; the state may be reset instantaneously and the system enters mode q_2 where it then flows according to $\dot{x} = f_2(x)$. The problem we are concerned with

M.D. Di Benedetto, A. Sangiovanni-Vincentelli (Eds.): HSCC 2001, LNCS 2034, pp. 204–217, 2001.
© Springer-Verlag Berlin Heidelberg 2001

a)   b)

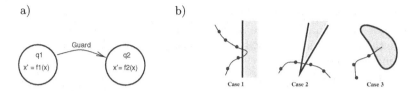

Fig. 1. (a) Conceptual model of a generic Hybrid System, (b) three situations for which popular simulators fail to properly detect or localize events.

is correctly detecting the discrete transitions. More formally: problem Given $f : R^n \rightarrow R^n$, $x_0 = x(t_0) \in R^n$ and $g : R^n \rightarrow R$ such that $g(x_0) < 0$, simulate $\dot{x} = f(x)$, for the time interval $[t_0, t^*]$ where t^* must be computed as the *first* time instant such that $g(x(t)) \geq 0$. problem We assume the guard set has a non-empty interior and is described as $Guard = \{x : g(x) \geq 0\}$ where $g(x)$ is a continuously differentiable. See [12] for an interesting discussion of the unique difficulties associated with solving such problems. It is well known that systems of differential equations with nonlinear guards can be transformed to a equivalent systems with linear guards by appending a new state variable $z = g(x)$ then the new system is

$$\dot{x} = f(x) \iff \dot{x} = f(x), \ \dot{z} = \frac{\partial g}{\partial x} \cdot f(x)$$
$$g(x) \geq 0 \qquad z \geq 0. \tag{1}$$

Most hybrid system simulators([1], [9], [18]) divide the task into an event *detection* phase followed by an event *localization* phase. They proceed with the detection phase by checking if $g(x(t_0)) \geq 0$. If the condition is false, numerically integrate the differential equation through one time step, to $t_1 = t_0 + h$ and check if $g(x(t_1)) \geq 0$. This procedure is repeated until a step is taken for which $g(x(t_k)) \geq 0$ is true, at which point an event is assumed to have occured in the interval $(t_{k-1}, t_k]$. Note that the step size h is selected *without* considering the guard dynamics. Some tools then activate a localization phase to determine the time of occurrence more precisely, but some simply assume the event occured at t_k. The localization phase is typically a variant on the bisection or bracketing algorithms found in the classical numerical analysis literature. Once the event is localized the integration is stopped, and the transitions occur.

Although this basic technique, first introduced in [4], seems to work well for many problems there are several situations in which it is prone to failure. The situations, discussed below, are illustrated in Figure 1b. The first case is when the trajectory is sufficiently oscillatory that the guard has an even number of roots in the interval $t^* \in (t_k, t_{k+1}]$. A similar situation occurs when the guard set is "thin" or has sharp corners. These two cases are essentially equivalent. Both are situations in which many of the most common *detection* methods can fail. As second class of problems for which the standard technique fails, consider the case when the right hand side of the differential equation is ill-defined for some x such that $g(x) \geq 0$. Perhaps the nature of the system is such that model is only valid in certain regions of the state space. Since the right hand side of the ODE cannot be evaluated at the new point, bisection methods cannot be used to locate the root more precisely. In this situation, almost all common event *localization* methods fail.

Cellier [4] was the first to note that state events warrant special treatment and advocated the discontinuity locking approach still used today. Gear [8] demonstrated the inefficiencies that can result if special techniques are not used. Carver [3] was the first person to notice that the rate of change of the event function along the flow field (*i.e.* the Lie derivative) was a critical quantity in event detection. The idea of differentiating the guard and appending it as an extra state variable to be integrated was introduced there as well. In each of these cases events were detected by simply looking for sign changes in the guard after integrating through one step. As a result they fail to detect an event when there are multiple transitions in a single step. Building on this work, Shampine and his colleagues [12] exploit the fact that interpolation polynomials can be generated for the guard dynamics and are able to correctly identify event occurrences using Strum sequences when the guards are of polynomial expressions but do not use this information to select step sizes. Several similar algorithms for event detection in differential algebraic equations were evaluated in [15]. These techniques are able to detect multiple transition however they tend to be expensive. Most recently, Park and Barton [17] combine some of these ideas and uses methods from interval arithmetic to create efficient tests to determine intervals where it is possible an event had occured. This event detection method seems to be the most reliable technique in the literature, it is streamlined and well suited to stiff problems. However since all of the techniques use the discontinuity locking approach, none of these provides a methodology to select step sizes to ensure that the state never crosses the event surface; thus all fail to localize and event which occurs in the neighborhood of a model singularity.

The idea in this paper is to develop an event detection technique that is not vulnerable to these pitfalls. Using an analogy to control theory we treat the simulated system as a control system, the integration step size as an input, and the guard as the output. The problem is the to select a "feedback law" (a rule for selecting step sizes) such that as the simulation proceeds the system approaches the event surface ($g(x) = 0$) asymptotically, without overshoot ($g(x) < 0$ always). Since the state approaches the guard asymptotically there is a better chance events are detected and since there is no overshoot there is no risk of crossing a model singularity. In Section 2 we review Linear Multistep numerical integration techniques and introduce the control theoretic concept of input/output linearization which our algorithm is inspired by; in Section 3 we develop in detail the ideas used in the method, culminating in a conceptual algorithm; in Section 4 we successfully solve two example problems which can be problematic for other methods and discuss some of the limitations of the proposed algorithm; finally in Section 5 we summarize our results and comment on future directions.

2 Key Concepts

In this section we review numerical integration of ordinary differential equations using Linear Multistep Methods, our prefered integration method. We also introduce the key idea behind our algorithm which draws on the control theoretic concept of input-output linearization.

2.1 Review: Numerical Integration with Linear Multistep Methods

Given the system $\dot{x} = f(x, t)$ and $x(0) = x_0$, it is customary to denote the approximate solution at the discrete time t_k as $x_k = x(t_k)$, and then the value of the time derivative may be written as $f_k = f(x_k)$. It is also convention to define the time step as $h_k = t_k - t_{k-1}$. The most general form of a m-step linear multistep method (LMSM) is $\sum_{j=0}^{m} \alpha_j x_{k-j+1} = h_k \sum_{j=0}^{m} \beta_j f_{k-j+1}$, where α_j and β_j are the coefficients of the method. Particular LMSM's differ in how α and β are selected. LMSM's can be broadly divided into two categories: if $\beta_0 = 0$ the method is called *explicit*, otherwise if $\beta_0 \neq 0$ the method is called *implicit*. Although the techniques presented here can be applied to the entire class of explicit LMSM's, the explicit Adams family is by far the most popular and will be used for the purposes of illustration. In such a method, $\alpha_0 = 1$, $\alpha_1 = -1$, and $\alpha_j = 0$ for $j > 1$. The β_j's are then selected such that the difference equation

$$x_{k+1} = x_k + h_{k+1} \sum_{j=1}^{m} \beta_j f_{k-j+1}, \tag{2}$$

would *exactly* reproduce the analytical solution $x(t)$ if it were a polynomial of order m or lower. In general the accuracy of the method is proportional to $(h_k)^m$. The Adams family of methods is very popular due to their large region of stability and efficiency. See any numerical analysis text for further details [10]. Often in text books, values of β will be supplied as constants; however this is only the case when the step size is constant. In general, β is a rational polynomial function of the previous m step sizes, $\beta_j(h_k, \ldots, h_{k-m})$. Multistep methods, as opposed to Runge-Kutta methods, are a natural choice for simulating hybrid systems because the polynomial expressions for β_j can be used as interpolants to approximate the solution at off-mesh points.

2.2 Feedback Linearization Analogy in Continuous Time

One feature of explicit LMSM's, not present in some other methods, is the fact that x_{k+1} is defined by a difference equation which is affine in the step size h_k. This property allows one to draw comparison with nonlinear control systems which often are affine in the input. Following this analogy the difference equation of the numerical method would be the system dynamics, the step size is viewed as the input and the guard function is considered to be the output equation.

For the purposes of illustrating our method, let us imagine for a moment that, instead of belonging to the set of positive integers, we let the step number,

k, take on a continuum of values, $k \in [0, \infty)$. Further suppose that t_k is then a continuous function of the real variable k, denoted by $t(k)$. Naturally it follows that we would then write $x(t(k))$, and $g(x(t(k)))$. Analogous to the discrete case we then find that the "step size", which is our input variable, can be viewed as $h(k) = \frac{dt}{dk}$. The dynamics of the event function (our output function) are then

$$\frac{dg}{dk} = \left(\frac{\partial g}{\partial x} \frac{dx}{dt} \right) \frac{dt}{dk}, \tag{3}$$

since by definition $\frac{dx}{dt} = f(x)$ this can be rewritten as,

$$\frac{dg}{dk} = (L_f g)\, h(k). \tag{4}$$

Note that the Lie derivative, $L_f g = \frac{\partial g}{\partial x} \cdot f$, has a geometric interpretation here as the time derivative of $g(x)$ along trajectories of the ODE.

We would like to select $h(k)$ in such a way as to ensure that $g(x) \to 0$ as $k \to \infty$. This may be accomplished by a technique from nonlinear control theory called feedback linearization (see for example [2]). Assuming the Lie derivative is non-zero, selecting

$$h(k) = -\gamma \frac{g(x)}{L_f g}, \tag{5}$$

and substituting into eq.(4) results in

$$\frac{dg}{dk} = -\gamma g \tag{6}$$

where γ is some positive constant to be selected by the user. The solution to the ODE is then $g(k) = g(0) \exp^{-\gamma \cdot k}$; which implies $g(k) \to 0$ exponentially, as $k \to \infty$. Thus, by judicious selection of the input, one may cancel the nonlinearities and stabilize the guard dynamics. In terms of simulation, by selecting the step size appropriately using eq.(5) we are able to re-parameterize time in order to make the guard (as a function of the step number) behave as a linear differential equation which has a stable equilibrium point on the surface $g(x) = 0$.

3   Simulation Algorithm

In this section we describe the ideas used in our simulation algorithm: methods for computing step sizes depending on the form of the guards (Sect. 3.1– 3.3), computation of candidate step sizes (Sect. 3.4), dealing with boolean combinations of guards (Sect. 3.5), merging the candidate step size for event detection with the ideal step sizes computed for integration accuracy and other implementation details (Sect. 3.6 and 3.7). Finally, in Section 3.8 these ideas are presented as a concrete algorithm.

While Sect. 2.2 contains a useful way of thinking of such systems, the simulated system evolves in discrete time. For a linear multistep method the dynamics are

$$x(t_k + h_{k+1}) = x_{k+1} = x_k + h_{k+1}\{\sum_{j=1}^{m} \beta_j f_{k-j+1}\} \tag{7}$$

which implies the guard dynamics are

$$g(x(t_k + h_{k+1})) = g_{k+1} = g(x_k + h_{k+1}\{\sum_{j=1}^{m} \beta_j f_{k-j+1}\}). \tag{8}$$

Selecting h_{k+1} to produce the desired behavior is somewhat more difficult in discrete time.

3.1 Symbolic Inverse

In theory, provided the guard is an invertible function (with respect to time along a given integral curve), we can select

$$h_{k+1} = \frac{-x_k + g^{-1}(\gamma g(x_k))}{\bar{f}_\beta} \tag{9}$$

where the vector $\bar{f}_\beta = \sum_{j=1}^{m} \beta_j f_{k-j+1}$, yielding the *difference* equation $g_{k+1} = \gamma g_k$, which has the solution $g_k = g_0 \gamma^k$ and converges exponentially to $g = 0$ provided $0 \le \gamma < 1$. This naturally assumes one can compute the symbolic inverse of the guard, $g^{-1}(h_{k+1})$, which is an unrealistic assumption in practice.

3.2 Exact Linearization

While it is unlikely that one would have a symbolic expression for the inverse of $g(x(t))$, exact linearization is possible for all guards with Taylor series expansions of finite length (i.e polynomial or linear guards). We illustrate this idea with linear guards, since they can be used to model a wide class of systems either through approximation or by transforming nonlinear guards to linear ones using eq.(1). If our event function is of the form $g(x) = a \cdot x + b$, where $a \in R^n$ and $b \in R$ are constant eq.(4) becomes

$$g_{k+1}(h_{k+1}) = g_k + h_{k+1}\frac{\partial g}{\partial x}\bar{f}_\beta \tag{10}$$

which is essentially a Taylor series expansion in h_{k+1} about x_k. Since $\frac{\partial g}{\partial x}\bar{f}_\beta$ is simply the Lie derivative $L_{\bar{f}_\beta}g$, select

$$h_{k+1} = \frac{(\gamma - 1)g_k}{L_{\bar{f}_\beta}g}. \tag{11}$$

Polynomial guards can be handled in a similar manner, by calculating and inverting their Taylor series expansions in h_{k+1}.

3.3   Approximate Linearization

If nonlinear guards with a Taylor series expansion of infinite length are not transformed to linear guards, an approximate linearization technique can be used. Approximations using a Taylor series expansion gives

$$g_{k+1}(h_{k+1}) = g(x_k) + L_{f_\beta} g h_{k+1} + \frac{1}{2} L_{f_\beta}^2 g h_{k+1}^2 + \dots \tag{12}$$

It is possible to compute the inverse of g as a function of h for the Taylor series expansion using a result due to Grobner often referred to as the Lie series

$$g^{-1}(h) = \sum_{p=0}^{\infty} \frac{1}{p!} \{ \frac{1}{\frac{\partial g}{\partial x} \cdot f} \frac{\partial}{\partial h} \}^p h \|_{x=x_k, h=0} \cdot [(\gamma - 1)g_k]^p. \tag{13}$$

While the result is defined as an infinite series, a finite number of terms can be used to compute an approximate linearization. One sided convergence is no longer guaranteed since uncanceled terms act as forcing functions, but by selecting a small value of γ the state still approaches the event surface slowly, increasing the likelihood that the event will be detected. This method seems to work well in practice since h is typically small implying that the higher order terms are usually correspondingly small

3.4   Computation of Step Sizes

As mentioned earlier, the β's for the Adams Method are only constant in the special case of constant step size. Since we are proposing to adjust the step size dynamically, the β's in the above discussion are not constant, but rather are rational polynomial functions of h_{k+1}. Computing the correct step size with eq.(11), for example, then entails finding the roots of a polynomial in h_{k+1}. For example in the case of two step Adams method $\beta_1 = (2h_k)/h_{k+1}$ and $\beta_2 = 1 - (2h_k)/h_{k+1}$. Substituting the expressions for β into eq.(11) and rearranging gives

$$z = Roots[ah_{k+1}^2 + bh_{k+1} + c] \tag{14}$$

where $a = 1/2 \cdot h_k[\partial g/\partial x \cdot (f_k + f_{k-1})]$, $b = \partial g/\partial x \cdot f_k$ and $c = -(\gamma - 1)g(x_k)$. Eq.(14) must be solved for h_{k+1} at every time step. Similar polynomials can be constructed using eq.(9) or eq.(13). Various algorithms for computing the roots of polynomials exist, most involve constructing the companion matrix and computing its eigenvalues. In general the polynomial equation determining h_{k+1} will have m roots (for an m-step multistep method), however only positive real roots should be considered as candidates for event times, since negative roots correspond to past events, while complex roots are physically meaningless. Assume the positive real roots have been ordered from smallest to largest $\{r_1, r_2, \dots, r_p\} \subset z$, then in the simplest case of a single guard, r_1 corresponds to the first event and hence is the proper choice for h_{k+1}. If there are no positive real roots set $h_{k+1} = \infty$.

3.5   Boolean Combinations of Guards

In many realistic system models, complex guards may be composed of several algebraic inequalities joined or modified by boolean operators (*e.g.* polyhedrals or semi-algebraic sets). If the guard is $(g^a(x) \geq 0) \bigvee (g^b(x) \geq 0)$, the situation is accommodated by computing r_1^a and r_1^b, the smallest positive real roots for eq.(14) using $g^a(x)$ and $g^b(x)$, and selecting $h_{k+1} = \min[r_1^a, r_1^b]$.

In the case of $(g^a(x) \geq 0) \bigwedge (g^b(x) \geq 0)$, we compute at time t_k the sets of positive ordered real roots $\{r_1^a, r_2^a, \ldots, \}$ and $\{r_1^b, r_2^b, \ldots, \}$ using eq.(14). Then

1. if $g^a(x_k) < 0$ but $g^b(x_k) \geq 0$; and if $r_1^a < r_1^b$, let $h_{k+1} = r_1^a$.
2. if $g^b(x_k) < 0$ but $g^a(x_k) \geq 0$; and if $r_1^b < r_1^a$, let $h_{k+1} = r_1^b$.
3. if both $g^a(x) < 0$ and $g^b(x) < 0$; and if *either* $r_1^a < r_1^b < r_2^a$ or $r_1^b < r_1^a < r_2^b$; let $h_{k+1} = r_2^b$ or r_2^a respectively.

Guards prefaced with a ¬ operator can be converted to the standard form by changing their sign, that is by using $-g(x) \geq 0$ rather than $g(x) \geq 0$.

3.6   Final Selection

In practice, event considerations are not the only criteria which determine the appropriate step size to be used in simulation. Often the simulation will specify some minimum step size, $h_{\min}$, below which roundoff errors affect the stability of the computation. In addition, most modern numerical integrators estimate an ideal step size based on truncation error considerations, h_{err}. The resulting step size selected by our algorithm based on event detection, h_{k+1}, can be easily incorporated into existing integration algorithms by selecting the actual step size as

$$h = \max[h_{\min}, \min(h_{k+1}, h_{err})]. \qquad (15)$$

In this way the original accuracy and stability properties of the integration algorithm are preserved.

3.7   Termination Criteria

In cases where the guards have a Taylor series expansion of finite length, $\gamma = 0$ will yield exact and rapid convergence to the event surface; therefore the algorithm should be terminated when $g(x_{k+1}) = 0$ If the guards are more general nonlinear functions , exact convergence is not guaranteed. In such situations, conservatively selecting $0 < \gamma < 1$ will cause the simulator to take successively smaller steps toward the surface. However, selecting γ too large results in slow convergence rate and a very small γ can risk overshooting the guard, in practice we have found $0.05 < \gamma < 0.5$ to be a good selection. Slowing down the simulation in this manner has the effect of dramatically increasing the chances an event will be properly detected and may event be useful when exact linearization is possible. Since steps are taken in such a way that the value of the guard approaches zero asymptotically, it may take an infinite number of steps to reach zero exactly. Therefore the user must set a small threshold $\epsilon \geq 0$ such that the procedure is terminated when $g(x) \geq -\epsilon$. Alternatively one could choose to stop the procedure once the computed time step is smaller than h_{min}.

3.8   Algorithm

All of these ideas are assembled into an algorithm and implemented in Matlab.
Given by the user upon initialization:

- A set of atomic propositions of the form $g^a(x) \leq 0$, $g^b(x) \leq 0$, $g^c(x) \leq 0$,
  ... joined or modified using the operators $\vee$, $\wedge$, and $\neg$.
- the gain, $0 \leq \gamma < 1$; and termination tolerance $\epsilon \geq 0$.

Preprocessing

1. convert any guards of the form $\neg g(x) \leq 0$ to $-g(x) \leq 0$.
2. *if desired*, convert any nonlinear guards to linear guards, using the transformation described in eq.(1), by appending an extra state variable.

Repeat until termination

Get from the integration algorithm at each iteration:

- m previous derivatives used in the multistep integration method, f_k, f_{k-1}, ... , f_{k-m}
- ideal step size for controlling the truncation error, h_{err} and minimum allowable step size, h_{min}

Main Algorithm

1. for each atomic proposition g^a, g^b, ..., g^i, ... compute a candidate step size using the appropriate method:
   a) *symbolic inverse $o(g^i(x))^{-1}$ given by user* –

   $$Roots\,[h\bar{f}_\beta(h) + x_k - (g^i)^{-1}(\gamma g^i(x_k))] = z^i$$

   b) $g^i(x)$ *is linear or has been converted to linear form and* $L_{\bar{f}_\beta}g \neq 0$ –

   $$Roots\,[hL_{\bar{f}_\beta(h)}g^i - (\gamma - 1)g^i(x_k)] = z^i$$

   c) $g^i(x)$ *is a polynomial of order N* –

   $$Roots\,[\sum_{p=1}^{N} L^p_{\bar{f}_\beta(h)}g^i \frac{h^p}{p!} - (\gamma - 1)g^i(x_k)] = z^i$$

   d) *nonlinear $g^i(x)$* – compute roots, z^i, using Lie series (eq. 13).
2. for each set of roots from the previous step z^a, z^b, etc. discard any negative or complex roots. If there are no positive real roots for a given z^i set $h^i = \infty$; otherwise sort the positive real roots in ascending order $r^i = \{r_1, r_2, \ldots\}$.
3. Using $r^a, r^b, \ldots$, recursively compute a composite step size, r^* for each boolean conjunction using the rules in section 3.5.
4. combine this result with the step size computed in the integration algorithm using $h = \max[h_{min}, \min(r^*, h_{err})]$
5. integrate through one step of size h. If $g(x_{k+1}) \geq -\epsilon$ terminate; else, repeat

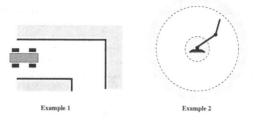

Fig. 2. Two examples: (1) an autonomous robot navigating a corridor; (2) a planar two link manipulator with workspace limitations.

4   Examples and Discussion

In this section we illustrate the effectiveness of our algorithm using the two examples shown in Figure 2. The first, controlling a car-like robot, represents a situation in which other event detection methods fail, because the guard set possesses "sharp" corners. The second, a planar manipulator with workspace limitations, illustrates a situation in which many event localization methods fail due to a model singularity. We also discuss some shortcomings of the proposed algorithm.

Example 1. Consider the nonholonomic cart trying to navigate an indoor environment as shown in Figure 2. The kinematic equations are

$$
\begin{bmatrix} \dot{x} \\ \dot{y} \\ \dot{\theta} \end{bmatrix} = \begin{bmatrix} \cos(\theta)\ 0 \\ \sin(\theta)\ 0 \\ 0\ \ 1 \end{bmatrix} \begin{bmatrix} u_1 \\ u_2 \end{bmatrix} \tag{16}
$$

where the inputs u_1 and u_2 are the forward velocity and turning rate. The details of the robot control problem and the history of u_1 and u_2 are omitted here, but it is assumed to be provided by a controller. The goal here is to verify the efficacy of the controller and in particular, to verify that the robot does not collide with the obstacles. For the sake of simplicity, we ignore the physical size of the robot and simply think of it as a point. Thus the guard(s) for the simulation are given by the equations of the walls

$$
((y - 0.5 \geq 0) \bigvee (x - 3.5 \geq 0)) \bigvee ((-y - 0.4 \geq 0) \bigwedge (2.8 - x \geq 0)). \tag{17}
$$

Figure 3a displays a situation for which the standard algorithm fails. Integration points are computed which happen to land just outside the guard region. Thus the simulator detects no collision when in fact the robot has collided with the walls, near the corner ($x = 2.8$, $y = -0.4$). Figure 3b illustrates the method presented in this paper. Observe how the integrator slows down as it approaches the event surface. Note that in this example the gain was selected in such a way as to produce a very gradual slow down, for the purposes of illustrating the technique. In practice, since the guards are linear, a gain of $\gamma = 0$ could have been used to force fast convergence.

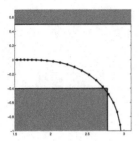 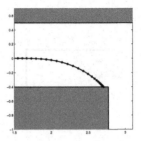

Fig. 3. Simulations of the mobile robot in example 1: (a) standard simulation technique fails to detect the collision; (b) our method slows down as it approaches the event surface.

Example 2. Consider the planar two link manipulator, as shown in Figure 2, with the kinematic equations

$$\begin{bmatrix} \dot{\theta}_1 \\ \dot{\theta}_2 \end{bmatrix} = \begin{bmatrix} \omega_1 \\ \omega_2 \end{bmatrix} \tag{18}$$

desired (x, y) positions for the end point are fed to the controller from a high level planner and the model is required to calculate θ_1 and θ_2 to achieve these positions. If the length of the proximal link is l_1 and the distal link is l_2, the appropriate inverse kinematics relation to compute θ_1, θ_2 as a function of (x, y) are

$$\theta_1 = \arctan 2 \left[\frac{-y}{\sqrt{x^2 + y^2}}, \frac{-x}{\sqrt{x^2 + y^2}} \right] \pm \cos^{-1} \left[\frac{-(x^2 + y^2 + l_1^2 - l_2^2)}{2l_1 \sqrt{x^2 + y^2}} \right] \tag{19}$$

$$\theta_2 = \arctan 2 \left[\frac{y - l_1 \sin(\theta_1)}{l_2}, \frac{x - l_1 \cos(\theta_1)}{l_2} \right] - \theta_1 \tag{20}$$

Note that it is possible for the high level planner to be unaware of the specifics of the manipulator and specify (x, y) points which are outside the set of reachable positions of the manipulator, in such cases the arguments of the $\cos^{-1}$ function would fall outside of the range of $[-1, 1]$ and the right hand side of the differential equation becomes ill-defined. In this case, given $l_1 > l_2$ the guard would be

$$(\sqrt{(x^2 + y^2)} \le (l_1 + l_2)) \bigwedge (\sqrt{(x^2 + y^2)} \ge (l_1 - l_2)) \tag{21}$$

with $x = l_1 \cos \theta_1 + l_2 \cos(\theta_1 + \theta_2), y = l_1 \sin \theta_1 + l_2 \sin(\theta_1 + \theta_2)$.

Figure 4a displays a simulation of the two link manipulator attempting to track a reference trajectory, which is a straight line in Cartesian space. In this case the reference trajectory eventually falls outside the workspace of the manipulator, where the right hand side of the differential equation becomes complex. The traditional integrator generates a point near the edge of the workspace and its next point falls outside the workspace. Because the vector field is ill-defined there, it is unable to correctly compute this new point, nor is it able to activate

a)

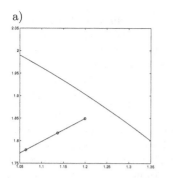

b)

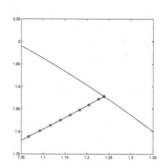

Fig. 4. Simulations of the two link manipulator from example 2: (a) root bracketing methods cannot be used since the vector field is ill-defined out side the workspace; (b) our method approaches the surface asymptotically without every requiring a function evaluation outside the workspace.

its root finding algorithm (bracketing technique) since it requires an initial point on each side of the guard. The output of our algorithm is shown in Figure 4b. Successively smaller steps are taken as the state approaches the boundary of the workspace.

Discussion. It should be said that, although our method is capable of terminating the simulation at t_k such that $g(x_k) = 0$ exactly, in some situations, or coming arbitrarily close to it in others, it can only be considered accurate insofar as the underlying integration method accurately reproduces the exact solution to the differential equation. That is to say that while $g(x_k)$ will equal zero exactly, x_k itself is not exact since it is generated through an approximation algorithm, as in all numerical analysis. Other limitations include:

- In eq.(11), which determines the step size, one must divide by the quantity $L_{\bar{f}_\beta}g$. Obviously the method is not applicable when this quantity is zero. Infact, by the inverse function theorem, $L_{\bar{f}_\beta}g = 0$ implies that the inverse of $g(t)$ used in eq.(9) does not exist. Geometrically, the differential equation is flowing purely tangential to the boundary of the guard set, an alternative method is required.
- The method requires solving for roots of eq.(14) at every step, despite the fact that that specialized algorithms exist, this computation can be a bit time consuming for higher order methods (higher order polynomials). We feel that given the importance of discrete event detection in accurate simulation this additional effort is worthwhile although an efficient exclusion test would improve the performance.

5   Conclusions and Future Work

It has been observed that there are a variety of situations in which one of the most popular hybrid simulation methods can fail to properly detect or localize the occurrence of discrete events: either due to a multiple number of zero crossings within a single step or because of model singularities. We present a method for detecting discrete events which, using techniques borrowed from control theory, selects integration step sizes in such a way that the simulation slows down as it approaches a guard. Our method guarantees that the simulation will land *exactly* on the event surface for any guard which has a Taylor series expansion of finite length. Given that any nonlinear guard can be transformed to a linear form, this technique is applicable to a broad class of systems. Even in situations where nonlinear guards have not been transformed to the canonical form, the method is still quite useful in practice. We show how to extend the method to complex guards which are built up from many simple algebraic inequalities using the boolean operators *and, or* and *not*. In this way polyhedral or semi-algebraic guards sets can be handled. The technique is easily used in combination with existing integration algorithms and does not adversely affect the underlying accuracy or stability of the numerical integration technique. Ultimately the framework presented here will be coded in Java (presently written in Matlab) and incorporated into the CHARON [16] simulation suite.

While our method requires a variable step size integration method, it has been observed that when simulating large systems such as Automated Highway Systems with 1000+ vehicles, traditional variable step size schemes are unacceptable since they require all components to be simulated at the same rate. Thus if only two of the vehicles actually necessitate a step size reduction, the entire system must be slowed down to the smallest common step size, creating gross inefficiencies. To address this problem, we are currently considering using the techniques presented here in conjunction with *multirate integration methods* such as those presented in [7]. When integrating a systems of ODEs, multirate methods use a different step size for each component. Thus, when a particular component of the set of equations is changing rapidly a small step size may be used without unnecessarily slowing down the integration rate for other slowly changing components. Multirate implementation would prevent agents not involved in the event from being simulated at an unnecessarily slow rate. We believe that these two techniques complement each other and can be used to develop a powerful simulation tool for multiagent and hierarchical hybrid systems.

Acknowledgments. We gratefully acknowledge support from DARPA grant MOBIES F33615-00-C1707 and NSF CDS-97-03220. The first author is also partially supported by a DoE GAANN grant.

References

1. A. Gollu A. Deshpande and L. Semenzato. Shift programming language and runtime system for dynamic networks of hybrid automata. *California PATH*, 1995.
2. A.Isidori. *Nonlinear Control Systems*. Springer, London, 1995.
3. M.B. Carver. Efficeint integration over discontinuities in ordinary differential equation simulations. *Mathematics and Computers in Simulation*, XX:190–196, 1978.

4. F. Cellier. *Combined discrete/ continuous system simulation by use of digital computers: techniques and tools.* PhD thesis, ETH Zurich, Zurich, Switzerland, 1979.
5. A. Chutinam and B. Krogh. Verification of polyhedral-invariant hybrid automata using polygonal flow pipe approximations. In F. Vaandrager and J. H. van Schuppen, editors, *Hybrid Systems : Computation and Control*, volume 1569 of *Lecture Notes in Computer Science*. Springer Verlag, 1999.
6. T. Dang and O. Maler. Reachability analysis via face lifting. In T. Henzinger and S. Sastry, editors, *Hybrid Systems : Computation and Control*, volume 1386 of *Lecture Notes in Computer Science*, pages 96–109. Springer Verlag, Berlin, 1998.
7. J. Esposito and V. Kumar. Efficient dynamic simulation of robotic systems with hierarchy. submitted to International Conference on Robotics and Automation 2001.
8. C.W. Gear and O.Osterby. Solving ordinary differential equations with discontinuities. Technical report, Dept. of Comput. Sci., University of Illinois, 1981.
9. D. Bruck H. Elmqvist and M. Otter. Dymola – user's manual. Dynasim AB Research Park Ideon, Lund Switzerland, 1996.
10. S. Campbell K.Benan and L. Petzold. *Numerical solutions of initial value problems.* North Holland, London, 1989.
11. S. Kowaleski, M.Fritz, H. Graf, J.Preubig, S.Simon, O.Stursberg, and H.Treseler. A case study in tool-aided analysis of discretely controled continuous systems: the two tanks problem. In *Hybrid Systems V*, Lecture Notes in Computer Science. Springer Verlag, 1998.
12. L.F.Shampine, I.Gladwell, and R.W.Brankin. Reliable solution of special event location problems for ODEs. *ACM transactions on Mathematical Software*, 17(1):11–25, March 1991.
13. Ian Mitchell and Claire Tomlin. Level set methods for computation in hybrid systems. In N. Lynch and B. H. Krogh, editors, *Hybrid Systems : Computation and Control*, volume 1790 of *Lecture Notes in Computer Science*, pages 310–323. Springer Verlag, 2000.
14. P.Mosterman. An overview of hybrid simulation phenomena and their support by simulation packages. In F.W. Vaandrager and J. H. van Schuppen, editors, *Hybrid Systems : Computation and Control*, volume 1569 of *Lecture Notes in Computer Science*, pages 163–177. Springer Verlag, 1999.
15. A.J. Preston and M.Berzins. Algorithms for the location of discontinuities in dynamic simualtion problems. *Computers in Chemical Engineering*, 15(10):701–713, 1991.
16. R.Alur, R. Grosse, Y.Hur, V. Kumar, and I. Lee. Modular specification of hybrid systems in charon. *Hybrid Systems Computation and Control: Third international workshop*, 3:6–19, 2000.
17. T.Park and P.Barton. State event location in differential-algebraic models. *ACM transactions on modeling and computer simulation*, 6(2):137–165, 1996.
18. J.Liu X.Lui, T.J.Koo, B.Sinopoli, S.Sastry, and E.A.Lee. A hierarchical hybrid system model and its simulation. *Proceedings of the 38th Conference on Decision and Control*, pages 2407–2411, 1999.

A Clustering Technique for the Identification of Piecewise Affine Systems

Giancarlo Ferrari-Trecate[1], Marco Muselli[2],
Diego Liberati[2], and Manfred Morari[1]

[1] Institut für Automatik,
ETH - Swiss Federal Institute of Technology, ETL,
CH-8092 Zürich, Switzerland,
Tel. +41-1-6327812, Fax +41-1-6321211
{ferrari,morari}@aut.ee.ethz.ch
[2] Istituto per i Circuiti Elettronici,
Consiglio Nazionale delle Ricerche,
Via De Marini, 6, 16149 Genova, Italy,
Tel: +39-010-6475213, Fax : +39-010-6475200
{liberati,muselli}@ice.ge.cnr.it

Abstract. We propose a new technique for the identification of discrete-time hybrid systems in the Piece-Wise Affine (PWA) form. The identification algorithm proposed in [10] is first considered and then improved under various aspects. Measures of confidence on the samples are introduced and exploited in order to improve the performance of both the clustering algorithm used for classifying the data and the final linear regression procedure. Moreover, clustering is performed in a suitably defined space that allows also to reconstruct different submodels that share the same coefficients but are defined on different regions.

1 Introduction

In this paper we address the problem of identifying discrete-time hybrid systems in the Piece-Wise Affine (PWA) form. The class of systems admitting a PWA description is broad since PWA systems provide an equivalent representation for interconnections of linear systems and finite automata [23], linear complementarity systems [14] and hybrid systems in the *Mixed Logic Dynamical (MLD)* form [1]. In particular, the MLD representation is suitable to solve, via optimization techniques, many analysis and synthesis problems like model predictive control [2], state estimation [9], formal verification [3], observability, controllability and stability tests [1,19].

In Section 2 we introduce the class of Piece-Wise AutoRegressive eXogenous (PWARX) models that provide an input-output description of PWA systems. PWARX models are obtained by partitioning the space of the regressors in a finite number of polyhedral region and by considering an affine submodel on each region. Therefore, the identification problem can be formulated as the

M.D. Di Benedetto, A. Sangiovanni-Vincentelli (Eds.): HSCC 2001, LNCS 2034, pp. 218–231, 2001.

reconstruction of a possibly discontinuous PWA map with a multi-dimensional domain.

In the last few years, the Neural Network community developed algorithms to solve regression problems with PWA maps. Among them, one may cite Breiman's hinging Hyperplanes [7] and multilayer neural networks with PWA activation functions [13]. However all such algorithms focus on the estimation of a *continuous* PWA function. A key feature of PWARX models is that the output-update map can be discontinuous along the boundary of the regions. This is due to the fact that many logic conditions can be represented through discontinuities in the state-update and output maps of a PWA system. To the authors' knowledge, regression with discontinuous PWA maps received very little attention so far. In [22] an algorithm based both on adaptive and competitive learning for the on-line identification of PWARX models was proposed. However, its performance strongly depends on the initialization and the choice of the learning parameters. Off-line procedure for the reconstruction of special classes of PWARX models can be found in [16] and [4]. In a very recent work [12] a regression problem with monodimensional PWA maps was considered whereas a multilayer neural networks with logic gates was proposed in [21].

An off-line procedure for the identification of general PWA systems was derived by the authors of the present paper in [10]. The main difficulty in reconstructing PWA maps is that estimation of the linear submodels cannot be separated from the problem of classifying the data, i.e. of assigning each datapoint to the submodel that more likely generated it. In order to accomplish both tasks, an algorithm that exploits the combined use of clustering and linear identification techniques was derived in [10]. The key idea of this algorithm lies in a procedure that reduces the problem of classifying the data to an optimal clustering problem.

Optimal clustering is known to be computationally prohibitive [8], and the common practice is to resort to suboptimal but efficient algorithms like K-means (see [8,11] for comprehensive reviews of various clustering techniques). However, all the classical procedures suffer from two drawbacks: first, poor initialization allows the algorithms to be trapped in local minima, second, their performance may be compromised by the presence of outliers. In this paper, we propose a "K-means"-like algorithm that exploits confidence measures on the points that have to be clustered in order to reduce the influence of outliers and poor initializations. Moreover, differently from [10], clustering is not performed in the space of the model coefficients, but in an extended space that takes also into account the spatial localization of the models. This allows to distinguish between submodels that share the same coefficients but are defined on different regions.

Once the data have been classified, linear regression can be used to compute the final submodels. However, pure least squares are not the optimal choice since they are sensitive to outliers [15] that may be present because of classification errors. In order to alleviate this shortcoming, we employ weighted least squares, using as weights suitably defined confidence measures on the datapoints. Finally, in order to find the shape of the regions, we use, as in [10], linear support vector machines [24] that find the optimal separating hyperplanes between the classified datapoints.

The various steps of the main algorithm and two illustrative examples are reported in Section 3. Moreover, in Section 4 we discuss the proposed procedure highlighting future research directions and possible modifications in order to estimate also the number of submodels and the model orders from the data set.

2   Problem Statement

We consider the problem of identifying Piecewise AutoRegressive eXogenous (PWARX) systems that are defined relying on the s submodels

$$
y(k) = \begin{cases}
a_{1,1}y(k-1) + a_{1,2}y(k-2) + \ldots + a_{1,n_a}y(k-n_a) + b'_{1,1}u(k-1) + \\
\quad + b'_{1,2}u(k-2) + \ldots + b'_{1,n_b}u(k-n_b) + f_1 + \epsilon_k \\
\vdots \\
a_{s,1}y(k-1) + a_{s,2}y(k-2) + \ldots + a_{s,n_a}y(k-n_a) + b'_{s,1}u(k-1) + \\
\quad + b'_{s,2}u(k-2) + \ldots + b'_{s,n_b}u(k-n_b) + f_s + \epsilon_k
\end{cases}
\tag{1}
$$

where $u \in \mathbb{R}^q$ and $y \in \mathbb{R}$ are the inputs and the output respectively, f_i are displacements and ϵ_k are noise samples. We consider a simple noise model by assuming that ϵ_k are Gaussian, independent and identically distributed random variables with zero mean and variance σ^2. The n-dimensional vector of the regressors is denoted by

$$
x(k) \triangleq \begin{bmatrix} y(k-1)\, y(k-2) \,\ldots\, y(k-n_a)\, u'(k-1)\, u'(k-2) \ldots\, u'(k-n_b) \end{bmatrix}'
$$

and we assume that the regressors lie in a bounded polyhedron, called *regressor set* and denoted by $\mathcal{X}$. In order to specify a PWARX model completely, a polyhedral partition $\{\mathcal{X}_i\}_{i=1}^{s}$ of $\mathcal{X}$ is given and the switching law between the models is specified by the rule: if $x(k) \in \mathcal{X}_i$, the i-th dynamic of (1) is active. When an input/output pair $(x(k), y(k))$ is such that $x(k) \in \mathcal{X}_i$ we say that the pair belongs to the i-th submodel. As discussed in [10], one advantage of PWARX models is that it is possible to map them into the standard state-space form of PWA systems by using classical realization theory. Therefore, all the tools for analysis and synthesis for hybrid systems in the MLD/PWA form can be directly applied to the identified model.

Throughout this paper we assume that N input/output points $(y(k), u(k))$, $k = 0, \ldots, N$, have been collected in the dataset $\mathcal{S}$. These are the data available for the identification of the PWARX model.

Assumption 1 *The data are generated from the PWARX model (1) specified by the orders $\bar{n}_a$, $\bar{n}_b$, the number of submodels $\bar{s}$, the parameter vectors*

$$
\bar{\theta}_i = \begin{bmatrix} \bar{a}_{i,1}\, \bar{a}_{i,2} \,\ldots\, \bar{a}_{i,\bar{n}_a} \bar{b}'_{i,1}\, \bar{b}'_{i,2} \,\ldots\, \bar{b}'_{i,\bar{n}_b} \bar{f}_i \end{bmatrix}'
\tag{2}
$$

and the sets $\bar{\mathcal{X}}$, $\bar{\mathcal{X}}_i$, $i = 1, \ldots, \bar{s}$,

Remark 1. If the data are generated according to Assumption 1 and $\bar{n}_a$, $\bar{n}_b$, $\bar{s}$, $\bar{\mathcal{X}}$ and $\bar{\mathcal{X}}_i$, $i = 1, \dots, \bar{s}$, are known, the identification problem amounts to reconstruct the $\bar{s}$ ARX submodels in (1) and this can be done by using standard algorithms for the identification of linear models [17]. In fact, since the sets $\bar{\mathcal{X}}_i$ are known, we can *classify* the points $(x(k), y(k))$, i.e., collect together the datapoints belonging to the i-th affine submodel and use them for its identification.

The identification problem becomes non-trivial if we do not know all the quantities mentioned in Remark 1. As discussed in [10] a fair scenario for the identification of PWARX models is given by the following Assumption.

Assumption 2 *Assumption 1 holds and the number of submodels $\bar{s}$, the orders $\bar{n}_a$, $\bar{n}_b$ and the regressor set $\bar{\mathcal{X}}$ are known. Moreover, $s = \bar{s}$, $n_a = \bar{n}_a$, $n_b = \bar{n}_b$ and $\mathcal{X} = \bar{\mathcal{X}}$.*

The number of models depends on the number of operative conditions in which the data are collected. For instance one can know in advance that the systems may only switch between a normal and a faulty operating condition, i.e., $s = 2$. The assumption that the model orders n_a and n_b are known is less realistic but will allow us to concentrate on the peculiarities of the identification of PWARX models without introducing the difficulties due to the estimation of the model orders. The shape of the set $\mathcal{X}$ describes the physical constraints on the inputs and the output of the system. In practice, constraints are often specified on each input/output sample or on each input/output increment and from these bounds it is easy to derive the set $\mathcal{X}$ once the orders n_a and n_b have been chosen [10].

3   The Main Algorithm

Based on the previous discussion, the identification problem we consider reads as

Problem 1. Assume that the data $(y(k), u(k))$, $k = 0, \dots, N$, are generated according to Assumption 1 and that Assumption 2 holds. Estimate the partition $\mathcal{X}_i$, $i = 1, \dots, s$, and the parameter vectors

$$\theta'_i = \left[a_{i,1}\ a_{i,2} \ \dots \ a_{i,n_a} b'_{i,1}\ b'_{i,2} \ \dots \ b'_{i,n_b} f_i \right] \tag{3}$$

characterizing the PWARX model (1).

The main difficulty in solving Problem 1 is that the estimation of the regions $\mathcal{X}_i$ cannot be decoupled from the identification of each submodel. A first algorithm to solve Problem 1 was proposed in [10]. Hereafter we summarize this procedure and propose modifications that improve the identification results. The underlying rationale will be illustrated by using the following simple example.

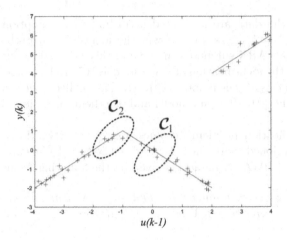

Fig. 1. The PWARX system (4) (-) and the dataset (crosses)

Example 1. The data are generated by the PWARX system

$$
y(k) = \begin{cases}
\begin{bmatrix} 1 & 2 \end{bmatrix} \begin{bmatrix} u(k-1) & 1 \end{bmatrix}' + \epsilon(k) & \text{if } u(k-1) = x(k) \in \bar{\mathcal{X}}_1 = [-4, -1] \\
\begin{bmatrix} -1 & 0 \end{bmatrix} \begin{bmatrix} u(k-1) & 1 \end{bmatrix}' + \epsilon(k) & \text{if } u(k-1) = x(k) \in \bar{\mathcal{X}}_2 = (-1, 2) \quad (4) \\
\begin{bmatrix} 1 & 2 \end{bmatrix} \begin{bmatrix} u(k-1) & 1 \end{bmatrix}' + \epsilon(k) & \text{if } u(k-1) = x(k) \in \bar{\mathcal{X}}_3 = [2, 4]
\end{cases}
$$

where $\bar{s} = 3$, $\bar{n}_a = 0$, $\bar{n}_b = 1$, $\bar{\mathcal{X}} = [-4, 4]$, and the input samples $u(k) \in \mathbb{R}$ are generated randomly according to the uniform distribution on $\bar{\mathcal{X}}$.

The system and a data set of 50 samples with noise variance $\sigma^2 = 0.05$ are depicted in Figure 1.

The first step of the identification algorithm is to cluster the datapoints $(x(k), y(k))$ in a suitable way [10]. In fact, a PWA map is *locally linear*. Thus, small subsets of points $x(k)$ that are close to each other are likely to belong to the same region $\bar{\mathcal{X}}_i$ [20]. For each datapoint $(x(j), y(j))$, $j = 1, \dots, N$, we build a cluster $\mathcal{C}_j$ collecting $(x(j), y(j))$ and the $c - 1$ distinct datapoints $(\tilde{x}, \tilde{y})$ that satisfy

$$
\forall (\tilde{x}, \tilde{y}) \in \mathcal{C}_j, \quad \|x(j) - \tilde{x}\|^2 \leq \|x(j) - \hat{x}\|^2, \quad \forall (\hat{x}, \hat{y}) \in \mathcal{S} \backslash \mathcal{C}_j. \quad (5)
$$

Note that each cluster $\mathcal{C}_j$ can be labeled with the point $x(j)$ so having a bijective map between datapoints and clusters. The parameter c has to be fixed by the user and this is a knob of our algorithm that can be adjusted. Some clusters will collect only data belonging to a single submodel (for instance the cluster $\mathcal{C}_1$ in Figure 1). Those clusters will be referred to as *pure* clusters. Clusters collecting data generated by different submodels will be called *mixed* clusters (see the cluster $\mathcal{C}_2$ in Figure 1).

We assume that $c > n$ so that we can identify an affine model by using the samples contained in each cluster. For this purpose every linear regression technique can be used and we adopt least squares estimation. The vector of coefficients $\theta^{LS,j}$ estimated from the data in $\mathcal{C}_j$ is then computed through the well-known formula

$$\theta^{LS,j} = (\Phi'_j \Phi_j)^{-1} \Phi'_j y_{\mathcal{C}_j}, \quad \Phi_j = \begin{bmatrix} x_1 & x_2 & \cdots & x_c \\ 1 & 1 & \cdots & 1 \end{bmatrix}' \tag{6}$$

where x_i are the vectors of regressors belonging to $\mathcal{C}_j$ and $y_{\mathcal{C}_j}$ is the vector of the output samples in $\mathcal{C}_j$. A classical result in least squares theory ensures that the estimated vectors of coefficients are Gaussian random vectors with mean $\theta^{LS,j}$. Moreover, their empirical covariance matrix can be computed as [17]

$$V_j = \frac{SSR_j}{c - n + 1}(\Phi'_j \Phi_j)^{-1}, \quad SSR_j = y'_{\mathcal{C}_j}\left(I - \Phi_j(\Phi'_j \Phi_j)^{-1}\Phi'_j\right)y_{\mathcal{C}_j} \tag{7}$$

Differently from the rationale described in [10], we also introduce the scatter matrices [8]

$$Q_j = \sum_{(x,y)\in\mathcal{C}_j}(x - m_j)(x - m_j)', \quad m_j = \frac{1}{c}\sum_{(x,y)\in\mathcal{C}_j} x, \quad j = 1,\ldots,N \tag{8}$$

that measure the sparsity of the $\mathcal{X}$-points in the clusters $\mathcal{C}_j$.

Both V_j^{-1} and Q_j^{-1} are related to the confidence we should have in the fact that θ_j is derived by using data belonging to a *single submodel*. In fact, the covariance of the $\theta^{LS,j}$ based on pure clusters depends only on the noise level and is expected to be smaller than the covariance of the $\theta^{LS,j}$ based on mixed clusters [10]. The reason is that, in the latter case, we are fitting with a single hyperplane datapoints generated by at least two hyperplanes: If they do not coincide, V_j will also take into account the model mismatch that increases the sum of the squared residual SSR_j. On the other hand, the confidence level on θ_j should also depend on the sparsity of the $\mathcal{X}$-points in the cluster $\mathcal{C}_j$. Indeed, scattered clouds of $\mathcal{X}$-points are more likely to belong to different submodels than dense clouds. Therefore the confidence level should be also proportional to the "magnitude" of Q_j^{-1}. In order to illustrate this point, consider the scenario depicted in Figure 2 where a two dimensional set $\mathcal{X}$ (partitioned in three regions) is shown together with the collected $\mathcal{X}$-datapoints.

If the true coefficient vectors $\bar{\theta}_1$ and $\bar{\theta}_3$ coincide (i.e., the same model is defined on the regions $\mathcal{X}_1$ and $\mathcal{X}_3$) it is impossible to assign a lower confidence to $\theta^{LS,2}$ than to $\theta^{LS,1}$ on the basis of the matrices V_1 and V_2 alone. Indeed, even if $\mathcal{C}_2$ is a mixed cluster, there is no model mismatch. However it is expected that Q_1^{-1} will be "larger" than Q_2^{-1} and this indicate that is more likely that $\theta^{LS,1}$ is based on a pure cluster than $\theta^{LS,2}$.

Consider now the vectors $\xi_j = [(\theta^{LS,j})', m'_j]'$, $\forall j = 1,\ldots,N$. Following the previous discussion we can approximatively model ξ_j as the realization of Gaussian random vectors with mean ξ_j and variance

$$R_j = \begin{bmatrix} V_j & 0 \\ 0 & Q_j \end{bmatrix} \tag{9}$$

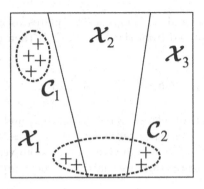

Fig. 2. Clusters in a two-dimensional region $\mathcal{X}$. Crosses: sampled points.

A scalar measure of the confidence level we assign to the point ξ_j is then given by

$$w_j = \frac{1}{\sqrt{(2\pi)^{(2n_a+2n_b+1)}\det(R_i)}}, \tag{10}$$

that is the peak of the Gaussian centered in ξ_j and with covariance R_j.

If the data are corrupted by a small amount of noise, if c is small enough and if the sampling schedule is "fair" (see the discussion in Section 4), then a picture of the vectors ξ_j, $j = 1,\ldots,N$, should show s major clusters and some isolated points hereafter referred to as *outliers*. In fact we observe that if two clusters C_{j_1} and C_{j_2} are pure and collect datapoints belonging to the same submodel, then θ^{LS,j_1} and θ^{LS,j_2} should be similar (in the limit case of noiseless data all such vectors coincide). The outliers correspond to ξ_j points computed from mixed clusters. However, the information provided by the θ-vectors alone may be misleading, since it can also happen that the *same* vector of coefficients $\bar{\theta}$ characterize submodels defined on different regions (see the first and the third submodels in the Example 1). In this case the estimated θ-vectors collapse into a single cluster. The separation of the corresponding ξ-points is achieved because of the vectors m_j that measure the spatial localization of the models based on different clusters C_j. Since the models are defined in different regions, the m_j vectors will be different even if the coefficients $\theta^{LS,j}$ are not. This fact can be noticed by looking at the plot in Figure 3(a) of the vectors ξ_j obtained for Example 1 with $c = 6$.

Remark 2. The parameter c should be suitably chosen in order to obtain non-overlapping clusters in the ξ-space. The optimal value of c is always a trade-off between two phenomena. Increasing c improves the estimation of the θ_j coefficients based on pure clusters yielding noise rejection benefits. However, at the same time, a large c increases also the number of mixed-clusters (in fact, for $c = N$ all the clusters become mixed) and of the outliers in the ξ-space. For a thorough discussion on the role of the parameter c we defer the reader to [10].

The next step of the algorithm amounts to clustering the ξ-points into s disjoint subsets $\mathcal{D}_i$. For this purpose, in principle, any clustering algorithm can be used (see [8,11] for comprehensive reviews) but the accuracy of the results can be spoiled either by a poor initialization (that lets the algorithm be trapped in local minima) or by the presence of outliers. In our case we can exploit the measures of the confidence on each ξ-point in order to alleviate these shortcomings.

The clustering technique we propose is a variation of the batch K-means algorithm [18,6,11].

Algorithm 1

Initialize the centers μ_i, $i = 1, \ldots, s$, and fix a threshold $\epsilon > 0$

1. compute the clusters $\mathcal{D}_i$ of ξ-points that minimize

$$J = \sum_{i=1}^{s} \sum_{\xi_j \in \mathcal{D}_i} \|\xi_j - \mu_i\|_{R_j^{-1}}^2. \tag{11}$$

2. update the centers according to the formula

$$\tilde{\mu}_i = \frac{\sum_{j:\xi_j \in \mathcal{D}_i} \xi_j w_j}{\sum_{j:\xi_j \in \mathcal{D}_i} w_j} \tag{12}$$

3. if $\max\|\tilde{\mu}_i - \mu_i\| < \epsilon$, $\forall i = 1, \ldots, s$, exit, else set $\mu_i = \tilde{\mu}_i$ and go to 1.

The main differences between Algorithm 1 and the classical K-means are the rule (11) for assigning the vectors ξ_j to the clusters $\mathcal{D}_i$ and the formula (12) for updating the centers μ_i of the clusters. However, it is important to note that these modifications do not spoil the computational efficiency of K-means.

The use of the norms $\|\cdot\|_{R_i^{-1}}$ in (11) allows assigning little influence to the ξ-points based on mixed clusters. Similar considerations justify the use of the weights w_j in (12). Then, it is expected that the centers μ^j will mainly depend on the ξ-points based on pure clusters. We can exploit the confidence weights also to provide a good initialization of the centers in Algorithm 1. We suggest to randomly assign the ξ_j vectors to s sets $\mathcal{D}_i^0$ (in a way such that each set collects approximatively N/s samples) and to compute the initial centers μ_i as the weighted means of the elements in $\mathcal{D}_i^0$ (i.e. analogously to formula (12)). If the number of ξ-points based on pure clusters is much larger than the number of outliers, it is expected that, because of the averaging procedure, the centers will be little influenced by the outliers. In practice, we noticed that this initialization procedure gives very good results compared to other common strategies like choosing the centers randomly from the $\mathcal{X}$-points in $\mathcal{S}$. The result of Algorithm 1 applied to Example 1 is plotted in Figure 3(b).

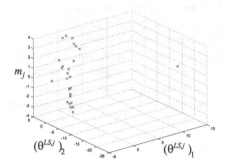
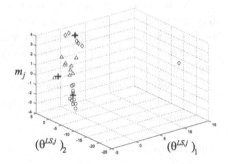

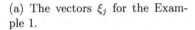

(a) The vectors ξ_j for the Example 1.

(b) Clustering of the vectors ξ_j with Algorithm 1. Clusters: triangle, diamonds, circles. The crosses are the centers of each cluster.

Fig. 3. Clustering of the vectors ξ_j, $j = 1, \ldots, 50$

Clustering in the ξ-space allows to classify the original datapoints with the procedure reported in [10]. In fact, each point ξ_j is associated to a single cluster $\mathcal{C}_j$ that is labeled with the datapoint $(x(j), y(j))$. Therefore we can form disjoint subsets $\mathcal{F}_i$, $i = 1, \ldots, s$, of $\mathcal{S}$ according the following rule: if $\xi_j \in \mathcal{D}_i$, then $(x(j), y(j)) \in \mathcal{F}_i$. The classified datapoints for the Example 1 are shown in Figure 4.

Since the original data are now classified, it is possible to identify the final s ARX submodels. More precisely the i-th submodel is estimated on the basis of the datapoints collected in the set $\mathcal{F}_i$. Again one can use least squares to accomplish this task. This allows also checking the goodness of each submodel by estimating the covariance of the final parameters θ_i and using standard criteria like confidence intervals. However one of the main drawbacks of least squares lies in the sensitivity of the method to outliers [15] that may be present due to classification errors. We can reduce the harmful effect of the outliers by using once more the confidence levels w_j in the weighted least squares algorithm [17]. Therefore, each vector θ_i is computed as the minimizer of

$$\sum_{(x(j),y(j))\in\mathcal{F}_i} w_j \|y(j) - \theta_i' \left[x'(j) \; 1 \right]' \|^2 \tag{13}$$

For Example 1 we obtained the following estimates

$$\theta_1' = \begin{bmatrix} 0.9659 & 1.9100 \end{bmatrix}, \quad \theta_2' = \begin{bmatrix} -0.9873 & -0.0240 \end{bmatrix}, \quad \theta_3' = \begin{bmatrix} 0.9580 & 2.2596 \end{bmatrix}$$

that provide a good approximation of the PWARX system (4).

So far we have obtained an estimate of each affine submodel of the PWARX representation. The final step is to look for the shape of the polyhedral regions $\mathcal{X}_i$. To accomplish this task we used the pattern recognition procedure proposed in [10] based on linear support vector machines and linear programming. Since the data have been classified, the problem of estimating the sets $\mathcal{X}_i$ amounts to a pattern recognition problem [6]. Note that there is a hyperplane that separates the set $\mathcal{X}_i$ from the set $\mathcal{X}_j$, $\forall j \neq i$ because all the sets $\mathcal{X}_i$ are polyhedral and convex. We can estimate such hyperplanes by applying a linear pattern recognition algorithm that separates the x-points in $\mathcal{F}_i$ from the x-points in $\mathcal{F}_j$, $\forall j \neq i$. The equation of the estimated hyperplane separating $\mathcal{F}_i$ from $\mathcal{F}_j$ is denoted with $M_{ij}x = m_{ij}$ where M_{ij} and m_{ij} are matrices of suitable dimensions. Moreover, we assume that the points in $\mathcal{X}_i$ belong to the half-space $M_{ij}x \leq m_{ij}$.

Due to errors in clustering, it may not be possible to find all the separating hyperplanes. Therefore, the classification algorithm should look for the hyperplanes that minimize the number of misclassified samples. For the classification we used linear Support Vector Machines [24] because they are appealing from a computational point of view (they can be solved through Linear or Quadratic Programming) and they isolate, as a byproduct, the misclassified samples.

Remark 3. Note that classification errors arise only when the sets $\mathcal{F}_i$ and $\mathcal{F}_j$ with $j \neq i$ are not linearly separable. Since Assumption 1 holds, this means that there were errors in the clustering of the ξ-vectors. In other words, the fact that the sets $\mathcal{X}_i$ are polyhedral and convex allows detecting *a posteriori* clustering errors (that are likely to be caused by the ξ-points based on mixed clusters $\mathcal{C}_k$). Then, in order to improve the overall performance of the algorithm, it is possible to remove the misclassified points $(x(k), y(k))$ from the dataset and repeat the overall identification procedure on the reduced set of datapoints.

In order to obtain a description of the set $\mathcal{X}_i$ in terms of linear inequalities, it is then enough to consider the bounded polyhedron

$$\left[M'_{i1} \; \ldots \; M'_{is} \, M' \right]' x \leq \left[m'_{i1} \; \ldots \; m'_{is} \, m' \right]'. \tag{14}$$

where $Mx \leq m$ are the linear inequalities describing $\mathcal{X}$. In (14) there may be redundant constraints that can be eliminated by using standard linear programming techniques.

For Example 1, the following estimated sets were obtained

$$\mathcal{X}_1 = [-4, -0.68], \quad \mathcal{X}_2 = [-0.68, 2.1], \quad \mathcal{X}_3 = [2.1, 4]. \tag{15}$$

The error in detecting the boundary at -1 between $\bar{\mathcal{X}}_1$ and $\bar{\mathcal{X}}_2$ is due to the fact that the datapoint $(-0.994, 0.608)$ was misclassified. However, as can be noticed by visual inspection in Figure 1, it is really hard to decide if the datapoint belongs to the first or the second submodel because the boundary is a point of continuity for the PWARX system. The results of the identification algorithm are shown in Figure 4.

We conclude the section by reporting the identification results for a more complex PWARX system.

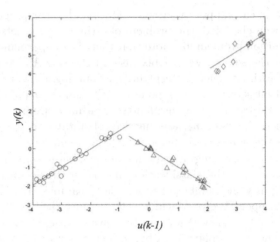

Fig. 4. Classified datapoints (triangles, diamonds, circles) and estimated model (-).

Example 2. The data are generated by the PWARX system

$$
y(k) = \begin{cases}
\begin{bmatrix} 0.9\, 0.2\, 0 \end{bmatrix} \begin{bmatrix} y(k-1)\ u(k-1)\ 1 \end{bmatrix}' + \epsilon(k) & \text{if } x(k) \in \bar{\mathcal{X}}_1 \\
\begin{bmatrix} 0.3 -0.3 -5 \end{bmatrix} \begin{bmatrix} y(k-1)\ u(k-1)\ 1 \end{bmatrix}' + \epsilon(k) & \text{if } x(k) \in \bar{\mathcal{X}}_2 \\
\begin{bmatrix} 0.5\, 0.4\, 2 \end{bmatrix} \begin{bmatrix} y(k-1)\ u(k-1)\ 1 \end{bmatrix}' + \epsilon(k) & \text{if } x(k) \in \bar{\mathcal{X}}_3
\end{cases} \quad (16)
$$

where $x(k) = \begin{bmatrix} y(k-1)\ u(k-1) \end{bmatrix}'$, $\bar{s} = 3$, $\bar{n}_a = 1$, $\bar{n}_b = 1$, $\bar{\mathcal{X}} = [-30, 40] \times [-40, 40]$ and the regions $\bar{\mathcal{X}}_1$, $\bar{\mathcal{X}}_2$, $\bar{\mathcal{X}}_3$ are shown in Figure 5(a). The input samples $u(k) \in \mathbb{R}$ are generated randomly according to the uniform distribution on $[-30, 40]$ and the variance of the noise affecting the output is $\sigma^2 = 0.2$. The model and the dataset of 100 samples are depicted in Figure 5(a).

The final results were computed (with a non-optimized code) in 11.88 s on a Pentium II 400 running Matlab 5.3. The identified submodels and the classified datapoints for $c = 9$ are shown in Figure 5(b). The estimated coefficients are

$$
\theta'_1 = \begin{bmatrix} 0.9108\ 0.1839\ 0.4301 \end{bmatrix},
$$
$$
\theta'_2 = \begin{bmatrix} 0.2926\ -0.2489\ -4.0013 \end{bmatrix},
$$
$$
\theta'_3 = \begin{bmatrix} 0.4826\ 0.3834\ 2.2510 \end{bmatrix}.
$$

4   Discussion and Concluding Remarks

The proposed algorithm is composed of six steps: build small clusters of the original data; identify a parameter vector based on each cluster; partition the

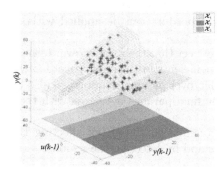

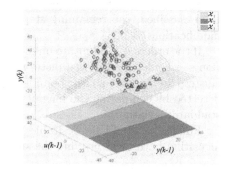

(a) The true model and the data-point (crosses)

(b) Classified datapoints (triangles, diamonds, circles) and estimated model.

Fig. 5. The PWARX system (16) and the identification results

parameter vectors in s clusters; classify the original data; estimate the s sub-models; estimate the partition $\mathcal{X}_i$, $i = 1, \ldots , s$, by using a linear classification algorithm.

For the clustering in the ξ-space, we propose a modified K-means algorithm, although other procedures can be considered to cope with the problem of ending in local minima. For instance, one can resort to soft competitive clustering algorithms that are less sensitive to initialization [11]. In order to improve the performance of the clustering algorithm, it is also possible to exploit the measures of confidence on the ξ-points in order to detect the outliers in the ξ-space, eliminate them from the set of the ξ-points and eliminate the corresponding datapoints from the clusters $\mathcal{F}_i$. In fact, the clusterization of the outliers may have a high degree of uncertainty and classification errors may spoil the accuracy of the final classification procedure.

The proposed algorithm gives good results under the implicit assumption that the sampling in the $\mathcal{X}$-space is "fair", i.e. that the input is persistently exciting and that the x-points are not all concentrated around the boundary of the sets $\mathcal{X}_i$. In fact, in the latter case it may happen that all the clusters $\mathcal{C}_j$ become mixed even if a large number of samples belonging to each submodel has been collected. We point out that the problem of input design for hybrid systems is quite difficult because all reachable modes have to be sufficiently excited. A thorough characterization of such conditions will be the subject of further research.

In the previous Sections we assumed that the number of models $\bar{s}$ is given. If it is unknown it should be estimated from the dataset. This can be done by replacing the modified K-means algorithm with a clustering algorithm where the number of clusters is not fixed a priori such as the Growing Neural Gas [11] or the MDL-based procedure proposed in [5]. In such methods the number of clusters is automatically detected. It is apparent that once the ξ-points have been classified, the remaining steps of our procedure can be applied without modifications.

If the orders n_a and n_b are unknown, we expect that their under/over estimation can be detected from a picture of the coefficients in the dual space (i.e. the clusters do not have a clear boundary). Under/over parametrization can also be detected by comparing the magnitude of the final parameter vectors with their standard deviation.

Finally, it would be desirable to have bounds on the errors affecting the algorithm both in identifying the submodels and in detecting the regions.

Acknowledgments. The research of G. Ferrari-Trecate has been supported by the Swiss National Science Foundation. D. Liberati and M. Muselli have been supported by the Italian National Research Council.

References

1. A. Bemporad, G. Ferrari-Trecate, and M. Morari. Observability and controllability of piecewise affine and hybrid systems. *IEEE Trans. on Automatic Control*, 45(10):1864–1876, 2000.
2. A. Bemporad and M. Morari. Control of systems integrating logic, dynamics, and constraints. *Automatica*, 35(3):407–428, March 1999.
3. A. Bemporad and M. Morari. Verification of hybrid systems via mathematical programming. In F.W. Vaandrager and J.H. van Schuppen, editors, *Hybrid Systems: Computation and Control*, volume 1569 of *Lecture Notes in Computer Science*, pages 31–45. Springer Verlag, 1999.
4. A. Bemporad, J. Roll, and L. Ljung. Identification of hybrid systems via mixed-integer programming. Technical Report AUT00-28, Automatic Control Laboratory http://control.ethz.ch/, 2000.
5. H. Bischof, A. Leonardis, and A. Selb. MLD principle for robust vector quantisation. *Pattern Analysis & Applications*, 2:59–72, 1995.
6. C.M. Bishop. *Neural networks for pattern recognition*. Clarendon press, Oxford, 1995.
7. L. Breiman. Hinging hyperplanes for regression, classification, and function approximation. *IEEE Trans. Inform. Theory*, 39(3):999–1013, 1993.
8. R.O. Duda and P.E. Hart. *Pattern Classification and Scene Analysis*. Wiley, 1973.
9. G. Ferrari-Trecate, D. Mignone, and M. Morari. Moving Horizon Estimation for Piecewise Affine Systems. *Proceedings of the American Control Conference*, 2000.
10. G. Ferrari-Trecate, M. Muselli, D. Liberati, and M. Morari. Identification of piecewise affine and hybrid systems. Technical Report AUT00-21, http://control.ethz.ch, ETH Zürich, 2000.
11. B. Fritzke. Some competitive learning methods. Technical report, Institute for Neural Computation. Ruhr-Universit at Bochum., 1997. http://www.neuroinformatik.ruhr-uni-bochum.de/ini/VDM/research/gsn/Java%Paper/.
12. R.E. Groff, D.E. Koditschek, and P.P. Khargonekar. Piecewise linear homeomorphisms: The scalar case. *Proc. Int. Joint Conf. on Neural Networks*, 2000.
13. S. Haykin. *Neural networks - a comprehensive foundation*. Macmillan, Englewood Cliffs, 1994.

14. W.P.M.H. Heemels and B. De Schutter. On the equivalence of classes of hybrid systems: Mixed logical dynamical and complementarity systems. Technical Report 00 I/04, Dept. of Electrical Engineering, Technische Universiteit Eindhoven, June 2000.

15. P.J. Huber. *Robust Statistics*. Wiley, 1981.

16. T.A. Johansen and B.A. Foss. Identification of non-linear system structure and parameters using regime decomposition. *Automatica*, 31(2):321–326, 1995.

17. L. Ljung. *System Identification - Theory For the User*. Prentice Hall, Upper Saddle River, N.J., 1999. 2nd ed.

18. J. MacQueen. On convergence of K-means and partitions with minimum average variance. *Ann. Math. Statist.*, 36:1084, 1965. Abstract.

19. D. Mignone, G. Ferrari-Trecate, and M. Morari. Stability and Stabilization of Piecewise Affine and Hybrid Systems: An LMI Approach. *Conference on Decision and Control*, 2000. 12-15 December, Sydney, Australia.

20. M. Muselli and D. Liberati. Training digital circuits with Hamming clustering. *IEEE Trans. Circuits and Systems - Part I*, 47(4):513–527, 2000.

21. K. Nakayama, A. Hirano, and A. Kanbe. A structure trainable neural network with embedded gating units and its learning algorithm. *Proc. Int. Joint Conf. on Neural Networks*, 2000.

22. A. Skeppstedt, L. Ljung, and M. Millnert. Construction of composite models from observed data. *Int. J. Control*, 55(1):141–152, 1992.

23. E.D. Sontag. Interconnected automata and linear systems: A theoretical framework in discrete-time. In R. Alur, T.A. Henzinger, and E.D. Sontag, editors, *Hybrid Systems III - Verification and Control*, number 1066 in Lecture Notes in Computer Science, pages 436–448. Springer-Verlag, 1996.

24. V. Vapnik. *Statistical Learning Theory*. John Wiley, NY, 1998.

Lateral Inhibition through Delta-Notch Signaling: A Piecewise Affine Hybrid Model*

Ronojoy Ghosh and Claire J. Tomlin

Stanford University, Stanford, CA 94305, USA
ronojoy,tomlin@stanford.edu

Abstract. Biological cell networks exhibit complex combinations of both discrete and continuous behaviors: indeed, the dynamics that govern the spatial and temporal increase or decrease of protein concentration inside a single cell are continuous differential equations, while the activation or deactivation of these continuous dynamics are triggered by discrete switches which encode protein concentrations reaching given thresholds. In this paper, we model as a hybrid system a striking example of this behavior in a biological mechanism called Delta-Notch signaling, which is thought to be the primary mechanism of cell differentiation in a variety of cell networks. We present results in both simulation and reachability analysis of this hybrid system. We emphasize how the hybrid system model is computationally superior (for both simulation and analysis) to other nonlinear models in the literature, without compromising faithful modeling of the biological phenomena.

1 Introduction

1.1 Lateral Inhibition and Developmental Biology

The emergence of differentiated cell types from an initially homogeneous population is a well-studied phenomenon. Differentiation occurs in all animal and plant embryonic tissue, particularly such species as *Drosophila melanogaster* (fruit fly) and *Xenopus laevis* (South African claw-toed frog) have been extensively studied. Genes control cell fate by controlling the type and amount of proteins made in a cell. Proteins in turn affect gene activity by turning "on" or "off" gene expression thereby affecting the production of proteins themselves. Hence differential gene activity is considered the key to cell differentiation (Wolpert [1]) and protein concentrations in a cell are a good measure of gene activity. The idea that lateral signaling between cells through the Delta-Notch protein pathway is responsible for some cell fate decisions has gained wide acceptance.

A concise description of the biological background follows (Lewis[2]): Delta is a transmembrane protein that binds and activates its receptor, the transmembrane protein Notch, in neighboring cells. The activation of Notch has a "direct

---

* The authors would like to acknowledge Harley McAdams, Mikael Johansson, David Dill and Henny Sipma. This research is supported by DARPA under the Bio:Info:Micro program, grant MDA972-00-1-0032.

M.D. Di Benedetto, A. Sangiovanni-Vincentelli (Eds.): HSCC 2001, LNCS 2034, pp. 232–246, 2001.
© Springer-Verlag Berlin Heidelberg 2001

and immediate" effect on gene expression. Hence Notch signaling directly controls switching in genetic networks and cascades. The activation of Notch in a cell affects the production of Notch ligands (i.e. Delta) both in itself and its neighbors. In the classical lateral inhibition case, high Notch levels inhibit ligand production in the cell and thus a cell producing more ligands forces its neighboring cells to produce less. However, Notch signaling can also be responsible for a phenomenon called lateral induction where activation of Notch promotes ligand production and thus a group of cells cooperate to produce uniformly high amounts of ligand and Notch, causing all-or-none behavior that promotes sharp gene expression boundaries.

Inter and intra cellular signaling has been postulated to be the mechanism for pattern formation in an incredibly wide range of organisms: emergence of ciliated cells in *Xenopus* embryonic skin (Marnellos et al[3]), neurogenesis in *Drosophila* (Luthi et al[4] and Marnellos et al[5]), sensory cell differentiation in the zebrafish ear (Haddon et al[6]), chick feather array (Crowe et al[7]), wing vein morphogenesis in *Drosophila* (Huppert et al[8]), etc. An example of the distinctive "salt-and-pepper" pattern formed due to lateral inhibition is the *Xenopus* epidermal layer where a regular set of ciliated cells form within a matrix of smooth epidermal cells as seen in Fig. 1. Apart from pattern formation, Delta and its homologues (Fringe, for example, proposed by Moloney et al[9]) interact with Notch (and its homologues) to produce other phenomenon like lineage decisions and boundary formation (Bray[10]), as well as stem cell function and formation of skin appendages (Lewis[2]).

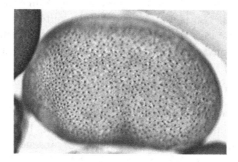

Fig. 1. *Xenopus* embryo labeled by *α-tubulin*, a marker for ciliated cell precursors seen as black dots. Photograph courtesy of P. D. Vize (*The Xenopus Molecular Marker Resource*, http://vize222.zo.utexas.edu)

1.2   Previous Work: Mathematical Models

Most classical models (including Turing's[11] seminal work on morphogenesis) depend on the phenomenon of local autocatalysis with lateral inhibition (LALI). These are grouped (Oster[12]) as neural models, diffusion-reaction models and mechanical models and produce very similar results in spite of widely different internal mechanics. Though successful in predicting pattern formation, they suffer from two main drawbacks: (a) they are phenomenological models which usually do not replicate the low-level protein dynamics and (b) analysis is usually intractable because nonlinear differential (or partial differential) equations are involved. Hence they are restricted to numerical solutions and predictions through simulation.

Previous work on Delta-Notch lateral inhibitory networks focus on nonlinear mathematical models of the protein concentration dynamics. Both Collier et al[13] and Marnellos et al[3,5] have coupled first order nonlinear differential equations which govern protein production and decay. The nonlinearities of both their models derive from the fact that the Delta-Notch protein production in a cell is controlled by a switching function which depends on the weighted sum of Delta-Notch protein levels. The necessity of including nonlinear sigmoid functions to capture this switching phenomenon makes analytical proofs of stability intractable. This issue has been addressed by Collier[13] by analyzing the system for either a small number of cells (actually a pair of cells) or linearizing the system about an equilibrium.

Marnellos et al[3,5] do not focus on mathematical analysis but stress the experimental validation of their model. The model proposed by Mjolsness[14], and used by Marnellos, is an attractive starting point for a hybrid model because of the fairly sharp sigmoid switching function and the introduction of switching thresholds (not used by Collier). Weighted interconnections are crucial to their model and the crux of their method is to train the weights in a network to obtain specific patterns. This is a very time-consuming task and convergence is not guaranteed. For completeness, the cellular automata model developed by Luthi et al[4] must be mentioned. However this model has discretized dynamics and no stability or convergence analysis has been done for it.

1.3   Motivation for Hybrid Model

A wide range of cell regulatory and signaling mechanisms seem to be ideal candidates for hybrid systems models. The physical reasons behind this include: gene expressions are represented by the existence (or absence) of certain proteins; protein concentration dynamics are described by constant exponential growth and decay rates coupled with discrete switches; protein production is switched on or off depending on the expression of other genes, i.e. presence or absence of other proteins in sufficient concentrations; complexity is introduced by the massive interconnections in the *discrete* switching circuit and logic (it is not uncommon to find complicated repressive and promoter feedback channels forming genetic circuits, e.g. McAdams and Arkin[15]). These observations suggest that a piecewise affine hybrid model would be a very good choice for modeling these systems. Using simple continuous dynamics and lumping the complexity into the discrete inputs gives us the capability (current and future) to: analyze the model mathematically and prove reachability and convergence for a wide set of initial conditions, extract important parameters and predict their effects on the system evolution without simulation, and suggest biological experiments to validate the model as well as refine it.

The validity of our assumptions in developing the hybrid model are, of course, open to question and we will justify them as we go deeper into model development, analysis and verification. Our current research demonstrates the applicability of hybrid systems modeling and analysis to a potentially limitless field, that of cell cycle regulation and control. This paper describes our first steps in defining the hybrid automata for Delta-Notch signaling and the analysis of some simpler cases which show how certain parameters critically affect the steady state behavior of the system. It also contains simulation results and comparison with previous nonlinear continuous models which clearly show that our hybrid models faithfully replicate the physical phenomena.

2   Model

The hybrid system model that we develop models the effect of intercellular Delta-Notch signaling on the intracellular concentrations of those proteins. The following properties, based on experimental data, are incorporated in the model: (a) direct contact between cells is a prerequisite for Delta-Notch signaling to occur. Thus only neighboring cells (in addition to feedback from the cell itself) affect the protein concentration dynamics of a cell, (b) Notch production is triggered by high Delta levels in neighboring cells, (c) Delta production is triggered by low Notch concentrations in the same cell, (d) high Delta concentrations lead to differentiated cells and low Delta levels to undifferentiated cells and (e) both proteins decay exponentially.

These properties are fairly orthodox (Lewis[2]) and are used in the model developed by Collier et al[13]. Our model, presented in the next section, is similar to that of Marnellos[3], with the exception that we replace his continuous sigmoid switching curve for protein production (and gene expression) by a discrete switch or signum function. While experimentally, the gene expression switch is determined to be a fairly steep sigmoid, as shown in Fig. 2(b), we will show by comparison with the nonlinear model that the signum function is justified. The signum allows us to model the system as a piecewise affine hybrid system since, in the absence of switching, the continuous dynamics are affine and consistent with the simple constant production and exponential decay postulated (a more accurate model of the continuous dynamics can be derived from chemical kinetics as outlined by Tyson et al[16]). The "direct contact" assumption restricts the discrete inputs of the automaton to be a function of chemical concentrations in neighboring cells and in the cell itself.

For a more biologically faithful model, we have approximated the sigmoid by a piecewise linear switching function (of which the signum is a limiting case). Preliminary analysis shows that the parameter constraints are modified from those derived with the signum switch by a term related to the *slope* of the switch. In the limiting case, when the slope of the switch tends to infinity, the constraints converge to those for the signum. However, these results are not discussed here and will be the subject of a future publication.

The spatial layout of the embryonic cell epidermal layer is two dimensional (planar), in which the cells are arranged in a hexagonal close-packed lattice as shown in Fig. 2(a). The indexing scheme for each cell and its six nearest neighbors is also given in Fig. 2(a).

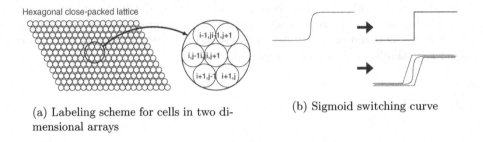

(a) Labeling scheme for cells in two dimensional arrays

(b) Sigmoid switching curve

Fig. 2. Spatial layout and switching curve of the model

A note regarding notation: the variable naming convention follows Marnellos et al[3] and the formal definition of the hybrid automata strictly follows the conventions given by Tomlin[17].

2.1   Model of a Single Cell, Two Cell and $N \times N$ Cell Network

Each biological cell is modeled as a four state piecewise affine hybrid automaton. The four states capture the property that Notch and Delta protein production can be individually switched on or off at any given time. It is assumed that there is no command-actuation delay in the mode switching. The formal definition of the hybrid automaton is given by:

$$H_1 = (Q_1, X_1, \Sigma_1, V_1, Init_1, f_1, Inv_1, R_1)$$

$$Q_1 = \{q_1, q_2, q_3, q_4\}$$

$$X_1 = (v_D, v_N)^T \in \mathbb{R}^2$$

$$\Sigma_1 = \left\{ u_D, u_N : u_D = -v_N, u_N = \sum_{i=1}^{6} v_D^i \right\}$$

$$V_1 = \emptyset$$

$$Init_1 = Q_1 \times \{X_1 \in \mathbb{R}^2 : v_D, v_N > 0\}$$

$$f_1(q, x) = \begin{cases} [-\lambda_D v_D; -\lambda_N v_N]^T & \text{if } q = q_1 \\ [R_D - \lambda_D v_D; -\lambda_N v_N]^T & \text{if } q = q_2 \\ [-\lambda_D v_D; R_N - \lambda_N v_N]^T & \text{if } q = q_3 \\ [R_D - \lambda_D v_D; R_N - \lambda_N v_N]^T & \text{if } q = q_4 \end{cases}$$

$$Inv_1 = \{q_1, \{u_D < h_D, u_N < h_N\}\} \cup \{q_2, \{u_D \geq h_D, u_N < h_N\}\}$$
$$\cup \{q_3, \{u_D < h_D, u_N \geq h_N\}\} \cup \{q_4, \{u_D \geq h_D, u_N \geq h_N\}\}$$

$$R_1 : \begin{bmatrix} R_1(q_1, \{u_D \geq h_D \land u_N < h_N\}) \in q_2 \times \mathbb{R}^2 \\ R_1(q_1, \{u_D < h_D \land u_N \geq h_N\}) \in q_3 \times \mathbb{R}^2 \\ R_1(q_1, \{u_D \geq h_D \land u_N \geq h_N\}) \in q_4 \times \mathbb{R}^2 \\ R_1(q_2, \{u_D < h_D \land u_N < h_N\}) \in q_1 \times \mathbb{R}^2 \\ R_1(q_2, \{u_D < h_D \land u_N \geq h_N\}) \in q_3 \times \mathbb{R}^2 \\ R_1(q_2, \{u_D \geq h_D \land u_N \geq h_N\}) \in q_4 \times \mathbb{R}^2 \\ R_1(q_3, \{u_D < h_D \land u_N < h_N\}) \in q_1 \times \mathbb{R}^2 \\ R_1(q_3, \{u_D \geq h_D \land u_N < h_N\}) \in q_2 \times \mathbb{R}^2 \\ R_1(q_3, \{u_D \geq h_D \land u_N \geq h_N\}) \in q_4 \times \mathbb{R}^2 \\ R_1(q_4, \{u_D < h_D \land u_N < h_N\}) \in q_1 \times \mathbb{R}^2 \\ R_1(q_4, \{u_D \geq h_D \land u_N < h_N\}) \in q_2 \times \mathbb{R}^2 \\ R_1(q_4, \{u_D < h_D \land u_N \geq h_N\}) \in q_3 \times \mathbb{R}^2 \end{bmatrix}$$

where, v_D and v_N: Delta and Notch protein concentrations, respectively, in a cell; v_D^i: Delta protein concentration in i^{th} neighboring cell; λ_D and λ_N: Delta and Notch protein decay constants respectively; R_D and R_N: constant Delta and Notch protein production rates, respectively; h_D and h_N: switching thresholds for Delta and Notch protein production, respectively. R_D, R_N, λ_D and λ_N are experimentally-determined constants. The switching thresholds h_D and h_N are unknown and we derive possible ranges for them which are biologically consistent. In the single cell, $v_D^i = 0, \forall i \in \{1, \ldots 6\}$. The inputs u_D and u_N are the physical realization of properties (b) and (c) of the model outlined before. Fig. 3(a) shows the transition diagram for the hybrid automaton H_1, in which the transition labels have been omitted for figure clarity.

The two cell hybrid automaton H_2 is the composition of two single cell automata, to form a model with four continuous states and 16 discrete modes.

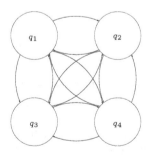

(a) Transition diagram for a single cell automaton: 4 discrete modes.

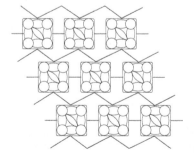

(b) Hybrid automaton for a 3×3 array: 4^9 discrete modes.

Fig. 3. Hybrid systems model of a single cell and a planar array.

Here, $v_D^1 \neq 0$ for each of the two cells, and thus the Delta level of each cell is communicated to its neighbor to control Notch production. Modeling the full two dimensional layer of cells involves composing $N \times N$ single cell hybrid automata with interconnections as shown in Fig. 3(b). The simulation results which follow are from this planar cell array model.

3   Simulation Results

Using the model defined in the previous section, extensive simulations were carried out for different size cell arrays. In a biological sample, it is usually assumed that the initial conditions on protein concentrations are nearly homogeneous, thus in our simulation the initial protein concentrations in the cells are taken randomly from a normal distribution with unity mean and a variance of 0.05. We assume that the protein concentrations at the boundary cells are initially at zero (though periodic protein concentrations at the boundary have also been simulated). The rate constants R_D, R_N, λ_D and λ_N are set to unity (the equations are assumed to be normalized) and the switching thresholds are $h_D = -0.5$ and $h_N = 0.2$ which are in the range which produces sensible biological results; these we derive in the next section.

The emergent steady state behavior of a 20×20 network is shown in Fig. 4(a)and a 50 cell loop in Fig. 4(b). The grey cells are differentiated cells with high Delta and low Notch concentrations while the white ones have high Notch and low Delta concentrations. The model accurately captures the salt-and-pepper pattern of the real biological event.

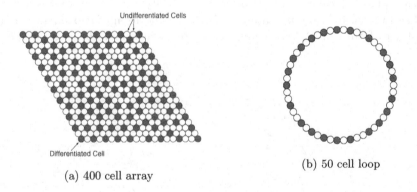

(a) 400 cell array   (b) 50 cell loop

Fig. 4. Simulation results showing the steady state of each cell. Grey indicates a differentiated cell and white indicates an undifferentiated cell.

The key results from the simulation runs are: (a) near-regular pattern formation emerges, especially for larger array sizes, (b) each cell hybrid automaton H_1 is bistable, i.e. it converges to the equilibrium in either state q_2 or q_3 and stays locked there. No oscillations were encountered in the simulations (with one exception, discussed later). This nicely models the fact that cells eventually produce either Delta or Notch proteins but not both, (c) the emergent patterns are very sensitive to the initial conditions for small array sizes. But this sensitivity decreases as the array size increases. This result is similar to that reported by Collier et al[13], (d) the steady state patterns for the cell network follow the rules that: *no two differentiated cells lie next to each other* and *no undifferentiated cell can be completely surrounded by other undifferentiated cells*. This result is important from the biological point of view as experiments show that this is the preferred steady state in organisms. We show later that this result is dependent on the switching threshold values h_D and h_N and (e) another interesting result which emerges from the simulations is the following phenomenon: the cell differentiation seems to start at the boundary and propagates inwards in the network. This might have biological significance and is also reported by Collier et al[13].

4 Analysis

In this section we will analyze the equilibria for a single cell and a two cell network by performing an existence and reachability (convergence) analysis for the hybrid automaton in each case. From now on, we define boundary conditions to be the discrete inputs of the automaton (the Notch protein concentration from the same cell, and Delta protein concentrations from neighboring cells).

4.1 Single Cell Hybrid Automaton

Proposition 1 (Existence of equilibria of H_1). *The equilibria (v_D^*, v_N^*) of H_1 depend on the switching threshold h_D, and are as given in Table 1.*

Proof. We prove this by constructing an algebraic test for the existence of equilibria in each mode. The equilibrium point exists if and only if it satisfies the constraints defining the mode, given by Inv_1. We substitute the equilibrium for each mode into the corresponding invariant for each mode which gives the condition for its existence. For example, for mode q_1 the equilibrium is given by $(v_D^* = 0, v_N^* = 0)$. The invariant for the mode is $\{u_D < h_D, u_N < h_N\}$. Since $u_D = -v_N$, we substitute $u_D = 0$ in the invariant to derive the condition $0 < h_D \wedge u_N < h_N$. Similarly, we perform the computation on q_2, q_3, q_4 to give the conditions in Table 1. $\square$

Table 1. Existence conditions for equilibrium points of H_1

Mode	Equilibrium	Existence condition	Label
q_1	$v_D^* = 0, v_N^* = 0$	$0 < h_D \wedge u_N < h_N$	dead cell
q_2	$v_D^* = \frac{R_D}{\lambda_D}, v_N^* = 0$	$0 \geq h_D \wedge u_N < h_N$	differentiated cell
q_3	$v_D^* = 0, v_N^* = \frac{R_N}{\lambda_N}$	$-\frac{R_N}{\lambda_N} < h_D \wedge u_N \geq h_N$	undifferentiated cell
q_4	$v_D^* = \frac{R_D}{\lambda_D}, v_N^* = \frac{R_N}{\lambda_N}$	$-\frac{R_N}{\lambda_N} \geq h_D \wedge u_N \geq h_N$	"confused" cell

Note from Table 1 that the existence of equilibria can be directly influenced only through manipulating h_D, since u_N is an external input over which the cell has no direct control. Another important observation is that the constraints on h_D are mutually exclusive for modes (q_1, q_2) and (q_3, q_4). From the biological point of view, a dead (no proteins being produced) or confused (both proteins are being produced) steady state should be excluded from the model. By restricting the switching threshold $h_D : -\frac{R_N}{\lambda_N} < h_D \le 0$, we can eliminate the equilibria for modes q_1 and q_4. This ensures that the cell can only converge to a differentiated or undifferentiated steady state depending on the environment (acting through u_N).

In the following, recall that $\Diamond$ means "eventually".

Proposition 2 (Reachability and convergence of H_1). *If $\Diamond(u_N < h_N) \lor \Diamond(u_N \ge h_N)$, then H_1 converges to an equilibrium in either mode q_2 or mode q_3.*

Proof. We first construct the pruned transition diagram by eliminating from the full transition diagram of Fig. 3(a) the transitions for each model which are never enabled. For example, in mode q_2, Notch protein concentration v_N is exponentially decaying and the invariant implies $-v_N \ge h_D$. Hence the transitions $R_1(q_2, \{u_D < h_D \land u_N < h_N\}) \in q_1 \times \mathbb{R}^2$ and $R_1(q_2, \{u_D < h_D \land u_N \ge h_N\}) \in q_3 \times \mathbb{R}^2$ are never enabled because the condition $u_D(= -v_N) < h_D$ is always false, where h_D is a given negative constant. Repeating this across all q_i, the pruned transition map is given by:

$$R_1 : \begin{bmatrix} R_1(q_1, \{u_D \ge h_D \land u_N < h_N\}) \in q_2 \times \mathbb{R}^2 \\ R_1(q_1, \{u_D < h_D \land u_N \ge h_N\}) \in q_3 \times \mathbb{R}^2 \\ R_1(q_1, \{u_D \ge h_D \land u_N \ge h_N\}) \in q_4 \times \mathbb{R}^2 \\ R_1(q_2, \{u_D \ge h_D \land u_N \ge h_N\}) \in q_4 \times \mathbb{R}^2 \\ R_1(q_3, \{u_D < h_D \land u_N < h_N\}) \in q_1 \times \mathbb{R}^2 \\ R_1(q_4, \{u_D < h_D \land u_N < h_N\}) \in q_1 \times \mathbb{R}^2 \\ R_1(q_4, \{u_D \ge h_D \land u_N < h_N\}) \in q_2 \times \mathbb{R}^2 \\ R_1(q_4, \{u_D < h_D \land u_N \ge h_N\}) \in q_3 \times \mathbb{R}^2 \end{bmatrix}$$

The transition diagram drawn in Fig. 6(a) represents this pruned transition diagram, and reachability and convergence can be deduced by tracing executions through it. We analyze the case in which after finite time the boundary condition u_N either always stays less than h_N or always stays greater than or equal to h_N. The continuous dynamics of H_1 is exponentially stable and will converge to the equilibrium in mode q_2 or mode q_3 depending on whether $u_N < h_N$ or $u_N \ge h_N$, respectively, as shown by the phase portraits given in Fig. 5. Note that the phase portraits show that the natural tendency for an isolated cell *in vacuo* is to become differentiated.   □

When the environment is time-varying with variation outside bounds on h_N, there is no guarantee of global convergence to a particular equilibrium. Since there is no equilibrium common to both phase portraits when $u_N < h_N$ and

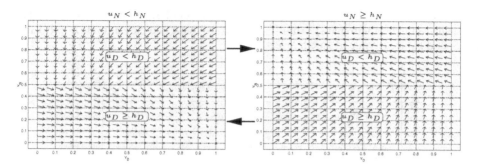

Fig. 5. Phase portrait for a single cell hybrid automaton

$u_N \geq h_N$, by varying u_N the environment can force the system out of an equilibrium point. A particularly diabolic environment could keep the automaton cycling through the modes indefinitely. For example, from Fig. 6(a) we can identify the cyclic sub-graph $\cdots \rightarrow q_1 \rightarrow q_2 \rightarrow q_4 \rightarrow q_3 \rightarrow q_1 \rightarrow \cdots$ which the environment might force the automaton to take for an indefinite interval of time. The reason for this behavior lies in the reductionism involved in the model. By isolating the cell from a larger system we have made it reactive to external inputs but removed its ability to influence the environment. Given that the environment is largely made up of cells like itself, the lack of two-way signaling clearly hampers analysis. If more cells are explicitly included in the model, as we shall see in subsequent sections, the behavior of the cells are more predictable and can be shown to be globally stable. A more elegant solution is to try to model the environment as a "super-cell" which is reactive to external inputs and replicates, at a higher level of abstraction, the dynamics of a large population of cells. Another approach might be to eliminate the continuous dynamics altogether and work with a discrete transition system. Both of these solutions are subjects of ongoing and future research.

4.2   Two Cell Hybrid Automaton

Proposition 3 (Existence of equilibria of H_2). *Existence of equilibria of the continuous dynamics of H_2 depends on the switching thresholds h_D and h_N, and is given in Table 2 for zero boundary conditions.*

Proof. The proof is similar to that for the single cell automaton. Each equilibrium must satisfy its modal invariant which provides an algebraic test for existence: we solve for the equilibrium of each mode and substitute it into the modal invariant. For example, in mode q_7 the equilibrium is given by $(x_1^* = \frac{R_D}{\lambda_D}, x_2^* = 0, x_3^* = 0, x_4^* = \frac{R_N}{\lambda_N})$. We substitute this into the invariant for q_7: $\{x_1 \geq h_N, -x_2 \geq h_D, x_3 < h_N, -x_4 < h_D\}$. This gives the required condition for existence of the equilibrium in q_7: $h_N \leq \frac{R_D}{\lambda_D} \wedge h_D \leq 0 \wedge h_N > 0 \wedge h_D > -\frac{R_N}{\lambda_N}$. This is performed for all 16 modes and the constraints are given in Table 2. $\square$

Table 2. Existence conditions for equilibrium points of H_2 (the composition of two single-cell hybrid automata). Note: x_1 and x_2 are Delta and Notch levels in cell 1 and x_3 and x_4 are Delta and Notch levels in cell 2

Mode	Equilibrium $x_1^*, x_2^*, x_3^*, x_4^*$	Existence condition	Comment
q_1	$0,0,0,0$	$h_N > 0 \wedge h_D > 0$	
q_2	$0,0,\frac{R_D}{\lambda_D},0$	$h_N > 0 \wedge h_D > 0 \wedge h_N > \frac{R_D}{\lambda_D} \wedge h_D \le 0$	unsatisfiable
q_3	$0,0,0,\frac{R_N}{\lambda_N}$	$h_N \le 0 \wedge h_D > 0 \wedge h_N > 0 \wedge h_D > -\frac{R_N}{\lambda_N}$	unsatisfiable
q_4	$0,0,\frac{R_D}{\lambda_D},\frac{R_N}{\lambda_N}$	$h_N \le 0 \wedge h_D > 0 \wedge h_N > \frac{R_D}{\lambda_D} \wedge h_D \le -\frac{R_N}{\lambda_N}$	unsatisfiable
q_5	$\frac{R_D}{\lambda_D},0,0,0$	$h_N > \frac{R_D}{\lambda_D} \wedge h_D \le 0 \wedge h_N > 0 \wedge h_D > 0$	unsatisfiable
q_6	$\frac{R_D}{\lambda_D},0,\frac{R_D}{\lambda_D},0$	$h_N > \frac{R_D}{\lambda_D} \wedge h_D \le 0$	
q_7	$\frac{R_D}{\lambda_D},0,0,\frac{R_N}{\lambda_N}$	$h_N \le \frac{R_D}{\lambda_D} \wedge h_D \le 0 \wedge h_N > 0 \wedge h_D > -\frac{R_N}{\lambda_N}$	
q_8	$\frac{R_D}{\lambda_D},0,\frac{R_D}{\lambda_D},\frac{R_N}{\lambda_N}$	$h_N \le \frac{R_D}{\lambda_D} \wedge h_D \le 0 \wedge h_N > \frac{R_D}{\lambda_D} \wedge h_D \le -\frac{R_N}{\lambda_N}$	unsatisfiable
q_9	$0,\frac{R_N}{\lambda_N},0,0$	$h_N > 0 \wedge h_D > -\frac{R_N}{\lambda_N} \wedge h_N \le 0 \wedge h_D > 0$	unsatisfiable
q_{10}	$0,\frac{R_N}{\lambda_N},\frac{R_D}{\lambda_D},0$	$h_N > 0 \wedge h_D > -\frac{R_N}{\lambda_N} \wedge h_N \le \frac{R_D}{\lambda_D} \wedge h_D \le 0$	
q_{11}	$0,\frac{R_N}{\lambda_N},0,\frac{R_N}{\lambda_N}$	$h_N \le 0 \wedge h_D > -\frac{R_N}{\lambda_N}$	
q_{12}	$0,\frac{R_N}{\lambda_N},\frac{R_D}{\lambda_D},\frac{R_N}{\lambda_N}$	$h_N \le 0 \wedge h_D > -\frac{R_N}{\lambda_N} \wedge h_N \le \frac{R_D}{\lambda_D} \wedge h_D \le -\frac{R_N}{\lambda_N}$	unsatisfiable
q_{13}	$\frac{R_D}{\lambda_D},\frac{R_N}{\lambda_N},0,0$	$h_N > \frac{R_D}{\lambda_D} \wedge h_D \le -\frac{R_N}{\lambda_N} \wedge h_N \le 0 \wedge h_D > 0$	unsatisfiable
q_{14}	$\frac{R_D}{\lambda_D},\frac{R_N}{\lambda_N},\frac{R_D}{\lambda_D},0$	$h_N > \frac{R_D}{\lambda_D} \wedge h_D \le -\frac{R_N}{\lambda_N} \wedge h_N \le \frac{R_D}{\lambda_D} \wedge h_D \le 0$	unsatisfiable
q_{15}	$\frac{R_D}{\lambda_D},\frac{R_N}{\lambda_N},0,\frac{R_N}{\lambda_N}$	$h_N \le \frac{R_D}{\lambda_D} \wedge h_D \le -\frac{R_N}{\lambda_N} \wedge h_N \le 0 \wedge h_D > -\frac{R_N}{\lambda_N}$	unsatisfiable
q_{16}	$\frac{R_D}{\lambda_D},\frac{R_N}{\lambda_N},\frac{R_D}{\lambda_D},\frac{R_N}{\lambda_N}$	$h_N \le \frac{R_D}{\lambda_D} \wedge h_D \le -\frac{R_N}{\lambda_N}$	

It can be seen that 10 out of the 16 equilibria cannot exist because the associated constraints on h_D and h_N are unsatisfiable. In addition, the constraints are mutually exclusive for all except the equilibria for modes q_7 and q_{10}. These equilibria represent one differentiated and one undifferentiated cell exactly and are inseparable due to symmetry. Hence, if the thresholds are selected such that the equilibria in q_7 and q_{10} exist, all other equilibrium points are unreachable. The constraints so chosen are given by,

$$h_D, h_N : -\frac{R_N}{\lambda_N} < h_D \le 0 \wedge 0 < h_N \le \frac{R_D}{\lambda_D}$$

An analysis of the automaton H_2 was done regarding the effect of boundary conditions on the reachable equilibria. Using the same equilibrium analysis methods used in previous sections it was determined that the set of reachable equilibria depend critically on the boundary conditions, i.e. levels of protein concentration in the environment. If the switching thresholds h_D and h_N are chosen so as to give a biologically consistent equilibrium for zero boundary conditions, then some interesting results were observed. If the Delta protein boundary conditions for both cells were below the chosen h_N value, then the automaton evolves as if the cells were *in vacuo*. However, if any one of the neighboring Delta levels exceeds the chosen h_N then the automaton admits only one reachable equilibrium which is that in which the cell next to the high Delta boundary condition becomes undifferentiated and the other cell becomes differentiated. However, if both boundary conditions have high Delta level then H_2 has only one reachable equilibrium which is that in which both cells have high Notch and low Delta level, i.e. both cells are undifferentiated. This is consistent with the patterns observed in simulations.

Proposition 4 (Existence of Zeno state). *For the hybrid automaton H_2, all executions with $Init_2 = Q_2 \times \left\{ X_2 \in \mathbb{R}^4 : x_1 = x_3, x_2 = x_4 \right\}$ are Zeno executions and $\left(\hat{q}, \hat{x} : \hat{q} = q_{16}, \hat{x} = [h_N \; - h_D \; h_N \; - h_D]^T \right)$ is a Zeno state.*

We prove that the state is Zeno by computing the execution of the automaton with the given initial states and show that it is a cyclic transition $(\cdots \rightarrow q_1 \rightarrow q_6 \rightarrow q_{16} \rightarrow q_{11} \rightarrow q_1 \rightarrow \cdots)$ with infinite transitions in finite time. The proof has to be omitted due to space constraints. Note that the Zeno state is a vestige of the mathematical model and not observable in nature due to noise. Interestingly, this Zeno state corresponds to a saddle equilibrium in the nonlinear model.

Proposition 5 (Reachability and convergence of H_2). *For zero boundary conditions, all executions, except the Zeno execution, of the two cell hybrid automaton H_2 eventually converge to the equilibrium in mode q_7 or mode q_{10}.*

Proof. The construction of the pruned transition diagram follows the same procedure as that for the single cell automaton. Due to space constraints the explicit pruning procedure is omitted. Figure 6(b) gives the transition map for H_2. Convergence is deduced by tracing executions through the map. The equilibrium-containing modes are invariant under continuous flow and hence have no escape transitions (modes q_7 and q_{10} in Fig. 6(b)). It can be shown that all executions (except the Zeno execution indicated by the dashed grey transitions in Fig. 6(b)) reach one of the two equilibria. Thus the automaton is bistable. Note: the proof can be extended to include boundary conditions by constructing the pruned transition maps for those cases. □

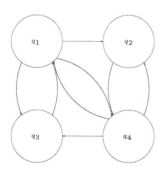

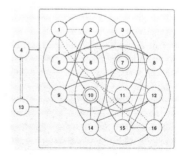

(a) Pruned transition diagram for a single cell hybrid automaton

(b) Transition diagram for two cell automaton with zero boundary conditions.

Fig. 6. Pruned transition diagrams

4.3 $N \times N$ Cell Hybrid Automaton

While we performed the equilibrium and reachability analysis for the single and two-cell networks by hand (by enumerating the vector fields over the discrete modes), as we analyze larger networks of cells this becomes difficult. However, because the continuous dynamics are affine, time-invariant, with diagonal A matrices (which admit analytic solutions), the equilibrium and reachability analysis may be automated. We are currently designing a "model checker" based on these principles for this specialized system, to automate these analyses.

5   Comparison with Nonlinear Model

The steady state behavior of the hybrid model and the nonlinear models are similar in simulation. To establish our model on a firmer base it is necessary to compare it with one of the benchmark nonlinear models, that developed by Collier et al[13]. The nonlinear model uses nonlinear differential equations coupled through sigmoid switching functions. Collier proves convergence of the model by determining the equilibria of the system and then using a set of "instantaneous" phase portrait projections showing the flow field around those equilibria. Figure 7(a) displays the flow field in the d_1(Delta of cell 1)-d_2(Delta of cell 2)-plane with two sinks and a saddle point. The hybrid model successfully captures this phase portrait, as shown in Fig. 7(b), with an exception: the saddle point is converted to a Zeno state. The hybrid model similarly approximates the dynamics of the nonlinear model in all projections of the state space. Hence this model is as expressive in simulation as the benchmark nonlinear model, yet it admits simpler analysis.

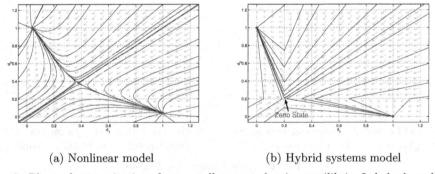

(a) Nonlinear model   (b) Hybrid systems model

Fig. 7. Phase plane projections for two cell system showing equilibria. Labels d_1 and d_2 are the Delta protein concentrations in cell 1 and 2 respectively.

6   Conclusion

The research presented in this paper gives a glimpse of the immense opportunities for hybrid modeling in biological systems. It presents work done to systematically model a well-known intercellular signaling pathway with some success. The faithful replication of biological events is demonstrated through simulation and the validity of the model is emphasized by comparison to a benchmark nonlinear model. The preliminary analysis of the model is promising and has resulted in the identification of the threshold parameters as an important and direct arbiter of cell fate, which might suggest possible experiments in the future.

Future work will concentrate on the development of an automated tool for equilibrium and convergence analysis using the specific geometric properties of this system, which we anticipate will lead to the development of a mathematically correct discrete abstraction of the hybrid model. The first step in this direction has been taken by mapping out the transition diagram for the two cell automata. The next is to convert it to a pure finite automata. If that analysis is extended to higher dimensional systems, we may reap enormous computational and analytical benefits without losing sight of the underlying biology.

We are hopeful that these techniques will not only apply to the specific example presented here, but also to a wide range of systems in which protein growth and decay, and protein interaction, is the key to the development of the biological system.

References

1. Lewis Wolpert. *Principles of Development*. Current Biology Ltd and Oxford University Press, 1998.
2. Julian Lewis. Notch signalling and the control of cell fate choices in vertebrates. *Seminars in Cell & Developmental Biology*, 9:583–589, 1998.
3. G. Marnellos, G. A. Deblandre, E. Mjolsness, and C. Kintner. Delta-notch lateral inhibitory patterning in the emergence of ciliated cells in *Xenopus*: experimental observations and a gene network model. In *Pacific Symposium on Biocomputing*, pages 5:326–337, 2000.
4. Pascal O. Luthi, Bastien Chopard, Anette Preiss, and Jeremy J. Ramsden. A cellular automaton model for neurogenesis in *Drosophila*. *Physica D*, (118):151–160, 1998.
5. G. Marnellos and E. Mjolsness. A gene network approach to modeling early neurogenesis in *Drosophila*. In *Pacific Symposium on Biocomputing*, pages 3:30–41, 1998.
6. Catherine Haddon, Yun-Jin Jiang, Lucy Smithers, and Julian Lewis. Delta-notch signalling and the patterning of sensory cell differentiation in the zebrafish ear: evidence from the *mind bomb* mutant. *Development*, 125:4637–4644, 1998.
7. Rebecca Crowe, Domingos Henrique, David Ish-Horowicz, and Lee Niswander. A new role for notch and delta in cell fate decisions: pattering the feather array. *Development*, 125:767–775, 1998.
8. Stacey S. Huppert, Thomas L. Jacobsen, and Marc A. T. Muskavitch. Feedback regulation is central to delta-notch signalling required for *Drosophila* wing vein morphogenesis. *Development*, 124:3283–3291, 1997.

9. Daniel J. Moloney, Vladislav M. Panin, Stuart H. Johnston, Jihua Chen, Li Shao, Richa Wilson, Yang Wang, Pamela Stanley, Kenneth D. Irvine, Robert S. Haltiwanger, and Thomas F. Vogt. Fringe is a glycosyltransferase that modifies notch. *Nature*, 406(27):369–375, July 2000.

10. Sarah Bray. Notch signalling in *Drosophila*: three ways to use a pathway. *Seminars in Cell & Developmental Biology*, 9:591–597, 1998.

11. A. M. Turing. The chemical basis of morphogenesis. *Philos. Trans. R. Soc. Lond. B*, 237(641):37–72, August 1952.

12. George F. Oster. Lateral inhibition models of developmental processes. *Mathematical Biosciences*, 90:265–286, 1988.

13. Joanne R. Collier, Nicholas A. M. Monk, Philip K. Maini, and Julian H. Lewis. Pattern formation by lateral inhibition with feedback: a mathematical model of delta-notch intercellular signalling. *J. theor. Biol.*, (183):429–446, 1996.

14. Eric Mjolsness, David H. Sharp, and John Reinitz. A connectionist model of development. *J. theor. Biol.*, 152:429–453, 1991.

15. Harley H. McAdams and Adam Arkin. Simulation of prokaryotic genetic circuits. *Annu. Rev. Biophys. Biomol. Struct.*, 27:199–224, 1998.

16. John J. Tyson, Bela Novak, Garrett M. Odell, Kathy Chen, and C. Dennis Thron. Chemical kinetic theory: understanding cell-cycle regulation. *TIBS*, 21:89–96, March 1996.

17. C. Tomlin, J. Lygeros, and S. Sastry. Controller design for hybrid systems. *Proceedings of the IEEE*, 88(7), July 2000.

Supervision of Event-Driven Hybrid Systems: Modeling and Synthesis

José M. E. González[1], Antonio E.C. da Cunha[1],
José E.R. Cury[1], and Bruce H. Krogh[2]

[1] Departamento de Automação e Sistemas, Universidade Federal de Santa Catarina,
Caixa Postal 470, 88040-001 Florianópolis, SC, Brasil
{jose,aecc,cury}@lcmi.ufsc.br
[2] ECE Department, Carnegie Mellon University,
15213 Pittsburgh, PA, USA
krogh@ece.cmu.edu

Abstract. This paper presents a formulation and solution of a supervisory control problem for a class of hybrid systems in which threshold-crossing events in the continuous state space force discrete-state transitions. The continuous dynamics are in turn determined by a discrete condition determined by the current discrete state of the system. The problem is to construct a supervisor that restricts the discrete-state transitions in the hybrid system so that the possible sequences of threshold events are contained in a given set of sequences (the desired threshold event language of the closed-loop system). Formally, the hybrid system supervisor can be synthesized using the theory of supervisor synthesis for discrete event systems. This procedure is described, and a computational approach to solve the problem is illustrated with an example.

1 Introduction

Several types of control problems can be formulated for hybrid systems. In this paper, we consider the problem of synthesizing a supervisor that restricts the selection of the continuous dynamics in the hybrid system so that the sequence of output events (generated when the continuous state crosses specified thresholds) is contained within a given set of sequences (the desired threshold event language). This is a generalization of the problem considered in [1] where the hybrid plant contained only continuous-state dynamics. Similar supervisory control problems were also considered in [2,3] for systems with discrete-time continuous-state dynamics, and in [4] for synthesis of discrete event supervisors for continuous and discrete time systems. In this paper, the hybrid plant to be controlled includes both continuous-state and discrete-state dynamics in continuous time.

The presentation of this paper is organized as follows. The problem is developed in Sect. 2 using the formalism of condition/event (C/E) systems [5]. C/E systems provide a framework for defining continuous-time systems as the interconnection of subsystems with discrete-valued input and output signals. Condition signals are piecewise constant, whereas event signals assume non-null

M.D. Di Benedetto, A. Sangiovanni-Vincentelli (Eds.): HSCC 2001, LNCS 2034, pp. 247–260, 2001.
© Springer-Verlag Berlin Heidelberg 2001

values only at isolated instants of time. The language for a C/E system is defined by the sequences of the values of the input-output signals recorded at their points of discontinuity.

Section 3 describes how the supervisor synthesis problem for the hybrid system can be solved, at least formally, using the theory of supervisory control for discrete event systems (DESs). The difficulty in computing and constructing the supervisor arises from the fact that in general there may not be finite-state generators for languages derived from C/E systems. This problem can be dealt with using a finite-state generator for conservative (outer) approximations to the language for the DES plant, as described in Sect. 4. The procedure is illustrated by an example in Sect. 5. The concluding section summarizes the contribution of this paper.

2 Problem Formulation

Consider the class of hybrid systems illustrated by Fig. 1. The hybrid plant $\hat{\mathcal{H}}$ is composed by interconnection of a continuous dynamic subsystem $\mathcal{H}_c$ and a discrete dynamic subsystem $\hat{\mathcal{H}}_d$. The input signal to the continuous subsystem

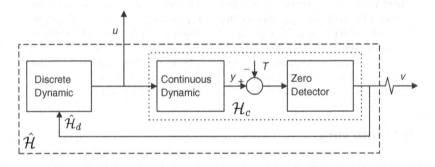

Fig. 1. Hybrid plant.

$\mathcal{H}_c$ is a piecewise constant, right continuous, condition signal $u(\cdot)$, taking on values on a finite set of conditions U [5]. The space of all condition signals $u(\cdot)$ for $[0, \infty)$ is denoted by $\mathcal{U}$. The *continuous dynamic* is defined by the *continuous state trajectory* $x(\cdot)$ that evolves in $X = R^n$. At each instant t, the continuous state trajectory satisfies the differential equation $\dot{x}(t) = \hat{f}_{u(t)}(x(t))$ selected by the input condition $u(t)$, where $\hat{f}_u : R^n \to R^n$ for all $u \in U$. The set of possible initial values of the state trajectory is $X_0 \subseteq R^n$. The set of all possible trajectories for a given input signal $u(\cdot) \in \mathcal{U}$ starting from any state in a set $X' \subset X$ is denoted by $\mathcal{X}_{u(\cdot)}(X')$. The function $\hat{g} : X \to R^m$ generates the *continuous output signal* $y(\cdot)$ from the state trajectory. Each component of $y(\cdot)$ is compared to a threshold defined by a *threshold vector* $T \in R^m$, and the event output signal is generated by a *zero detector*, defined for each component of the output signal

$y(\cdot)$ as $v(0) = v_0$ and for $t > 0$ and $1 \le i \le m$:

$$v_i(t) = \begin{cases} 1, & y_i(t) - T_i = 0 \wedge (\exists \Delta > 0)(\forall \delta \in (0, \Delta)) : y_i(t - \delta) - T_i < 0 \\ 0, & \text{otherwise} \end{cases} \tag{1}$$

For each instant where any $v(t) \ne 0$ it is said that a threshold event occurs, otherwise it is assumed a *null event* occurrence. Let v_0 be the *initialization event*, an event which occurs only once at $t = 0$, and is associated to the nondeterministic choice of the initial state $x(0)$. Thus, the threshold event signal $v(\cdot)$ assumes values over the set $V = \{0, 1\}^m \cup \{v_0\}$ at isolated points of time, and the space of all threshold event signals $v(\cdot)$ in $[0, \infty)$ is denoted by $\mathcal{V}$.

The input signal to $\mathcal{H}_c$ is determined by the discrete subsystem $\hat{\mathcal{H}}_d$. The system $\hat{\mathcal{H}}_d$ is a purely discrete dynamic system which maps nondeterministically event signals $v(\cdot) \in \mathcal{V}$ into condition signals $u(\cdot) \in \mathcal{U}$. The feedback of event signals from $\mathcal{H}_c$ to $\hat{\mathcal{H}}_d$ models physical constraints of the continuous subsystem which restricts the range of allowable input signals. It is assumed that $\hat{\mathcal{H}}_d$ can change the input signal if and only if a threshold event is observed. It is also assumed that the feedback on Fig. 1 doesn't lead to chattering, which means that on any finite interval of time there are at most a finite number of threshold events.

The hybrid plant is modeled as a Condition/Event (C/E) system in the sense of [5] as follows. The continuous subsystem $\mathcal{H}_c$ is defined as a subset of $\mathcal{V} \otimes \mathcal{U}$, the time synchronous cross product of $\mathcal{V}$ and $\mathcal{U}$, the set of all pairs $(v(\cdot), u(\cdot))$ such that discontinuities in $u(\cdot)$ occur only at instants when $v(\cdot)$ is nonzero. The pair $(v(\cdot), u(\cdot)) \in \mathcal{H}_c$ if and only if there exists a state trajectory $x(\cdot) \in \mathcal{X}_{u(\cdot)}(X_0)$ such that the resulting event signal is $v(\cdot)$.

We introduce the *discrete trace representation* for $\mathcal{H}_c$ as the 4-tuple (W, f, h, W_0) described as follows. A piecewise constant, right continuous, condition signal $w(\cdot)$ taking on values on $W = R^n$, and with initial values in $W_0 = X_0$, records the value of the corresponding state trajectory at instants of discontinuity in $(v(\cdot), u(\cdot)) \in \mathcal{H}_c$. The transition function $f : W \times U \to W$ for $w(\cdot)$ is such that

$$f(w(t^-), u(t^-)) = \begin{cases} \Phi_{u(t^-)}(t, w(t^-)) & \text{if for some } i,\ 1 \le i \le m \\ & \hat{g}_i(\Phi_{u(t^-)}(t, w(t^-))) - T_i = 0 \text{ and} \\ & (\exists \Delta > 0)(\forall \delta \in (0, \Delta)) : \\ & \hat{g}_i(\Phi_{u(t^-)}(t - \delta, w(t^-))) - T_i < 0 \\ w(t^-) & \text{otherwise.} \end{cases} \tag{2}$$

where $\Phi_u(t, x(t_0))$ is the solution of the differential equation $\dot{x} = \hat{f}_u(x)$ for $u \in U$, $t \ge t_0$ and initial value $x(t_0)$. The event output function $h : W \times W \to V$ is defined as

$$v(t) = h(w(t^-), w(t)) \tag{3}$$

which outputs the corresponding threshold event at the instant of the state transition of $w(\cdot)$, and is null at any other time. This discrete trace model is similar to the discrete state model of [5] except for the existence of an infinite and uncountable set of states.

Similarly, $\hat{\mathcal{H}}_d \subseteq \mathcal{V} \otimes \mathcal{U}$, and its *discrete state model* is (Q, δ, ϕ, q_0), where Q is the discrete state set, countable and possibly infinite, $q_0 = q(0^-)$ is the initial state, and

$$q(t) \in \hat{\delta}(q(t^-), v(t))$$
$$u(t) = \phi(q(t)) \tag{4}$$

are the state transition and condition output functions [5].

The hybrid plant $\hat{\mathcal{H}} \subseteq \mathcal{V} \otimes \mathcal{U}$ is obtained by the cascade and feedback connection of $\hat{\mathcal{H}}_d$ and $\mathcal{H}_c$ following [5].

Consider now the supervisory control scheme for the hybrid plant shown in Fig. 2. The supervisor $\mathcal{S}$ applies a control input to the discrete subsystem $\mathcal{H}_d$

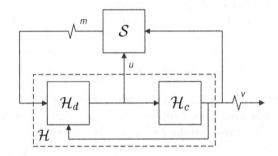

Fig. 2. Supervisory Control scheme for Hybrid Plant.

of the hybrid plant $\mathcal{H}$ to restrict the range of possible input conditions to the continuous subsystem $\mathcal{H}_c$. The control input to the controlled discrete subsystem is an event signal $m(\cdot) \in \mathcal{M}$ taking on values on $M = 2^U$, and is interpreted as the set of allowed conditions to be chosen by $\mathcal{H}_d$. It is assumed that the supervisor applies a control input if and only if a threshold event is observed, which makes the discontinuities in $m(\cdot)$ and $v(\cdot)$ synchronous. At the occurrence of the event $v(t) \in V$, a control input $m(t) \subseteq U$ is applied by the supervisor, and if $\mathcal{H}_d$ is at state $q(t^-)$, the set of next possible input conditions is constrained to $m(t) \cap \phi(\hat{\delta}(q(t^-), v(t)))$. It is assumed that any input condition to $\mathcal{H}_d$ can be disabled, but the supervisor control action cannot disable all possible conditions for a given event v.

The controlled discrete subsystem is now defined as $\mathcal{H}_d \subseteq \mathcal{V} \otimes \mathcal{M} \otimes \mathcal{U}$, where the only difference in the discrete state model from the uncontrolled version is the transition function, defined as:

$$\delta(q(t^-), v(t), m(t)) = \{q(t) \in \delta(q(t^-), v(t)) : \phi(q(t)) \in m(t)\} \tag{5}$$

The controlled hybrid plant is also given by $\mathcal{H} \subseteq \mathcal{V} \otimes \mathcal{M} \otimes \mathcal{U}$ obtained by interconnection of $\mathcal{H}_c$ and $\mathcal{H}_d$, which incorporates the influence of m in $\hat{\mathcal{H}}$.

The C/E supervisor is a *deterministic* C/E system $S \subseteq V \otimes M \otimes U$, whose discrete state model is (Z, ξ, ψ, z_0), where Z is the discrete state set of the supervisor, $z_0 = z(0^-)$ is the initial state, and

$$
\begin{aligned}
z(t) &= \xi(z(t^-), u(t^-), v(t)) \\
m(t) &= \psi(z(t^-), z(t))
\end{aligned}
\tag{6}
$$

are the state transition and event output functions.

The closed loop C/E system is $S/\mathcal{H} \subseteq V$, built by cascade and feedback connection of S and $\mathcal{H}$, following [5].

In order to introduce our supervisory control problem, we express the discrete behavior of the systems in terms of a language. Given the C/E system $\mathcal{D}$ the *language* of $\mathcal{D}$, denoted by $\mathcal{L}(\mathcal{D})$, is the prefix closure over the finite length strings of records of the values of the input/output signals at the point of discontinuities. We consider the following problem.

Supervisor Synthesis for Hybrid Systems (SSHS). Given $\mathcal{H}$ (controlled hybrid plant) and $A, E \subseteq V^*$ (specifications), find a C/E supervisor S such that $A \subseteq \mathcal{L}(S/\mathcal{H}) \subseteq E$.

3   DES Approach

In this section, the SSHS is translated to a purely discrete event control framework, and a solution is proposed. The procedure of this section is purely formal and conceptual, since the state space of the models may be infinite. Finite-state practical approaches will be subject of the next section.

The DES model for the hybrid plant is a prefix closed language L and a control structure Γ. The language is defined as $L = \mathcal{L}(\hat{\mathcal{H}}) \subseteq (V \times U)^*$. The control structure is a map $\Gamma : L \to 2^{2^{V \times U}}$, such that for all $s \in L$, $\Gamma(s) \subseteq 2^{V \times U}$, and $\gamma \in \Gamma(s)$ is such that $\forall v \in V_L(s) = \{v \in V : (\exists u \in U) s \circ vu \in L\}$, it is always true that $\emptyset \subset \{u \in U : vu \in \gamma\} \subset \{u \in U : s \circ vu \in L\}$. The control structure captures the idea that for each active event $v \in V$ the supervisor may enable any nonempty possibility of $u \in U$ that can be selected by the discrete subsystem for a give event $v \in V$. The following proposition states the logical equivalence of the controlled hybrid plant and the DES model.

Proposition 1. *The DES model for the hybrid plant (L, Γ) and the C/E model $\mathcal{H} \subseteq V \otimes M \otimes U$ are logically equivalent, in the sense that:*

1. *$\forall w = v_1 m_1 u_1 \circ \ldots \circ v_k m_k u_k \in (V \times M \times U)^*$, $w \in \mathcal{L}(\mathcal{H})$, if and only if $s = v_1 u_1 \circ \ldots \circ v_k u_k \in L$, and*
2. *$\forall w = v_1 m_1 u_1 \circ \ldots \circ v_k m_k u_k \in \mathcal{L}(\mathcal{H})$ and $\alpha = vmu \in V \times M \times U$, $w \circ \alpha \in \mathcal{L}(\mathcal{H})$ if and only if for $s = v_1 u_1 \circ \ldots \circ v_k u_k \in L$, $\exists \gamma \in \Gamma(s)$ such that $m = \{u \in U : vu \in \gamma\}$.*

The DES supervisor for the hybrid plant is a map $f : L \to 2^{V \times U}$, such that for $s \in L$, $f(s) \in \Gamma(s)$. The DES supervisor is represented by a state machine $F = (P, V \times U, \rho, p_0)$ where P is the set of states, p_0 is the initial state, and the transition function $\rho : P \times V \times U \to P$ is such that for $p \in P$ and $\sigma \in V \times U$, $\rho(p, \sigma)$ is defined if and only if $\sigma = f(s)$ and $s \in (V \times U)^*$ is such that $\hat{\rho}(p_0, s) = p$, where $\hat{\rho}$ stands for the extension of the transition function to strings in $(V \times U)^*$. Thus, the supervisor control action is implicit in the machine transitions. We introduce a formal procedure to get the C/E supervisor $\mathcal{S}$, given by (Z, ξ, ψ, z_0), logically equivalent to the DES supervisor. The procedure exploits the state machine representation of the C/E supervisor, given by $((Z \times U) \cup \{z_0\}, V \times M \times U, \xi^D, z_0)$, where the transition function $\xi^D : ((Z \times U) \cup \{z_0\}) \times (V \times M \times U) \to ((Z \times U) \cup \{z_0\})$ is such that $L(S) = \mathcal{L}(\mathcal{S})$ [5].

Consider the state machines representing the DES supervisor and the corresponding C/E supervisor in Fig. 3. Assume that each state in the DES supervisor

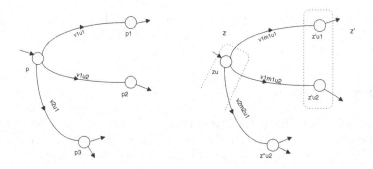

Fig. 3. Sample correspondence between DES supervisor (right) and C/E supervisor (left).

has a unique value for the input condition signal associated with it on p's incoming arcs in the DES supervisor, such that for a DES state p, let $u(p)$ denote such value. Each state z in the C/E supervisor is associated with a set of states in the DES supervisor, let's denote the set by $P(z)$. Let $V(p)$ be the set of events on arcs leaving state p, and for $v \in V(p)$, let $U(v, p)$ be the set of all condition values on the arcs labeled vu.

It can be proved that the previous algorithm terminates in a finite number of steps, and the following proposition states the logical equivalence of the DES supervisor and C/E supervisor.

Proposition 2. *The C/E supervisor $\mathcal{S} \subseteq \mathcal{V} \otimes \mathcal{M} \otimes \mathcal{U}$ obtained by Alg. 1 is logically equivalent to the DES supervisor f in the sense that $\forall s = v_1 u_1 \circ \ldots \circ v_k u_k \in (V \times U)^*$ and $\sigma = vu \in V \times U$, $\sigma \in f(s)$ if and only if $\exists w = v_1 m_1 u_1 \circ \ldots \circ v_k m_k u_k \in (V \times M \times U)^*$ and $\alpha = vmu \in V \times M \times U$ such that $w \circ \alpha \in \mathcal{L}(\mathcal{S})$*

Algorithm 1 Recursion to construct a C/E supervisor from the DES supervisor

$Z \leftarrow \{z_0\}$; $P(Z_0) \leftarrow \{p_0\}$; $Z' \leftarrow Z$
$\xi = \emptyset$; $\psi \leftarrow \emptyset$; {Sets to store the state transition and output information}
while $Z' \neq \emptyset$ **do**
   Select and remove z from Z'
   for $p \in P(z) \wedge v \in V(p)$ **do**
      $m \leftarrow U(p, v)$;
      $P' \leftarrow \cup \rho(p, vu)$, $u \in m$; {Set of states reached by arcs with v}
      if For all $z \in Z$, $P' \neq P(z)$ **then**
         Add new state z' to Z and Z' with $P(z') = P'$
      end if
      Select z' from Z such that $P(z') = P'$
      $\xi(z, u(p), v) \leftarrow z'$;
      $\psi(z, z') \leftarrow m$;
   end for
end while

The closed behavior in the DES framework $L^f \subseteq V^*$ is defined recursively as:

1. $\epsilon \in L^f$, and
2. $\forall t = v_1 \circ \ldots \circ v_k \in V^*$ and $\forall v \in V$, $t \circ v \in L^f$ if and only if $t \in L^f \wedge \exists s = v_1 u_1 \circ \ldots \circ v_k u_k \in (V \times U)^*$ and $\exists \sigma = vu \in V \times U$ such that $s \circ \sigma \in L$ and $\sigma \in f(s)$.

Proposition 3. $L^f = \mathcal{L}(\mathcal{S}/\mathcal{H})$.

Proposition 3 indicates that the SSHS can be solved by solving an equivalent DES supervisory control problem.

SCP Given a hybrid plant with control input represented by a pair (L, Γ) and $A, E \subseteq V^*$ (specification languages), find a supervisor f such that $A \subseteq L^f \subseteq E$.

Given the language $L \subseteq (V \times U)^*$ and the language $E \subseteq V^*$, E is said to be *controllable with respect to L*, or just controllable, if for all $t = v_1 \circ \ldots \circ v_k \in \overline{E}$, exists $s = v_1 u_1 \circ \ldots \circ v_k u_k \in L$, where $u_1 \circ \ldots \circ u_k \in U^*$, such that

$$V_E(t) = V_L(s) \tag{7}$$

A threshold crossing event language is controllable if the plant can follow its prefix by applying determined sequences of conditions. This definition of controllable language is consistent with the existence of a control structure Γ as defined above. For example, consider the language $L = [v_1 u_1 \circ (v_2 u_1 + v_2 u_3)] + [v_1 u_2 \circ (v_3 u_1 + v_2 u_2)]$. The language $E_1 = v_1 \circ v_2$ is controllable with respect L and the language $E_2 = v_1 \circ v_3$ is not controllable with respect to L.

Since it can be proved that the control structure Γ for L is closed for the union for each $s \in L$, then for $E \subseteq V^*$, the class of controllable sublanguages

$C(E)$ is nonempty and closed for the union, and has a unique supremal element, the maximal controllable language $\sup C(E)$. Thus, the following results bring a formal solution for the SCP [6].

Theorem 1. *Given a hybrid plant with control input represented by (L, Γ) and a specification language $E \subseteq V^*$, there is a supervisor f such that $L^f = E$ if and only if E is controllable and prefix closed.*

Theorem 2. *SCP is solvable if and only if $\sup C(E) \supseteq A$.*

The supervisor which implements $\sup C(E)$ is the optimal solution of the SCP, in the sense of being minimally restrictive. Finally, from the development of this section, we state a solution for the SSHS as follows.

Corollary 1. *The SSHS is solvable if and only if the equivalent SCP is solvable. Furthermore, given the DES supervisor f as a solution for SCP, the C/E supervisor S obtained by Alg. 1 is the corresponding solution for the SSHS.*

4   Finite State Approximations for the HS DES Plant

In this section, finite state approximations are proposed to find a computable solution for the SSHS.

Suppose there is a finite state machine H describing the logical behavior of the hybrid plant $\mathcal{H}$, i.e., $L(H) \subseteq (V \times U)^*$. Then, for a specification language $E \subseteq V^*$, the language $\sup C(E)$ can be computed in a finite set of steps by an algorithm of polynomial complexity in the number of states of both H and the corresponding representation for E [6].

The state space of the state machine H is possibly infinite. This is one of the main problems in hybrid systems theory since, in general, the convergence of algorithms involving state models is only guaranteed over finite spaces. Recent approaches, e.g. [7], propose the use of finite conservative approximations for the behavior of the hybrid system to solve verification problems. In the context of synthesis of supervisors Cury et al. [1,8] show that, given a conservative (finite) approximation H' of H, i.e., such that $L(H) \subseteq L(H')$, it is verified $L(H')^f \subseteq E$ then also holds $L(H)^f \subseteq f$. In other words, a supervisor solution for the approximation H', is also a solution for the original problem, since the desired containment relation $L(H)^f \subseteq E$ is preserved. Thus, a supervisor solution for the approximation H', is also a solution for the original problem.

Given a conservative approximation H' of the behavior of a plant H with infinite state space, and a language specifying the target behavior E, the synthesis procedure is applied over A and E. If there is no solution for this problem this means that the approximation H' is too coarse or that the specification E is too restrictive (it can not be satisfied no matter how accurate the approximation is) and needs to be relaxed. Assuming the specification can be met, a refinement of the approximation is indicated in [8], such that another conservative approximation can be computed and the process can be repeated repeated until a solution is found.

5   Example

This section presents an example of the class of hybrid systems under consideration. By this example, the computational approach for the supervisor synthesis for hybrid systems will be illustrated.

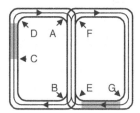

Fig. 4. Trains example.

The system consists of two trains over cyclic tracks sharing a piece of track (Fig. 4). The trains can travel at two speeds: *fast* or *slow*. There are sensors over the tracks that register the crossing of the trains at the locations A, B, C and D which, in turn, correspond to the events associated to train 1; similarly, E, F and G are the events indicating crossings of train 2. At the instant of the occurrence of any event, each train can accept speed change commands. The slow mode can only be issued between the locations C-D (for train 1) and G-E (for train 2), as indicated by the gray shade in Fig. 4. The problem is to guarantee mutual exclusion on the shared track, between the locations A-B and E-F.

In order to solve this supervisory control problem, the following procedure was applied, whose steps are detailed in the following.

1. Build the Hybrid System model in *CheckMate*;
2. Generation of the finite state machine approximation by *CheckMate*, and
3. Synthesis of the Supervisor.

We first model the open-loop hybrid system using *CheckMate*. *CheckMate* is a verification tool for event-driven hybrid systems for *Matlab/Simulink* environment, recently developed at Carnegie Mellon University[7]. The resulting model is illustrated in figure 5.

The middle box of figure 5, named *trains*, corresponds to a Switched Continuous Block (SCSB) modeling the continuous subsystem. The state vector x models the position of the trains, the measured distances over the track to predefined origins set to D and G respectively. The continuous dynamic is defined, for the input signal u, as satisfying $\dot{x} = f_u(x)$ for $x \in R^2$. The input signal is a multiplexed vector u with four signals, each one assuming a positive integer value associated to certain speed mode of operation. In this 4-tuple, two signals take values on the modes of operation *fast* and *slow*; the other two signals take values on the *up* and *down* modes. The later, are two artificial modes introduced

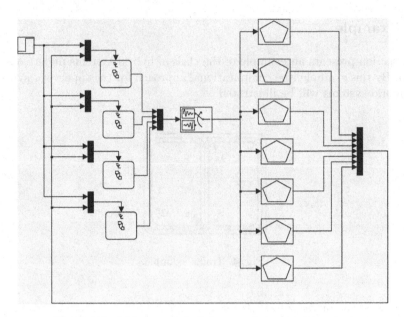

Fig. 5. CheckMate model of the open-loop hybrid system.

for modeling the position variable in such a manner that it assumes values only in certain range $[0, max]$ without introducing jumps in the trajectory. For a given position value of maximal position, max, we associate to each component of the position vector a positive (up) mode in the range $[0, max/2]$ and a negative (down) mode in the range $[max/2, max]$. The switching function which returns the derivative of the state vector for each values of u is specified in a m-file that basically associates to each values of the 4-tuple an specific *clock dynamic*, see [7], given by $\dot{x} = [\pm v_1 \ \pm v_2]^T$, where $v_1, v_2 \in \{v_{fast}, v_{slow}\}$ and v_{fast} and v_{slow} are the possible trains' speeds.

The seven boxes aligned at the right of the SCSB in Fig. 5 correspond to Polyhedral Threshold Blocks (PTHBs). Each PTHB represents a convex polyhedron parameterized by the matrix pair (C, d). The output of the block is a boolean signal that indicates whether the continuous state vector x (the block input signal) lies within the polyhedron defined by $Cx \le d$. In this example, each convex polyhedron defines just a line restriction associated to each position of the sensors over the tracks. As a consequence, the continuous space is divided in regions. For instance, considering $x = [x_1 \ x_2]^T$ the polyhedron defined by the pair (C, d), where $C = [-1 \ 0]$ and $D = [-A \ 0]^T$, defines the line constraint $-x_1 \le -A$ or $x_1 > A$. For this example of PTHB, the output signal is true only for values $x_1 > A$. Observe that each PTHB of the figure is labeled according to this criterion.

The four boxes aligned at the left of Fig. 5 correspond to Finite State Machine Blocks (FSMB) modeling the discrete subsystem. The input events of these blocks are multiplexed signals with the events from the PTHBs. The triggering criterion adopted for all events is rising edge. The two upper FSMBs represent the *up/down* logic. In particular, we model the behavior of the system in such a way that the occurrence of event D (G) forces the *up* mode, turns positive the variable related to the position of train 1 (2). Also, the occurrence of event B (F) forces the *down* mode, i.e., turns negative the variable related to the position of train 1 (2). For convenience, locations B and F are also associated to the middle of the trajectory of each train. Figure 6 shows two FSMBs representing *up/down* logic for each train.

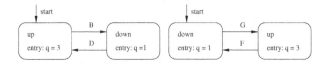

Fig. 6. FSMBs representing the *up/down* logic of each train.

In Figure 7 the two FSMBs represent a nondeterministic logic for the *slow/fast* modes. Note, for instance, that when event C (G) happens there is a nondeterministic choice of the next mode, *fast* or *slow*, for train 1 (2). At the other hand the occurrence of event D (E) forces the retaking of the fast mode of train 1 (2). The occurrence of other events leads to nondeterministic choices. Note that the representation of the discrete part of the hybrid system through four FSMBs simplifies enormously and results in a more intuitive model.

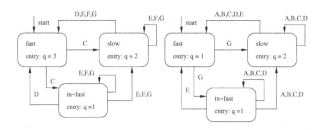

Fig. 7. FSMBs representing the *slow/fast* logic of each train.

The model in *CheckMate* can be simulated according to the rules of *Matlab*'s *Simulink* environment. For simulation purposes, we set up the following values to the hybrid plant model: **Sensors:** $x_1 = 20$m (A), $x_1 = 40$m (B), $x_1 = 10$m (C), $x_1 = 0$m (D); $x_2 = 30$m (E), $x_2 = 50$m (F) and $x_2 = 0$m (G); **Modes** *fast/slow*: 1.0m/s and 0.2m/s; and **Initial Conditions**: Train 1 at $x_1 = 0$m and Train 2 at $x_2 = 40$m, in *down* mode. Note that the values assigned to the sensors are consistent with the *up/down* modes of the position variable. Not considering these artificial modes results in an *extended model*, with sensors values given by $x_1 = 20$m (A), $x_1 = 40$m (B), $x_1 = 70$m (C), $x_1 = 80(0)$m (D);

$x_2 = 30$m (E), $x_2 = 50$m (F) and $x_2 = 100(0)$m (G). The extended model is useful for visualization of simulation results. For instance, Fig. 9 shows in the extended model some results for a simulation time $t = 450s$ and under the above parameters, where the possibility of train collision is clearly pointed. Obviously, in this case the order of events causing nondeterminism was defined so that the *fast* mode was forced to be the *preferred* choice.

The calculation of a finite state approximation for the hybrid plant is accomplished by running a verification procedure in *CheckMate*. In the case of the trains example, after two iterations of approximation and refinement, a finite state machine with 817 states and 936 transitions is obtained. The approximation obtained in *CheckMate* must be treated before the application of the supervisor synthesis procedure, since it is nondeterministic, non minimal, and has spurious transitions. A set of basic functions of a C++ Library for manipulation of state machines called *Grail* [9] was extended and applied for it. A finite state deterministic and minimal machine representing the system of trains with 44 states and 92 transitions is obtained for the example.

The specification of the desired mutual exclusion (shown in Fig. 8) simply states that the trains are not allowed to enter the shared piece of track at the same time. This specification is given over the output alphabet V.

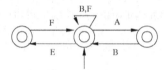

Fig. 8. Specification of the desired behavior.

By application of supervisor synthesis procedure described in [6], implemented also in a *Grail* function, a supervisor with 18 states and 27 transitions is found. The resulting supervisor represents the DES supervisor of Sec. 3, and by application of Alg. 1, the C/E supervisor can be found.

After the succeeding synthesis of the supervisor for the hybrid system, it is possible to simulate the closed loop behavior in *CheckMate*. The C/E supervisor, as defined in Sec. 2, cannot be implemented directly in *CheckMate* due to the assumption of synchronicity of signals that is not respected in the simulation of two interconnected FSMB. Substitution of the original discrete subsystem by the synthesized supervisor would be a valid simulation option, if the synthesis procedure had not been based in approximations of the plant, since approximations include additional sequences in the original and closed-loop system. The synchronous composition of supervisor and discrete subsystem, connected to the continuous subsystem is, in general, a correct simulation option, due to the synchronicity assumption of Sec. 2. Figure 9 shows a simulation case for the closed loop of last case, putting in evidence the speed changes (fast to slow mode) of train 1 in order to avoid collisions.

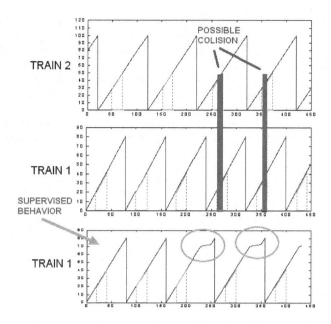

Fig. 9. Sample simulation of the open-loop and closed-loop system.

6   Discussion

This paper presents the solution to a class of supervisory control problems for hybrid systems with both continuous and discrete dynamics. The approach is illustrated with an in example which, to our knowledge, is the first published example of the computation of a discrete-state supervisor directly from a computer model of a hybrid system.

References

[1] José E. R. Cury, Bruce H. Krogh, and Toshihiko Niinomi. Synthesis of supervisory controllers for hybrid systems based on approximating automata. *IEEE Transactions on Automatic Control*, 43(4):564–568, April 1998.

[2] T. Moor, J. Raisch, and S. D. O'Young. Supervisory control of hybrid systems via *l*-complete approximations. In *WODES'98- International Workshop on Discrete Event Systems*, pages 426–431, 1998.

[3] J. Raisch and S. D. O'Young. Discrete approximation and supervisory control of continuous systems. *IEEE Trans. on Automatic Control*, 43(4):569–573, April 1998.

[4] X.D. Koutsoukos, P.J. Antsaklis, J.A. Stiver, and M.D. Lemmon. Supervisory control of hybrid systems. *Proceedings of the IEEE*, 88(7):1026–1049, July 2000.

[5] R. S. Sreenivas and B. H. Krogh. On condition/event systems with discrete state realizations. *Discrete Event Dynamic Systems: Theory and Applications*, 1:209–236, 1991.

[6] Jose Miguel Eyzell González. *Aspectos de Síntese de Supervisores para Sistemas a Eventos Discretos e Sistemas Híbridos*. Tese (doutorado), Programa de Pós Graduação em Engenharia Elétrica, Universidade Federal de Santa Catarina, Florianópolis, Brasil, Abril 2000.

[7] A. Chutinan and B.H. Krogh. Infinite-state transition system verification using approximate quotient transition systems. To appear IEEE Transactions on Automatic Control., 2000.

[8] J. E. R. Cury and B. H. Krogh. Synthesizing supervisory controllers for hybrid systems. *Journal of the Society of Instrument and Control Engineers*, 38(3):161–168, March 1999.

[9] D. Raymond and W. Derick. Grail: A c++ library for automata and expressions. *Journal of Symbolic Computation*, 11, 1995.

Control of Piecewise-Linear Hybrid Systems on Simplices and Rectangles[*]

Luc C.G.J.M. Habets[1,2] and Jan H. van Schuppen[1]

[1] CWI — Centrum voor Wiskunde en Informatica,
P.O. Box 94079, 1090 GB Amsterdam, The Netherlands
{L.C.G.J.M.Habets, J.H.van.Schuppen}@cwi.nl
[2] Eindhoven University of Technology,
Department of Mathematics and Computing Science,
P.O. Box 513, 5600 MB Eindhoven, The Netherlands

Abstract. A necessary and sufficient condition for the reachability of a piecewise-linear hybrid system is formulated in terms of reachability of a finite-state discrete-event system and of a finite family of affine systems on a polyhedral set. As a subproblem, the reachability of an affine system on a polytope is considered, with the control objective of reaching a particular facet of the polytope. If the polytope is a simplex, necessary and sufficient conditions for the solvability of this problem by affine state feedback are described. If the polytope is a multi-dimensional rectangle, then a solution is obtained using continuous piecewise-affine state feedback.

Keywords and Phrases: Piecewise-linear hybrid systems, polyhedral set, simplex, multi-dimensional rectangle, facet, reachability, control law.

1 Introduction

The purpose of this paper is to present results on the reachability and control synthesis of piecewise-linear hybrid systems.

Many engineering systems can in a first approximation be described by a piecewise-linear hybrid system. The computational and complexity issues of this class of systems seem comparatively simple. Therefore this class merits attention for the development of control theory.

Hybrid systems have been investigated since the 1980's, see [5] for references. The class of piecewise-linear hybrid systems studied in this paper may be considered as a subclass of the class of piecewise-linear systems, introduced by Sontag in [14] (see also [16]). Piecewise-linear hybrid systems are, in regard to the geometry of the spaces, based on polyhedral sets. The fact that polyhedral sets can be described by finite-dimensional parameters, makes these sets a suitable class of objects for control and system theory of hybrid systems. The class of piecewise-linear hybrid systems is therefore useful both because many engineering systems can be modelled by it and because of its mathematical properties.

---

[*] Research is supported in part by the Project Verification of Hybrid Systems (VHS, Esprit Project 26270) of the European Commission.

M.D. Di Benedetto, A. Sangiovanni-Vincentelli (Eds.): HSCC 2001, LNCS 2034, pp. 261–274, 2001.
© Springer-Verlag Berlin Heidelberg 2001

Although control synthesis for hybrid systems has been investigated by many researchers (e.g. by S. Sastry and co-workers), it is fair to say that the current status of control theory for hybrid systems is far from satisfactory. No review of the available literature will be presented here. The reader is referred to the proceedings of workshops [17,12].

The results of the paper concern reachability of piecewise-linear hybrid systems. First, the approach of [19] is used to show that reachability of a hybrid system is equivalent to reachability of a discrete-event system and of a family of continuous-space affine systems. The result is based on a natural decomposition of a hybrid system involving the concepts of arrival set, departure set, and of a discrete-event system for the switches from departure sets to arrival sets. Motivated by this result, the reachability problem for a continuous-space affine system is formulated as whether there exists a control law such that the closed-loop system reaches from an arbitrary initial state a particular facet of the polyhedral set, without reaching other facets first. Particular attention is payed to the situations, where the state set is a simplex or a multi-dimensional rectangle. On a simplex, the solvability of the continuous-state reachability problem using affine state feedback is equivalent to the existence of a solution of a set of linear inequalities corresponding to input vectors at the vertices of the simplex. This solution is treated in full detail in a separate paper, see [7]; it is a nice application of linear system theory and of convex analysis. Reachability of affine systems on multi-dimensional rectangles can be handled similarly, provided that continuous piecewise-affine state feedback is allowed. The proof is based on the fact that any polytope admits a triangulation in terms of simplices.

This paper is organized as follows. Section 2 contains a definition of a continuous-time piecewise-linear hybrid system and the formulation of the reachability problem. Concepts and a theorem on the reachability of a hybrid system are stated in Section 3. In Section 4 reachability and control of affine systems on simplices and multi-dimensional rectangles is considered. Conclusions are stated in Section 5.

2   Problem Formulation

In this section a definition of a piecewise-linear hybrid system is stated and the problem of reachability of such a system is formulated.

Throughout the paper, the notion of polyhedral sets plays a prominent role. Polyhedral sets are subsets of $\mathbb{R}^N$, ($N \in \mathbb{N}$), described by a finite number of linear equalities and inequalities. A polyhedral set that is bounded is a polytope, and is characterized as the convex hull of a finite number of points: the vertices of the polytope. A facet of a polyhedral set $P_N \subset \mathbb{R}^N$ is the intersection of P_N with a supporting hyperplane, such that the dimension of the intersection is $N-1$. For further terminology on polyhedral sets see [13,15,21].

Definition 2.1. *A (time-invariant continuous-time) piecewise-linear hybrid system (PLHS) consists of an automaton $(Q, E_{in} \cup E_{cd}, f)$, in combination with a $|Q|$-tuple of affine systems $(A(q), B(q), C(q), D(q), a(q), c(q))$, $(q \in Q)$, interacting in the following way.*

Given a mode $q \in Q$, the continuous state x_q evolves according to the affine differential equation

$$\dot{x}_q(t) = A(q)x_q(t) + B(q)u(t) + a(q), \quad x_q(t_0) = x_q^+, \tag{1}$$
$$y(t) = C(q)x_q(t) + D(q)u(t) + c(q),$$

with $x_q \in X_q$ and $u \in U$. The state set X_q and the input set U are assumed to be polyhedral sets. As soon as a discrete input event $e \in E_{in}$ is applied, or an event $e \in E_{cd}$ (i.e. an event generated by the continuous dynamics) occurs, because the continuous state has reached the guard $G_q(e) \subseteq \partial X_q$, a discrete transition takes place according to the transition map f:

if $x_{q^-}^- = \lim_{s \uparrow t} x_{q^-}(s) \in G_{q^-}(e)$ or if $e \in E_{in}$ occurs, then
$q^+ = f(q^-, x_{q^-}, e).$

In the new discrete mode q^+, the evolution of the new continuous state x_{q^+} is described by differential equation (1), with q replaced by q^+, and with initial value $x_{q^+}^+$ determined by the affine reset map

$$x_{q^+}^+ = A_r(q^-, e, q^+)x_{q^-}^- + b_r(q^-, e, q^+).$$

In order to make the system well defined, we assume that:

1. *At any fixed time only a finite number of discrete transitions can occur.*
2. *On any finite interval only a finite number of discrete transitions can occur (non-Zenoness).*

In the definition of a PLHS the input set U and the state sets $X_q \subseteq \mathrm{I\!R}^{N_q}$, $(q \in Q)$, are polyhedral sets. In Section 4 attention is first restricted to state sets that are simplices and later on multi-dimensional rectangles are considered.

Control problems for hybrid systems require conditions for their solvability. A condition that is required for the solution of many such problems is that the system is reachable, according to the definition provided below. Before computing a control law one often determines whether the considered system is reachable, although in the approach of the present paper, checking reachability and construction of a control law may be combined. However, verification of reachability of a PLHS is theoretically and practically difficult, because of the extent of the external behavior of a PLHS and because of the complexity of computations for this class of systems.

Definition 2.2. *Consider a PLHS.*

(a) The state $(q_1, x_{q_1,1}) \in Q \times X$ is said to be reachable *from the initial state $(q_0, x_{q_0,0}) \in Q \times X$ if there exist two finite sequences,*

$$\{(t_i, e_i) \in T \times E_{in} | i = 1, \ldots, m\}, \ \{u_i : [t_i, t_{i+1}) \to U | i = 1, \ldots, m\},$$

such that the PLHS, starting at state $(q_0, x_{q_0,0})$ and with discrete and continuous input functions the sequences above, moves to state $(q_1, x_{q_1,1}) \in Q \times X$ at time t_{m+1}, or, stated differently, at time $t_{m+1}, q = q_1$ and $x_{q_1}(t_{m+1}) = x_{q_1,1}$.

(b) The PLHS is said to be reachable from the initial state $(q_0, x_{q_0,0}) \in Q \times X$
if every $(q_1, x_{q_1,1}) \in Q \times X$ *is reachable from the initial state.*

Problem 2.1. Consider a PLHS. Determine necessary and sufficient conditions
on this system such that it is reachable from the initial state.

Problem 2.1 is motivated by, for example, path planning for robots and by
chemical process control. Because the class of PLHS has a large extent, an analytic solution is likely to be intractable. Thus, the reachability problem may be
undecidable or, if decidable, of large complexity.

A major contribution to the reachability problem for hybrid systems was presented by G. Lafferriere, G. Pappas, and S. Sastry in [9,10]. That approach uses
the notion of O-minimality in combination with the concept of bisimulation. It
is shown that the reachability problem is decidable if the hybrid system satisfies
certain conditions. The approach of the present paper differs from that using
the O-minimality approach in several respects: (1) The approach concerns only
piecewise-linear hybrid systems. (2) The reset map is an affine map. (3) A particular decomposition method is used that is not considered in the O-minimality
approach. The work is inspired by examples of hybrid systems that are models
of engineering systems.

The problem of reachability of PLHS or closely related systems has also
been investigated by other researchers. O. Maler, T. Dang, and co-workers have
developed an approach to approximate reachability (see [1]), based on over approximating the reachable set by an orthogonal polyhedron. A. Bemporad, M.
Morari, and F. Torrisi have developed a computational approach to determine
reachability of discrete-time PLHS (see e.g. [2], [3]). For a polyhedral set of initial
states they numerically approximate the subset of reachable states at subsequent
times. This method is effective for a comparatively small number of time steps
and for PLHS with state sets of relatively low dimension.

3   Reachability of Hybrid Systems

The approach to the reachability problem discussed in this paper is to decompose
it into a reachability problem for an automaton on the one hand, and a finite
set of reachability problems for continuous-time polyhedral linear systems on
the other. The reachability problem for the automaton is easily solved by direct
computation. The resulting reachability problem for affine systems requires some
analysis and will be discussed in the next section.

The approach to the reachability problem presented in this section was first
described by the second author in [19] but, compared with that reference, several
definitions have been sharpened and the theorem strengthened.

Definition 3.1. *Consider a PLHS.*

(a) A departure set *(or* exit set*) of this system is defined to be either a guard,*
$G_q(e) \subseteq \partial X_q$, $\forall e \in E_{cd}$, $q \in Q$, *or a set of the form*

$$D(q^-, e, q^+, A_{q^+}^+)$$

$$= \begin{cases} x_{q^-}^- \in X_{q^-} | q^+ = f(q^-, x_{q^-}^-, e), \\ A_r(q^-, e, q^+) x_{q^-}^- + b_r(q^-, e, q^+) \in A_{q^+}^+ \end{cases},$$

$$\forall e \in E_{in}, \; A_{q^+}^+ \subseteq X_{q^+} \text{ a polyhedral set}, \; \forall q^-, q^+ \in Q, \; q^- \neq q^+.$$

(b) An arrival set *(or* entry set*) is defined to be a set of the form*

$$AR(q^-, e, q^+, D^-)$$
$$= \begin{cases} x_{q^+}^+ \in X_{q^+} | \exists x_{q^-}^- \in D^- \subseteq X_{q^-} \text{ such that,} \\ q^+ = f(q^-, x_{q^-}^-, e), \; x_{q^+}^+ = A_r(q^-, e, q^+) x_{q^-}^- + b_r(q^-, e, q^+) \end{cases},$$

$$\forall q^-, q^+ \in Q, \; q^- \neq q^+, \; \forall e \in E_{in} \cup E_{cd}, \; \forall D^- \subseteq X_{q^-} \text{ a polyhedral set}.$$

A departure set in X_q may be interpreted as a set from which the state trajectory may leave the state set X_q. Such a departure takes place either at a guard by a continuous-dynamics event $e \in E_{cd}$ or from a departure set by application of an input event $e \in E_{in}$. An arrival set is a subset in which the state trajectory will enter the state set X_q directly after a transition.

Definition 3.2. *Consider a PLHS. The* controllability set *for* $(q, x_{q,1}) \in Q \times X$ *is defined to be the set of all states* $x_{q,0} \in X_q$ *from which* $x_{q,1}$ *can be reached without leaving* X_q:

$$\text{Conset}((q, x_{q,1}))$$
$$= \begin{cases} (q, x_{q,0}) \in Q \times X_q | \exists t_0, t_1 \in T, \; t_0 < t_1, \exists u : [t_0, t_1) \to U, \text{ such that,} \\ x_q(t_0) = x_{q,0}, \; x_q(t_1) = x_{q,1}, \; \forall t \in (t_0, t_1), \; x_q(t) \in X_q \end{cases}.$$

The controllability set *of a subset* $S_q \subseteq X_q$ *is defined to be the set*

$$\text{Conset}((q, S_q)) = \cup_{x_{q_1} \in S_q} \text{Conset}((q, x_{q,1}))$$

Definition 3.3. *Consider a PLHS. Assume there exists a* finite *collection of disjoint sets of the form*

$$A = \{A(q, k) \subseteq X_q | k \in \{1, \ldots, n_q\}, \; q \in Q\}.$$

Assume further that for every arrival set $AR(q^-, e, q^+, X_{q^-})$, *for* $q^-, q^+ \in Q$, *and* $e \in E_{in} \cup E_{cd}$, *there exists a subset of the A-sets such that*

$$AR(q^-, e, q^+, X_{q^-}) \subseteq \cup_{k \in \{1, \ldots, n_{q^+}\}} A(q^+, k). \tag{2}$$

The collection is called a collection of A-sets. *Define the corresponding* A-automaton *as a possibly non-deterministic finite automaton* $(A, E_{in} \cup E_{cd}, f_A, A_0)$, *with initial state* $A_0 \in A$, *and partial function* $f_A : A \times (E_{in} \cup E_{cd}) \to A$, *defined by*

$$f_A(A(q^-, k), e) = \begin{cases} A(q^+, m), \text{ if} \\ \text{either } A(q^-, k) \subseteq \text{Conset}(D(q^-, e, q^+, A(q^+, m))), \\ \text{or } A(q^-, k) \subseteq \text{Conset}(G_{q^-}(e)) \wedge \\ \qquad A_r(q^-, e, q^+) x_{q^-}^- + b_r(q^-, e, q^+) \in A(q^+, m), \\ \text{for all } x_{q^-}^- \in G_{q^-}(e). \end{cases} \tag{3}$$

In the case of a piecewise-linear hybrid system, boundaries of departure sets and guards are assumed to be facets of the relevant polyhedral state set. Otherwise the polyhedral state set must be further decomposed into smaller polyhedral sets such that boundaries of departure sets and guards are facets. The question is thus: how to determine the controllability set of a facet of a polyhedral set? In Section 4 this problem is studied for state sets that are simplices or multi-dimensional rectangles. A condition is formulated that is equivalent to the controllability set of a facet being the full state set. In this situation, condition (3) in Definition 3.3 of the A-automaton is always satisfied. This implies that an A-automaton exists, but its state set may be infinite. Definition 3.3 imposes a restriction because the state set is assumed to be finite. This is discussed again below.

Theorem 3.1. *Consider a PLHS. Assume that there exists a* finite *collection of sets of the form*

$$A = \{A(q,k) \subseteq X_q | k \in \{1, \ldots, n_q\}, \ q \in Q\},$$

such that the conditions of Definition 3.3 hold. Then the PLHS is reachable from any initial state if and only if:

1. *The A-automaton is reachable (every state $A_1 \in A$ is reachable from any initial state $A_0 \in A$);*
2. *for any $(q_1, x_{q_1,1}) \in Q \times X$ there exists a set $A(q_1, k) \in A$ such that $(q_1, x_{q_1,1})$ is reachable from all initial states in $A(q_1, k)$ without leaving X_{q_1}; equivalently, for any $(q_1, x_{q_1,1}) \in Q \times X$ there exists a set $A(q_1, k) \in A$ such that $A(q_1, k) \subseteq \text{Conset}((q_1, x_{q_1,1}))$.*

Theorem 3.1 is a strengthened version of [19, Th. 8]. It provides a necessary and sufficient condition for reachability of a piecewise-linear hybrid system in terms of conditions and calculations. The main assumption for this result is the existence of a finite collection of A-sets. It is related to the concept of O-minimality and the approach to reachability developed by G. Lafferriere, G. Pappas, and S. Sastry, see [9,10]. The first condition for reachability of the PLHS, reachability of the A-automaton, is simple to check by a computer program. The second condition is a new problem. The problem is whether there exists an input that transfers the system from an A-set to a final state. This problem has been investigated in control theory in some generality but not for piecewise-linear systems on polyhedral sets as far as the authors know. An approach to this problem is to construct a Lyapunov function that assures convergence to a point. For an affine system on a simplex, further inspiration for tackling this problem may be taken from the discussion in Section 4.

Example 3.1. Control of a conveyor belt system. This example has been described in detail in [18]. There, a conveyor belt system was modelled as a piecewise-linear hybrid system. The arrival sets are simple to formulate because they correspond mostly to the arrival of a tray with manufacturing parts at either the front end of the belt or at the mid-point of the belt. The A-automaton based on arrival sets as A-sets has about 26 states and 84 transitions, and was checked to be reachable, using the computer program UMDES, developed by S. Lafortune at the University of Michigan. Reachability of any of the continuous-time systems is also easily verified: the guards can be reached by switching on the motor that drives the belt and the departure sets equal the full state set.

A first approach for constructing the A-sets is to take them equal to the full arrival sets,

$$A(q, r) = AR(q^-, e, q, X_{q^-}), \text{ for } r \in \mathbb{N} \text{ an index, and } q^-, q \in Q, \ e \in E.$$

In some examples, like Example 3.1, this choice suffices, but in general it is too restrictive. Recall from Definition 3.3 that a transition between A-sets is not defined if an arrival set is not fully contained in a corresponding controllability set. Hence it seems useful to split an arrival set into two or more subsets and to take these subsets as new A-sets. This approach is formulated in Algorithm 3.1 below. The construction of A-sets is similar to the bisimulation algorithm, see [9], except that it refers to the splitting of arrival sets only.

Algorithm 3.1. *Consider a PLHS and the collection of arrival sets*

$$AR = \left\{ \begin{array}{l} AR(q^-, e, q^+, D) \subseteq X_{q^+} | q^-, q^+ \in Q, \ q^- \neq q^+, \\ \text{and either } \{e \in E_{in} \text{ and } D = D(q^-, e, q^+, X_{q^+})\} \\ \text{or } \{e \in E_{cd} \text{ and } D = G_{q^-}(e)\} \end{array} \right\}.$$

Consider further a terminal state $(q_f, x_{q_f,f}) \in Q \times X$ *to be reached.*

1. Initialization set

$$A_0(q_f, k) = AR(q^-, e, q_f, D) \cap \text{Conset}((q_f, x_{q_f,f})),$$
$$\text{for } q^- \in Q, \ e \in E_{in} \cup E_{cd},$$
$$D = G_{q^-}(e) \text{ or } D = D(q^-, e, q_f, X_{q_f}),$$
$$A_0(q, k) = AR(q^-, e, q, D),$$
$$\text{if } q^-, q \in Q, \ q \neq q_f, \ q^- \neq q, \ e \in E_{in} \cup E_{cd},$$
$$D = G_{q^-}(e) \text{ or } D = D(q^-, e, q, X_q).$$

2. Backward recursion. Construct the sets,

$$B_{k+1}(q, m) = A_k(q^-, m_1) \cap \text{Conset}(D(q^-, e, q, A_k(q, m_2))),$$
$$q, q^- \in Q, \ e \in E_{in} \cup E_{cd}, \ m, m_1, m_2 \in \mathbb{N}.$$

Then produce a disjoint collection of the collection of B_{k+1} sets and denote these by

$$A_{k+1} = \{A_{k+1}(q, m) \subseteq X_q | m \in \{1, \ldots, n_{k+1}\}, q \in Q\}.$$

Define the map,

$$h : Pwrset(Pwrset(Q \times X)) \to Pwrset(Pwrset(Q \times X)), \ A_{k+1} = h(A_k).$$

Two questions for the above algorithm require further study:

1. Does the algorithm terminate in a finite number of steps?
2. If the algorithm terminates (thus $A_K = h(A_K)$ for some $K \in \mathbb{N}$), is the resulting collection A_K finite, i.e. does there exist $m_A \in \mathbb{N}$ such that

$$A_K = \{A_K(q, m) \subseteq X_q | m \in \{1, \ldots, m_A\}, \ q \in Q\}?$$

If both questions have been answered affirmatively, Theorem 3.1 provides an equivalent condition for reachability. Note however that for the construction of A-sets, the computation of controllability sets is required. In the next section we will consider this issue, in case the set to be reached is a facet of the state set. Often the state set can be partitioned in such a way that reachability of a polyhedral subset can be reformulated as reachability of a facet. In these situations the discussion of Section 4 facilitates the construction of A-sets. As soon as Algorithm 3.1 terminates, and the required collection of A-sets is obtained, the reachability of a piecewise-linear hybrid system may be verified by checking (1) the reachability of the A-automaton and (2) the reachability of a finite set of systems.

4   Reaching Departure Sets Using Feedback Control

In this section we focus our attention on one particular discrete mode of a piecewise-linear hybrid system, and study the continuous dynamics at that specific mode. There the continuous evolution of the system is described by an affine differential equation

$$\dot{x}(t) = Ax(t) + Bu(t) + a, \tag{4}$$

with $A \in \mathbb{R}^{N \times N}$, $B \in \mathbb{R}^{N \times m}$ and $a \in \mathbb{R}^N$. We assume that the state set X is a (full-dimensional) convex polytope P_N in $\mathbb{R}^N$. Also the choice of inputs $u \in \mathbb{R}^m$ is restricted to a polyhedral set U.

As soon as the state x crosses one of the facets of P_N, a discrete-event occurs, transferring the system to a different mode with different continuous dynamics. So the facets of P_N completely consist of departure sets. We will assume that every facet of P_N consists of exactly one departure set, meaning that the discrete transition to another mode only depends on the facet of P_N through which the state x leaves the polytope P_N. So, to steer the overall hybrid system to a particular state, using the approach of Section 3, we first have to answer the question whether it is possible to steer the affine system (4) to a specific facet/departure set. Preferably, this steering should be implemented by a static state feedback. So, in this section we will study the following problem:

Problem 4.1. Consider the system (4) with $x \in P_N$, and let F_1 be a facet of P_N, with normal vector n_1, pointing out of P_N. For any initial state $x_0 \in P_N$, find a time-instant $T_0 \geq 0$ and an input function $u : [0, T_0] \longrightarrow U$, such that at time T_0 the state x leaves P_N through the facet F_1, i.e.

(i) $\forall t \in [0, T_0]:\ x(t) \in P_N$,

(ii) $x(T_0) \in F_1$, and T_0 is the smallest time-instant in the interval $[0, T_0]$ for which $x(t) \in F_1$,

(iii) $n_1^T \dot{x}(T_0) > 0$, i.e. the velocity vector $\dot{x}(T_0)$ at the point $x(T_0) \in F_1$ has a positive component in the direction of n_1.

Furthermore, this input function u should be realized by the application of a continuous feedback law $u = f(x)$, with f independent of the initial state x_0.

Problem 4.1 is related to, but different from the existence of a control law for an affine system, such that the closed-loop system is invariant on a polytope, see [4,6,20].

Since the class of all continuous feedback laws is very large, we will focus on solutions of Problem 4.1, using affine feedback (if P_N is a simplex) or continuous piecewise-affine feedback (if P_N is a multi-dimensional rectangle). This restriction enables us to construct feedback solutions, by making extensive use of the convexity of the problem. First however, we formulate a set of necessary conditions for the solvability of Control Problem 4.1.

Proposition 4.1. *Let P_N be a full-dimensional polytope in $\mathbb{R}^N$ with vertices $v_1, \ldots, v_M$, $(M \geq N + 1)$. Let $F_1, \ldots, F_L$ denote the facets of P_N, with normal vectors $n_1, \ldots, n_L$, respectively, pointing out of the polytope P_N. For $i \in \{1, \ldots, L\}$, let $V_i \subset \{1, \ldots, M\}$ be the index set such that $\{v_j \mid j \in V_i\}$ is the set of vertices of the facet F_i. Conversely, for every $j \in \{1, \ldots, M\}$, the set $W_j \subset \{1, \ldots, L\}$ contains the indices of all facets of which v_j is a vertex. Assume that F_1 is the exit facet of P_N. If Control Problem 4.1 is solvable by a continuous state feedback f, i.e. if irrespective of the initial state $x_0 \in P_N$, the closed-loop system*

$$\dot{x} = Ax + Bf(x) + a, \qquad x(0) = x_0,$$

has a solution x, satisfying conditions (i)—(iii) of Problem 4.1, then there exist inputs $u_1, \ldots, u_M \in U$ such that

(1) $\forall j \in V_1: n_1^T(Av_j + Bu_j + a) > 0$,

(2) $\forall i \in \{2, \ldots, L\}\ \forall j \in V_i: n_i^T(Av_j + Bu_j + a) \leq 0$,

(3) $\forall j \in \{1, \ldots, M\} \backslash V_1\ \exists i \in W_j: n_i^T(Av_j + Bu_j + a) < 0$.

Proof. Suppose that the continuous feedback $f : P_N \longrightarrow U$ solves Problem 4.1. Then the inputs $u_j = f(v_j)$, $(j = 1, \ldots, M)$ satisfy (1), (2), and (3).

Indeed, at the exit facet F_1 the velocity vector field of the closed-loop system has a positive component in the n_1-direction, hence (1) holds. Furthermore, the state of the closed-loop system cannot leave P_N through any of the other facets, irrespective of the initial state x_0. This implies that on these facets the velocity vector field of the closed-loop system has to point into the polytope P_N. This condition remains valid at the vertices of a facet, and therefore (2) holds. Finally, the state of the closed-loop system should reach the exit facet F_1 in finite time. If (3) would not hold, then there would exist a vertex v of P_N, not belonging to F_1, such that the velocity vector field of the closed-loop system in v is equal to 0. Hence $x(t) \equiv v$ would be a solution of the closed-loop system, never reaching the exit-facet F_1. This leads to a contradiction. $\qquad \square$

Our next goal is to derive sufficient conditions for the solvability of Problem 4.1. For this purpose, we first consider the case where the convex polytope P_N is a *simplex* S_N, i.e. a full-dimensional polytope in $\mathbb{R}^N$, with exactly $N+1$ vertices. In this situation, the necessary conditions of Proposition 4.1 turn out to be sufficient for the construction of an affine feedback solution to Problem 4.1.

Lemma 4.1. *Let S_N be a full-dimensional simplex in $\mathbb{R}^N$ with affinely independent vertices $v_1, \ldots, v_{N+1}$, and let*

$$T_{N+1} := \{(\lambda_1, \ldots, \lambda_{N+1}) \in [0,1]^{N+1} \mid \sum_{j=1}^{N+1} \lambda_j = 1\}.$$

For every $x \in S_N$ there exists a unique $(\lambda_1, \ldots, \lambda_{N+1}) \in T_{N+1}$ such that $x = \sum_{j=1}^{N+1} \lambda_j v_j$. Moreover, the corresponding mapping $\varphi : S_N \longrightarrow T_{N+1}$ is affine, and thus continuous.

Proposition 4.2. *Consider the dynamical system $\dot{x}(t) = Ax(t) + Bu(t) + a$, with $x \in S_N$ and $u \in U$, and assume that there exist inputs $u_1, \ldots, u_{N+1} \in U$, such that at the vertices $v_1, \ldots, v_{N+1}$ of the simplex S_N, conditions (1)—(3) of Proposition 4.1 are satisfied. Define the affine mapping*

$$\psi : T_{N+1} \longrightarrow U : \psi(\lambda_1, \ldots, \lambda_{N+1}) = \sum_{j=1}^{N+1} \lambda_j u_j.$$

Then the mapping $f : S_N \longrightarrow U$, defined by $f = \psi \circ \varphi$, is an affine feedback solution of Control Problem 4.1.

Proof. For notational convenience we assume that the vertices $v_1, \ldots, v_{N+1}$ of S_N are numbered in such a way, that for $i = 1, \ldots, N+1$, v_i is the only vertex of S_N, not belonging to the facet F_i.

First we prove that the state x of the closed-loop system $\dot{x} = Ax + Bf(x) + a$ cannot leave the simplex S_N through any of the facets $F_2, \ldots, F_{N+1}$. Let $i \in \{2, \ldots, N+1\}$, and consider the facet F_i with normal vector n_i. Let $p \in F_i$ and $(\lambda_1, \ldots, \lambda_{N+1}) = \varphi(p)$, with $\lambda_i = 0$. Then condition (2) of Proposition 4.1 guarantees that

$$n_i^T \dot{x} \mid_p = n_i^T (Ap + Bf(p) + a)$$

$$= n_i^T \left(A \sum_{j=1, j\neq i}^{N+1} \lambda_j v_j + B \sum_{j=1, j\neq i}^{N+1} \lambda_j u_j + \sum_{j=1, j\neq i}^{N+1} \lambda_j a \right)$$

$$= \sum_{j=1, j\neq i}^{N+1} \lambda_j n_i^T (Av_j + Bu_j + a) \leq 0.$$

Hence, on every facet $F_2, \ldots, F_{N+1}$, the velocity vector field of the closed-loop system is pointing into the simplex S_N, so the state x cannot escape from S_N through any of these facets.

Next we show that the exit facet F_1 is reached within finite time. For this proof we need the fact that the normal vector n_1 can be written as a negative linear combination of $n_2, \ldots, n_{N+1}$ (see e.g. [7, Lemma A.3]). Let $p \in S_N$ with $\varphi(p) = (\lambda_1, \ldots, \lambda_{N+1})$. Then conditions (1), (2), and (3) of Proposition 4.1 and an argument imply that

$$n_1^T \dot{x} \mid_p = n_1^T (Ap + Bf(p) + a) = n_1^T \left(A \sum_{j=1}^{N+1} \lambda_j v_j + B \sum_{j=1}^{N+1} \lambda_j u_j + \sum_{j=1}^{N+1} \lambda_j a \right)$$

$$= \lambda_1 n_1^T (Av_1 + Bu_1 + a) + \sum_{j=2}^{N+1} \lambda_j n_1^T (Av_j + Bu_j + a) > 0.$$

Moreover, the simplex S_N is compact, so $\min\{n_1^T \dot{x} \mid_p \mid p \in S_N\}$ exists and is positive. Therefore the state x reaches the exit facet F_1 in finite time.   □

Remark 4.1. Given inputs $u_1, \ldots, u_{N+1} \in U$ at the vertices $v_1, \ldots, v_{N+1}$ of the simplex S_N, satisfying conditions (1)—(3) of Proposition 4.1, an affine feedback law $u = Fx + g$ with $F \in \mathbb{R}^{m \times N}$ and $g \in \mathbb{R}^m$ that solves Control Problem 4.1, can be computed directly by solving the linear equations $u_j = Fv_j + g$, $(j = 1, \ldots, N + 1)$, for F and g.

Example 4.1. Control to a facet. Let S_2 be the triangle in $\mathbb{R}^2$, with vertices $v_1 = (-1, 0)^T$, $v_2 = (1, 1)^T$, and $v_3 = (1, -1)^T$, and consider the affine system

$$\dot{x} = \begin{pmatrix} -1 & -1 \\ -2 & 1 \end{pmatrix} x + \begin{pmatrix} 2 \\ -2 \end{pmatrix} u + \begin{pmatrix} 3 \\ 1 \end{pmatrix},$$

with state $x \in S_2$ and scalar input $-1 \leq u \leq 1$. Consider Control Problem 4.1, with F_1, the facet between v_2 and v_3, as exit-facet. This problem is solvable if and only if there exist inputs u_1, u_2, u_3 at the vertices v_1, v_2, v_3, respectively, such that condition (1), (2), and (3) of Proposition 4.1 are satisfied. In this example these inequalities become $\frac{1}{3} \leq u_1 \leq 1$, $-\frac{1}{6} \leq u_2 \leq 1$, and $-1 \leq u_3 \leq -\frac{1}{2}$. Upon choosing $u_1 = \frac{1}{2}$, $u_2 = 0$, and $u_3 = -\frac{3}{4}$, an affine feedback solution of Problem 4.1 is given by

$$u = \begin{pmatrix} -\frac{7}{16} & \frac{3}{8} \end{pmatrix} \begin{pmatrix} x_1 \\ x_2 \end{pmatrix} + \frac{1}{16}.$$

The idea of the proof of Proposition 4.2 can be extended to multi-dimensional rectangles, if we also allow continuous piecewise-affine functions $f : P_N \longrightarrow U$ as possible feedback solutions.

Proposition 4.3. *Let P_N be a full-dimensional convex polytope in $\mathbb{R}^N$ with vertices $v_1, \ldots, v_M$, $(M \geq N + 1)$, and define*

$$T_M := \{(\lambda_1, \ldots, \lambda_M) \in [0, 1]^M \mid \sum_{j=1}^M \lambda_j = 1\}.$$

Then there exists a continuous and piecewise-affine mapping $\varphi : P_N \longrightarrow T_M$ such that for all $x \in P_N$:

$$x = \sum_{j=1}^{M} \varphi(x)_j v_j. \tag{5}$$

The fact that any point $x \in P_N$ may be written as a convex combination of the vertices of P_N is obvious. Note however that such a convex combination is in general not unique, unless $M = N + 1$. If $M > N + 1$, one may construct $\varphi : P_N \longrightarrow T_M$, satisfying (5), by subdividing P_N in simplices (triangulation, see e.g. [11]). Then every $x \in P_N$ is uniquely represented as a convex combination of those vertices, that are vertices of all the simplices of which x is an element. This representation yields a continuous and piecewise-affine mapping φ, satisfying (5).

Proposition 4.4. Let R_N be the multi-dimensional rectangle defined by

$$R_N := \{x \in \mathbb{R}^N \mid \forall i = 1, \ldots, N : a_i \leq x_i \leq b_i\},$$

and consider the dynamical system $\dot{x}(t) = Ax(t) + Bu(t) + a$, with $x \in R_N$ and $u \in U$. Let $F_1 := R_N \cap \{x \in \mathbb{R}^N \mid x_1 = b_1\}$ be the exit facet of R_N with normal vector e_1. The normal vectors on the other facets are $-e_1$ and $\pm e_i$, $(i = 2, \ldots, N)$. Denote $M = 2^N$, and let $\varphi : R_N \rightarrow T_M$ be a continuous and piecewise-affine mapping, satisfying (5). Assume that there exist inputs $u_1, \ldots, u_M \in U$, such that at the vertices $v_1, \ldots, v_M$ of R_N, conditions (1)—(3) of Proposition 4.1 are satisfied, and additionally

(4) $\forall j = 1, \ldots, M : e_1^T (Av_j + Bu_j + a) > 0.$

Define the affine mapping

$$\psi : T_M \longrightarrow U : \psi(\lambda_1, \ldots, \lambda_M) = \sum_{j=1}^{M} \lambda_j u_j.$$

Then the mapping $f : R_N \longrightarrow U$, defined by $f = \psi \circ \varphi$, is a continuous and piecewise-affine feedback law, solving Control Problem 4.1.

The proof of Proposition 4.4 is analogous to the proof of Proposition 4.2. Condition (4) is required to guarantee that the state of the closed-loop system reaches the exit-facet F_1 in finite time. However, for multi-dimensional rectangles condition (4) is almost implied by conditions (1) and (2); at the vertices of the exit facet conditions (1) and (4) are the same, and at the other vertices (the vertices of the facet $R_N \cap \{x \in \mathbb{R}^N \mid x_1 = a_1\}$ with normal vector $-e_1$), condition (2) states that $e_1^T (Av_j + Bu_j + a) \geq 0$. The only difference with condition (4) is a $>$-sign instead of a $\geq$-sign. So the necessary and sufficient conditions of Propositions 4.1 and 4.4 are almost equivalent. Furthermore, in Proposition 4.4 condition (3) may be omitted, because it is implied by (4).

Remark 4.2. The design method of Proposition 4.4 for the construction of a continuous piecewise-affine feedback solving Problem 4.1 is applicable to arbitrary full-dimensional convex polytopes P_N. However, if P_N is not a simplex or a multi-dimensional rectangle, the sufficient condition (4) becomes restrictive.

Propositions 4.1, 4.2, and 4.4 yield necessary and sufficient conditions for the solution of Control Problem 4.1 for simplices and rectangles. So, if for a hybrid system the state-set at each discrete mode belongs to this class, the question of reachability of a departure set may be translated into the solvability of a system of linear inequalities. Therefore, the verification may be carried out, using existing software packages, e.g. [8].

5 Conclusions

The contribution of this paper to control of hybrid systems concerns reachability and control law synthesis. First, an equivalent condition for reachability of a piecewise-linear hybrid system was formulated in terms of reachability of a finite-state discrete-event system and of a finite family of affine systems on a polyhedral set. Next, an equivalent condition for reachability of an affine system on a simplex was derived, for the control objective of reaching a particular facet of the simplex. This result was extended to multi-dimensional rectangles. The solution is based on the construction of a continuous (piecewise) affine control law.

Further research is required into the reachability of an affine system on a general polytope. Computational aspects of the construction of a control law should be studied. For this, triangulation of polyhedral sets is needed, involving concepts of discrete and computational geometry. Symbolic computation seems well suited for this operation. Application of the results to engineering systems also requires attention.

References

1. E. Asarin, O. Bournez, T. Dang, and O. Maler. Approximate reachability analysis of piecewise-linear hybrid systems. In N. Lynch and B.H. Krogh, editors, *Hybrid Systems: Computation and Control*, volume 1790 of *Lecture Notes in Computer Science*, pages 20–31, Berlin, 2000. Springer-Verlag.
2. A. Bemporad, G. Ferrari-Trecate, and M. Morari. Observability and controllability of piecewise affine and hybrid systems. In *Proceedings of the 38th IEEE Conference on Decision and Control*, pages 3966–3971, New York, 1999. IEEE Press.
3. A. Bemporad and M. Morari. Control of systems integrating logic, dynamics, and constraints. *Automatica*, 35:407–427, 1999.
4. L. Berardi, E. De Santis, and M.D. Di Benedetto. Control of switching systems under state and input constraints. In *Proc. European Control Conference (ECC99)*, 1999.
5. M.S. Branicky. *Studies in hybrid systems: Modeling, analysis, and control*. PhD thesis, M.I.T., Cambridge, MA, 1995.
6. E.B. Castelan and J.C. Hennet. On invariant polyhedra of continuous-time linear systems. *IEEE Trans. Automatic Control*, 38:1680–1685, 1993.
7. L.C.G.J.M. Habets and J.H. van Schuppen. A control problem for affine dynamical systems on a full-dimensional simplex. Report PNA-R0017, CWI, Amsterdam, 2000. www.cwi.nl/ftp/CWIreports/PNA/PNA-R0017.ps.Z
8. B. Jeannet. Convex polyhedra library. Report, Verimag, Université Joseph Fourier, Grenoble, 1999.

9. G. Lafferriere, G.J. Pappas, and S. Sastry. Subanalytic stratifications and bisimulations. In T.A. Henzinger and S. Sastry, editors, *Hybrid systems: Computation and control*, volume 1386 of *Lecture Notes in Computer Science*, pages 205–220, Berlin, 1998. Springer-Verlag.

10. G. Lafferriere, G. Pappas, and S. Sastry. O-minimal hybrid systems. *Math. Control Signals Systems*, 13:1–21, 2000.

11. C.W. Lee. Subdivisions and triangulations of polytopes. In J.E. Goodman and J. O'Rourke, editors, *Handbook of discrete and computational geometry*, pages 271–290. CRC Press, Boca Raton, NY, U.S.A., 1997.

12. N. Lynch and B.H. Krogh. *Hybrid Systems: Computation and Control*. Volume 1790 of *Lecture Notes in Computer Science*. Springer-Verlag, Berlin, 2000.

13. R.T. Rockafellar. *Convex analysis*. Princeton University Press, Princeton, 1970.

14. E.D. Sontag. Nonlinear regulation: The piecewise linear approach. *IEEE Trans. Automatic Control*, 26:346–358, 1981.

15. E.D. Sontag. Remarks on piecewise-linear algebra. *Pacific J. Math.*, 98:183–201, 1982.

16. E.D. Sontag. Interconnected automata and linear systems: A theoretical framework in discrete-time. In R. Alur, T.A. Henzinger, and E.D. Sontag, editors, *Hybrid Systems III: Verification and Control*, volume 1066 of *Lecture Notes in Computer Science*, pages 436–448, Berlin, 1996. Springer-Verlag.

17. F.W. Vaandrager and J.H. van Schuppen, editors. *Hybrid systems: Computation and control (HSCC'99)*. Volume 1569 of *Lecture Notes in Computer Science*. Springer-Verlag, Berlin, 1999.

18. J.H. van Schuppen. Control for a class of hybrid systems. Report PNA-R9716, CWI, Amsterdam, 1997. www.cwi.nl/ftp/CWIreports/PNA/PNA-R9716.ps.Z

19. J.H. van Schuppen. A sufficient condition for controllability of a class of hybrid systems. In T.A. Henzinger and S. Sastry, editors, *Hybrid systems: Computation and control*, volume 1386 of *Lecture Notes in Computer Science*, pages 374–383, Berlin, 1998. Springer-Verlag.

20. M. Vassilaki and G. Bitsoris. Constrained regulation of linear continuous-time dynamical systems. *Systems & Control Lett.*, 13:247–252, 1989.

21. G.M. Ziegler. *Lectures on polytopes*. Volume 152 of *Graduate Texts in Mathematics*. Springer-Verlag, Berlin, 1995.

Assume-Guarantee Reasoning
for Hierarchical Hybrid Systems*

Thomas A. Henzinger, Marius Minea, and Vinayak Prabhu

Dept. of EECS, University of California, Berkeley, CA 94720, USA
{tah,marius,vinayak}@eecs.berkeley.edu
www.eecs.berkeley.edu/~{tah,marius,vinayak}

Abstract. The assume-guarantee paradigm is a powerful divide-and-conquer mechanism for decomposing a verification task about a system into subtasks about the individual components of the system. The key to assume-guarantee reasoning is to consider each component not in isolation, but in conjunction with assumptions about the context of the component. Assume-guarantee principles are known for purely concurrent contexts, which constrain the input data of a component, as well as for purely sequential contexts, which constrain the entry configurations of a component. We present a model for hierarchical system design which permits the arbitrary nesting of parallel as well as serial composition, and which supports an assume-guarantee principle for mixed parallel-serial contexts. Our model also supports both discrete and continuous processes, and is therefore well-suited for the modeling and analysis of embedded software systems which interact with real-world environments. Using an example of two cooperating robots, we show refinement between a high-level model which specifies continuous timing constraints and an implementation which relies on discrete sampling.

1 Introduction

In the automatic verification of systems with very large state spaces, the model-checking task needs to be decomposed into subtasks of manageable complexity. It is natural to decompose the verification task following the component structure of the design. However, an individual component often does not satisfy its requirements unless the component is put into the right context. Thus, in order to verify each component individually, we need to make assumptions about its context, namely, about the other components of the design. This reasoning is circular: component A is verified under the assumption that context B behaves correctly, and symmetrically, B is verified assuming the correctness of A. The assume-guarantee paradigm provides a systematic theory and methodology for ensuring the soundness of the circular style of postulating and discharging assumptions in component-based reasoning.

---

* Support for this research was provided in part by the AFOSR MURI grant F49620-00-1-0327, and the DARPA SEC grant F33615-C-98-3614, the MARCO GSRC grant 98-DT-660, the NSF ITR grant CCR-0085949.

M.D. Di Benedetto, A. Sangiovanni-Vincentelli (Eds.): HSCC 2001, LNCS 2034, pp. 275–290, 2001.

When components are composed in parallel, context assumptions constrain the inputs to a component. Assume-guarantee principles for parallel composition are advocated, among others, by [MC81,AL95,McM97,AH99], and by [TAKB96, AH97] in a real-time setting. If components are composed in series, context assumptions constrain the entry configurations of a component. An assume-guarantee principle for serial composition is given in [AG00]. In hierarchical design, it is often useful to nest parallel and serial composition. This is especially true for embedded software, where serial composition occurs at multiple levels of granularity (e.g., software procedures; modes of operation; exception handling), and so does parallel composition (e.g., hardware modules; software threads; environment interaction). We provide an assume-guarantee principle for the case where a context can contain both parallel and serial components, arbitrarily nested.

For this purpose, we use a formal model which is called Masaccio, in honor of the Italian fresco painter who is credited with inventing perspective. The Masaccio language was defined in [Hen00]; we modify it slightly in order to obtain a general assume-guarantee principle. Masaccio is a formal model for hybrid dynamical systems which are built from atomic discrete components (difference equations) and atomic continuous components (differential equations) by parallel and serial composition, arbitrarily nested. Data is represented by variables; control by locations. The syntax of components includes six operations: besides parallel and sequential composition, data connections are built by variable renaming, control connections by location renaming, data abstractions by variable hiding, and control abstractions by location hiding. The formal semantics of each component consists of an interface, which determines the possible ways of using the component, and a set of executions, which define the possible behaviors of the component in real time. The intended use of Masaccio is to provide a formal, structured model for software and hardware that interacts with a physical environment in real time. Parallel composition is conjunctive: it typically combines actors (software threads, sensors, actuators, etc.); serial composition is disjunctive: it typically combines modes of operation (time-triggered and event-triggered mode switching, degraded and fault modes, etc.). Masaccio conservatively extends Reactive Modules [AH99,AH97], which provide parallel but no serial composition, and it inherits the mixing of discrete and continuous behavior from Hybrid Automata [ACH+95,Hen96], which are not hierarchical. The parallel composition of Masaccio is synchronous; asynchronicity can be modeled as in [AH99].

We demonstrate that Masaccio supports hierarchical, component-based design and analysis. In particular, we prove the soundness of (noncircular) compositional proof rules for both parallel and serial composition, and the soundness of a (circular) assume-guarantee proof rule, which permits assumptions about mixed parallel-serial contexts. Several key insights are necessary to enable the assume-guarantee principle. First, assume-guarantee reasoning is sound only for components that cannot deadlock internally. We therefore equip the interface of a component with entry conditions and insist that a location can be hidden only if the corresponding entry condition is valid. Second, if two components A

and B are composed in series, the assume-guarantee principle is sound only if each trace of the composite system $A + B$ can be assigned uniquely to either A or B. This can be achieved by requiring that for all locations common to A and B, the entry conditions are disjoint. Third, if A and B are composed in parallel, we wish to model the fact that either component may preempt the other on termination, causing $A\|B$ to terminate. Therefore, in refinement, B is more specific than C not only if every trace of B is a trace of C, but also if every trace of B has a prefix (possibly generated if B is preempted) which is a trace of C. This novel notion of refinement is consistent with sequential composition: a trace may terminate at an exit location of a component, and the serial addition of another component can then provide it with a continuation. Thus, a prefix of a trace is more general than the trace itself, since it potentially allows several different continuations. It will follow that both parallel and serial composition are congruences with respect to refinement.

We illustrate our formalism by modeling at different levels of detail a system of two cooperating robots, one of which is always following the other. The specification requires that a request by one robot to lead is honored within a certain time bound by the other robot starting to follow. We give an implementation that relies on periodic sampling of the robot states, and show how assume-guarantee reasoning simplifies the task of refinement checking between implementation and specification.

Related work. Concurrent and sequential hierarchies have long been nested in informal and semiformal ways (for instance, Statecharts [Har87], UML [BRJ98], Ptolemy [DGH+99]). While these languages enjoy considerable acceptance as good engineering practice, the most widely used versions of these languages do not support compositional formal analysis. For Statecharts, variants with compositional semantics have been defined (see, e.g., [US94]), but an assume-guarantee paradigm is not known. Hierarchic Modules [AG00] provide an assume-guarantee principle for serial composition, and parallel composition is reduced to serial composition. No continuous behaviors are considered. The languages Shift [DGV97] and Charon [AGH+00] support the hierarchical design of hybrid systems, but its emphasis is on simulation, and serial and parallel composition cannot be nested arbitrarily. The model of Hybrid I/O Automata [LSVW96] offers compositionality in a setting without serial composition.

2   The Masaccio Model for Embedded Components

In Masaccio, a system model is built out of *components*. We illustrate Masaccio by modeling parts of a system with two communicating robots, which will be used in Section 4; the formal definition of Masaccio is given in the appendix. The semantics of a component is defined by its interface ("structure") and its set of executions ("behavior"). The executions are *hybrid*: the state of a component may evolve by any sequence of discrete transitions (so-called *jumps*) and continuous evolutions (*flows*).

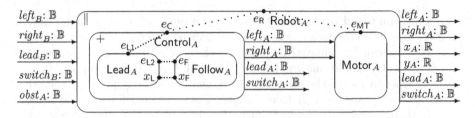

Fig. 1. Robot specification

The interface of a component. The interface of a component determines how the component can be composed (i.e., can interact) with other components. In Masaccio, control and data are handled separately. The interface of a component A contains a set V_A of variables partitioned into *input variables* and *output variables*, and a set L_A of *interface locations*, through which control can enter and/or exit the component. All variables are typed, with domains such as the booleans $\mathbb{B}$, the natural numbers $\mathbb{N}$, and the reals $\mathbb{R}$. While control resides inside a component, the input variables are updated by the environment (such as another component put in parallel), and the output variables are updated by the component. The component interface specifies a *dependency relation* $\prec_A$ between I/O variables and output variables. If $x \prec_A y$, then the value of y can depend without delay on the value of x. Specifically, with each jump, the new value of output y can depend on the new value of (say) input x, and during a flow, the derivative of output y can depend on the simultaneous derivative of input x. The dependency relation must be acyclic, in order to guarantee the existence of suitable output values and output curves.

An I/O state of the component is a value assignment to the variables in V_A. The component interface specifies for each location $a \in L_A$ a *jump entry condition* $\psi_A^{jump}(a)$ and a *flow entry condition* $\psi_A^{flow}(a)$. The component can be entered by a jump iff the jump entry condition is satisfied by the current I/O state, and by the new values of the input variables; the component can be entered by a flow iff the flow entry condition is satisfied by the current I/O state. The length of a flow may be constrained by the component, but whenever the flow entry condition is satisfied, at least a flow of duration 0 is possible. Control can exit the component at every location. In typical designs, the exit points are the locations with unsatisfiable entry conditions.

As an example, we portray a scenario in which two similar robots, structured as in Figure 1, move around in an environment with obstacles. The robots jointly choose the strategy of one leading and the other following, and their roles can switch. The interface of robot A consists of five input and six output variables. It contains a unique location e_R, with jump entry condition true (not represented). Once entered, the robot will react and execute forever, without control exiting. The inputs $lead_B$ and $switch_B$ indicate whether robot B is in the lead mode, or about to switch from follow to lead. The input $obst_A$ indicates if an obstacle is encountered. The component Motor_A, shown in Figure 2, controls the motion of the two wheels based on the signals $left_A$ and $right_A$, which allow the robot to

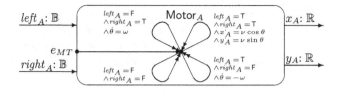

Fig. 2. Motor specification

go straight, halt, or turn in either direction. The outputs x_A and y_A give the position of the robot.

The executions of a component. The behavior of a component A is described by a set E_A of finite executions; the treatment of infinite behaviors for the study of liveness issues, such as nonzenoness [Hen96], is deferred for now. An *execution* is either a triple (a, w, b) or a pair (a, w) defined by an origin location $a \in L_A$, a nonempty finite sequence w of execution steps and, possibly, a destination location $b \in L_A$. An execution step is either a jump or a flow. A *jump* consists of a source I/O state and a sink I/O state; a *flow* consists of a real duration $\delta \geq 0$ together with a differentiable curve f that maps every real time in the compact interval $[0, \delta]$ to an I/O state. For types other than $\mathbb{R}$, we assume that only constant functions are differentiable. The source of the flow is the I/O state $f(0)$, and the sink is $f(\delta)$. For any two successive execution steps, the sink of the first must coincide with the source of the second. In figures, arrows with double tips denote flows, whereas normal arrows represent jumps.

The set E_A of executions is *prefix-closed*. Indeed, if a component permits a flow of a certain duration, then all restrictions of the flow to shorter durations, including the restriction to duration 0, are also permitted. Every component is *deadlock-free*, in the sense that (1) if the jump entry condition of a location a is satisfiable at an I/O state q, then there is an execution with origin a which starts with a jump with source q, (2) if the flow entry condition of location a is true at q, then there is an execution with origin a which starts with a flow with source q, and (3) every execution that does not end in a destination location can be prolonged by either a destination or a jump. Indeed, the stronger condition of *input-permissiveness* holds, which asserts that a component cannot deadlock no matter how the environment decides to change the inputs, by either jumping or flowing. Prefix-closure, deadlock-freedom, and input-permissiveness are formally defined and proved in the full version of this paper. They are essential properties of every component, because the environment (another component) may decide to interrupt a flow at any time to perform a jump, in which case the component must be prepared to match the environment jump by a local jump.

Atomic components. Every component in Masaccio is built from two kinds of atomic components, with discrete and continuous behavior, respectively. An atomic component has an arbitrary number of input and output variables, but only two locations, which serve as origin and destination, respectively, for its executions, all of which contain a single step. For an atomic discrete component, that step is a jump; for an atomic continuous component, a flow. The legal jumps of an *atomic discrete component* are defined by a jump predicate, which constrains the output values of the sink depending on the source I/O state and on input values of the sink. Such a predicate is typically specified by a difference equation. The legal flows of an *atomic continuous component* are defined by a flow predicate, which constrains the time derivatives of output variables depending on the current I/O state and on the current time derivatives of input variables. Such a predicate is typically specified by a differential equation, as in Figure 2. A flow predicate may also constrain the values of output variables, so that a flow must not go on for any duration that would violate this "invariant" condition. Both jump predicates and flow predicates may allow nondeterminism.

Operations on components. *Discrete components* are built from atomic discrete components using the six operations of parallel and serial composition, variable and location renaming, and variable and location hiding, arbitrarily nested. The discrete components conservatively extend Reactive Modules [AH99] by serial composition. *Hybrid components* are built from both discrete and continuous atomic components using the same six operations.

Parallel composition is defined synchronously, as conjunction, with static await dependencies between outputs and inputs preventing circularity. For two components A and B, an execution of the parallel composition $A\|B$ starts at a common location in $L_A \cap L_B$. The execution is synchronous in both components: each jump of A must be matched by a concurrent jump of B, and each flow of A must be matched by a concurrent flow of B with the same duration. Control exits the parallel composition when it exits any one of the two components. If the execution of A reaches a destination location, then the concurrent execution of B is preempted and terminated; if B reaches a destination location, then the concurrent execution of A is terminated; if both A and B simultaneously reach destination locations, then the result is nondeterministic. When constructing a parallel composition $A\|B$, inputs of A can be identified with outputs of B, and vice versa, by renaming variables. Such identifications are depicted by solid lines in the figures. Similarly, locations of A can be identified with locations of B by renaming locations; these identifications are depicted by dotted lines. We write $A[x := y]$ for the component that results from renaming the variable x in A to y, and $A[a := b]$ for the component that results from renaming the location a in A to b.

In Figure 1, the component Robot_A is the parallel composition of the components $\mathsf{Control}_A$ and Motor_A. Before composition, the two entry locations e_C and e_{MT} are renamed to a common location e_R.

Serial composition and location hiding can be used to achieve the sequencing of components. Serial composition represents disjunctive choice between the executions of two components. For two components A and B, an execution of the

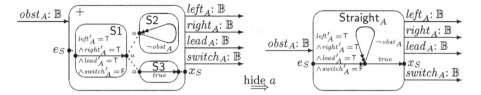

Fig. 3. Serial composition and location hiding

serial composition $A + B$ is either an execution of A or an execution of B. Hiding renders a location internal to a component, and inaccessible (invisible) from the outside. The executions of the resulting component are obtained by stringing together at that location any finite number of executions of the original component. To avoid internal deadlock, a location a can be hidden only if its jump entry condition is valid, so that it can always take another jump at a. We write $A \backslash a$ for the component that results from hiding a in A.

Figure 3 shows how a sequential component (representing the straight movement of the robot in the lead mode) is obtained by the serial composition of several components, followed by location hiding. Let $\mathsf{Straight}_A = (\mathsf{S1} + \mathsf{S2} + \mathsf{S3}) \backslash a$, where S1 and S3 are atomic discrete components, and S2 is obtained from an atomic continuous component by renaming destination location to origin location. The resulting component initializes its output variables by a jump, flows (without output changes) for any amount of time as long as the input $obst_A$ remains false, and nondeterministically exits with a jump. In the same way, any "automaton structure" can be built from individual "edges" (i.e., atomic components) using serial composition, location renaming, and location hiding.

Variable hiding builds an abstract component by turning some outputs of a component into internal state. Hidden variables, however, do not maintain their values from one exit of a component to a subsequent entry, but they are nondeterministically reinitialized upon every entry to the component so as to satisfy the applicable entry condition. We write $A \backslash x$ for the component that results from hiding the output variable x of the component A.

3 Assume-Guarantee Refinement between Components

If component A refines component B, then B can be viewed as a more abstract (permissive) version of A, with some details (constraints) left out in B which are spelled out in A. In particular, in the trace-based semantics of concurrent systems, refinement is taken to be the containment relation on trace sets. If A refines B, then A is a more specific description of system behavior than B in the sense that A may be equivalent to $B \| C$ for some parallel context C which constrains the inputs to B. In analogy, in the trace-based semantics of sequential systems, refinement ought to be interpreted as prefix relation on trace sets. If A refines B, then A is a more specific description of system behavior than B in the sense that A may be equivalent to $B + C$ for some serial context C which constrains the continuations of B. Consequently, in Masaccio, if A refines B, then A may specify fewer traces and longer traces than B.

The refinement relation. Component A *refines* component B if the following two conditions are satisfied:

1. Every output variable of B is an output variable of A, every input variable of B is an I/O variable of A, and the dependency relation of B is a subset of the dependency relation of A.
2. For every execution $(a, \boldsymbol{w})$ (or $(a, \boldsymbol{w}, b)$, respectively) of A, either $(a, \boldsymbol{w}[V_B])$ (or $(a, \boldsymbol{w}[V_B], b)$, respectively, where $\boldsymbol{w}[V_B]$ is the projection of $\boldsymbol{w}$ to the variables of B) is an execution of B, or there exist a proper, nonempty prefix $\boldsymbol{w}'$ of $\boldsymbol{w}$ and an interface location $c \in L_B$ such that $(a, \boldsymbol{w}'[V_B], c)$ is an execution of B.

Note that the second condition implies that every interface location of A is an interface location of B. Furthermore, by input-permissiveness, if A refines B, then for every location a of A, the jump entry condition of a in A implies the jump entry condition of a in B, and the flow entry condition of a in A implies the flow entry condition of a in B.

Compositionality. All six operations on components are compositional.

Theorem 1. *Let A and B be components, let x and y be variables, and let a and b be locations so that the following expressions are all well-defined. If A refines B, then $A\|C$ refines $B\|C$; and $A + C$ refines $B + C$; and $A[x := y]$ refines $B[x := y]$; and $A[a := b]$ refines $B[a := b]$; and $A\backslash x$ refines $B\backslash x$; and $A\backslash a$ refines $B\backslash a$.*

More generally, define a *context* to be a component expression that can take a component as a parameter. For instance, if $(A + B)\|D$ is well-defined, we can regard $C[\cdot] = ([\cdot] + B)\|D$ as a context for component A.

Corollary 1. *Let $C[\cdot]$ be a context for both A_1 and A_2. If A_1 refines A_2, then $C[A_1]$, refines $C[A_2]$.*

Assume-guarantee reasoning. Our assume-guarantee rule states that for discrete components, if two components can be individually replaced in a context while maintaining refinement, then both can be replaced simultaneously. Therefore, in order to show that a complex component $C[A_1, B_1]$ (the "implementation") refines a simpler component $C[A_2, B_2]$ (the "specification"), it suffices to look at simplified versions of the implementation one at a time. First, we prove that A_1 refines its specification B_1, under the "assumption" B_2; then, we prove that A_2 refines its specification B_2, under the "assumption" B_1. This reasoning is inherently circular. A special case is the assume-guarantee rule for the parallel composition of Reactive Modules [AH99]: take the context $C[\circ, \bullet]$ in the following theorem to be $\circ\|\bullet$. The proof relies on the deadlock-freedom and input-permissiveness of components. It also requires that each execution of a serial composition can be uniquely assigned to one of the components. This can be achieved by disjoint entry conditions. We say that the serial composition $A + B$ is *jump-deterministic* if for all common interface locations $a \in L_A \cap L_B$, the conjunction $\psi_A^{jump}(a) \wedge \psi_B^{jump}(a)$ is unsatisfiable, and *flow-deterministic* if $\psi_A^{flow}(a) \wedge \psi_B^{flow}(a)$ is unsatisfiable for all $a \in L_A \cap L_B$. The serial composition $A + B$ is *deterministic* if it is both jump-deterministic and flow-deterministic.

For hybrid modules, we need to break the circularity of the rule, by relaxing one assumption, say, B_2, to allow arbitrary flows at all hidden locations. We write $rlax(B_2)$ for the component that results from B_2 by (1) replacing every flow predicate in B_2 by *true*, and (2) serially composing every hidden location a of B_2 which is not the origin location of any flow, with an atomic continuous component that permits all flows from origin a to destination a.

Theorem 2. *Let $C[\circ, \bullet]$ be a context whose arguments are not in the scope of any variable or location hiding. Suppose that all input variables of $C[A_2, B_2]$ are variables of $C[A_1, B_1]$, and that within $C[A_2, B_2]$ the context arguments are not within the scope of any nondeterministic serial composition. If $C[A_1, rlax(B_2)]$ refines $C[A_2, rlax(B_2)]$, and $C[A_2, B_1]$ refines $C[A_2, B_2]$, then $C[A_1, B_1]$ refines $C[A_2, B_2]$.*

Linear components. If all flows are specified by linear differential equations, and no degenerate flows of 0 duration can be enforced, then the existence of unique solutions allows us to strengthen the assume-guarantee rule. In this case, we can make circular assumptions about the flows. An *open linear condition* on a set V of real-valued variables is a conjunction of boolean variables and strict ($<$ or $>$) comparisons between linear combinations of the variables in V. Consider a flow action F (consult the appendix for a definition). The atomic continuous component $A(F)$ is *linear* if (1) all variables in $V_{A(F)}$ have the type $\mathbb{R}$, and (2) the flow predicate φ_F^{flow} has the form $\alpha(X_F) \wedge (\dot{Z}_F = \beta(X_F, \dot{Y}_F))$, where α is an open linear condition, called *invariant*, on the source variables X_F, and β is a set of linear combinations, one for the derivative $\dot{z} \in \dot{Z}_F$ of each controlled flow variable, of the source variables X_F and the derivatives $\dot{Y}_F$ of the uncontrolled flow variables. A component is *linear* if (1) all its atomic continuous components are linear, and (2) all its serial compositions are flow-deterministic. Let $rlax'$ be defined like $rlax$, with the difference that only the invariants rather than the flow predicates are replaced with *true*.

Theorem 3. *Let $C[\circ, \bullet]$ be a context whose arguments are not in the scope of any variable or location hiding. Suppose that $C[A_1, B_1]$ and $C[A_2, B_2]$ are linear components, that all input variables of $C[A_2, B_2]$ are variables of $C[A_1, B_1]$, and that within $C[A_2, B_2]$ the context arguments are not within the scope of any nondeterministic serial composition. If $C[A_1, rlax'(B_2)]$ refines $C[A_2, rlax'(B_2)]$, and $C[A_2, B_1]$ refines $C[A_2, B_2]$, then $C[A_1, B_1]$ refines $C[A_2, B_2]$.*

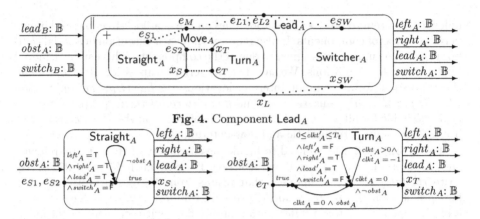

Fig. 4. Component Lead_A

Fig. 5. Components Straight_A and Turn_A

4   A Two-Robot Example

We continue the presentation of the two-robot system whose overall view was given in Section 2. Robot A (Figure 1) starts out as the leader. After a while it may move from Lead_A to Follow_A, as indicated by the dotted line connecting location x_L (with an unsatisfiable entry condition, which is not shown) and location e_F. It may then move back to lead mode (line $x_F{-}e_{L2}$). Robot B has the same structure, except that it starts out in follow mode. Within the subcomponent Move_A (Figure 4), the robot can execute in Straight_A arbitrarily long while there is no obstacle. Upon sensing an obstacle, control is passed to the component Turn_A, which commands the robot to rotate for an amount of time given by timer variable $clkt_A$. Control then returns to the component Straight_A. The sequence of straight moves and turns continues until robot B switches to leading status. This event is modeled by the boolean signal $switch_B$, which is monitored by the component Switcher_A. We require the switcher unit to preempt execution of the lead mode within a specified amount of time T_{sw} after the other robot has signaled its intention to lead. Once Lead_A is exited, control enters the component Follow_A, which samples the values of $left_B$ and $right_B$ and drives its own motor signals $left_A$ and $right_A$. The robot may stay in the follow mode arbitrarily long, provided that $obst_A$ is false. At any time it may also issue the signal $switch_A$, exit the component Follow_A and switch back to lead mode.

We now present a robot implementation that contains a modified component Lead_A^I, which does not continuously observe the $switch$ signal (Figure 7). Instead, the implementation samples the leading indicators of both robots with a period T_{ed}, as measured by the global clock clk. If both robots are leading, a correction is made by the component Errordetect_A. The new state depends on the last sampled values of the leading signals: the robot that had been leading before now switches to follow mode.

We wish to show that when composed together, two robot implementations refine the parallel composition of two robot specifications, provided that $T_{ed} < T_{sw}$. The specification of robot A is $\text{Control}_A \| \text{Motor}_A$, and the implementation

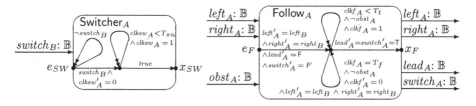

Fig. 6. Components $\mathsf{Switcher}_A$ and Follow_A

of robot A is $\mathsf{Control}_A^I\|\mathsf{Motor}_A$, where $\mathsf{Control}_A = (\mathsf{Lead}_A + \mathsf{Follow}_A)\backslash e_{L2}\backslash e_F$ and $\mathsf{Control}_A^I = (\mathsf{Lead}_A^I + \mathsf{Follow}_A)\backslash e_{L2}\backslash e_F$. Robot B is specified and implemented symmetrically. Denoting the parallel composition with the motor by the context $C_A[\cdot] = \cdot\|\mathsf{Motor}_A$, and similarly for C_B, we wish to prove that

$$C_A[\mathsf{Control}_A^I]\|C_B[\mathsf{Control}_B^I] \quad \text{refines} \quad C_A[\mathsf{Control}_A]\|C_B[\mathsf{Control}_B].$$

Note that $C_A[\mathsf{Control}_A^I]$ does not refine $C_A[\mathsf{Control}_A]$, because a robot implementation meets the specification only when composed with a symmetric robot. This is where assume-guarantee reasoning helps. All continuous components in the system are linear. Hence by Theorem 3, it suffices to discharge the simpler assertions

$$C_A[\mathsf{Control}_A^I]\|C_B[\mathsf{Control}_B'] \quad \text{refines} \quad C_A[\mathsf{Control}_A]\|C_B[\mathsf{Control}_B']$$
$$C_A[\mathsf{Control}_A]\|C_B[\mathsf{Control}_B^I] \quad \text{refines} \quad C_A[\mathsf{Control}_A]\|C_B[\mathsf{Control}_B],$$

where $\mathsf{Control}_B' = rlax'(\mathsf{Control}_B)$. We simplify further using compositionality (Theorem 1), and are left to prove that

$$\mathsf{Control}_A^I \parallel \mathsf{Control}_B' \quad \text{refines} \quad \mathsf{Control}_A \parallel \mathsf{Control}_B'$$
$$\mathsf{Control}_A \parallel \mathsf{Control}_B^I \quad \text{refines} \quad \mathsf{Control}_A \parallel \mathsf{Control}_B,$$

two proof obligations that involve simpler components than the original one. The power of the assume-guarantee rules of Theorems 2 and 3 stems from the fact that they can be applied to components arbitrarily deep in the design hierarchy, creating proof obligations which have smaller differences between the two components which are supposed to refine each other.

Acknowledgments. We thank Rajeev Alur, Radu Grosu, and Edward Lee for many stimulating discussions.

References

[ACH+95]   R. Alur, C. Courcoubetis, N. Halbwachs, T.A. Henzinger, P.-H. Ho, X. Nicollin, A. Olivero, J. Sifakis, and S. Yovine. The algorithmic analysis of hybrid systems. *Theoretical Computer Science*, 138:3–34, 1995.

[AG00]   R. Alur and R. Grosu. Modular refinement of hierarchic reactive machines. In *Principles of Programming Languages*, pp. 390–402, ACM Press, 2000.

[AGH+00]   R. Alur, R. Grosu, Y. Hur, V. Kumar, and I. Lee. Modular specification of hybrid systems in Charon. In *Hybrid Systems: Computation and Control*, LNCS 1790, pp. 130–144, Springer-Verlag, 2000.

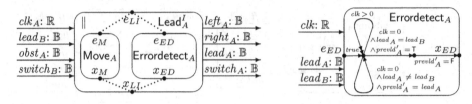

Fig. 7. Components Lead_A^I and Errordetect_A

[AH97]   R. Alur and T.A. Henzinger. Modularity for timed and hybrid systems. In *Concurrency Theory*, LNCS 1243, pp. 74–88, Springer-Verlag, 1997.

[AH99]   R. Alur and T.A. Henzinger. Reactive modules. *Formal Methods in System Design*, 15:7–48, 1999.

[AL95]   M. Abadi and L. Lamport. Conjoining specifications. *ACM Transactions on Programming Languages and Systems*, 17:507–534, 1995.

[BRJ98]   G. Booch, J. Rumbaugh, and I. Jacobson. *The Unified Modeling Language User Guide*. Addison-Wesley, 1998.

[DGH+99] J. Davis, M. Goel, C. Hylands, B. Kienhuis, E.A. Lee, J. Liu, X. Liu, L. Muliadi, S. Neuendorffer, J. Reekie, N. Smyth, J. Tsay, and Y. Xiong. Overview of the Ptolemy project. Tech. Rep. UCB/ERL M99/37, University of California, Berkeley, 1999.

[DGV97]   A. Deshpande, A. Göllü, and P. Varaiya. Shift: A formalism and a programming language for dynamic networks of hybrid automata. In *Hybrid Systems*, LNCS 1273, pp. 113–134, Springer-Verlag, 1997.

[Har87]   D. Harel. Statecharts: A visual formalism for complex systems. *Science of Computer Programming*, 8:231–274, 1987.

[Hen96]   T.A. Henzinger, The theory of hybrid automata. In *Logic in Computer Science*, pp. 278–292, IEEE Computer Society Press, 1996.

[Hen00]   T.A. Henzinger. Masaccio: A formal model for embedded components. In *Theoretical Computer Science*, LNCS 1872, pp. 549–563, Springer Verlag, 2000.

[LSVW96] N.A. Lynch, R. Segala, F. Vaandrager, and H.B. Weinberg. Hybrid I/O Automata. In *Hybrid Systems*, LNCS 1066, pp. 496–510, Springer-Verlag, 1996.

[McM97]   K.L. McMillan. A compositional rule for hardware design refinement. In *Computer-aided Verification*, LNCS 1254, pp. 24–35, Springer-Verlag, 1997.

[MC81]   J. Misra and K.M. Chandy. Proofs of networks of processes. *IEEE Transactions on Software Engineering*, 7:417–426, 1981.

[TAKB96] S. Tasiran, R. Alur, R.P. Kurshan, and R.K. Brayton. Verifying abstractions of timed systems. In *Concurrency Theory*, LNCS 1119, pp. 546–562, Springer-Verlag, 1996.

[US94]   A.C. Uselton and S.A. Smolka. A compositional semantics for Statecharts using labeled transition systems. In *Concurrency Theory*, LNCS 836, pp. 2–17, Springer-Verlag, 1994.

Appendix: Formal Definition of Masaccio

Let V be a set of typed variables. For a variable $x \in V$, denote by x' its primed version, and denote by $\dot{x}$ its dotted version. The type of x' is the same as the type of x. The type of $\dot{x}$ is $\mathbb{R}$ if the type of x is $\mathbb{R}$, and $\{0\}$ otherwise. This is because on types other than $\mathbb{R}$, we assume that only the constant functions are differentiable. Let $V' = \{x' \mid x \in V\}$ be the set of primed versions of the variables in V, and let $\dot{V} = \{\dot{x} \mid x \in V\}$ be the set of dotted versions of the variables in V. Let $[V]$ be the set of type-conforming value assignments to the variables in V: if $x \in V$ and $q \in [V]$, let $q(x)$ be the value assigned by q to x.

The interface of a component. The *interface of a component* A consists of:

- A finite set V_A^i of typed *input variables*.
- A finite set V_A^o of typed *output variables*, such that $V_A^i \cap V_A^o = \emptyset$. Let $V_A = V_A^i \cup V_A^o$ be the set of *I/O variables*. The value assignments in $[V_A]$ are called *I/O states*.
- An *dependency relation* $\prec_A \subseteq V_A \times V_A^o$ between I/O variables and output variables, such that the transitive closure $\prec_A^*$ is asymmetric. A set $U \subseteq V_A$ of I/O variables is *dependency-closed* if $x \prec_A y$ and $y \in U$ implies $x \in U$.
- A finite set L_A of *interface locations*.
- For each location $a \in L_A$, a predicate $\psi_A^{jump}(a)$ on the variables in $V_A \cup V_A^{i'}$, called *jump entry condition*, and a predicate $\psi_A^{flow}(a)$ on the variables in V_A, called *flow entry condition*.

The executions of a component. A *jump* of a component A is a pair $(p, q) \in [V_A]^2$ of I/O states. The I/O state p is the *source* of the jump, and q is the *sink*. A *flow* of A is a pair (δ, f) consisting of a nonnegative real $\delta \in \mathbb{R}_{\geq 0}$, and a function $f: \mathbb{R} \to [V_A]$ from the reals to I/O states which is differentiable, with time derivative f', on the compact interval $[0, \delta] \subset \mathbb{R}$. The real δ is the *duration* of the flow, the I/O state $f(0)$ is the *source*, and $f(\delta)$ is the *sink*. A *step* of A is either a jump or a flow of A. The step w is *successive* to the step v if the sink of v is equal to the source of w. An *execution* of A is either a pair $(a, \boldsymbol{w})$ or a triple $(a, \boldsymbol{w}, b)$, where $a, b \in L_A$ are interface locations, and $\boldsymbol{w} = w_0 \cdots w_n$ is a finite, nonempty sequence of steps of A such that (1) every step w_i, for $1 \leq i \leq n$, is successive to the preceding step w_{i-1}, and (2) the first step w_0 satisfies the entry conditions of location a: if $w_0 = (p, q)$ is a jump, then $\psi_A^{jump}(a)$ is true if each I/O variable $x \in V_A$ is assigned the value $p(x)$, and each primed input variable $y' \in V_A^{i'}$ is assigned the value $q(y)$; if $w_0 = (\delta, f)$ is a flow, then $\psi_A^{flow}(a)$ is true if each I/O variable $x \in V_A$ is assigned the value $f(0)(x)$. The location a is the *origin* of the execution, the sequence $\boldsymbol{w}$ is the *trace*, and the location b (when present) is the *destination*. Given a trace $\boldsymbol{w}$ and a set $U \subseteq V_A$ of I/O variables, we write $\boldsymbol{w}[U]$ for the projection of $\boldsymbol{w}$ to the variables in U,

Atomic discrete components. An *atomic discrete component* is specified by a jump action. A *jump action* J consists of a finite set X_J of *source variables*, a finite set Y_J of *uncontrolled sink variables*, a finite set Z_J of *controlled sink variables* disjoint from Y_J, and a predicate φ_J^{jump} on the variables in $X_J \cup Y_J' \cup Z_J'$, called *jump predicate*. The jump action J specifies the component $A(J)$. The *interface of the component* $A(J)$ is defined as follows:

- $V^i_{A(J)} = (X_J \setminus Z_J) \cup Y_J$.
- $V^o_{A(J)} = Z_J$.
- $y \prec_{A(J)} z$ iff $y \in Y_J$ and $z \in Z_J$.
- $L_{A(J)} = \{from, to\}$.
- $\psi^{jump}_{A(J)}(from) = (\exists Z'_J)\,\varphi^{jump}_J$ and $\psi^{flow}_{A(J)}(from) = false$.
- $\psi^{jump}_{A(J)}(to) = \psi^{flow}_{A(J)}(to) = false$.

The *executions of the component $A(J)$* are defined as follows. The pair $(a, \boldsymbol{w})$ is an execution of $A(J)$ iff $a = from$ and the trace $\boldsymbol{w}$ consists of a single jump (p, q) such that φ^{jump}_J is true if each source variable $x \in X_J$ is assigned the value $p(x)$, and each primed sink variable $y' \in Y'_J \cup Z'_J$ is assigned the value $q(y)$. The triple $(a, \boldsymbol{w}, b)$ is an execution of $A(J)$ iff the pair $(a, \boldsymbol{w})$ is an execution of $A(J)$, and $b = to$.

Atomic continuous components. An *atomic continuous component* is specified by a flow action. A *flow action F* consists of a finite set X_F of *source variables*, a finite set Y_F of *uncontrolled flow variables*, a finite set Z_F of *controlled flow variables* disjoint from Y_F, and a predicate φ^{flow}_F on the variables in $X_F \cup \dot{Y}_F \cup \dot{Z}_F$, called *flow predicate*. The flow action F specifies the component $A(F)$. The *interface of the component $A(F)$* is defined as follows:

- $V^i_{A(F)} = (X_F \setminus Z_F) \cup Y_F$.
- $V^o_{A(F)} = Z_F$.
- $y \prec_{A(F)} z$ iff $y \in Y_F$ and $z \in Z_F$.
- $L_{A(F)} = \{from, to\}$.
- $\psi^{jump}_{A(F)}(from) = false$ and $\psi^{flow}_{A(F)}(from) = (\exists \dot{Y}_F, \dot{Z}_F)\,\varphi^{flow}_F$.
- $\psi^{jump}_{A(F)}(to) = \psi^{flow}_{A(F)}(to) = false$.

The *executions of the component $A(F)$* are defined as follows. The pair $(a, \boldsymbol{w})$ is an execution of $A(F)$ iff $a = from$ and the trace $\boldsymbol{w}$ consists of a single flow (δ, f) such that the following holds: if $\delta = 0$, then $(\exists \dot{Y}_F, \dot{Z}_F)\,\varphi^{flow}_F$ is true if each source variable $x \in X_F$ is assigned the value $f(0)(x)$; if $\delta > 0$, then for all $\varepsilon \in [0, \delta]$, the flow predicate φ^{flow}_F is true if each source variable $x \in X_F$ is assigned the value $f(\varepsilon)(x)$, and each dotted flow variable $\dot{y} \in \dot{Y}_F \cup \dot{Z}_F$ is assigned the value $f'(\varepsilon)(y)$. The triple $(a, \boldsymbol{w}, b)$ is an execution of $A(F)$ iff the pair $(a, \boldsymbol{w})$ is an execution of $A(F)$, and $b = to$.

Parallel composition. Two components A and B *can be composed in parallel* if their interfaces satisfy the following conditions:

- $V^o_A \cap V^o_B = \emptyset$.
- There are no two variables $x \in V^o_A$ and $y \in V^o_B$ such that both $x \prec^*_B y$ and $y \prec^*_A x$.

- For all $a \in L_A$, if $\psi_A^{jump}(a)$ or $\psi_A^{flow}(a)$ is satisfiable, then $a \in L_B$. For all $a \in L_B$, if $\psi_B^{jump}(a)$ or $\psi_B^{flow}(a)$ is satisfiable, then $a \in L_A$. For all $a \in L_A \cap L_B$, the projections of the entry conditions of a in A and B to the common variables are equivalent: $(\exists V_A \setminus V_B)(\exists V_A^{i'} \setminus V_B^{i'}) \psi_A^{jump}(a)$ is equivalent to $(\exists V_B \setminus V_A)(\exists V_B^{i'} \setminus V_A^{i'}) \psi_B^{jump}(a)$, and $(\exists V_A \setminus V_B) \psi_A^{flow}(a)$ is equivalent to $(\exists V_B \setminus V_A) \psi_B^{flow}(a)$.

The *interface* of $A\|B$ is defined from the interfaces of A and B:

- $V_{A\|B}^i = (V_A^i \setminus V_B^o) \cup (V_B^i \setminus V_A^o)$.
- $V_{A\|B}^o = V_A^o \cup V_B^o$.
- $\prec_{A\|B} = \prec_A \cup \prec_B$.
- $L_{A\|B} = L_A \cup L_B$.
- If $a \in L_A \cap L_B$, then $\psi_{A\|B}^{jump}(a) = \psi_A^{jump}(a) \wedge \psi_B^{jump}(a)$ and $\psi_{A\|B}^{flow}(a) = \psi_A^{flow}(a) \wedge \psi_B^{flow}(a)$. If $a \in L_A \setminus L_B$ or $a \in L_B \setminus L_A$, then $\psi_{A\|B}^{jump}(a) = \psi_{A\|B}^{flow}(a) = false$.

The *executions* of $A\|B$ are defined from the executions of A and B. The pair (a, w) is an execution of $A\|B$ iff $(a, w[V_A])$ is an execution of A and $(a, w[V_B])$ is an execution of B. The triple (a, w, b) is an execution of $A\|B$ iff either $(a, w[V_A], b)$ is an execution of A and $(a, w[V_B])$ is an execution of B, or $(a, w[V_B], b)$ is an execution of B and $(a, w[V_A])$ is an execution of A.

Serial composition. Two components A and B *can be composed in series* if $V_A^o = V_B^o$. The *interface* of $A + B$ is defined from the interfaces of A and B:

- $V_{A+B}^i = V_A^i \cup V_B^i$.
- $V_{A+B}^o = V_A^o = V_B^o$.
- $\prec_{A+B} = \prec_A \cup \prec_B$.
- $L_{A+B} = L_A \cup L_B$.
- If $a \in L_A \cap L_B$, then $\psi_{A+B}^{jump}(a) = \psi_A^{jump}(a) \vee \psi_B^{jump}(a)$ and $\psi_{A+B}^{flow}(a) = \psi_A^{flow}(a) \vee \psi_B^{flow}(a)$. If $a \in L_A \setminus L_B$, then $\psi_{A+B}^{jump}(a) = \psi_A^{jump}(a)$ and $\psi_{A+B}^{flow}(a) = \psi_A^{flow}(a)$. If $a \in L_B \setminus L_A$, then $\psi_{A+B}^{jump}(a) = \psi_B^{jump}(a)$ and $\psi_{A+B}^{flow}(a) = \psi_B^{flow}(a)$.

The *executions* of $A + B$ are defined from the executions of A and B. The pair (a, w) is an execution of $A + B$ iff either $(a, w[V_A])$ is an execution of A, or $(a, w[V_B])$ is an execution of B. The triple (a, w, b) is an execution of $A + B$ iff either $(a, w[V_A], b)$ is an execution of A, or $(a, w[V_B], b)$ is an execution of B.

Variable renaming. The variable $x \in V_A$ can be *renamed* to y in component A if y has the same type as x, and either y is not an I/O variable of A, or x and y are both input variables; that is, if $y \in V_A$, then $x, y \in V_A^i$. The *interface of the component* $A[x := y]$ is defined from the interface of A. If $x \in V_A^i$, then $V_{A[x:=y]}^i = (V_A^i \setminus \{x\}) \cup \{y\}$ and $V_{A[x:=y]}^o = V_A^o$; if $x \in V_A^o$, then $V_{A[x:=y]}^i = V_A^i$ and

$V^o_{A[x:=y]} = (V^o_A \setminus \{x\}) \cup \{y\}$. In either case, let $L_{A[x:=y]} = L_A$, and let $\prec_{A[x:=y]}$ and $\psi^{jump}_{A[x:=y]}$ and $\psi^{flow}_{A[x:=y]}$ result from renaming x to y, and x' to y', in $\prec_A$ and ψ^{jump}_A and ψ^{flow}_A, respectively. The *executions of the component* $A[x := y]$ result from renaming x to y in the traces of the executions of A.

Location renaming. The interface location $a \in L_A$ *can be renamed to* b in component A if either b is not an interface location of A, or the entry conditions of a and b are disjoint; that is, if $b \in L_A$, then both $\psi^{jump}_A(a) \wedge \psi^{jump}_A(b)$ and $\psi^{flow}_A(a) \wedge \psi^{flow}_A(b)$ are unsatisfiable. The *interface of the component* $A[a := b]$ is defined from the interface of A: let $V^i_{A[a:=b]} = V^i_A$; let $V^o_{A[a:=b]} = V^o_A$; let $\prec_{A[a:=b]} = \prec_A$; let $L_{A[a:=b]} = (L_A \setminus \{a\}) \cup \{b\}$; let $\psi^{jump}_{A[a:=b]}(b) = \psi^{jump}_A(a) \vee \psi^{jump}_A(b)$ and $\psi^{flow}_{A[a:=b]}(b) = \psi^{flow}_A(a) \vee \psi^{flow}_A(b)$ if $b \in L_A$, let $\psi^{jump}_{A[a:=b]}(b) = \psi^{jump}_A(a)$ and $\psi^{flow}_{A[a:=b]}(b) = \psi^{flow}_A(a)$ if $b \notin L_A$, and let $\psi^{jump}_{A[a:=b]}(c) = \psi^{jump}_A(c)$ and $\psi^{flow}_{A[a:=b]}(c) = \psi^{flow}_A(c)$ for all locations $c \in L_A \setminus \{a, b\}$. The *executions of the component* $A[a := b]$ result from renaming a to b in the origins and destinations of the executions of A.

Variable hiding. The variable $x \in V_A$ *can be hidden* in the component A if $x \in V^o_A$. The *interface of the component* $A \backslash x$ is defined from the interface of A: let $V^i_{A \backslash x} = V^i_A$; let $V^o_{A \backslash x} = V^o_A \setminus \{x\}$; let $\prec_{A \backslash x}$ be the intersection of the transitive closure $\prec^*_A$ with $V_{A \backslash x} \times V^o_{A \backslash x}$; let $L_{A \backslash x} = L_A$; let $\psi^{jump}_{A \backslash x}(a) = (\exists x)\, \psi^{jump}_A(a)$ and $\psi^{flow}_{A \backslash x}(a) = (\exists x)\, \psi^{flow}_A(a)$ for all locations $a \in L_A$. The *executions of the component* $A \backslash x$ are defined from the executions of A. The pair $(a, \boldsymbol{w})$ is an execution of $A \backslash x$ iff $(a, \boldsymbol{w}[V_{A \backslash x}])$ is an execution of A. The triple $(a, \boldsymbol{w}, b)$ is an execution of $A \backslash x$ iff $(a, \boldsymbol{w}[V_{A \backslash x}], b)$ is an execution of A.

Location hiding. The interface location $c \in L_A$ *can be hidden* in the component A if the jump entry condition $\psi^{jump}_A(c)$ is equivalent to *true*. The *interface of the component* $A \backslash c$ is defined from the interface of A: let $V^i_{A \backslash c} = V^i_A$; let $V^o_{A \backslash c} = V^o_A$; let $\prec_{A \backslash c} = \prec_A$; let $L_{A \backslash c} = L_A \setminus \{c\}$; let $\psi^{jump}_{A \backslash c}(a) = \psi^{jump}_A(a)$ and $\psi^{flow}_{A \backslash c}(a) = \psi^{flow}_A(a)$ for all locations $a \in L_{A \backslash c}$. The *executions of the component* $A \backslash c$ are defined from the executions of A. The pair $(a, \boldsymbol{w})$ is an execution of $A \backslash c$ iff $c \neq a$ and either $(a, \boldsymbol{w})$ is an execution of A, or there is a finite sequence $\boldsymbol{w}_1, \ldots, \boldsymbol{w}_n$ of traces, $n \geq 2$, such that $\boldsymbol{w} = \boldsymbol{w}_1 \cdots \boldsymbol{w}_n$ and the following are executions of A: the triple $(a, \boldsymbol{w}_1, c)$, the triples $(c, \boldsymbol{w}_i, c)$ for $1 < i < n$, and the pair $(c, \boldsymbol{w}_n)$. The triple $(a, \boldsymbol{w}, b)$ is an execution of $A \backslash c$ iff $c \notin \{a, b\}$ and $(a, \boldsymbol{w}, b)$ is an execution of A, or there is a finite sequence $\boldsymbol{w}_1, \ldots, \boldsymbol{w}_n$ of traces, $n \geq 2$, such that $\boldsymbol{w} = \boldsymbol{w}_1 \cdots \boldsymbol{w}_n$ and the following are executions of A: the triple $(a, \boldsymbol{w}_1, c)$, the triples $(c, \boldsymbol{w}_i, c)$ for $1 < i < n$, and the triple $(c, \boldsymbol{w}_n, b)$.

Hybrid Modeling of TCP
Congestion Control*

João P. Hespanha[1], Stephan Bohacek[1], Katia Obraczka[2], and Junsoo Lee[1]

[1] University of Southern California, Los Angeles, CA 90089-2563, USA
[2] University of California, Santa Cruz, CA 95064, USA

Abstract. In this paper we propose a hybrid model for TCP's congestion control mechanism operating under drop-tail queuing policy. Using
this model we confirmed the standard formula $T := \frac{1.23}{\overline{RTT}\sqrt{p}}$ used by
TCP-friendly congestion control algorithms, which relates the average
packet drop rate p, the average round-trip time $\overline{RTT}$, and the average
throughput T. The hybrid model also allows us to understand the transient behavior and theoretically predict the flow synchronization phenomena that have been observed in simulations and in real networks
but, to the best of our knowledge, have not been theoretically justified.
This model can also be used to detect abnormalities in TCP traffic flows,
which has important applications in network security.

1 Introduction

Consider the computer network shown in Figure 1. In this topology, n TCP flows
are generated at a source node n_1 and are directed towards a sink node n_2. All
the flows compete for the finite bandwidth B that characterizes the link ℓ that
connects the nodes. This configuration is known as a *dumbbell topology* and is
typically used to analyze TCP's congestion control. In more realistic networks,
a path of several links (and intermediate nodes) would connect the source and
destination nodes. However, to analyze congestion control mechanisms, one often ignores the existence of all the intermediate links, except for the *bottleneck
link*, i.e., the link that has the smallest bandwidth. In the dumbbell topology, ℓ
represents precisely this link.

The basic problem in congestion control is to determine sending rates for each
of the n flows that result in an optimal utilization of the available bandwidth,
avoiding a catastrophic collapse under very heavy load. The transport layer of
the TCP/IP protocol stack is responsible for solving this problem and the sending rates are determined by n congestion controllers. Each congestion controller
adjusts the sending rate of one particular flow, based on the number of packet
drops that this flow is suffering. Packet drops occur when the sending rates of

* This research was supported by the Defense Advanced Research Projects Agency
and the Office of Naval Research. The views presented here are those of the authors
and do not represent the views of the funding agencies.

M.D. Di Benedetto, A. Sangiovanni-Vincentelli (Eds.): HSCC 2001, LNCS 2034, pp. 291–304, 2001.
© Springer-Verlag Berlin Heidelberg 2001

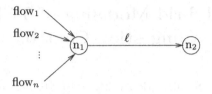

Fig. 1. Dumbbell topology

the flows are too large and the source node n_1 is unable to process all the packets received. The congestion controller becomes aware of packet drops because, each time a packet is received by the destination node, it sends an *acknowledgment* packet back to the source node. When a data packet is dropped, its acknowledgment is never received and the congestion controller should take some action. The congestion control problem is nontrivial because of the following:

1. The bandwidth B associated with the link ℓ and the total number of flows n competing for this bandwidth are not known by the congestion controllers. Moreover, these parameters are likely to change over time.
2. The exchange of information among congestion controllers and between the congestion controllers and the nodes is undesirable. This is because the control information would compete with the data for the available bandwidth.

Every computer connected to the Internet runs some version of TCP congestion control. It is therefore not surprising to find that a significant body of literature is devoted to this topic. However, many basic questions remain poorly understood. These include:

1. Does TCP congestion control work? In particular, is it able to prevent a catastrophic collapse of the network under very heavy load.
2. Is TCP congestion control fair? In particular, does it result in approximately equal throughput for all competing flows.
3. Is TCP optimal or close to optimal? This question is particularly difficult because there is no universally accepted notion of optimality. Small drops rates, small delays, approximately constant flow rates, and fast adaptation to changes in the network are certainly desirable properties. However, these criteria are self-contradictory and therefore trade-off solutions are required.

In this paper we provide a hybrid model for Reno congestion control [1,2,3] that sheds light in some of the questions formulated above. Reno is one of the more popular versions of TCP congestion control and is generally accepted to perform well. The model proposed also applies to more recent variations on Reno such as New Reno, Sack [4], and general AIMD [5].

The model proposed provides a new derivation for the now fairly standard formula

$$T = \frac{1.23}{RTT\sqrt{p}} \tag{1}$$

that relates the average packet drop rate p, the average round-trip time $\overline{RTT}$, and the average throughput T [6,7,8,9]. Formulas such as (1) have been used to design congestion control mechanisms that are TCP-friendly but produce more constant sending rates, making them more suitable, e.g., for streaming multimedia over the Internet [10]. Unlike previous derivations, ours considers the effect of queuing and the coupling between the competing flows.

The hybrid model presented here also predicts that the dumbbell topology in Figure 1, with drop-tail queuing at node n_1, leads to flow synchronization, i.e., the sending rates of all the flows exhibit in-phase periodic variations. This produces undesirably large variations of the round-trip time and poor utilization of the queue. This type of behavior has been observed before [11] and actually led to the development of Random Early Detection/Drop active queuing [12, 13]. To the best of our knowledge, this is the first time that the synchronization phenomena are theoretically explained.

2   Hybrid Model for Congestion Control

In this paper, we consider Reno congestion control. We describe next a simplified version of this algorithm that is sufficient for the purposes of this paper. Each congestion controller possesses an internal state known as the *window size*. We denote by w_i, $i \in \{1, 2, \ldots, n\}$, the window size of the congestion controller associated with the ith flow. The window size determines the maximum number of unacknowledged packets for that flow. E.g., if $w_i = 3$, then the congestion controller can send 3 packets immediately, but must wait for one acknowledgment to arrive before a 4th packet can be sent. The algorithm to update the window size w_i is as follows: While no drops occur, the window size is incremented by a fixed constant $a \geq 1$ for each w_i acknowledgments received (typically $a = 1$). This is known as *additive increase*. When it is detected that a drop occurred (because an acknowledgment packet is missing) the window size is multiplied by a constant $m \in (0, 1)$ (typically $m = 1/2$). This is known as *multiplicative decrease*. We are ignoring Reno's initial adjustment of the window size—known as *slow start*—because it has little impact on the system after a brief initial period. The reader is referred to [1,2,3] for a detailed description of Reno congestion control.

Although the window size takes discrete values, it is convenient to regard it as a continuously varying variable. Let us call *round-trip time*, denoted by RTT, the time interval measured from the moment a packet is sent until an acknowledgment for that packet is received. As we will see below, the round-trip time is a time-varying quantity. Suppose that at some time t, the congestion controller for the ith flow sends one packet and fills its window. This means that w_i packets are now unacknowledged for. Assuming that there are no drops, after one round-trip time the acknowledgment for this packet is received, as well as the acknowledgments for the previous $w_i - 1$ packets. Since w_i acknowledgments were received, the window size must have increased by a. On average, each w_i

thus increases at a rate of $\frac{a}{RTT}$ packets per second. The following hybrid model provides a good approximation of the ith window size dynamics: While the ith flow suffers no drops we have

$$\dot{w}_i = \frac{a}{RTT}, \tag{2}$$

and, if a drop is detected on this flow at time t, we have $w_i(t) = m\, w_i^-(t)$, where $w_i^-(t)$ denotes the limit from below of $w_i(s)$ as $s \uparrow t$.

We proceed to determine the evolution of the round-trip time $RTT(t)$. Typically, the round trip time has two components: a fixed *propagation time* T_p that is determined by the physical length of the link ℓ and the speed of light, and a variable *service time* T_s that accounts for the time the nodes take to process the packet. The service time is usually dominated by the *queue time* T_q, i.e., the time a packet stays in the output queue of node n_1 before it is sent to the link. Denoting by $q(t)$ the size of this queue at time t, and by B the bandwidth of link ℓ in packets per second, the queuing time is given by

$$T_q(t) = \frac{q(t)}{B},$$

because $q(t)$ packets need to be transmitted (each taking $1/B$ seconds) before a new packet can also be transmitted. We assume here that the bandwidth B is measured in packets per second. The round-trip time is then given by

$$RTT(t) = T_p + \frac{q(t)}{B}. \tag{3}$$

In this formula, we incorporated in T_p any fixed component of the service time.

As mentioned above, the ith flow receives w_i acknowledgment packets in one round-trip time. Therefore, in average, it sends w_i packets per round-trip time. This means that the output queue at node n_1 receives a total of $\frac{\sum_i w_i}{RTT}$ packets per second and is able to send B packets to the link in the same period. The difference between these two quantities determines the evolution of $q(t)$. In particular,

$$\dot{q} = \begin{cases} 0 & q = 0,\ \frac{\sum_i w_i}{RTT} < B \quad \text{or} \quad q = q_{\max},\ \frac{\sum_i w_i}{RTT} > B \\ \frac{\sum_i w_i}{RTT} - B & \text{otherwise} \end{cases} \tag{4}$$

The first branch in (4) takes into account that the queue size cannot become negative nor should it exceed the *maximum queue size* $q_{\max}$. When $q(t)$ reaches $q_{\max}$ drops occur. These will be detected by the congestion controllers some time later.

To complete our model it remains to understand how many drops occur and in which flows. As mentioned above, drops will occur whenever q reaches the maximum queue size $q_{\max}$ and the rate of incoming packets to the queue $\frac{\sum_i w_i}{RTT}$

exceeds the rate B of outgoing packets. Since a drop will only be detected after one round-trip time, the rate of incoming packets will not change for a period of length RTT and multiple drops are expected. It turns out that, in most operating conditions, exactly one drop per flow will occur [11]. To understand why, we must recall that in every round-trip time the window size of each flow will increase because each flow will receive as many acknowledgments as its window size. When the acknowledgment that triggers the increase of the window size by $a \geq 1$ arrives, the congestion controller will attempt to send two packets *back-to-back*. The first packet is sent because the acknowledgment that just arrived decreased the number of unacknowledged packets and therefore a new packet can be sent. The second packet is sent because the window size just increased, allowing the controller to have an extra unacknowledged packet. However, at this point there is a very fragile balance between the number of packets that are getting in and out of the queue, so two packets will not fit in the queue and the second packet is dropped. This, of course, assumes a drop-tail queuing policy. Although this behavior is essentially caused by the discreteness of the queue mechanism, we can incorporate it in our hybrid model by considering two modes for the system: One mode corresponds to the situation when the queue is not full and therefore the system evolves according to (2), (3), (4). The other mode of operation corresponds to the situation where the queue is full and one drop will occur in each flow. This mode of operation is active for RTT seconds. When the system leaves this mode all window sizes are multiplied by m because of the multiplicative decrease caused by the drops. In reality, the multiplicative decrease of all flows does not occur exactly at the same time instant. However, this model provides a very good approximation for the time scales considered here.

Figure 2 contains a graphical representation of the overall hybrid system. In this figure, each node represents one of the two discrete states: *queue-full* and *queue-not-full*. The continuous state of the hybrid system consists of the queue size q, the window sizes w_i, $i \in \{1, 2, \cdots, n\}$, and a timing variable t_T used to enforce that the system remains in the *queue-full* state for RTT seconds. The differential equations for these variables in each discrete state are shown inside the corresponding nodes. The links in the figure represent discrete transitions, which are labeled with their enabling conditions and any necessary reset of the continuous state that must take place when the transition occurs. We assume here that a jump always occurs when the transition condition is enabled. This model falls in several of the general hybrid systems frameworks proposed in the literature [14,15,16,17,18,19,20,21,22]. For simplicity we assume here that the queue size q never reaches zero.

Remark 1. For a very large number of flows, a single drop per flow may not be sufficient to produce the decrease in the window size required to make the queue size drop below q_{max} after the multiplicative decrease. In this case, the model in Figure 2 is not valid. However, we shall see in Section 4 that, for most operating conditions, this model accurately matches packet-level simulations performed

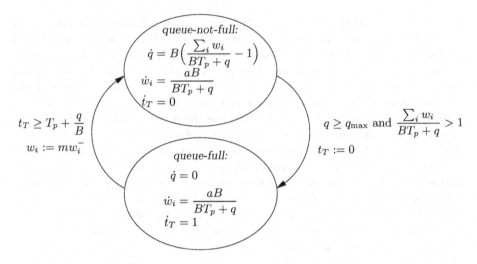

Fig. 2. Hybrid model for Reno congestion control

using the ns-2 network simulator [23]. In fact, this hybrid model only fails when the number of flows is so large that the drop rates take unusually large values.

3   Dynamics in Normalized Time

The dynamics for the hybrid system in Figure 2 are nonlinear essentially because of the dependence of RTT on q. However, it is possible to make them linear by normalizing the time variable. To this effect we introduce a new time variable τ, called the *normalized time*[1], defined by

$$\frac{\mathrm{d}t}{\mathrm{d}\tau} = RTT = T_p + \frac{q}{B}, \qquad \tau(0) = 0. \tag{5}$$

This means that an interval with duration $d\tau$ in the variable τ corresponds to an interval of duration $dt = RTT d\tau$ in the variable t. We can think of τ as a time variable normalized so that one unit of τ corresponds to one round-trip time. Figure 3 shows the dynamics of the hybrid system in normalized time. In this figure, $'$ denotes the derivative $\frac{\mathrm{d}}{\mathrm{d}\tau}$ with respect to the normalized time τ. In Figure 3, we also used the fact that in the *queue-full* state, $q = q_{\max}$ and therefore, waiting until t_T reaches $T_p + \frac{q_{\max}}{B}$ from zero with $t_T' = RTT = T_p + \frac{q_{\max}}{B}$, is equivalent to waiting until τ_T reaches 1 from zero with $\tau_T' = 1$.

---

[1] Formally, there is a bijective function f that maps normalized time τ into real time t. This function is actually defined by (5). With some abuse of notation, when we write $q(\tau)$ for some normalized time τ, we really mean $q(f(\tau))$. Similar notation is used for the remaining time-dependent variables.

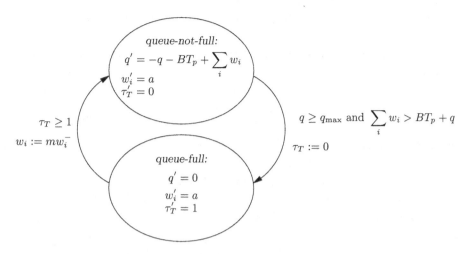

Fig. 3. Hybrid model for Reno congestion control in normalized time.

It is interesting to note that the equation that models the queue dynamics in the *queue-not-full* state is stable. This is an important property of window-based congestion control, as opposed to other congestion control mechanisms that adapt the packets sending rates directly (instead of indirectly through the window size).

Let us denote by $\{\tau_k : \tau_k \leq \tau_{k+1}, k \geq 1\}$ the set of normalized times at which the system leaves the *queue-full* mode. Using the fact that the system dynamics is essentially linear at each discrete mode, it is somewhat tedious but nevertheless straightforward to show that

$$\tau_{k+1} - \tau_k = f^{-1}(s_k) + 1, \qquad\qquad k \geq 1, \qquad\qquad (6)$$

where

$$s_k := \frac{q_{\max} + BT_p - \sum_{i=1}^{n} w_i(\tau_k)}{an}, \qquad\qquad (7)$$

and $f : [0, \infty) \rightarrow [0, \infty)$ denotes the smooth bijection

$$x \mapsto \begin{cases} \frac{x}{1-e^{-x}} - 1 & x \neq 0 \\ 0 & x = 0 \end{cases}.$$

The reader is referred to [24] for the detailed derivation of (6). We proceed to analyze the evolution of the $w_i(\tau_k)$. To this effect, suppose that the system left the *queue-full* mode at some normalized time τ_k, $k \geq 1$. Since it takes $f^{-1}(s_k)+1$ units of normalized time until the system leaves the *queue-full* state again and during this time $w_i' = a$, $i \in \{1, 2, \ldots, n\}$, we conclude that

$$w_i^-(\tau_{k+1}) = w_i(\tau_k) + af^{-1}(s_k) + a, \qquad\qquad i \in \{1, 2, \ldots, n\},$$

and therefore

$$w_i(\tau_{k+1}) = m\left(w_i(\tau_k) + af^{-1}(s_k) + a\right), \qquad i \in \{1, 2, \ldots, n\}. \tag{8}$$

From (7) and (8) we then conclude that

$$s_{k+1} = m\left(s_k - f^{-1}(s_k)\right) + \frac{1-m}{an}(q_{\max} + BT_p) - m. \tag{9}$$

It turns out that, as long as

$$q_{\max} + BT_p \geq \frac{2ma}{1-m}n,$$

the map $g : [0, \infty) \to [0, \infty)$, defined by

$$s \mapsto m\left(s - f^{-1}(s)\right) + \frac{1-m}{an}(q_{\max} + BT_p) - m,$$

is a contraction. In particular,

$$|g(s) - g(\bar{s})| = m|s - \bar{s} - f^{-1}(s) + f^{-1}(s_s)| \leq m|s - \bar{s}|, \qquad s, \bar{s} \geq 0. \tag{10}$$

Since (9) can also be written as $s_{k+1} = g(s_k)$, using the Contraction Mapping Theorem [25, p. 126] we conclude that the s_k converges to the unique fixed point s_∞ of g, which is the unique solution to

$$s_\infty = m\left(s_\infty - f^{-1}(s_\infty)\right) + \frac{1-m}{an}(q_{\max} + BT_p) - m. \tag{11}$$

The convergence is as fast as m^k. From this and (8) we conclude that the following theorem holds:

Theorem 1. *Let $\{t_k : t_k \leq t_{k+1}, k \geq 1\}$ be the set of times at which the system leaves the queue-full. For $q_{\max} + BT_p \geq \frac{2ma}{1-m}n$, all the $w_i(t_k)$, $i \in \{1, 2, \ldots, n\}$ converge exponentially fast to*

$$w_\infty := \frac{ma}{1-m}(f^{-1}(s_\infty) + 1),$$

as $k \to \infty$ and the convergence is as fast as m^k.

The condition $q_{\max} + BT_p \geq \frac{2ma}{1-m}n$ essentially limits the maximum number of flows under which the one-drop-per-flow is valid. When this condition is violated, i.e., when $n > \frac{1-m}{2ma}(q_{\max} + BT_p)$, a single drop per flow may not be sufficient to produce a decrease in the sending rates that would make q drop below $q_{\max}$ after the multiplicative decrease.

A straightforward conclusion of Theorem 1 is that all the flows become synchronized as time goes to infinity. This is because the window sizes of all the flows asymptotically converge to the same limit cycle. This limit cycle corresponds to an increase of the window size from w_∞ to $\frac{1}{m}w_\infty$, lasting $f^{-1}(s_\infty) + 1$

units of normalized time, followed by an instantaneous decrease back to w_∞ due to drops.

Window size synchronization had been observed in [11] for Tahoe congestion control [4]. In [11], the authors defend that synchronization is closely related to the packet loss synchronization that we also use in our model. In fact, they provide an informal explanation—supported by packet-level simulations—of how synchronization is a self-sustained phenomenon. Although [11] only deals with Tahoe, the arguments used there also apply to Reno congestion control. Theorem 1 goes further because it demonstrates that the limit cycle that corresponds to flow synchronization is globally exponential stable. This means that synchronization will occur even if the flows start unsynchronized or lose synchronization because of some temporary disturbance. Moreover, the convergence to the limit cycle is very fast and is reduced by at least m (typically $1/2$) on each cycle. In fact, initially the convergence is even faster because the upper bound in (10) is conservative for large $|s - \bar{s}|$.

4   Steady-State Behavior

We proceed now to derive steady-state formulas—such as the ones found in [6,7,8,9]—that relate the average throughput, the average drop rate (i.e., the percentage of dropped packets), and the average round-trip time. In this section we concentrate on the case where s_∞ is much larger than one and therefore

$$f^{-1}(s_\infty) \approx s_\infty + 1. \tag{12}$$

This approximation is valid when

$$q_{\max} + BT_p \gg \frac{2man}{1 - m} \tag{13}$$

and results in the system remaining in the state *queue-not-full* for, at least, a few round-trip times[2]. In practice, this is quite common and a deviation from (13) results in very large drop rates.

Suppose then that the steady-state has been reached and let us consider an interval $[t_k, t_{k+1}]$ between two consecutive time instants at which the system enters the *queue-not-full* state. Somewhere in this interval lies the time instant $\bar{t}_k$ at which the system enters the *queue-full* state and drops occur. During the interval $[t_k, t_{k+1}]$, the instantaneous rate r at which the nodes are successfully transmitting packets is given by

$$r(t) = \begin{cases} \frac{\sum w_i(t)}{RTT(t)} & t \in [t_k, \bar{t}_k) \\ B & t \in [\bar{t}_k, t_{k+1}] \end{cases} \tag{14}$$

---

[2] When the system remains in the *queue-not-full* for at least 4 round-trip times, (12) already yields an error smaller than 2%.

The total number of packets N_k sent during the interval $[t_k, t_{k+1}]$ can then be computed by

$$N_k := \int_{t_k}^{t_{k+1}} r(t)dt = \int_{\tau_k}^{\tau_{k+1}} r(\tau)RTT(\tau)d\tau \tag{15}$$

$$\approx \frac{1-m^2}{2an}(q_{max} + BT_p + 2an)^2.$$

We used here the change of integration variable defined by (5) to work with quantities in normalized time. Details on the computation of the integrals in (15) and in (17) below are given in [24]. Since n drops occur in the interval $[t_k, t_{k+1}]$, the average drop rate p is then equal to

$$p := \frac{n}{N_k} \approx \frac{2a}{1-m^2}\left(\frac{n}{q_{max} + BT_p + 2an}\right)^2. \tag{16}$$

Another quantity of interest is the average round-trip time $\overline{RTT}$. We consider here a packet-average, rather than a time-average, because the former is the one usually measured in real networks. This distinction is important since the sending rate r is not constant. In fact, when the sending rate is higher, the queue is more likely to be full and the round-trip time is larger. This results in the packet-average being larger than the time-average. The *packet-average round-trip time* can then be computed as

$$\overline{RTT} := \frac{\int_{t_k}^{t_{k+1}} r(t)RTT(t)dt}{N_k} = \frac{\int_{\tau_k}^{\tau_{k+1}} r(\tau)RTT(\tau)^2 d\tau}{N_k}$$

$$\approx \frac{1}{T}\left(\frac{2}{3}\frac{1-m^3}{1-m^2}\frac{q_{max} + BT_p + 2an}{n} - a\frac{1-m}{1+m}\right), \tag{17}$$

where $T := \frac{B}{n}$ is the average throughput of each flow. We recall that, because the queue never empties, the total throughput is precisely the bandwidth B of the bottleneck link.

It is interesting to note that the average drop rate p can provide an estimate for the quantity $\frac{n}{q_{max}+BT_p+2an}$. In particular, we conclude from (16) that

$$\frac{q_{max} + BT_p + 2an}{n} \approx \sqrt{\frac{2a}{(1-m^2)p}}. \tag{18}$$

This, in turn, can be used together with (17) to estimate the average throughput T. In fact, from (17) and (18) we conclude that

$$T \approx \frac{1}{\overline{RTT}}\left(\frac{2}{3}\frac{1-m^3}{1-m^2}\sqrt{\frac{2a}{(1-m^2)p}} - a\frac{1-m}{1+m}\right) \tag{19}$$

For $a = 1$ and $m = 1/2$, (19) becomes $T \approx \frac{1}{\overline{RTT}}\left(\frac{1.27}{\sqrt{p}} + \frac{1}{3}\right)$. For reasonable drop rates, the term $\frac{1.27}{\sqrt{p}}$ dominates over $1/3$ and (19) matches closely similar formulas derived in [6,7,8,9]. It should be emphasized that the derivations in these references do not take queuing into account nor its effect in the variation of the round-trip time. The coupling between the n competing flows is also ignored and therefore no theoretically-supported claim is made to the extent that the steady-state solution is actually reached in an asymptotic sense. The hybrid model introduced here also leads to a more complete description of the steady-state behavior of TCP through the explicit formulas (16) and (17) for the average round-trip time $\overline{RTT}$ and the drop rate p as a function of the number of flows n. It is important to emphasize that $\overline{RTT}$ in (17) denotes the *average* round-trip time. It turns out that the actual round-trip-time RTT varies quite significantly around this average because of fluctuations on the queue size. These large variations in the queue size (which are amplified by synchronization) produce a large delay jitter. These phenomena, which have significant implications in the design of congestion control mechanisms for applications that require stricter service guarantees from the network, have not been accurately captured in most existing models [9,26,27,10,28].

To verify the formulas derived above, we simulated the dumbbell of Figure 1 using the ns-2 network simulator [23]. Figure 4 summarizes the results obtained for a network with the following parameters: $B = \frac{10^7 \text{ bits/sec}}{8 \text{ bits/char} \times 1000 \text{ char/packet}} = 1250$ packets/sec, $T_p = .04$ sec, $q_{max} = 250$ packets, $a = 1$ packet/RTT, $m = 1/2$. As seen in the Figure 4, the theoretical predictions given by (16), (17), (19) match the simulation results quite accurately. Some mismatch can be observed for large number of flows. However, this mismatch only starts to become significant when the drop rates are around 1%, which is an unusually large value. This mismatch is mainly due to two factors: the quantization of the window size and a crude modeling of the fast-recovery algorithm [2]. We are now in the process of incorporating these two features into our hybrid model to obtain formulas that are accurate also in very congested networks.

5   Conclusion

In this paper we proposed a hybrid model for Reno congestion control. Using this model, we analyzed both the transient and the steady-state behavior of n TCP flows competing for the available bandwidth on a dumbbell network topology. Our model confirmed formulas for the steady-state behavior that can be found in the literature and also derive new relationships between the several quantities of interest. We were also able to explain the flow synchronization phenomena that have been observed in simulations and in real networks but, to the best of our knowledge, have not been theoretically justified. We were also able to demonstrate that the limit cycle that corresponds to flow synchronization is globally exponential stable. This means that synchronization will occur even if the flows start unsynchronized or lose synchronization because of some temporary disturbance.

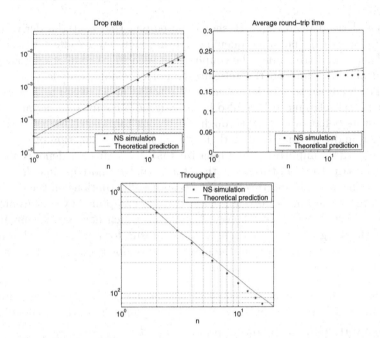

Fig. 4. Comparison between the predictions obtained from the hybrid model and the results from `ns-2` simulations.

We are now in the process of generalizing the analysis presented here to different network topologies; other congestion control mechanisms (such as Tahoe, Vegas, and Equation-Based); and different queuing policies (such as drop-head, Random Drop, RED, and SRED). We are also exploring mechanisms that can be used to avoid the undesirable synchronization. Another application of the hybrid model derived here is the detection of abnormalities in TCP traffic flows. This has important applications in network security.

Appendix

To derive equation (6), suppose that drops occurred at some normalized time τ_k at which the system entered the *queue-not-full* state and therefore that $q(\tau_k) = q_{\max}$. Denoting by $\bar{\tau}_k$ the normalized time at which the next drop occurs, for $\tau \in [\tau_k, \bar{\tau}_k)$, we have

$$w_i(\tau) = w_i(\tau_k) + a(\tau - \tau_k), \qquad i \in \{1, 2, \ldots, n\},$$

$$q(\tau) = e^{-(\tau - \tau_k)}\left(q_{\max} + BT_p + an - \sum_{i=1}^{n} w_i(\tau_k)\right) +$$

$$+ an(\tau - \tau_k) + \sum_{i=1}^{n} w_i(\tau_k) - BT_p - an.$$

We assumed here that q remains positive during the whole interval. Since a new drop occurs at the normalized time $\bar{\tau}_k$, we must have $q(\bar{\tau}_k) = q_{\max}$. Because of q's continuity, we must then have

$$
q_{\max} = e^{-(\bar{\tau}_k - \tau_k)} \left(q_{\max} + BT_p + an - \sum_{i=1}^{n} w_i(\tau_k) \right) +
$$

$$
+ an(\bar{\tau}_k - \tau_k) + \sum_{i=1}^{n} w_i(\tau_k) - BT_p - an.
$$

We can then solve this equation to compute the normalized time interval $\bar{\tau}_k - \tau_k$ and obtain

$$
\frac{q_{\max} + BT_p - \sum_{i=1}^{n} w_i(\tau_k)}{an} = \frac{\bar{\tau}_k - \tau_k}{1 - e^{-(\bar{\tau}_k - \tau_k)}} - 1,
$$

which is equivalent to $\bar{\tau}_k - \tau_k = f^{-1}(s_k)$. Equation (6) is a consequence of this and the fact that the system enters the *queue-not-full* state again at time $\tau_{k+1} := \bar{\tau}_k + 1$. $\qquad \square$

References

1. V. Jacobson, "Congestion avoidance and control," in *Proc. of SIGCOMM*, vol. 18.4, pp. 314–329, Aug. 1988.
2. V. Jacobson, "Modified TCP congestion avoidance algorithm." Posted on end2end-interest mailing list, Apr. 1990.
   Available at ftp://ftp.ee.lbl.gov/email/vanj.90apr30.txt.
3. M. Allman, V. Paxson, and W. Stevens, "TCP congestion control," *RFC 2581*, p. 13, Apr. 1999.
4. K. Fall and S. Floyd, "Simulation-based comparisons of Tahoe Reno and SACK TCP," *Computer Communication Review*, vol. 27, pp. 5–21, July 1996.
5. Y. Yang and S. Lam, "General AIMD congestion control. technical report," Tech. Rep. TR-200009, Department of Computer Science, University of Texas at Austin, May 2000.
6. T. Ott, J. H. B. Kemperman, and M. Mathis, "Window size behavior in TCP/IP with constant loss probability," in *Proc. of the DIMACS Workshop on Performance of Realtime Applications on the Internet*, Nov. 1996.
7. J. Mahdavi and S. Floyd, "TCP-friendly unicast rate-based flow control." Technical note sent to the end2end-interest mailing list, Jan. 1997.
8. T. V. Lakshman, U. Madhow, and B. Suter, "Window-based error recovery and flow control with a slow acknowledgment channel: A study of TCP/IP performance," in *Proc. of INFOCOMM*, Apr. 1997.
9. M. Mathis, J. Semke, J. Mahdavi, and T. Ott, "The macroscopic behavior of the TCP congestion avoidance algorithm," *Computer Communication Review*, vol. 27, July 1997.
10. S. Floyd, M. Handley, J. Padhye, and J. Widmer, "Equation-based congestion control for unicast applications." To appear in SIGCOMM, May 2000.

11. L. Zhang, S. Shenker, and D. D. Clark, "Observations on the dynamics of a congestion control algorithm: The effects of two-way traffic," in *Proc. of SIGCOMM*, Sept. 1991.

12. S. Floyd and V. Jacobson, "On traffic phase effects in packet-switched gateways," *Internetworking: Research and Experience*, vol. 3, pp. 115–116, Sept. 1992.

13. S. Floyd and V. Jacobson, "Random early detection gateways for congestion avoidance," *IEEE/ACM Trans. on Networking*, vol. 1, pp. 397–413, Aug. 1993.

14. L. Tavernini, "Differential automata and their discrete simulators," *Nonlinear Anal. Theory, Methods, and Applications*, vol. 11, no. 6, pp. 665–683, 1987.

15. A. S. Morse, D. Q. Mayne, and G. C. Goodwin, "Applications of hysteresis switching in parameter adaptive control," *IEEE Trans. Automat. Contr.*, vol. 37, pp. 1343–1354, Sept. 1992.

16. A. Back, J. Guckenheimer, and M. Myers, "A dynamical simulation facility for hybrid systems," in Grossman *et al.* [29].

17. A. Nerode and W. Kohn, "Models for hybrid systems: Automata, topologies, stability," in Grossman *et al.* [29], pp. 317–356.

18. P. J. Antsaklis, J. A. Stiver, and M. D. Lemmon, "Hybrid system modeling and autonomous control systems," in Grossman *et al.* [29], pp. 366–392.

19. R. W. Brockett, "Hybrid models for motion control systems," in *Essays in Control: Perspectives in the Theory and its Applications* (H. L. Trentelman and J. C. Willems, eds.), pp. 29–53, Boston: Birkhäuser, 1993.

20. M. S. Branicky, V. S. Borkar, and S. K. Mitter, "A unified framework for hybrid control: Background, model and theory," in *Proc. of the 33rd Conf. on Decision and Contr.*, vol. 4, pp. 4228–4234, Dec. 1994.

21. M. S. Branicky, *Studies in Hybrid Systems: Modeling, Analysis, and Control.* PhD thesis, MIT, Cambridge, MA, June 1995.

22. J. Lygeros, C. Tomlin, and S. Sastry, "Multi-objective hybrid controller synthesis: Least restrictive control," in *Proc. of the 36th Conf. on Decision and Contr.*, vol. 1, pp. 127–132, Dec. 1997.

23. The VINT Project, a collaboratoin between researchers at UC Berkeley, LBL, USC/ISI, and Xerox PARC, *The ns Manual (formerly ns Notes and Documentation)*, Oct. 2000.
    Available at http://www.isi.edu/nsnam/ns/ns-documentation.html.

24. J. P. Hespanha, S. Bohacek, K. Obraczka, and J. Lee, "Hybrid modeling of tcp congestion control," tech. rep., University of Southern California, Los Angeles, CA, Oct. 2000.

25. A. W. Naylor and G. R. Sell, *Linear Operator Theory in Engineering and Science.* No. 40 in Applied Mathematical Sciences, New York: Springer-Verlag, 1982.

26. J. Padhye, V. Firoiu, D. Towsley, and J. Kurose, "Modeling TCP throughput: a simple model and its empirical validation," in *Proc. of SIGCOMM*, Sept. 1998.

27. V. Misra, W. Gong, and D. Towsley, "Stochastic differential equation modeling and analysis of TCP-windowsize behavior," in *In Proceedings of PERFORMANCE99*, (Istanbul, Turkey), 1999.

28. F. Baccelli and D. Hong, "TCP is max-plus linear," in *Proc. of SIGCOMM*, Sept. 2000.

29. R. L. Grossman, A. Nerode, A. P. Ravn, and H. Rishel, eds., *Hybrid Systems*, vol. 736 of *Lecture Notes in Computer Science*. New York: Springer-Verlag, 1993.

Hybrid Geodesics as Optimal Solutions to the Collision-Free Motion Planning Problem[*]

Jianghai Hu[1], Maria Prandini[2], Karl Henrik Johansson[3], and Shankar Sastry[1]

[1] Dept. of Electrical Engineering and Computer Sciences
University of California at Berkeley - Berkeley CA 94720, USA
{jianghai,sastry}@eecs.berkeley.edu
[2] Dept. of Electrical Engineering for Automation
University of Brescia - Brescia, Italy
prandini@ing.unibs.it
[3] Dept. of Signals, Systems and Sensors
Royal Institute of Technology - Stockholm , Sweden
kallej@s3.kth.se

Abstract. In this paper we address the problem of designing energy minimizing collision-free maneuvers for multiple agents moving on a plane. We show that the problem is equivalent to that of finding the shortest geodesic in a certain manifold with nonsmooth boundary. This allows us to prove that the optimal maneuvers are C^1 by introducing the concept of u-convex manifolds. Moreover, due to the nature of the optimal maneuvers, the problem can be formulated as an optimal control problem for a certain hybrid system whose discrete states consist of different "contact graphs". We determine the analytic expression for the optimal maneuvers in the two agents case. For the three agents case, we derive the dynamics of the optimal maneuvers within each discrete state. This together with the fact that an optimal maneuver is a C^1 concatenation of segments associated with different discrete states gives a characterization of the optimal solutions in the three agents case.

1 Introduction and Background

Many problems arising in practical situations have boundary constraints and can be described in the setting of manifolds with boundary. Here we are interested in certain geometric aspects of such manifolds, specifically those concerning the properties of *geodesics*, i.e., locally distance minimizing curves. It is intuitively clear that when the boundary consists of cells of various dimensions pieced together, a geodesic is in general "hybrid" in the sense that it is a concatenation of different segments, each one of which being a geodesic of a particular cell (in its own geometry). Thus in the hybrid systems terminology ([16]) , the geodesics can be naturally described as the executions of an underlying hybrid system.

[*] Research supported by NSF and DARPA. The authors would like to thank Ekaterina Lemch for the helpful discussions.

M.D. Di Benedetto, A. Sangiovanni-Vincentelli (Eds.): HSCC 2001, LNCS 2034, pp. 305–318, 2001.
© Springer-Verlag Berlin Heidelberg 2001

Note that our interpretation of a manifold with boundary as the domain for the continuous state of a hybrid system is the inverse of the procedure adopted in [21], where the concept of *hybrifold* is introduced by piecing together the domains corresponding to all the discrete modes of a hybrid system to form a single topological manifold. Another difference is that, in addition to the topological properties of the hybrid systems such as stability, zenoness, ergodicity, etc., we are also interested in their metric properties such as distance, curve length, angle, etc. Therefore when piecing domains together, isometries instead of merely diffeomorphisms are required as the identifying maps of the boundaries.

To be precise, let M be a connected m-dimensional C^∞ Riemannian manifold with boundary. The boundary of M can be either *smooth* or *nonsmooth*. Consider only those curves in M which are piecewise C^1, i.e., curves which can be partitioned into a countable number of C^1 segments. For such curves the arc length is well defined. The distance between two points in M is then defined as the infimum of the arc length of all the piecewise C^1 curves connecting them. A geodesic in M is a locally distance minimizing curve. More precisely, the curve $\gamma : (t_0, t_f) \to M$ is a geodesic if and only if for each $t \in (t_0, t_f)$, γ is the shortest curve between $\gamma(t_1)$ and $\gamma(t_2)$ for every t_1, t_2 belonging to a neighborhood of t with $t_1 < t < t_2$. Given two arbitrary points in M, the (globally) shortest curve connecting them is automatically a geodesic. However, it is well known that the converse is not true: a geodesic is not necessarily distance minimizing between its end points. In fact, even for manifolds without boundary, a geodesic is no longer distance minimizing after its first conjugate point ([5]).

Due to the presence of the boundary, regularity of geodesics in M is an issue. The special case of geodesics in manifolds with smooth boundary is dealt with in [2,3], to name a few. We now review briefly some of the results in these papers relevant to our study in the nonsmooth boundary case. For manifolds with smooth boundary, it is shown in [3] that geodesics are in general C^1 but not C^2. The simplest example is $\mathbb{R}^2$ with a unit disk removed. Two points across the disk and "invisible" to each other are connected by at most two shortest geodesics, which are C^1 everywhere but fail to be C^2 at exactly the points where geodesics switch from a line segment to a boundary arcs or *vice versa*. In [3] it is further suggested that a geodesic in a manifold M with smooth boundary can be decomposed into: (1) *interior segments*, which are geodesic segments belonging to the interior of M; (2) *boundary segments*, which are geodesic segments belonging to the boundary ∂M of M; (3) *switch points*, which are points where the geodesic switches from a boundary segment to an interior segment or *vice versa*; (4) *intermittent points*, which are accumulation points of the set of switch points. It is proved in [1] that when the boundary ∂M is locally analytic, a geodesic can have only a finite number of switch points in any segment of finite arc length, hence no intermittent points at all. In our interpretation of geodesics as the executions of an underlying hybrid system, switch points correspond to transitions between discrete states, and the existence of intermittent points in a geodesic implies that the corresponding execution, hence the hybrid system, is Zeno ([16]). Therefore the result in [1] can be rephrased by saying that a hybrid system whose executions correspond to geodesics in a manifold with locally analytic boundary is non-Zeno.

In this paper we study the problem of optimal collision-free motion planning for multiple agents moving on a plane, where a collision is the event that any two agents get closer than a minimum allowed distance. We show that each collision-free joint maneuver has a natural representation as a curve in a certain manifold with boundary, and among all such joint maneuvers the one with the least energy corresponds to a geodesic parameterized proportionally to arc length. Geodesics satisfying this property are called *normalized*. Unless otherwise stated, we assume throughout the paper that all geodesics are normalized.

The problem which inspired this work originally is the development of algorithms for aircraft conflict resolution. Aircraft flying at the same altitude must maintain a horizontal separation of at least 3 nautical miles (nmi) inside the terminal radar approach control facilities and 5 nmi in the en-route airspace ([20]). Moreover, the energy of an aircraft maneuver is closely related to practical aspects such as travel distance, fuel consumption, passenger comfort, etc. Numerous approaches have been suggested in the literature to deal with aircraft conflict resolution (see the survey paper [13]). Some of them ([6,8,11,17]) actually pose the problem as a constrained optimization problem. In particular, in [11] the geometric interpretation of aircraft motions as a braid is used in performing the optimality analysis. Optimal multi-agent coordination also finds applications in other transportation systems, for example [18]. Another related field is the motion planning for mobile robots. Most of the papers in this field focus on the feasibility and the algorithmic complexity aspect of the problem ([7,9,14,22]). Among those dealing with optimal coordination, [15] considers the case when each robot minimizes its own independent goal by using techniques from multi-objective optimization and game theory. [4] studies the problem of time-optimal control of multiple vehicles moving on a plane with constant speed and bounded curvature.

The rest of the paper is organized as follows. In Sect. 2, we describe the optimal collision-free motion planning problem and show how it can be reformulated as the problem of finding the shortest geodesic in a manifold M with nonsmooth boundary. Using the fact that M is a u-convex manifold, we are able to prove in Sect. 2.2 that the optimal motions for the agents are C^1. We then introduce in Sect. 3 the notion of "contact graph", which leads to a natural interpretation of the problem in the framework of optimal control for a certain hybrid system. The C^1 property implies that the reset maps of the hybrid system are all identity maps. The shortest geodesic can be obtained by appropriately piecing together geodesic segments in different discrete modes, and is the optimal execution for the hybrid system. In Sect. 3.1 necessary conditions are introduced to simplify the determination of such geodesics, which are then used in Sect. 3.2 and 3.3 to characterize the optimal collision-free motions for the two agents and three agents case respectively. Finally some concluding remarks are given in Sect. 4.

2   Problem Formulation

Consider the situation when n agents, numbered from 1 to n, are moving on a common plane $\mathbb{R}^2$. The n agents are required to start from positions $a_1, \dots, a_n \in \mathbb{R}^2$ at time t_0 and reach positions $b_1, \dots, b_n \in \mathbb{R}^2$ at a fixed time t_f. We assume that each one of the two sets $\{a_i\}_{i=1}^n$ and $\{b_i\}_{i=1}^n$ satisfies the r-*separation condition* for some positive r, in the sense that the minimum pairwise Euclidean distance in each set is at least r.

A *maneuver* for agent i, $1 \le i \le n$, is defined to be a piecewise C^1 map $\alpha_i : [t_0, t_f] \to \mathbb{R}^2$ satisfying $\alpha_i(t_0) = a_i$ and $\alpha_i(t_f) = b_i$. The set of all maneuvers for agent i is denoted as $\mathcal{P}_i$. Then $\mathcal{P} = \prod_{i=1}^n \mathcal{P}_i$ is the set of *joint maneuvers* for the n-agent system. Here we are interested in the subset $\mathcal{P}(r)$ of $\mathcal{P}$ consisting of all the *collision-free maneuvers*, i.e., those joint maneuvers $\alpha = (\alpha_1, \dots, \alpha_n) \in \mathcal{P}$ such that $\{\alpha_i(t)\}_{i=1}^n$ satisfies the r-separation condition at each time t, $t \in [t_0, t_f]$.

The *energy* of a joint maneuver $\alpha = (\alpha_1, \dots, \alpha_n) \in \mathcal{P}$ is defined as

$$J(\alpha) \triangleq \frac{1}{2} \sum_{i=1}^n \int_{t_0}^{t_f} \|\dot{\alpha}_i(t)\|^2 \, dt.$$

The goal is to find the collision-free maneuver $\alpha \in \mathcal{P}(r)$ with minimal energy. This leads to the following formulation of the problem:

$$\text{Minimize } J(\alpha) \text{ subject to } \alpha \in \mathcal{P}(r). \tag{1}$$

Notice that in formulating problem (1), we make the restrictive assumption that all the agents involved in the encounter reach their destinations at the same *known* time instant t_f. This is important in time-critical applications such as air traffic management. The issue of choosing t_f is not dealt with in this paper.

Remark 1. Problem (1) can be alternatively formulated as an optimal control problem with state constraints, and approached by using the corresponding techniques from optimal control theory. In this paper, however, we adopt a geometric point of view. The geometric method not only yields elegant results and proofs, but more importantly, by using information on the curvature of the domains, it also allows us to obtain deeper results concerning the global uniqueness of the optimal solutions under certain conditions (see [12]).

2.1   A Geometric Interpretation

Each joint maneuver $\alpha = (\alpha_1, \dots, \alpha_n)$ in $\mathcal{P}$ can be re-interpreted as a curve in $\mathbb{R}^{2n}$ defined by $\alpha(t) = (\alpha_1(t), \dots, \alpha_n(t))$, $t \in [t_0, t_f]$, which starts from $a = (a_1, \dots, a_n)$ and ends at $b = (b_1, \dots, b_n)$. If we use $(x_1, y_1, \dots, x_n, y_n)$ to denote the coordinates of a generic point in $\mathbb{R}^{2n}$, then the collision-free constraint on the joint maneuver α translates into the condition that α viewed as a curve in $\mathbb{R}^{2n}$ is strictly contained in M, a manifold with boundary obtained by removing from $\mathbb{R}^{2n}$ the "static obstacle" W given by

$$W = \{ \mathrm{P} \in \mathbb{R}^{2n} : \sqrt{(x_i - x_j)^2 + (y_i - y_j)^2} < r \text{ for some } 1 \le i < j \le n \}. \tag{2}$$

In other words, $M = \mathbb{R}^{2n} \backslash W$. Thus there is a one-to-one correspondence between maneuvers in $\mathcal{P}(r)$ and piecewise C^1 curves in M connecting a and b. Moreover, the energy of a joint maneuver $\alpha = (\alpha_1, \ldots, \alpha_n) \in \mathcal{P}$ can be expressed as $J(\alpha) = \frac{1}{2} \sum_{i=1}^{n} \int_{t_0}^{t_f} \|\dot{\alpha}_i(t)\|^2 \, dt = \frac{1}{2} \int_{t_0}^{t_f} \|\dot{\alpha}(t)\|^2 \, dt$, which coincides with the usual definition of the energy of α viewed as a curve in $\mathbb{R}^{2n}$. Hence (1) is equivalent to the following geometric problem:

Find the energy minimizing curve α in M joining point a to point b.   (3)

It is a standard result (see, e.g., [19]) that solutions to (3) are shortest curves in M from a to b parameterized proportionally to arc length, i.e., *minimizing geodesics* in M connecting a to b. We shall henceforth study problem (3) instead of (1) with the understanding that all the curves connecting a to b in M are parameterized so that they start from a at t_0 and end at b at t_f.

Notice that W defined in (2) is the union of $n(n-1)/2$ convex open cylinders, each one of the form $\{(x_1, y_1, \ldots, x_n, y_n) : \sqrt{(x_i - x_j)^2 + (y_i - y_j)^2} < r\}$ for some (i, j), with $i \neq j$. Therefore M obtained by removing W from R^{2n} is an instance of the following class of manifolds with boundary:

Definition 1 (u-convex manifolds). *A manifold with boundary is called u-convex if it is obtained by removing from some Euclidean space $\mathbb{R}^m$ a finite union of open convex subsets, each one of which has a smooth boundary.*

We will show in the next section that geodesics in u-convex manifolds are C^1, which implies that solutions to problem (3), hence (1), are C^1.

2.2 Geodesics in u-Convex Manifolds

In this section we study the properties of geodesics in u-convex manifolds. Many technicalities encountered in the general case can be avoided when analyzing this special case. For example, when the boundary of M is nonsmooth, geodesics in M are in general not C^1 since they can bend into sharp corners of the boundary. However, we next show that this is not the case for u-convex manifolds.

Suppose M is u-convex, i.e., $M = \mathbb{R}^m \setminus \cup_{i=1}^{k} D_i$ is the complement in $\mathbb{R}^m$ of the union of open convex bodies $D_1, \ldots, D_k \subset \mathbb{R}^m$, whose boundary ∂D_i is smooth for each $i = 1, \ldots, k$. Then at each point $x \in M$, we can define the *visible cone* of x to be the cone $V(x)$ with vertex x and consisting of all the rays which start from x and lie inside M within a sufficiently small distance. In other words, $V(x)$ is the region a viewer sitting at x can see if only local obstacles around x are considered. $V(x)$ can be obtained in the following way. If $x \in M$ lies on the boundary of D_i for exactly those i belonging to a subset $\mathcal{I}$ of $\{1, \ldots, k\}$, then the obstacles D_i, $i \in \mathcal{I}$, are called the *active* obstacles at x. For each active obstacle D_i, let $T_x(\partial D_i)$ be the plane tangent to ∂D_i at x and n_i be the unit normal vector of ∂D_i at x pointing outside of D_i. $T_x(\partial D_i)$ separates $\mathbb{R}^m$ into two open half spaces. We denote the one containing n_i as $P_{i,x}^+$ and its closure as $\overline{P_{i,x}^+}$. The convexity of D_i implies that $P_{i,x}^+$ and D_i are disjoint sets. Then $V(x)$ is given by

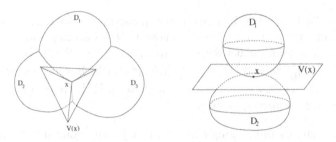

Fig. 1. Examples of visible cones. On the right a degenerate case.

$V(x) = \bigcap_{i \in \mathcal{I}} \overline{P_{i,x}^+}$. $V(x)$ is a closed convex cone since it is the finite intersection of closed convex sets (half spaces), and it can have an arbitrary dimension lower than m. Figure 1 shows examples of visible cones in $\mathbb{R}^3$. In the case when x is in the interior of M, $V(x) = \mathbb{R}^m$ since there are no active obstacles at x.

By using the notion of visible cone, one can prove the following result.

Theorem 1. *Suppose that M is u-convex. Then any geodesic in M is C^1.*

Proof. Let $\gamma : I \to M$ be a geodesic of M, where I is an open interval in $\mathbb{R}$. For each $s \in I$, the one-sided derivatives $\gamma'(s^-)$ and $\gamma'(s^+)$ of γ at s exist since γ is piecewise C^1. By using a reparameterization if necessary, we can assume that both of them are unit vectors. Construct the visible cone $V(x)$ of $x = \gamma(s)$. By definition, both $\gamma'(s^+)$ and $-\gamma'(s^-)$ based at x lie inside $V(x)$ and they span an angle $\theta \in [0, \pi]$. Suppose by contradiction that $\gamma'(s^-) \neq \gamma'(s^+)$, then $\theta < \pi$.

Fix a neighborhood U of x small enough so that only the active obstacles at x intersect U. Choose ϵ such that $\gamma|_{[s-\epsilon,s+\epsilon]} \subset U$. For each $t \in [s - \epsilon, s]$, let $\hat{\gamma}(t)$ be the projection of $\gamma(t)$ onto the line through x and along the direction $-\gamma'(s^-)$; for each $t \in [s, s + \epsilon]$, let $\hat{\gamma}(t)$ be the projection of $\gamma(t)$ onto the line through x and along the direction $\gamma'(s^+)$. Notice that $\hat{\gamma}|_{[s-\epsilon,s+\epsilon]}$ is a curve through x contained completely within M. By choosing ϵ small enough, one can ensure that the line segments $\overline{\gamma(s - \epsilon)\hat{\gamma}(s - \epsilon)}$ and $\overline{\gamma(s + \epsilon)\hat{\gamma}(s + \epsilon)}$ both lie completely inside M. Therefore by replacing the arc $\gamma|_{[s-\epsilon,s+\epsilon]}$ with the concatenation of $\overline{\gamma(s - \epsilon)\hat{\gamma}(s - \epsilon)}$, the arc $\hat{\gamma}|_{[s-\epsilon,s+\epsilon]}$, and $\overline{\hat{\gamma}(s + \epsilon)\gamma(s + \epsilon)}$, the total arc length is increased by at most $o(\epsilon)$. Notice further that we can short-cut $\hat{\gamma}|_{[s-\epsilon,s+\epsilon]}$ by the line segment $\overline{\hat{\gamma}(s - \epsilon)\hat{\gamma}(s + \epsilon)}$, which lies completely inside $V(x)$ (hence M) by the convexity of $V(x)$. Doing so can reduce the arc length of $\hat{\gamma}|_{[s-\epsilon,s+\epsilon]}$ by at least $2\epsilon(1 - \sin(\theta/2)) + o(\epsilon)$, where we use the fact that $\gamma'(s^-)$ and $\gamma'(s^+)$ are unit vectors. Therefore the concatenation of the line segments $\overline{\gamma(s - \epsilon)\hat{\gamma}(s - \epsilon)}$, $\overline{\hat{\gamma}(s - \epsilon)\hat{\gamma}(s + \epsilon)}$, and $\overline{\hat{\gamma}(s + \epsilon)\gamma(s + \epsilon)}$ is a curve in M shorter than the arc $\gamma|_{[s-\epsilon,s+\epsilon]}$ for ϵ small enough. This contradicts the fact that γ is locally distance minimizing. Thus $\theta = \pi$ and γ is C^1 everywhere.

To show the necessity of u-convexity in proving Theorem 1, we plot in Fig. 2 an example in which M is obtained by removing from $\mathbb{R}^3$ a nonconvex obstacle given by the exterior D_1 of a cylinder with axis l_1 and a convex obstacle given by

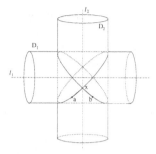

Fig. 2. Geodesic in a manifold with boundary that is not u-convex.

the interior D_2 of a cylinder with the same radius and with axis l_2 intersecting l_1 at a right angle. Hence M consists of all those points in $\mathbb{R}^3$ which lie inside the cylinder with axis l_1 but outside the cylinder with axis l_2, with the points on their boundaries included. The heavy-weighted curve in Fig. 2 is a geodesic in M with end points a and b, which is clearly not C^1 at x.

3   Hybrid System Solution

Now we go back to the discussion of the optimization problem (3) proposed in Sect. 2, where $M = \mathbb{R}^{2n} \setminus W$ with W defined in (2).

Consider a curve $\alpha = (\alpha_1, \ldots, \alpha_n)$ from a to b in M corresponding a collision-free maneuver in $\mathcal{P}(r)$. Fix a time instant $t \in [t_0, t_f]$. We say that agent i and agent j *contact* at time t if and only if $\|\alpha_i(t) - \alpha_j(t)\| = r$. A graph can be associated to α at time t in the following way. The graph has n vertices, numbered from 1 to n, each one corresponding to an agent, and an edge exists between vertex i and vertex j if and only if agent i and agent j contact at time t. We call this graph the *contact graph* of α at time t.

Let α^* be a curve from a to b in M that is a solution to problem (3). Suppose that there is a finite subdivision of $[t_0, t_f]$: $t_0 \leq t_1 \leq \ldots \leq t_{k-1} \leq t_k = t_f$, such that the contact graph of α^* over the subinterval (t_{h-1}, t_h) (which we denote as G_h) remains constant for all $h = 1, \ldots, k$, while contiguous subintervals have distinct contact graphs. In each subinterval, say (t_{h-1}, t_h), α^* moves on a certain part of M determined by G_h. If G_h has no edges, then α^* restricted to (t_{h-1}, t_h) is a straight line segment in the interior of M. If G_h has at least one edge, then α^* restricted to (t_{h-1}, t_h) moves on a portion of the boundary of M, which is a lower dimensional smooth submanifold of $\mathbb{R}^{2n}$ consisting of all the points $(x_1, y_1, \ldots, x_n, y_n)$ in $\mathbb{R}^{2n}$ such that $\sqrt{(x_i - x_j)^2 + (y_i - y_j)^2}$ is equal to r for (i, j) such that there is an edge between vertices i and j in G_h, and greater than r for all others (i, j), $i \neq j$. Moreover, α^* restricted to (t_{h-1}, t_h) is a minimizing geodesic in this submanifold. In this way we can associate to each type of contact graph a domain, i.e., the submanifold of M to which α^* belongs when its contact graph is of that type.

Based on the above analysis, α^* can be viewed as an execution of a certain hybrid system, whose continuous variable takes values in M, and whose discrete modes have a one-to-one correspondence with the different contact graphs for the n-agent system. For each discrete mode, the invariant set is the domain of the corresponding contact graph, and the dynamics is governed by the geodesic equation on that domain, which is a second-order ordinary differential equation. By Theorem 1, when a transition occurs between discrete modes, the position α and the velocity $\dot{\alpha}$ are reset by identity maps. α is an optimal solution to this hybrid system if it satisfies $\alpha(t_0) = a$ and $\alpha(t_f) = b$, and has minimal energy. The problem is to determine the initial velocity $\dot{\alpha}(t_0)$ and the time and sequence of the discrete switchings so that the corresponding execution of this hybrid system will generate the optimal solution.

3.1   Necessary Conditions for Optimality

We now derive some necessary conditions for α to be an optimal solution to problem (3), which can then be used to simplify the determination of optimal maneuvers for the two-agent and three-agent cases.

Proposition 1. *Suppose that α^* is a minimizing geodesic from a to b in M. Fix an arbitrary $w \in \mathbb{R}^2$. Then $\beta^* = (\beta_1^*, \dots, \beta_n^*)$ defined by*

$$\beta_i^*(t) = \alpha_i^*(t) + w\frac{t - t_0}{t_f - t_0}, \quad t \in [t_0, t_f], \quad i = 1, \dots, n, \tag{4}$$

is a minimizing geodesic from a to $b' = (b_1 + w, \dots, b_n + w)$ in M.

Proof. For each curve β from a to b' in M, define curve $\alpha = (\alpha_1, \dots, \alpha_n) = \mathcal{T}_{-w}(\beta)$ in $\mathbb{R}^{2n}$ as $\alpha_i(t) = \beta_i(t) - w\frac{t-t_0}{t_f-t_0}$, for $t \in [t_0, t_f]$ and $i = 1, \dots, n$. Then it is easily verified that α is a curve in M from a to b with energy

$$J(\alpha) = J(\beta) + \frac{w^T \left(\sum_{i=1}^n (a_i - b_i) - nw/2\right)}{t_f - t_0}. \tag{5}$$

The second term of the right hand side of (5) is a constant independent of β, which we shall denote as C. From (5) and the optimality of α^*, we have $J(\beta) = J(\alpha) - C \geq J(\alpha^*) - C = J(\beta^*)$, where the last equality follows by noticing that $\alpha^* = \mathcal{T}_{-w}(\beta^*)$. This is true for arbitrary β, hence the conclusion.

One important implication of Proposition 1 is that it suffices to solve problem (3) only for those a and b that are *aligned*, i.e., a and b with the same centroid $\frac{1}{n}\sum_{i=1}^n a_i = \frac{1}{n}\sum_{i=1}^n b_i \in \mathbb{R}^2$. In fact for non-aligned a and b, by choosing $w = \sum_{i=1}^n a_i - \sum_{i=1}^n b_i$, one can ensure that a and $b' = (b_1 + w, \dots, b_n + w)$ are aligned. Hence by Proposition 1, minimizing geodesics from a to b can be obtained from minimizing geodesics from a to b' by applying the inverse of the transformation (4).

Proposition 2. *Assume that α^* is a minimizing geodesic from a to b in M. Then*

$$\sum_{i=1}^{n} \alpha_i^*(t) = \frac{(t_f - t) \sum_{i=1}^{n} a_i + (t - t_0) \sum_{i=1}^{n} b_i}{t_f - t_0}, \quad \forall t \in [t_0, t_f].$$

Proof. Consider first the case when a and b are aligned. Define a piecewise C^1 map $g : [t_0, t_f] \to \mathbb{R}^2$ by $g(t) = \sum_{i=1}^{n} \alpha_i^*(t) - \sum_{i=1}^{n} a_i$, $t \in [t_0, t_f]$, which satisfies $g(t_0) = g(t_f) = 0$. For each $\lambda \in \mathbb{R}$, let $\beta_\lambda = (\beta_{\lambda,1}, \ldots, \beta_{\lambda,n})$ be given by $\beta_{\lambda,i}(t) = \alpha_i^*(t) + \lambda g(t)$, $t \in [t_0, t_f]$, $i = 1, \cdots, n$. Note that β_λ is a piecewise C^1 curve from a to b in M with energy

$$J(\beta_\lambda) = J(\alpha^*) + \frac{n\lambda^2}{2} \int_{t_0}^{t_f} \left\| \sum_{i=1}^{n} \dot{\alpha}_i^*(t) \right\|^2 dt + \lambda \int_{t_0}^{t_f} \left\| \sum_{i=1}^{n} \dot{\alpha}_i^*(t) \right\|^2 dt.$$

The difference $J(\beta_\lambda) - J(\alpha^*)$ is a quadratic function of λ which, by the optimality of α^*, must be nonnegative for all λ. Hence we have $\int_{t_0}^{t_f} \| \sum_{i=1}^{n} \dot{\alpha}_i^*(t) \|^2 dt = 0$, implying that $\sum_{i=1}^{n} \dot{\alpha}_i^*(t) = 0$ for almost all $t \in [t_0, t_f]$. After integration, this leads to the desired conclusion for the aligned case. In the case when a and b are not aligned, the result follows from Proposition 1 by considering a minimizing geodesic in M from a to $b' = (b_1 + w, \ldots, b_n + w)$ with $w = \sum_{i=1}^{n} a_i - \sum_{i=1}^{n} b_i$ and noticing that a and b' are aligned.

A geometric interpretation of the above results is as follows. Let N be the two dimensional subspace of $\mathbb{R}^{2n}$ spanned by vectors $(0, 1, \ldots, 0, 1)$ and $(1, 0, \ldots, 1, 0)$, and V be the orthogonal complement of N in $\mathbb{R}^{2n}$ such that $\mathbb{R}^{2n} = V \oplus N$. Then the condition that a and b are aligned is equivalent to the condition that $b - a$ belongs to V. Denote with V_a the $(n-2)$-plane through a and parallel to V. Then if a and b are aligned, they both belong to V_a, and by Proposition 2, a minimizing geodesic α^* in M from a to b lies in V_a completely. For non-aligned a and b, let b' be the orthogonal projection of b onto V_a. Then Proposition 1 and Proposition 2 say that a minimizing geodesic α^* between a and b in M can be decomposed into two parts: its projection onto V_a, which is a minimizing geodesic from a to b' in $V_a \cap M$; and its projection onto N, which is a straight line. These conclusions become evident under the following important observation: the obstacle W defined in (2) is cylindrical in the direction of N, i.e., $x \in W$ if and only if $x + N \subset W$.

As a result of the above analysis, we can focus on the case when a and b are aligned. Without loss of generality, we assume that a and b both belong to V. Since any minimizing geodesic between such a and b is contained in V, we can effectively reduce our space of consideration from M to $M_0 \triangleq V \cap M$, which is a cross section of M and two dimensions lower than M. This will make a difference when n is relatively small.

Remark 2. Optimal maneuvers for the n-agent system can be alternatively viewed as the outcomes of a mechanical experiment, in which n particles of unit mass move from positions $a_1, \ldots, a_n$ on a plane with certain initial velocities and no external force acting on them. In this interpretation, the result in

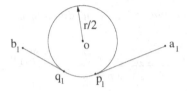

Fig. 3. Optimal α_1^* for two agents case.

Proposition 2 becomes the law of conservation of momentum. See [10] for further details.

3.2 Two Agents Case

Consider the simplest case when $n = 2$ with aligned $a = (a_1, a_2)$ and $b = (b_1, b_2)$ such that $a_1 + a_2 = b_1 + b_2 = 0$. If $\alpha^* = (\alpha_1^*, \alpha_2^*)$ is a solution to problem (3), then Proposition 2 implies that $\alpha_1^*(t)$ and $\alpha_2^*(t)$ are symmetric with respect to the origin for all $t \in [t_0, t_f]$. Hence specifying one of them, say α_1^*, is sufficient for describing α^*. Moreover, the r-separation constraint can be formulated as the condition that α_1^* can never enter the open ball $B(0, r/2)$ of radius $r/2$ around the origin. By noting that α_1^* and α_2^* give identical contributions to the total energy, we finally have a simplified but equivalent version of problem (3):

Find the energy minimizing curve α_1 in $\mathbb{R}^2 \setminus B(0, r/2)$ joining a_1 to b_1.   (6)

Figure 3 shows the geometric construction of a solution α_1^* to problem (6), which is a geodesic of $\mathbb{R}^2 \setminus B(0, r/2)$ and, depending on the positions of a_1 and b_1, may contain up to three segments: first a line segment from a_1 to p_1 tangent to $\partial B(0, r/2)$ at p_1; next from p_1 to q_1 along $\partial B(0, r/2)$; and finally the line segment from q_1 to b_1 tangent to $\partial B(0, r/2)$ at q_1. The case when b_1 is "visible" from a_1 is trivial.

3.3 Three Agents Case

The case $n = 3$ is more complicated. Figure 4 shows all the possible contact graphs and the transitions between them, with the "ground" symbol indicating that there is a transition relation with state 1. We now determine the geodesics in each one of the discrete states.

Geodesics in state 1. State 1 corresponds to the contact graph of three isolated vertices, hence its domain X_1 corresponds to $int(M)$, the interior of M. By the discussion in Sect. 3.1, we only consider $X_1 = V \cap int(M)$, which has dimension 4. Geodesics in X_1 are straight lines.

Geodesics in state 2, 3, and 4. States 2, 3 and 4 correspond to contact graphs where two vertices are connected to each other and the third one is isolated. Let us consider state 2. Its domain X_2 is:

$$X_2 = \{(x_1, y_1, x_2, y_2, x_3, y_3) : d_{12} = r, d_{13} > r, d_{23} > r\} \cap V$$

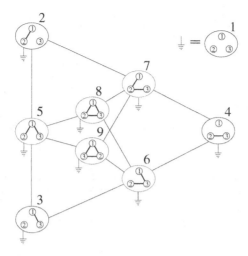

Fig. 4. State diagram.

where $d_{ij} \triangleq \sqrt{(x_i - x_j)^2 + (y_i - y_j)^2}$ denotes the distance between agent i and agent j. X_2 has dimension 3. As long as the boundary of X_2 is not reached, a geodesic in X_2 consists of a constant velocity motion for agent 3 since it is "free", while the motions for agents 1 and 2 are determined as in Sect. 3.2 for the two agents case, followed by a possible application of Proposition 1 if their starting and destination positions are not aligned. Similarly for X_3 and X_4.

Geodesics in state 5, 6, and 7. In states 5, 6 and 7, one agent, called the *pivotal agent*, contacts with both the other two agents, which do not contact each other themselves. The domain for state 5 is:

$$X_5 = \{(x_1, y_1, x_2, y_2, x_3, y_3) : d_{12} = r, d_{13} = r, d_{23} > r\} \cap V.$$

X_5 is a 2-dimensional submanifold with global coordinates $(\theta_{12}, \theta_{13})$ defined by

$$\theta_{12} = \arctan \frac{y_2 - y_1}{x_2 - x_1}, \quad \theta_{13} = \arctan \frac{y_3 - y_1}{x_3 - x_1}.$$

$(\theta_{12}, \theta_{13})$ takes values in $[0, 2\pi] \times [0, 2\pi]$ with opposite edges identified, i.e., the 2-torus T^2. In order to satisfy the constraint $d_{23} > r$, the shaded region (see Fig. 5) has to be removed from T^2, resulting in a subset $\hat{X}_5$ homeomorphic to $S^1 \times (0, 1)$. So topologically $\hat{X}_5$ (hence X_5) is an untwisted ribbon whose boundary consists of two disjoint circles.

Each $(\theta_{12}, \theta_{13}) \in \hat{X}_5$ determines a unique point $f(\theta_{12}, \theta_{13})$ in X_5 by

$$f(\theta_{12}, \theta_{13}) = \frac{r}{3}(-\cos \theta_{12} - \cos \theta_{13}, -\sin \theta_{12} - \sin \theta_{13}, 2 \cos \theta_{12} - \cos \theta_{13},$$

$$2 \sin \theta_{12} - \sin \theta_{13}, -\cos \theta_{12} + 2 \cos \theta_{13}, -\sin \theta_{12} + 2 \sin \theta_{13})^T,$$

which is an embedding of $\hat{X}_5$ into $\mathbb{R}^6$. The standard metric on $\mathbb{R}^6$ induces by f isometrically a metric on $\hat{X}_5$. A curve $(\theta_{12}(t), \theta_{13}(t))$ is a geodesic in $\hat{X}_5$ under

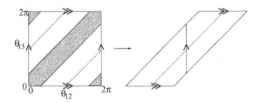

Fig. 5. The domain X_5 of discrete state 5.

the induced metric if and only if $\gamma(t) = f(\theta_{12}(t), \theta_{13}(t))$ is a geodesic in X_5. Using the fact that γ is a geodesic in X_5 if and only if its acceleration as a curve in $\mathbb{R}^6$ at each point is orthogonal to the tangent space of X_5 ([5]), we obtain after some calculations the geodesic equation on $\hat{X}_5$ as (see [11] for details)

$$\begin{cases} 2\ddot{\theta}_{12} - \cos(\theta_{12} - \theta_{13})\ddot{\theta}_{13} = \sin(\theta_{12} - \theta_{13})(\dot{\theta}_{13})^2 \\ 2\ddot{\theta}_{13} - \cos(\theta_{12} - \theta_{13})\ddot{\theta}_{12} = -\sin(\theta_{12} - \theta_{13})(\dot{\theta}_{12})^2. \end{cases} \tag{7}$$

There are certain symmetries in equation (7), which become evident by writing (7) in the new coordinates $\xi = \theta_{12} + \theta_{13}$ and $\eta = \theta_{12} - \theta_{13}$, leading to:

$$\begin{cases} (2 - \cos\eta)\ddot{\xi} = -\dot{\xi}\dot{\eta}\sin\eta \\ (2 + \cos\eta)\ddot{\eta} = \frac{1}{2}((\dot{\xi})^2 + (\dot{\eta})^2)\sin\eta. \end{cases} \tag{8}$$

Integrating the first equation in (8), we have

$$\dot{\xi}(2 - \cos\eta) = C_2, \tag{9}$$

for some constant C_2. On the other hand, since geodesics have constant speed, there exists another constant C_1 such that ([11])

$$(2 - \cos\eta)(\dot{\xi})^2 + (2 + \cos\eta)(\dot{\eta})^2 = 4C_1.$$

Substitution of (9) into the above equation leads to

$$(\dot{\eta})^2 = \frac{8C_1 - C_2^2 - 4C_1\cos\eta}{4 - \cos^2\eta}, \tag{10}$$

which together with (9) governs the dynamics of η and ξ respectively.

Geodesics in X_6 and X_7 can be obtained similarly.

Geodesics in state 8 and 9. Domains X_5, X_6 and X_7 share a common boundary consisting of two disjoint circles, which form the domains of state 8 and state 9 respectively. In both states, the three agents form an equilateral triangle centered at the origin. The only difference is their orientation. Agents 1, 2 and 3 are numbered counterclockwise in state 8 and clockwise in state 9.

Consider state 8 and its domain X_8. X_8 is a one dimensional circle and can be parameterized by σ, which is the angle between the line segment joining the

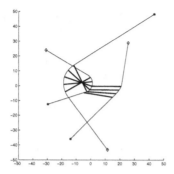

Fig. 6. Concatenation of geodesic segments.

origin to agent 1 and the positive x-axis. A geodesic in X_8 in this coordinate must then be of the form $\sigma(t) = \omega t$ for some constant angular velocity ω.

In summary, we have characterized geodesic segments in each one of the discrete states. By Theorem 1, the minimizing geodesics corresponding to the optimal collision-free maneuvers for the three agents are C^1 concatenation of such segments. One example of such concatenations is shown in Fig. 6, where the starting and destination positions of the three agents are marked with stars and diamonds respectively. A rod exists between two agents if and only their distance at the corresponding positions is r. However, it should be pointed out that the problem of finding when and where the switches between geodesic segments occur remains an open issue. In [11], we propose a numerical procedure to approximate the minimizing geodesics based on the successive optimization of piecewise linear curves in M. At each iteration a convex optimization problem is solved. By choosing a small step size for the piecewise linear curves, we can obtain a reasonably good approximation.

4   Conclusions

The problem of optimal collision-free maneuvers for multiple agents is formulated and shown to be equivalent to the problem of finding minimizing geodesics in a certain manifold with boundary, which can in turn be interpreted as an optimal control problem for a hybrid system. The solution is given for the two agents case. For the three agents system we derive the dynamics of the segment of optimal maneuver associated to each discrete state. The overall optimal maneuver is shown to be a C^1 concatenation of such segments.

References

1. F. Albrecht and I.D. Berg. Geodesics in Euclidean space with analytic obstacle. *Proceedings of the American Mathematics Society*, 113(1):201–207, 1991.
2. R. Alexander and S. Alexander. Geodesics in Riemannian manifolds-with-boundary. *Indiana University Mathematics Journal*, 30(4):481–488, 1981.

3. S.B. Alexander, I.D. Berg, and R.L. Bishop. Cauchy uniqueness in the Riemannian obstacle problem. In *Lecture notes in Math.*, vol.1209, pag.1-7. Springer-Verlag, 1985.

4. A. Bicchi and L. Pallottino. Optimal planning for coordinated vehicles with bounded curvature. In *Proc. Workshop on Algorithmic Foundations of Robotics*, Dartmouth, 2000.

5. M.P. de Carmo. *Riemannian geometry*. Birkhäuser Boston, 1992.

6. N. Durand, J.M. Alliot, and J. Noailles. Automatic aircraft conflict resolution using genetic algorithms. In *11th Annual ACM Conf. on Applied Computing*, 1996.

7. M. Erdmann and T. Lozano-Perez. On multiple moving objects (motion planning). *Algorithmica*, 2(4):477–521, 1987.

8. E. Frazzoli, Z.H. Mao, J.H. Oh, and E. Feron. Resolution of conflicts involving many aircraft via semidefinite programming. *AIAA J. of Guidance, Control and Dynamics*. To appear.

9. K. Fujimura. *Motion planning in dynamic environments*. Springer-Verlag, 1991.

10. J. Hu, M. Prandini, and S. Sastry. Optimal coordinated maneuvers for multiple agents moving on a plane. *Technical report*, Univ. of California at Berkeley, 2001.

11. J. Hu, M. Prandini, and S. Sastry. Optimal maneuver for multiple aircraft conflict resolution: a braid point of view. In *IEEE 39th Conf. on Decision and Control*, Sydney, Australia, 2000.

12. J. Hu and S. Sastry. Geodesics in manifolds with boundary: a case study. *In preparation*, 2001.

13. J. Kuchar and L.C. Yang. Survey of conflict detection and resolution modeling methods. In *AIAA Guidance, Navig., and Control Conf.*, New Orleans, LA, 1997.

14. J.-C. Latombe. *Robot motion planning*. Kluwer Academic Publishers, 1991.

15. S.M. LaValle and S.A. Hutchinson. Optimal motion planning for multiple robots having independent goals. *IEEE Trans. on Robotics and Aut.*, 14(6):912–925, 1998.

16. J. Lygeros, G.J. Pappas, and S. Sastry. An introduction to hybrid systems modeling, analysis and control. In *Preprints of the First Nonlinear Control Network Pedagogical School*, pag. 307-329, Athens, Greece, 1999.

17. P.K. Menon, G.D. Sweriduk, and B. Sridhar. Optimal strategies for free-flight air traffic conflict resolution. *AIAA J. of Guidance, Control and Dynamics*, 22(2):202–211, 1999.

18. A. Miele, T. Wang, C.S. Chao, and J.B. Dabney. Optimal control of a ship for collision avoidance maneuvers. *J. of Optim. Theory and App.*, 103(3):495–519, 1999.

19. J.W. Milnor. *Morse theory*. Annals of mathematics studies, 51. Princeton University Press, 1963. Based on lecture notes by M. Spivak and R. Wells.

20. Radio Technical Commission for Aeronautics. Minimum aviation system performance standards for automatic dependent surveillance-broadcast (ADS-B). *Technical report*, RTCA-186, 1997. DRAFT 4.0.

21. S. Simic, K.H. Johansson, S. Sastry, and J. Lygeros. Towards a geometric theory of hybrid systems. *Hybrid Systems: Computations and Control. Third International Workshop*, 2000. In Lecture Notes in Computer Science, number 1790.

22. B. Vronov, M. de Berg, A.F. van der Stappen, P. Svestka, and J. Vleugels. Motion planning for multiple robots. *Discrete & Comput. Geometry*, 22(4):502–525, 1999.

Nonlinear Adaptive Backstepping with Estimator Resetting Using Multiple Observers

Jens Kalkkuhl[1], Tor Arne Johansen[2], Jens Lüdemann[1], and Andreas Queda[1]

[1] DaimlerChrysler, Research and Technology, Berlin, Germany
{jens.kalkkuhl,jens.luedemann,andreas.queda}@DaimlerChrysler.com
[2] SINTEF Electronics and Cybernetics and
the Norwegian University of Sceince and Technology,
Trondheim, Norway
tor.arne.johansen@itk.ntnu.no

Abstract. A multiple model based observer/estimator for the estimation of parameters is used to reset the parameter estimation in a conventional Lyapunov based nonlinear adaptive controller. The advantage of combining both approaches is that the performance of the controller with respect to disturbances can be considerably improved while a reduced controller gain will increase the robustness of the approach with respect to noise and unmodeled dynamics. Several alternative resetting criteria are developed based on a control Lyapunov function.

1 Introduction

The use of multiple models to switch or reset parameter estimators has been proposed in order to speed up the convergence rate of certainty equivalence adaptive control of linear systems [1,2,3,4,5,6,7,8].

In this paper we present a hybrid approach to speed up transients in continuous Lyapunov based nonlinear adaptive control systems. Hereby, a multiple model observer (MMO) is used to reset the parameter estimation in a nonlinear adaptive controller. The advantage of combining both approaches is that transients due to adaptation can be damped out while the performance of the controller with respect to disturbances can be improved. As a consequence the gain of the continuous adaptive controller can be considerably lowered thus, increasing the robustness of the approach with respect to noise and unmodeled dynamics. The parameter resetting is based on a Control Lyapunov function and can guarantee asymptotic stability. The main contributions of the paper are

- an extension of multiple model based adaptive control to the class of parametric strict feedback nonlinear systems,
- the formulation of a set of sufficient closed loop stability conditions for resetting tuning function based nonlinear adaptive controllers,
- the introduction of a fast multiple model observer, from which even under transient conditions an accurate parameter estimate can be obtained.

M.D. Di Benedetto, A. Sangiovanni-Vincentelli (Eds.): HSCC 2001, LNCS 2034, pp. 319–332, 2001.
© Springer-Verlag Berlin Heidelberg 2001

The paper is organised as follows: In Section 2 some results of constructive nonlinear adaptive control are briefly reviewed and a motivation for discontinuous parameter resetting is given. This is followed by an analysis of the closed loop stability implications of resetting parameter estimates (Section 3) where a first order and a second order example are used to illustrate the results. Section 4 describes the concept of multiple model observers and gives for a special plant structure sufficient conditions for stability of parameter resetting. At the end discussions of a first order system as an application of the method and some simulation results are given.

2   Nonlinear Adaptive Backstepping

Consider the adaptive tracking problem for a parametric strict-feedback system [9]

$$\dot{x}_1 = x_2 + \varphi_1(x_1)^T\theta \tag{1}$$

$$\vdots$$

$$\dot{x}_{n-1} = x_n + \varphi_{n-1}(x_1, x_2, \ldots, x_{n-1})^T\theta$$

$$\dot{x}_n = \beta(x)u + \varphi_n(x)^T\theta$$

$$y = x_1$$

where $\theta \in \mathbb{R}^p$ is a vector of unknown constant parameters, β and $F = [\varphi_1, \ldots, \varphi_n]$ are smooth nonlinear functions taking arguments in $\mathbb{R}^n$. It has been shown that in a tuning function adaptive controller for such a system the adaptive control law and the parameter update law take the following form

$$u = \frac{1}{\beta(x)}\left[\alpha_n(x, \hat{\theta}, \bar{y}_r^{(n-1)}) + y_r^{(n)}\right] \tag{2}$$

$$\dot{\hat{\theta}} = \Gamma\tau_n(x, \hat{\theta}, \bar{y}_r^{(n-1)}) \tag{3}$$

where y_r is the reference signal to be tracked by the output y

$$\bar{y}_r^{(i)} = (y_r, \dot{y}_r, \ldots, y_r^{(i)}). \tag{4}$$

The control law and the tuning functions are given recursively by

$$z_i = x_i - y_r^{(i-1)} - \alpha_{i-1} \tag{5}$$

$$\alpha_i(\bar{x}_i, \hat{\theta}, \bar{y}_r^{(i-1)}) = -z_{i-1} - c_i z_i - w_i^T\hat{\theta} + \sum_{k=1}^{i-1}\left(\frac{\partial\alpha_{i-1}}{\partial x_k}x_{k+1} + \frac{\partial\alpha_{i-1}}{\partial y_r^{(k-1)}}y_r^{(k)}\right)$$

$$-\kappa_i|w_i|^2 z_i + \frac{\partial\alpha_{i-1}}{\partial\hat{\theta}}\Gamma\tau_i + \sum_{k=2}^{i-1}\frac{\partial\alpha_{k-1}}{\partial\hat{\theta}}\Gamma w_i z_k \tag{6}$$

$$\tau_i(\bar{x}_i, \hat{\theta}, \bar{y}_r^{(i-1)}) = \tau_{i-1} + w_i z_i \tag{7}$$

$$w_i(\bar{x}_i, \hat{\theta}, \bar{y}_r^{(i-1)}) = \varphi_i - \sum_{k=1}^{i-1}\frac{\partial\alpha_{i-1}}{\partial x_k}\varphi_k \tag{8}$$

$$i = 1\ldots n \tag{9}$$

where $\bar{x}_i = (x_1, \ldots, x_i)$, $\alpha_0 = 0$, $\tau_0 = 0$, $c_i > 0$. The control law together with the parameter update law render the time derivative of the Lyapunov function

$$V_n = \frac{1}{2} z^T z + \frac{1}{2} \tilde{\theta}^T \Gamma^{-1} \tilde{\theta} \quad \text{with} \quad \tilde{\theta} = \theta - \hat{\theta} \tag{10}$$

negative semidefinite along trajectories of the closed loop system:

$$\dot{V}_n = -\sum_{k=1}^{n} c_k z_k^2 - \sum_{k=i}^{n} \kappa_i |w_i|^2 z_i^2 \le -c_0 |z|^2 \quad \text{where} \quad c_0 = \min_{1 \le i \le n} c_i \tag{11}$$

Our main objective is to improve the transient performance of the closed loop system, in particular with respect to the unknown parameter vector θ which is assumed to be constant with respect to time.

It is a well known fact that for this adaptive control schemes the transient performance can be improved by increasing any of the design parameters c_i, κ_i and Γ. The higher the gain the faster the transient response of the control systems. In practical applications however, high gain should be avoided as there are always unmodelled dynamics or even time delays (related to computer implementation) in the system which may lead to instability if the loop gain is too high. Thus, other strategies of counteracting uncertainties are highly desirable.

Such a strategy is provided by the multiple model switching and tuning approach, where the estimates are taken from a finite set

$$\theta_i, \quad i = 1, \ldots, N.$$

The multiple model observer provides additional information on parameter uncertainies which can then be used to instanteneously reset the parameter estimate $\hat{\theta}$. Suppose the best estimate of the multiple model observer with respect to *prediction performance* is

$$\hat{\theta}^+ = \hat{\theta}_j.$$

Then a decision has to be made whether or not to use this additional information. In the case when the multiple model estimate is used the current continuous estimate $\hat{\theta}^-$ will be discarded and the continuous update law reset to the new value. This resetting decision should not be based on the modelling performance alone. It should also be guaranteed that the control performance and in particular the transient behaviour is improved via resetting.

In between the resetting events the parameter estimate will still be governed by the adaptation law and it will thus be piecewise continuous. This will result in discontinuous control and adaptation laws. Since the state transformation in Eq. (5) is parameterised by $\hat{\theta}$ the states $z_2, \ldots, z_n$ will be discontinuous in time.

In the remainder of the paper the implications of such a resetting strategy will be studied.

3   Stability Analysis of Parameter Resetting

3.1   Sufficient Conditions for Stability

Stability results for discontinuous Lyapunov functions exist, e.g. [10]. For stability it is sufficient that

1. $V(x)$ be continuous with respect to its arguments
2. $V(x)$ is non-increasing along trajectories in between switching events,
3. $V(x^+) \leq V(x^-)$ whenever there is a jump from $x^- = \lim_{t \downarrow t^*} x(t)$ to $x^+ = \lim_{t \uparrow t^*} x(t)$ at some time instant t^*.

Consider the Lyapunov function (10) of the tuning function approach

$$V_n(z, \theta, \hat{\theta}) = \frac{1}{2} z^T z + \frac{1}{2} \tilde{\theta}^T \Gamma^{-1} \tilde{\theta} \quad \text{with} \quad \tilde{\theta} = \theta - \hat{\theta}. \tag{12}$$

For the tuning function approach it can be easily shown that properties 1 and 2 hold due to the stability of the closed loop system when no resetting is applied. When the parameter estimate $\hat{\theta}$ is reset, the state variable z depending on $\hat{\theta}$ changes discontinuously with time. Then, to obtain a sufficient condition for stability it remains to be analysed whether

$$\Delta V_n = V_n(z(\hat{\theta}^+), \theta, \hat{\theta}^+) - V_n(z(\hat{\theta}^-), \theta, \hat{\theta}^-) \leq 0 \tag{13}$$

holds. If this is the case then a resetting of $\hat{\theta}$ from $\hat{\theta}^-$ to $\hat{\theta}^+$ is admissible. In general the state vector z will depend on $\hat{\theta}$ in a nonlinear way. In order to develop some stability criteria the following assumption may be made (it will be shown in later sections how this can be replaced by other assumptions):

Assumption 3.1. *Set the step change in parameter*

$$\Delta \hat{\theta} = \hat{\theta}^+ - \hat{\theta}^-. \tag{14}$$

There exist a matrix-valued function $M(z^-, \hat{\theta}^-, \bar{y}_r^{(i-1)})$ such that

$$\left(z^+\right)^T \left(z^+\right) \leq \left(z^- + M\Delta\hat{\theta}\right)^T \left(z^- + M\Delta\hat{\theta}\right) \tag{15}$$

for all $\Delta \hat{\theta} \in D \subseteq \mathbb{R}^p$.

Under assumption 3.1 the following bound on the step change of the Lyapunov function (10) can be given:

$$\Delta V_n = \left(z^+\right)^T \left(z^+\right) + \left(\theta - \hat{\theta}^+\right)^T \Gamma^{-1} \left(\theta - \hat{\theta}^+\right)$$
$$- \left(z^-\right)^T \left(z^-\right) - \left(\theta - \hat{\theta}^-\right)^T \Gamma^{-1} \left(\theta - \hat{\theta}^-\right) \tag{16}$$

$$\Delta V_n \leq 2 \left[M^T z^- - \Gamma^{-1} \tilde{\theta}^-\right]^T \Delta\hat{\theta} + \Delta\hat{\theta}^T \left[M^T M + \Gamma^{-1}\right] \Delta\hat{\theta} \tag{17}$$

$$\tilde{\theta}^- = \theta - \hat{\theta}^-$$

For positive definite $M^T M + \Gamma^{-1} > 0$ the sufficient condition for stability $\Delta V_n \leq 0$ is satisfied inside the hyper-ellipse

$$2 \left[M^T z^- - \Gamma^{-1} \tilde{\theta}^- \right]^T \Delta \hat{\theta} + \Delta \hat{\theta}^T \left[M^T M + \Gamma^{-1} \right] \Delta \hat{\theta} = 0 \qquad (18)$$

It can be easily verified that even in the case when $\hat{\theta}$ steps from $\hat{\theta}^-$ to the *correct parameter value* $\hat{\theta}^+ = \theta$ the condition for stability is not necessarily satisfied because in this case the requirement would be:

$$2(z^-)^T M \tilde{\theta}^- + (\tilde{\theta}^-)^T (M^T M - \Gamma^{-1}) \tilde{\theta}^- \leq 0. \qquad (19)$$

It has been shown above that the set of admissible parameter changes $\Delta \theta$ depends on the state z and on the parameter error $\tilde{\theta}$. While z^- and z^+ can be computed, additional information on the estimation error is necessary to check the admissibility of $\Delta \theta$. In the remainder of the paper two ways of obtaining the required knowledge of θ will be presented. The first approach is by exploiting properties of the closed loop system while the second approach uses additional information supplied by an multiple observer.

3.2 Reference Trajectory Resetting

The condition (13) on ΔV can be considerably simplified when resetting of the reference trajectory y_r is used in combination with the parameter resetting.

Reference trajectory resetting can be applied most easily in the case where y_r and its derivative are generated by a linear reference model which is driven by some external reference input signal $r(t)$. For the following calculations we assume the existence of a reference model since the states of such a system can be reset directly. In the other case where y_r and its derivatives are generated externally the reset is accomplished by modification of the reference signal using the output $\delta, \delta^{(1)}, \ldots, \delta^{(n-1)}$ of an additional linear asymptotically stable autonomous system $y_{rmod}^{(i)} = y_r^{(i)} + \delta^{(i)}$.

Reference trajectory initialisation is originally a tool for improving the transients in adaptive tuning function control systems [9]. In fact, by resetting the n values $y_r(t^+), \dot{y}_r(t^+), \ldots, y_r^{(n-1)}(t^+)$ an additional degree of freedom is obtained which enables us to set $z^+ = 0$. From Eq. (5) it can be seen that $z^+ = 0$ requires the solution of set of equations

$$y_r^{(i-1)}(t^+) = x_i - \alpha_{i-1}(\bar{x}_1, \ldots, x_{i-1}, \hat{\theta}^+, y_r(t^+), \ldots, y_r^{(i-2)}(t^+)), \quad i = 1, \ldots, n \qquad (20)$$

It can be shown [9] that the solution to these equations does not depend on the controller parameters.

The step change in the Lyapunov function with reference trajectory resetting is

$$\Delta V_n = \left(\theta - \hat{\theta}^+\right)^T \Gamma^{-1} \left(\theta - \hat{\theta}^+\right) - \left(z^-\right)^T \left(z^-\right) - \left(\theta - \hat{\theta}^-\right)^T \Gamma^{-1} \left(\theta - \hat{\theta}^-\right)$$
$$= \Delta\hat{\theta}^T \Gamma^{-1} \Delta\hat{\theta} - 2\left(\tilde{\theta}^-\right)^T \Gamma^{-1} \Delta\hat{\theta} - \left(z^-\right)^T \left(z^-\right) \tag{21}$$

for which we can obtain a controller independent upper bound

$$\Delta V_n \leq \Delta\hat{\theta}^T \Gamma^{-1} \Delta\hat{\theta} - 2\left(\tilde{\theta}^-\right)^T \Gamma^{-1} \Delta\hat{\theta} \tag{22}$$

When trajectory resetting is used, the Lipschitz assumption 3.1 (where M might be difficult to compute) is no longer required because $z^+ = 0$ in Eq. (16).

3.3   Application to a First Order System

Consider the tracking control of the first order system

$$\dot{x}_1 = \varphi_1(x_1)\theta + u \tag{23}$$

An adaptive tuning function controller is simply

$$u = -\varphi_1(x_1)\hat{\theta} - c_1 z_1 - \dot{y}_r \tag{24}$$
$$\dot{\hat{\theta}} = \gamma z_1 \varphi_1(x_1) = \gamma \tau_1 \tag{25}$$
$$z_1 = x_1 - y_r$$

This controller based on the control Lyapunov function

$$V = \frac{1}{2}z_1^2 + \frac{1}{2\gamma}\left(\theta - \hat{\theta}\right)^2 \tag{26}$$

renders the derivative of the Lyapunov function negative semi-definite

$$\dot{V} = -c_1 z_1^2 \leq 0.$$

The closed loop system is given by

$$\dot{z}_1 = -c_1 z_1 + \varphi_1(x_1)\tilde{\theta} \tag{27}$$

The time derivative of the squared error along the solution of (27) is

$$\frac{d}{dt}\left(\frac{1}{2}z_1^2\right) = z_1\dot{z}_1 = -c_1 z_1^2 + z_1\varphi_1(x_1)\tilde{\theta} \tag{28}$$

For the rest of the discussion of the first order case we assume that $\varphi_1(x_1) > 0$. This assumption is not necessary for the approach in general but it simplifies the switching law considerably.

For the first order system (23) and the Lyapunov function (26) we obtain by use of Eq. (16) the following sufficient stability condition:

$$\Delta V = V^+ - V^- = \frac{1}{2\gamma}\left(\hat{\theta}^+ - \hat{\theta}^-\right)^2 - \frac{1}{\gamma}\left(\left(\theta - \hat{\theta}^-\right)\left(\hat{\theta}^+ - \hat{\theta}^-\right)\right) \leq 0 \quad (29)$$

This gives the following bounds on the step change in the parameter estimate:

$$\mathrm{sgn}\left(\Delta\hat{\theta}\right) = \mathrm{sgn}\left(\tilde{\theta}^-\right) \quad (30)$$

$$\left|\Delta\hat{\theta}\right| \leq 2\left|\tilde{\theta}^-\right| \quad (31)$$

In general, condition (31) cannot be verified without additional information on the parameter estimate. However a switching law $S(z_1, \Delta\hat{\theta})$ can be designed such that condition (30) holds.

Using this switching law the parameter resetting law is constructed in the following way

$$\hat{\theta} = \hat{\theta}^- + \left(\hat{\theta}^+ - \hat{\theta}^-\right)S(z_1, \Delta\hat{\theta}) = \hat{\theta}^- + \Delta\hat{\theta}\, S(z_1, \Delta\hat{\theta}) \quad (32)$$

where S assumes the values 1 or 0 according to the following set of inequalities

$$S = 1 \quad \text{whenever} \quad \begin{cases} z_1 > \varepsilon_1 \ \wedge\ \Delta\hat{\theta} > \varepsilon_2 \\ \vee \\ z_1 < -\varepsilon_1 \wedge \Delta\hat{\theta} < -\varepsilon_2 \end{cases}$$

$$S = 0 \quad \text{elsewhere} \quad (33)$$

Condition (32) states that resetting occurs whenever the magnitude of the control error z_1 exceeds some threshold and at the same time there is a significant discrepancy between continuous parameter estimate and multiple model parameter estimate having the same sign as the control error.

Note that due to the assumption that φ is always positive we obtain from the closed loop error equation (27):

$$\dot{z}_1 z_1 > 0 \quad \text{implies} \quad \mathrm{sgn}(\dot{z}_1) = \mathrm{sgn}(\tilde{\theta}) \quad (34)$$

Thus, provided that $|z_1|$ is increasing while it crosses the threshold ε_1 the sign of $\dot{z}_1$ is a direct indicator of the sign of the parameter error $\tilde{\theta}$. In the general case, the sign of φ will be known and the resetting law can be modified accordingly.

This leads us to the following theorem

Theorem 3.2. *1. Consider the first order system (23) together with the continuous control law (24) and the update law (25). Assuming $\varphi_1(x_1) > 0$, $\gamma > 0$ and $c_1 > 0$. If the parameter $\hat{\theta}$ is reset under the condition*

$$z_1\mathrm{sgn}(\dot{z}_1) = \varepsilon_1 \bigwedge z_1\Delta\hat{\theta} > \varepsilon_1\varepsilon_2, \quad \varepsilon_1 > 0, \varepsilon_2 > 0 \quad (35)$$

then, the sign condition (30) is satisfied.

2. *Provided the sign condition is satisfied, then a decrease of V in Equation (26) at the switching instant is obtained provided that*

$$\left|\Delta\hat{\theta}\right| < 2\left|\tilde{\theta}^-\right| \tag{36}$$

holds. Thus a sufficient condition for stability is satisfied.

3. *If to the contrary*

$$\left|\Delta\hat{\theta}\right| \geq 2\left|\tilde{\theta}^-\right| \tag{37}$$

holds then the control error z_1 is driven towards zero as long as $|z_1| > \varepsilon_1$ despite of the increase in value of V.

Proof. The first and second part of the Theorem has been proven above.

If the assumptions of the third part of the theorem hold then, outside $|z_1| > \varepsilon_1$ we have along the solutions of the closed loop equation:

$$\frac{\mathrm{d}}{\mathrm{d}t}\left(\frac{1}{2}z_1^2\right) = z_1\dot{z}_1$$

$$= -c_1z_1^2 + z_1\varphi_1(x_1)\left[\tilde{\theta}^- - \Delta\hat{\theta}S(y, \Delta\hat{\theta})\right]$$

$$\leq -c_1z_1 + |z_1\varphi_1(x_1)|\left[\left|\tilde{\theta}^-\right| - \left|\Delta\hat{\theta}\right|\right] < 0 \tag{38}$$

due to (37) which implies that z_1 is driven towards the origin. ∎

As a remark, one might note, that case 3 of Theorem 3.2 implies stability but possibly with reduced transient performance and chattering.

The negative jump in the Lyapunov function could be interpreted as improved transient performance. This follows from the dependency of transient performance of the tuning function approach on the initial conditions which has been analysed in [9].

3.4   Application to a Second Order System

Consider the second order system with one parameter

$$\dot{x}_1 = x_2 + \varphi(x_1)\theta$$
$$\dot{x}_2 = u. \tag{39}$$

Designing the tuning function controller (2) for such a system requires one backstep. Assuming that the parameter estimate $\hat{\theta}$ can vary discontinuously with time we will thus have also discontinuous changes with time in α_1 and z_2 and in the corresponding Lyapunov function $V = \frac{1}{2}z_1^2 + \frac{1}{2}z_2^2 + \frac{1}{2\gamma}\tilde{\theta}^2$. The step change in the Lyapunov function can be expressed as

$$\Delta V = V^+ - V^- = z_2^-\varphi_1(x_1)\Delta\hat{\theta} + \frac{1}{2}\varphi_1^2(x_1)\Delta\hat{\theta}^2 - \frac{1}{\gamma}\tilde{\theta}^-\Delta\hat{\theta} + \frac{1}{2\gamma}\Delta\hat{\theta}^2$$

$$= \frac{1}{2}\left(\frac{1}{\gamma} + \varphi_1^2(x_1)\right)\Delta\hat{\theta}^2 - \left(\frac{1}{\gamma}\tilde{\theta}^- - z_2^-\varphi(x_1)\right)\Delta\hat{\theta} \tag{40}$$

This corresponds with Assumption 3.1 and Eq. (15) where

$$z^+ = z^- + M\Delta\hat{\theta}$$
$$M = \begin{pmatrix} 0 \\ \varphi_1(x_1) \end{pmatrix}, \qquad M^T M = \varphi_1^2(x_1).$$

The reset conditions discussed in sections 3.3 and 3.4 require the information whether the states of z_1 and z_2 cross some threshold from above or below. No explicit knowledge of the derivatives of the states is required. In case of noisy state measurement multiple crossing of the threshold may occur, however, by imposing an additional threshold on $\Delta\hat{\theta}$ a hysteresis is introduced and chattering cannot occur.

4   Multiple Model Observer (MMO)

As explained above a multiple observer approach can be used to avoid large transient errors in continuous adaptive control. Quite similar to the multiple model estimation described in [2,3,4,7], the idea is to construct a finite set of parallel observers each of which is designed for a fixed parameter value. In its simplest form the MMO constits of a set O of N individual observers o_i each parameterised with a fixed parameter value θ_i. All N observer cover the range of admissible parameter values. Figure (1) shows the structure of a multi-observer parameter estimation. Each of the N observer estimates the states of the system and is driven by the residual $e_{1i} = x_1 - \hat{x}_{1i}$. Since any mismatch between a single observer and the physical system will in general lead to a steady-state estimation error, this error can be used to determine the best observer for the actual system.

Using discontinuous output injection functions is common in sliding mode observers [11]. A hybrid observer using convergence information to switch between several discontinuous output injection functions for nonlinear systems has been reported in [12]. Here, we propose instead to use a set of observers with fixed output injection functions which can have considerably faster transients.

A performance index $Q_i(\hat{x}_i, y)$ is defined for each observer of the set O. The performance index weighs the output error of the observer, thus quantifies the mismatch between the plant and the individual observer. A switching logic L is used to determine the estimate θ_i of the multi-observer O. L satisfies two purposes:

1. selecting the coefficient θ_i corresponding to the observer o_i with the best performance.
2. providing a mechanism that ensures a convergence of the estimator after a finite number of switches.

In order to prevent chattering, two different approaches have been suggested in literature

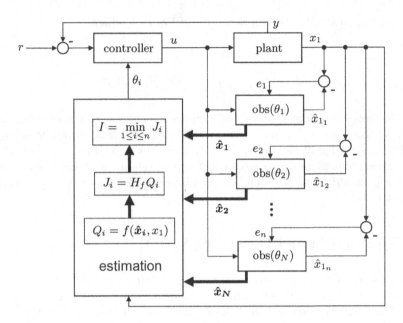

Fig. 1. Multiple model observer parameter estimation

- Dwell time switching [5] where after each switch for a certain period of time switching is prohibited.
- Hysteresis switching [1,13]: Let o_p be the valid observer at time t^- then a switch to a new observer o_i occurs only if $Q_i(t^+)(1+h) < Q_p(t^+)$ where $Q_p(t^+)$ is the current performance of the observer o_p and $h > 0$ is the hysteresis. Otherwise no switching will occur and o_p will remain valid.

4.1 Construction of the Individual Observers in the First Order Case

Consider the system (23) where the parameter θ is treated as an augmented state

$$\dot{x}_1 = \varphi_1(y)\theta + u$$
$$\dot{\theta} = 0$$
$$y = x_1 \tag{41}$$

It is assumed that $\varphi_1(y) > 0$ and that the parameter θ is contained in a closed interval $[\theta_{min}, \theta_{max}]$. The interval is discretised using a set of N parameter values $\theta_{min} < \theta_1 < \theta_2 < \ldots < \theta_N < \theta_{max}$. Each of the N individual observers of the multiple model observer will be centered around one of the discrete parameter values θ_i. For this purpose Eq. (41) is rewritten into

$$\dot{x}_1 = \varphi_1(y)\theta_i + \varphi_1(y)x_{2i} + u$$
$$\dot{x}_{2i} = 0 \tag{42}$$

where $x_{2i} = \theta - \theta_i$. Following the Lyapunov based observer design in [14] we propose to use the following individual nonlinear observer

$$\dot{\hat{x}}_{1i} = \varphi_1(y)\theta_i + 2\omega\varphi_1(y)(y - \hat{x}_{1i}) + u + \varphi_1(y)\hat{x}_{2i}$$
$$\dot{\hat{x}}_{2i} = \omega^2\varphi_1(y)(y - \hat{x}_{1i}), \qquad \omega > 0. \tag{43}$$

Defining the error $e_i = [e_{1i}, e_{2i}]^T = [y - \hat{x}_{1i}, x_{2i} - \hat{x}_{2i}]^T$ the observer will result in the bilinear error dynamics

$$\dot{e}_i = \varphi(y) \underbrace{\begin{pmatrix} -2\omega & 1 \\ -\omega^2 & 0 \end{pmatrix}}_{A} e_i. \tag{44}$$

where the matrix A is Hurwitz and $\varphi(y)$ represents the nonlinearity in the system output. The observer design renders the derivative of the Lyapunov function

$$V_i(e_i) = \frac{1}{2}e_i^T \begin{pmatrix} 1 & 0 \\ 0 & \omega^{-2} \end{pmatrix} e_i \tag{45}$$

negative definite $\dot{V}_i = -2\omega\varphi(y)e_{1i}^2 < 0$.

An important property of the error differential equation (44) is that its solution can be explicitly given. Knowing the measurable output error $e_{1i}(t - T)$ and $e_{1i}(t)$ at some time instant t the parameter estimation error

$$e_{2i}(t) = \frac{1}{y^*}\left[(1 + \omega y^*)e_{1i}(t) - e^{-\omega y^*}e_{1i}(t - T)\right] \tag{46}$$

can be determined, where $y^*(t - T, t) = \int_{t-T}^{t} \varphi_1(y(\tau))d\tau > 0$. Thus, even under observer transients a parameter estimate

$$\hat{\theta}_i = \theta_i + \hat{x}_{2i}(t) + e_{2i}(t) \tag{47}$$

can be computed.

Anti-windup is introduced for the observer state $\hat{x}_{2i}$ by defining the local bounds $\bar{\theta}_i$. The state equation $\dot{\hat{x}}_{2i}$ is set to zero if $\hat{x}_{2i} + \theta_i \notin [\bar{\theta}_{i-1}, \bar{\theta}_i]$ and $(y - \hat{x}_{1i})\hat{x}_{2i} > 0$. Hence, only one individual observer will have an output error converging to zero and consequently a cost index Q_i converging to zero independently of the particular cost index that is used.

The properties of the MMO can be used to derive the following resetting law:

Theorem 4.1. *Consider the control system (23) together with the control law (24), the parameter update law (25) and the MMO (43). Suppose that o_i is the observer that has been selected according to the cost index. Then, setting $\hat{\theta}^+ = \theta_i$ will result in a negative step of the Lyapunov function (26) if*

1. $x_{2i}(\tau)$ *does not saturate within the time intervall* $\tau \in [t - T, t]$.
2. $\bar{\theta}_{i-1} < \hat{\theta}_i < \bar{\theta}_i$.
3. *either (a)* $\hat{\theta}^- - \bar{\theta}_i > \bar{\theta}_i - \theta_i$ *or (b)* $\bar{\theta}_{i-1} - \hat{\theta}^- > \theta_i - \bar{\theta}_{i-1}$.

Proof. If condition 1 of the theorem holds, according to Eqs. (46) and (47) we have

$$\hat{\theta}_i = \theta_i + \hat{x}_{2i}(t) + e_{2i}(y^*(t, t - T), e_{1i}(t), e_{1i}(t - T)). \tag{48}$$

If in addition to this, condition 2 is satisfied, then it can be implied that the real parameter is contained in

$$\bar{\theta}_{i-1} < \theta < \bar{\theta}_i. \tag{49}$$

From condition 3 it follows that either 3a is satisfied in which case we obtain by adding $\hat{\theta}$ to both sides, rearranging and employing (49)

$$-\Delta\hat{\theta} = \hat{\theta}^- - \theta_i < 2(\hat{\theta} - \bar{\theta}_i) \leq 2(\hat{\theta}^- - \theta) = -2\tilde{\theta}^- \tag{50}$$

If on the other hand 3b is satisfied then by subtracting $\hat{\theta}$ from both sides and employing (49)

$$\Delta\hat{\theta} = \theta_i - \hat{\theta}^- < 2(\bar{\theta}_{i-1} - \hat{\theta}^-) \leq 2(\theta - \hat{\theta}^-) = 2\tilde{\theta}^-. \tag{51}$$

Consequently, conditions (30) and (31) are satisfied which is sufficient for stability. ∎

Note that the MMO approach does not rely on assumption 3.1.

5   First Order System

Consider the first order system (41) where $\varphi_1(x_1) = x_1^2$ together with the control law (24) and the update law (25). The design of the MMO (43) is done by using five parameter hypotheses $\theta_i \in \{-10, -5, 0, 5, 10\}$. The parameter estimate $\hat{\theta}$ is reset if the Theorem 4.1 together with (32) hold. The simulation results with and without parameter resetting are depicted in Figure (2). Consider the simulation scenario where the system should follow a ramp signal with the slope 0.1sec^{-1}. The parameter θ jumps at time $t = 4\text{sec}$ from $\theta = 9$ to $\theta = -8$ and at time $t = 7\text{sec}$ to $\theta = 4$. White noise is distributed to the system's output. Note that the scenario differs slightly from the above theoretical considerations where the parameter θ is assumed to be time invariant. The upper left picture in Figure (2) shows the control error for both cases with (fat black line) and without (gray line) using the MMO. The upper right picture shows the control signal respectively. The lower left picture depicts the real parameter value θ (dotted), the estimate of the MMO θ_i (dashed gray), the estimate $\hat{\theta}$ with parameter resetting (solid fat)and $\hat{\theta}$ without resetting (dashed fat line). Using the MMO estimation, $\hat{\theta}$ converges faster to the real parameter value and the control error is removed faster. The lower right picture of Figure (2) shows the faster decrease of the Lyapunov function (26) and the performance enhancement. The simulation shows an improved performance even for step disturbances in the parameter.

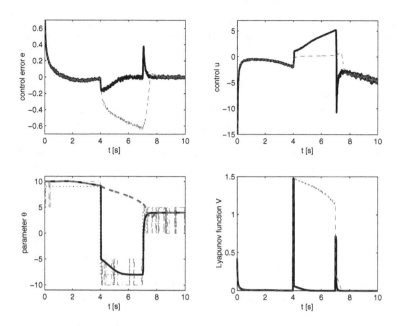

Fig. 2. First order example

6   Conclusions

The presented paper provided an extension of multiple model based adaptive control to the class of parametric strict feedback nonlinear systems. As a main contribution a set of sufficient closed loop stability conditions for resetting tuning function based nonlinear adaptive controllers was given. Also, a fast multiple model observer was introduced, from which even under transient conditions a parameter estimate can be obtained. A first order control example showed that recovering of the control error can be improved after instantaneous changes of the parameter.

Future work will be dedicated to the application of multiple observers in automotive wheel slip control where a fast recovery of wheel slip after instantaneous changes of the tyre/road friction coefficient is required.

Acknowledgments. This work has been supported by the European Union under the ESPRIT LTR funding scheme, project number 28104.

References

1. R. H. Middleton, G. C. Goodwin, D. J. Hill, and D. Q. Mayne, "Design issues in adaptive control," *IEEE Transactions on Automatic Control*, vol. 33, pp. 50–58, 1 1988.

2. K. S. Narendra and J. Balakrishnan, "Improving transient response of adaptive control systems using multiple models and switching," *IEEE Transactions on Automatic Control*, vol. 39, no. 9, pp. 1861–1866, 1994.

3. K. S. Narendra and J. Balakrishnan, "Intelligent control using fixed and adaptive models," in *Proceedings on the 33rd CDC, Lake Buena vista, Florida*, pp. 1680–1685, December 1994.

4. K. S. Narendra, J. Balakrishnan, and M. K. Ciliz, "Adaption and learning using multiple models, switching and tuning," *IEEE Control Systems Magazine*, vol. 15, no. 3, pp. 37–51, 1995.

5. A. S. Morse, "Supervisory control of families of linear set-point controllers–part 1: Exact matching," *IEEE Transactions on Automatic Control*, vol. 41, pp. 1413–1431, October 1996.

6. A. S. Morse, "Supervisory control of families of linear set-point controllers–part 2: Robustness," *IEEE Transactions on Automatic Control*, vol. 42, pp. 1500–1515, 10 1997.

7. K. S. Narendra and C. Xiang, "Adaptive control of discrete–time systems using multiple models," in *Proceedings on the 37th CDC Tampa, Florida*, pp. 3978–3983, December 1998.

8. P. V. Zhivoglyadov, R. H. Middleton, and M. Fun, "Localisation based switching adaptive control for time-varying discrete time systems," *IEEE Transactions on Automatic Control*, vol. 45, no. 4, pp. 752–755, 2000.

9. M. Krstić, I. Kanellakopoulos, and P. Kokotović, *Nonlinear Adaptive Control Design*. John Wiley & Sons Inc., 1995.

10. A. van der Schaft and H. Schumacher, *An Introduction to Hybrid Dynamical Systems*. London: Springer-Verlag, 2000.

11. S. D. V. Utkin, "Sliding mode observers. Tutorial," in *Proceedings of the 34th IEEE CDC, New Orleans*, pp. 3376–3378, 1995.

12. Y. Liu, "Switching observer design for uncertain nonlinear system," in *Proceedings of the 34th IEEE CDC, New Orleans*, pp. 1756–1761, 1995.

13. J. Hespanha, *Logic-Based Switching Algorithms in Control*. Dissertation, Graduate School, Yale University, December 1998.

14. C. de Wit, R. Horowitz, and P.Tsiotras, "Model-based observers for tire/road contact friction prediction," in *New Directions in Nonlinear Observer Design, Springer Lecture Notes on Control and Information Science No. 244*.

Mode Switching Synthesis
for Reachability Specifications

T. John Koo[1,2], George J. Pappas[1], and Shankar Sastry[2]

[1] Department of EE, University of Pennsylvania, Philadelphia, PA 19104
{jkoo,pappasg}@grasp.cis.upenn.edu,
[2] Department of EECS, University of California at Berkeley, Berkeley, CA 94704,
{koo,sastry}@eecs.berkeley.edu

Abstract. In many control applications, a specific set of output tracking controllers of satisfactory performance have already been designed and must be used. When such a collection of *control modes* is available, an important problem is to be able to accomplish a variety of high level tasks by appropriately switching between the low-level control modes. In this paper, we define a concept of control modes, and propose a framework for determining the sequence of control modes that will satisfy reachability tasks. Our framework exploits the structure of output tracking controllers in order to extract a finite graph where the mode switching problem can be efficiently solved, and then implement it using the continuous controllers. Our approach is illustrated on a helicopter example, where we determine the mode switching logic that achieves the high-altitude takeoff task from a hover mode.

1 Introduction

Large scale systems like automated highway systems, air traffic management systems, unmanned aerial vehicles are multi-agent, multi-objective systems that operate in many modes of operation. This results in systems of very high complexity which may dramatically limit the applicability of current analysis and design methods. A natural way to reduce the complexity of system design uses compositional methods which solve a complex problem by decomposing it into a sequence of smaller problems of manageable complexity. For example, in sophisticated flight management systems [3], modern aircraft fly from origin to destination while satisfying a large number of aerodynamic, scheduling, and air traffic constraints by switching among a finite set of *flight modes*, where each flight mode essentially corresponds to a different output tracking controller.

More generally, given a continuous control system, a *control mode* is defined as the operation of the system under a controller that is *guaranteed* to track a certain class of output trajectories. Different outputs of interest correspond to different control modes. Given a set of control modes, the mode switching problem attempts to find a finite *sequence* of the control modes as well as *switching conditions* in order to satisfy various tasks. In this paper, we focus on reachability tasks.

M.D. Di Benedetto, A. Sangiovanni-Vincentelli (Eds.): HSCC 2001, LNCS 2034, pp. 333–346, 2001.

Problem 1. Given a control system and a finite set of control modes for the system, determine whether there exists a finite sequence of modes that will steer the system from an initial control mode to a desired final control mode. If such a sequence exists, then determine the switching conditions.

Clearly, in this setup, many more interesting problems can be formulated. For example one can ask what are the optimal switching conditions, where optimality can mean minimum time, or minimum number of switchings. Furthermore, one can ask whether a set of modes is sufficient for performing a reachability, or more general, task. In this paper, we focus on Problem 1, while setting up the framework for considering these more general questions in the future.

In its full generality, Problem 1 can be tackled using controller synthesis methods for hybrid systems [1,7,12,14]. However, termination conditions for such synthesis procedures are limited [6], and the computational complexity of such procedures could be prohibitive due to nested reachability computations. It is therefore evident that in order to scale our methods to real-life examples, structure must be imposed on the system, and subsequently exploited in our analysis and synthesis methods.

In order to reduce the complexity of the mode switching problem, we start by assuming that output tracking control laws have been designed for each control mode. Feedback greatly simplifies the continuous models in each discrete location since the complexity of the continuous behavior is now reduced to the complexity of the trajectories we design. Therefore, many reachability computations that are required in our approach can be greatly simplified by properly *designing* the desired trajectories. Even though feedback control simplifies the continuous complexity, the problem of having nested reachability computations is still present. In order to avoid such expensive computations, we place a *consistency* condition in our mode switching logic which is reminiscent of the notion of *bisimulation*. We propose an algorithm which given an initial set of control modes, constructs a *control mode graph* which refines the initial control modes but is consistent. Construction of the mode graph can be done off-line or every time a new control mode is designed, allowing the mode switching problem to be efficiently solved on-line, in real time.

2   Problem Formulation

Throughout this paper, we consider a nonlinear system modeled by differential equations of the form

$$\dot{x}(t) = f(x(t)) + g(x(t))u(t), \quad x(t_0) = x_0, \quad t \geq t_0 \tag{2.1}$$

where $x \in \mathbb{R}^n$, $u \in \mathbb{R}^p$, $f(x) : \mathbb{R}^n \to \mathbb{R}^n$ and $g(x) : \mathbb{R}^n \to \mathbb{R}^n \times \mathbb{R}^p$. The system is assumed to be as smooth as needed. We now define a concept of control mode.

Definition 1 (Control Modes). *A control mode, labeled by q_i where $i \in \{1, \ldots, N\}$, is the operation of the nonlinear system (2.1) under a closed-loop feedback controller of the form*

$$u(t) = k_i(x(t), r_i(t)) \qquad (2.2)$$

associated with an output $y_i(t) = h_i(x(t))$ such that $y_i(t)$ shall track $r_i(t)$ where $y_i(t), r_i(t) \in \mathbb{R}^{m_i}$, $h_i : \mathbb{R}^n \to \mathbb{R}^{m_i}$, $k_i : \mathbb{R}^n \times \mathbb{R}^{m_i} \to \mathbb{R}^p$ for each $i \in \{1, \dots, N\}$. We assume that $r_i \in \mathcal{R}_i$, the class of output trajectories associated with the control mode q_i, when the initial condition of the system (2.1) starts in the set $S_i(r_i) \subseteq X_i$, output tracking is guaranteed and the state satisfies a set of state constraints $X_i \subseteq \mathbb{R}^n$.

The trajectory $r_i(t)$ is the desired output trajectory, and $y_i(t)$ is the output vector which shall track $r_i(t)$. Notice that in general the initial set may be a function of the trajectory r_i, thus we denote it as $S_i(r_i)$. This is because even though trajectory tracking controllers are guaranteed to converge for any initial condition, trajectory tracking in the presence of state constraints or input constraints can be guaranteed only if the initial tracking error is sufficiently small. In this paper we are interested in switching between controllers, rather than the design of output tracking controllers. We therefore make the following assumption.

Assumption 1 *For each control mode q_i, $i \in \{1, \dots, N\}$, we assume that a controller of the form (2.2) has been designed which achieves output tracking such that $y_i(t)$ shall track $r_i(t)$ where $r_i \in \mathcal{R}_i \neq \emptyset$, while the state satisfies the set of state constraints $x(t) \in X_i \subseteq \mathbb{R}^n$, when the initial condition of the system (2.1) starts in the set $S_i(r_i) \subseteq X_i \subseteq \mathbb{R}^n$.*

The above assumption is justified given the maturity of output tracking controllers for large classes of linear and nonlinear systems [15]. Based on different design methodologies, the notion of *output tracking* could be different as it could be uniform asymptotic, exponential, etc. Depending on the complexity on the computation, one may choose a specific notion of tracking for solving Problem 1. In order to motivate the discussion, we present a planar helicopter model and a set of controllers in which each controller satisfies Assumption 1 but with different output functions and state constraints.

Example 1. **Multi-Modal Control of a Planar Helicopter Model.** In this example, a helicopter model [4] described in longitudinal and vertical axes with simplified force and moment generation processes is considered. The x, z-axes of the spatial frame are pointing to north and down directions. The body x-axis is defined from the center of gravity to the nose of the helicopter, and body z-axis is pointing down from the center of gravity. The motion of the helicopter is controlled by main rotor thrust, T_M and longitudinal tilt path angle, a_M. The pitch angle is defined by θ. The equations of motion can be expressed as:

$$\begin{bmatrix} \ddot{p}_x(t) \\ \ddot{p}_z(t) \end{bmatrix} = \frac{1}{m} \begin{bmatrix} \cos\theta(t) & \sin\theta(t) \\ -\sin\theta)(t) & \cos\theta(t) \end{bmatrix} \begin{bmatrix} -T_M(t)\sin a_M(t) \\ -T_M(t)\cos a_M(t) \end{bmatrix} + \begin{bmatrix} 0 \\ g \end{bmatrix} \qquad (2.3)$$

$$\ddot{\theta}(t) = \frac{1}{I_y}(M_M a_M(t) + h_M T_M(t) \sin a_M(t)) \qquad (2.4)$$

The state vector and input vector are defined as $x = [p_x, \dot{p}_x, p_z, \dot{p}_z, \theta, \dot{\theta}]^T \in \mathbb{R}^6$ and $u = [T_M, a_M]^T \in \mathbb{R}^2$, respectively.

Control Mode	Output	Reference	Constraint
q_1: Hover	$y_1 = [p_x, p_z]^T$	r_1	X_1
q_2: Cruise	$y_2 = [\dot{p}_x, \dot{p}_z]^T$	r_2	X_2
q_3: Ascend	$y_3 = [\dot{p}_x, \dot{p}_z]^T$	r_3	X_3
q_4: Descend	$y_4 = [\dot{p}_x, \dot{p}_z]^T$	r_4	X_4

Define $X_1 = X_2 = \mathbb{R} \times (\underline{v}_x, \overline{v}_x) \times \mathbb{R} \times (\underline{v}_z, \overline{v}_z) \times (-\pi/2, \pi/2) \times \mathbb{R}$, $X_3 = \mathbb{R} \times (\underline{v}_x^{cr}, \overline{v}_x) \times \mathbb{R} \times (\underline{v}_z, \overline{v}_z^{as}) \times (-\pi/2, \pi/2) \times \mathbb{R}$, and $X_4 = \mathbb{R} \times (\underline{v}_x^{cr}, \overline{v}_x) \times \mathbb{R} \times (\underline{v}_z^{de}, \overline{v}_z) \times (-\pi/2, \pi/2) \times \mathbb{R}$ where $\underline{v}_x < 0 < \underline{v}_x^{cr} < \overline{v}_x$ and $\underline{v}_z < \underline{v}_z^{de} < 0 < \overline{v}_z^{as} < \overline{v}_z$. To satisfy Assumption 1, several control design methodologies can be used to design a controller for each discrete control mode q_i where $i \in \{1, 2, 3, 4\}$. Each controller implementation can be specified as $u = k_i(x, r_i)$ with $r_i \in \mathcal{R}_i$ where $\mathcal{R}_i$ defines the class of admissible output trajectories in mode q_i, and the performance of the closed-loop system can be specified by *initial set*, $S_i(r_i)$, and *flow*, $\phi_i(t, r_i, x_0)$ where $x_0 \in S_i(r_i)$.

Given two control modes, one cannot simply switch from one control mode to another due to incompatible constraints. A natural question is then whether this mode reachability task can be achieved by a *finite sequence* of modes. Based on the above example, we can now define the mode switching problem that we will address in this paper.

Problem 2 (Mode Switching Problem). Given an initial control mode q_S with desired reference r_S, does there exist a sequence of control modes such that the system can reach a desired mode q_F with reference r_F? If so, then determine a mode sequence $q_S \to \cdots q_i \to q_j \cdots \to q_F$ along with trajectories r_i for each control mode q_i, as well as conditions for switching between the control modes.

For the control modes defined in Example 1, one can define a task of having the Hover mode q_1 as an initial mode and ask for a finite control mode sequence to reach the Ascend mode q_3. Any solution to this problem leads to a feasible execution of the task called *high-altitude takeoff* according to flight instruction for helicopter pilots. Note that Problem 2 is a reachability problem. More generally, one can envision more complicated tasks that can be specified in temporal logic, but in this paper we restrict our attention to reachability specifications.

3   A Mode Switching Condition

In its full generality, Problem 2 can be posed as a controller synthesis problem for hybrid systems [7,12]. Such synthesis methods involve *nested*, and possibly *cyclic* reachability computations, where each reachability computation involves computing the capture set of a differential game. Furthermore, termination guarantees for controller synthesis methods are rather limited [6].

In our mode switching problem, however, there is enough structure to take advantage of in order to simplify the complexity of the synthesis task. First of all, the continuous controllers are assumed to have been designed, and therefore we do not have to design the continuous part of the system, but simply determine the mode switching conditions. Furthermore, by imposing certain conditions on the allowable mode switches, we reduce the complexity of the synthesis problem, by *maximally decoupling the discrete and continuous aspects of the synthesis*.

To address the problem, we have to characterize the reachable set of each mode and switching condition among them. Let $\phi_i(t, r_i, x_0)$ denote the *flow* of system (2.1) operating in mode q_i with the controller defined by (2.2) for initial condition x_0, and desired output trajectory r_i.

Definition 2 (Predecessor set). *Given a set $P \subseteq X_i$, a trajectory $r_i \in \mathcal{R}_i$, the reach set $Pre_i(P, r_i)$ in mode q_i is defined by*

$$Pre_i(P, r_i) = \{ \ x_0 \in X_i \ | \ \exists t \geq 0 \ \exists x \in P \ \text{ such that } \ x = \phi_i(t, r_i, x_0) \ \} \quad (3.1)$$

Therefore $Pre_i(P, r_i)$ consists of all states that can reach the set P in mode q_i for a given output trajectory r_i, at *some* future time. Furthermore, because of Assumption 1, we have a guarantee that throughout the whole trajectory, the state constraints are satisfied, that is $\phi_i(t, r_i, x_0) \in X_i$ for all $t \geq 0$.

Given control modes q_i, and q_j, one would typically allow a switch from mode q_i to q_j if during the operation of the system under mode q_i for some $r_i \in \mathcal{R}_i$, the state reaches the allowable set of initial conditions $S_j(r_j)$ for some $r_j \in \mathcal{R}_j$, *i.e.* there exist $r_i \in \mathcal{R}_i$ and $r_j \in \mathcal{R}_j$ such that

$$S_i(r_i) \cap Pre_i(S_j(r_j), r_i) \neq \emptyset. \quad (3.2)$$

If one allows this type of mode switching, then reachability critically depends on the particular choice of initial conditions since some initial conditions in $S_i(r_i)$ may reach the set $S_j(r_j)$ of mode q_j while others may not. If this is the case, then nested reachability computations seem necessary for the solution of the mode switching problem. However, such nested computations can be avoided if one places the following condition on mode switching.

Definition 3 (Consistent mode switching). *Assume that control mode q_i satisfies Assumption 1, that is $\phi_i(t, r_i, x_0) \in X_i$ for all $t \geq 0$ with initial conditions starting from $S_i(r_i)$ where $r_i \in \mathcal{R}_i$. A transition from mode q_i to mode q_j is allowed only if there exist $r_i \in \mathcal{R}_i$ and $r_j \in \mathcal{R}_j$ such that*

$$S_i(r_i) \subseteq Pre_i(S_j(r_j), r_i) \quad (3.3)$$

$$\Leftrightarrow \forall x_0 \in S_i(r_i) \ \exists t \geq 0 \ \exists x \in S_j(r_j) \ \text{ such that } \ x = \phi_i(t, r_i, x_0) \quad (3.4)$$

Therefore, if there exist trajectories r_i (in mode q_i) and r_j (in mode q_j) such that, if the system starts at *any* $x_0 \in S_i(r_i)$, then switching from mode q_i to q_j can occur at some time t such that $\phi_i(t, r_i, x_0) \in S_j(r_j)$. The consistent mode switching condition is shown in Figure 1. The condition expressed in Definition 3

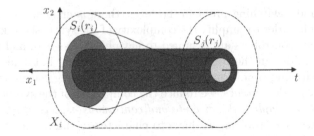

Fig. 1. Visualization of consistent mode switching condition

is a consistency condition that guarantees that our ability to get from mode q_i to mode q_j for the particular trajectory pair (r_i, r_j) is independent of the choice of initial condition in $S_i(r_i)$. The condition is reminiscent of the time-abstract bisimulation property from formal verification [8]. In this case, however, Definition 3 is quite different since no partitioning of the state space is involved. Now define

$$\mathcal{R}^{ij} = \{(r_i, r_j) \in \mathcal{R}_i \times \mathcal{R}_j \mid \text{condition (3.3) is satisfied }\} \qquad (3.5)$$

Hence, if $\mathcal{R}^{ij} \neq \emptyset$, then mode switching from q_i to q_j is possible since there exists a trajectory $r_i \in \mathcal{R}_i$ that will steer the system state to an initial set $S_j(r_j)$ with $r_j \in \mathcal{R}_j$ independently of where we start in $S_i(r_i)$. Therefore, *every* trajectory pair $(r_i, r_j) \in \mathcal{R}^{ij}$ will steer the system from mode q_i to mode q_j. For each $(r_i, r_j) \in \mathcal{R}^{ij}$, the only thing that depends on the initial condition is *when* the state will reach $S_j(r_j)$, but not *if* the state will reach $S_j(r_j)$.

To test the mode switching condition (3.3), and compute the sets $\mathcal{R}^{ij}$, one needs to compute the predecessor set $Pre_i(P, r_i)$. Even though there is extensive research in computing exactly, or approximately such reachable sets [7,9,12, 11,13], there is limited research for parametric reachability computations [10]. Furthermore, in our problem we take advantage of the fact that in each control mode, the output is tracking a reference trajectory r_i. Therefore, by designing trajectories we *design part of the reachable space* whereas the part of the state is not reflected in the output remains within the set X_i. Choosing simple, or better computable, classes of trajectories $\mathcal{R}_i$ will allow us to efficiently perform reachability computations for $Pre_i(P, r_i)$ with parameters $r_i \in \mathcal{R}_i$. To continue discussion, we assume that the Pre_i operators are available to us, and defer this important issue to Section 5.

4   Mode Sequence Synthesis

The mode switching condition (3.3) makes the mode switching problem much more tractable since we can ignore the initial sets and focus on the trajectory sets $\mathcal{R}^{ij}$. Furthermore, the construction presented in this section will abstract the mode switching logic into a purely discrete graph. Therefore one can first determine the sequence of modes using standard algorithms for discrete graph reachability, and then determine the continuous parameters r_i for each mode. This will decouple the discrete from the continuous aspects of the problem, and allow continuous techniques for continuous problems, and discrete techniques for discrete problems.

Given a collection of control modes $Q = \{q_1, \ldots, q_N\}$, the first attempt at solving the mode switching would construct a graph as $(Q, \rightarrow)$ where the vertices of the graph would be the set of control modes Q, and we would define the transition relation $\rightarrow \subseteq Q \times Q$ as

$$(q_i, q_j) \in \rightarrow \quad \Longleftrightarrow \quad \mathcal{R}^{ij} \neq \emptyset \qquad (4.1)$$

In other words, there would be a transition $q_i \rightarrow q_j$, if there exist trajectory pairs $(r_i, r_j) \in \mathcal{R}^{ij}$ that can transfer the system from mode q_i to q_j. This approach, however, leads immediately to problems because if $q_i \rightarrow q_j$ and $q_j \rightarrow q_k$ there may not exists a trajectory r_j, which will take a point $x \in S_i(r_i)$ to $S_k(r_k)$ via $S_j(r_j)$, if $\mathcal{R}^{ij} \cap \mathcal{R}^{jk} = \emptyset$. Hence, transitivity fails, and our mode switching graph is not a *consistent abstraction* as the high level mode switching logic is not implementable at the lower level by the continuous controllers.

In order to obtain a consistent *control mode graph*, denoted as $(Q_c, \rightarrow_c)$, that has feasible low level implementations, our original attempt must be refined. In particular, each control mode q_i gets refined to $2N$ *submodes*, where N submodes stand for entering mode q_i from any other mode q_j, and N more copies for exiting mode q_i towards any other mode q_j. This refinement is illustrated in Figure 2, where mode q_1 has two *submodes*, q_1^{12} which is the operation of the system in mode q_1 on the way to mode q_2, whereas q_1^{21} is the operation of the system under mode q_1 after being in mode q_2. Therefore, this control mode graph has some discrete memory, in the sense that each state represents not only which mode the system is in, but also which mode will either precede it or has preceded it.

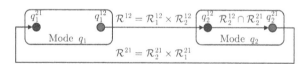

Fig. 2. Refining the mode switching logic by introducing submodes in order to obtain a consistent control mode graph

The N^2 pairwise reachability computations in order to compute the sets $\mathcal{R}^{ij}$, can immediately be embedded in the graph $(Q_c, \rightarrow_c)$. The computed sets $\mathcal{R}^{ij}$ can be used to go from submode q_i^{ij} to q_j^{ij}. After this initial step, the graph contains only isolated transition pairs between different modes as no transitions between submodes are considered.

If the set $\mathcal{R}^{ij}$ can be expressed as a decoupled product of the form $\mathcal{R}^{ij} = \mathcal{R}_i^{ij} \times \mathcal{R}_j^{ij}$ where $\mathcal{R}_i^{ij} = \{r_i \in \mathcal{R}_i \mid (r_i, r_j) \in \mathcal{R}^{ij}\}$ and $\mathcal{R}_j^{ij} = \{r_j \in \mathcal{R}_j \mid (r_i, r_j) \in \mathcal{R}^{ij}\}$, then the choice of trajectory $r_i \in \mathcal{R}_i^{ij}$ in mode q_i would work for any trajectory $r_j \in \mathcal{R}_j^{ij}$ in mode q_j, i.e.

$$\forall r_i \in \mathcal{R}_i^{ij} \; \forall r_j \in \mathcal{R}_j^{ij} \qquad \text{condition (3.3) is satisfied.}$$

This decoupling allows us to consider switching via submodes. In Figure 2, if $\mathcal{R}_2^{12} \cap \mathcal{R}_2^{21}$ is non empty, then that means that there exists a trajectory r_2 which is common for both submodes. Notice that in this case, we do not have to do any reachability computations, we simply have to compute intersections of trajectory sets. Therefore, within each mode, we can check for submode consistency by simply performing set intersections. Since there are maximally $2N$ submodes of N modes, a total of $N(N)^2 = N^3$ intesections must be computed. We now summarize the ideas and present an algorithm for constructing the consistent control mode garph. The algorithm starts with the pairwise reachability computations (3.3,3.5), and performs the submode interconnections.

Algorithm 1 : (Consistent Control Mode Graph)
Input Control Modes $Q = \{q_1, \ldots, q_N\}$
Output Control Mode Graph $(Q_c, \to_c)$
Initialize $Q_c := \emptyset$, $\to_c = \emptyset$

Determine Mode Interconnections
for $i = 1 : N$
    for $j = 1 : N$
        Compute sets $\mathcal{R}^{ij}$ using (3.3) and (3.5)
        if $\mathcal{R}^{ij} = \mathcal{R}_i^{ij} \times \mathcal{R}_j^{ij}$;
        $q_i^{ij} := q_i, \; q_j^{ij} := q_j$,
        $Q_c := Q_c \cup \{q_i^{ij}, q_j^{ij}\}$,
        $\to_c := \to_c \cup \{(q_i^{ij}, q_j^{ij})\}$
        end if
    end for
end for

Determine Submode Interconnections
for $j = 1 : N$
    for all $q_j^{ij} \in \{q^{nj} \in Q_c | \exists n \; s.t. \; (q_n^{nj}, q_j^{nj}) \in \to_c\}$
        for all $q_j^{jk} \in \{q^{jm} \in Q_c | \exists m \; s.t. \; (q_j^{jm}, q_k^{jm}) \in \to_c\}$
            if $\mathcal{R}_j^{ij} \cap \mathcal{R}_j^{jk} \neq \emptyset$;
            $\to_c := \to_c \cup \{(q_j^{ij}, q_j^{jk})\}$
            end if
        end for
    end for
end for

Overall, Algorithm 1 requires N^2 reachability computations for the mode interconnections, and N^3 set intersections for the submode interconnections. After applying Algorithm 1, we obtain a finite *control mode graph* $(Q_c, \rightarrow_c)$ which, as the following proposition shows, is *consistent*.

Proposition 1. *For any* $j \in \{1, \ldots, |Q|\}$, *if* $\exists q_i^{ij} \in \{q_j^{nj} \in Q_c | \exists n$ *such that* $(q_n^{nj}, q_j^{nj}) \in \rightarrow_c\}$, $\exists q_i^{jk} \in \{q_j^{jm} \in Q_c | \exists m$ *such that* $(q_j^{jm}, q_m^{jm}) \in \rightarrow_c\}$ *and* $\mathcal{R}_j^{ij} \cap \mathcal{R}_j^{jk} \neq \emptyset$, *then there exists* $r_i \in \mathcal{R}_i^{ij}$, $r_j \in \mathcal{R}_j^{ij} \cap \mathcal{R}_j^{jk}$ *and* $r_k \in \mathcal{R}_k^{jk}$ *such that*

$$S_i(r_i) \subseteq Pre_i(Pre_j(S_k, r_k), r_j).$$

Proof: Given $(q_i^{ij}, q_j^{ij}) \in \rightarrow_c$, we can pick any $r_i \in \mathcal{R}_i^{ij}$ and since $\mathcal{R}_j^{ij} \cap \mathcal{R}_j^{jk} \neq \emptyset$ we can pick any $r_j \in \mathcal{R}_j^{ij} \cap \mathcal{R}_j^{jk}$, so that $\forall x_0 \in S_i(r_i) \, \exists t \geq 0 \, \exists x \in S_j(r_j)$ such that $x = \phi_i(t, r_i, x_0)$. Then, pick any $r_k \in \mathcal{R}_k^{jk}$, since $(q_j^{jk}, q_k^{jk}) \in \rightarrow_c$, $r_j \in \mathcal{R}_j^{ij} \cap \mathcal{R}_j^{jk}$ and the switching occurs whenever $\phi_i(t, r_i, x_0) \in S_j(r_j)$, it can be easily seen that $\exists s \geq 0 \, \exists y \in S_k(r_k)$ *such that* $y = \phi_j(s, r_j, \phi_i(t, r_i, x_0)) = \phi_j(s, r_j, x)$. The choice on the trajectories is illustrated in Figure 3. Since by Assumption 1, $\phi_i(t, \cdot, \cdot) \in X_i$ and $\phi_j(s, \cdot, \cdot) \in X_j$ for the choice of initial conditions and reference trajectories, by directly applying the definition we have shown the result. $\square$

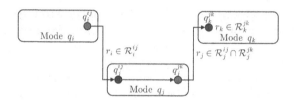

Fig. 3. Graphical illustration of feasible trajectories between control modes.

Without loss of generality, in the following discussion, we assume that the given initial and final control mode in Q can be represented by $q_S \in Q_c$ and $q_F \in Q_c$ respectively. Given an initial control mode $q_S \in Q_c$, the problem of whether we can reach control mode $q_F \in Q_c$, can be efficiently solved using standard reachability algorithms. Furthermore, one can determine the shortest path (minimum number of mode switches) between mode q_S and q_F, in the control mode graph. The structure that we have imposed on our control mode graph, immediately results in the following solution to the mode switching problem.

Theorem 1 (Mode Switching Solution). *Given a collection of control modes* Q, *consider the mode switching Problem 2. Construct the consistent control mode graph* $(Q_c, \rightarrow_c)$ *as described in Algorithm 1. If there exists a path in the consistent control mode graph between* q_S *and* q_F *with feasible trajectories* r_S *and* r_F, *then Problem 2 is solvable.*

Having determined the sequence of modes that can steer our system from q_S to q_F, we are left with the problem of determining the parameters r_i for each mode of the sequence. By construction, such parameters exist and may be selected from the computed sets. Furthermore, it is reasonable to pose the problem of choosing r_i within mode q_i as an optimization or an optimal control problem. A key issue for this approach (as well as for *most* controller synthesis approaches for hybrid systems), is to be able to compute $Pre_i(S_j, r_i)$ in order to check condition 3. This is the focus of the following section of this paper.

5   Reachability Computations

There has been a growing interest recently in computing reachable sets for various classes of systems [9,11,7,13]. In particular, the approach of [9] has been extended to classes of parametric linear control systems [10], which is highly relevant for computing the operator (3.1).

In our case, however, the continuous dynamics are those of output-tracking, closed-loop systems. Therefore part of the state is forced to converge to a trajectory that we get to design, and part of the trajectory is guaranteed to satisfy state constraints. This gives us the opportunity to obtain very reasonable approximations of the reachable sets, and even *design reachable sets* by appropriately designing output trajectories. The following example illustrates how continuous controller design results in reachability computations which are very easy to check.

Example 2. **Multi-Modal Control of a Helicopter Model(Continued)** Reconsider the four control modes shown in Example 1. We first present the controller design to illustrate how to compute the reachable sets, then we show how to check the consistent mode switching condition between control modes. In this example, we assume that all output trajectories are *constant* trajectories, therefore, all controllers are setpoint regulators. Choosing computable classes of trajectories makes the reachability computations simpler.

Given the specifications for the control modes, a nonlinear control scheme [5] based on outer flatness is applied for the design of the controllers. For each mode, the closed-loop dynamics with states defined by $x_{ex} = [p_x, \dot{p}_x, p_z, \dot{p}_z, \theta, \dot{\theta}, T_M, a_M]^T \in \mathbb{R}^8$ can be decoupled into an inner system and two outer subsystems which specify the dynamics in x and z directions. In the following presentation, the Hover mode is presented to illustrate how the reachable set can be computed.

For q_1, the output tracking controller is designed such that $y_1(t)$ shall track $r_1 = [r_{1x}, r_{1z}]^T$ and the output tracking error is uniformly ultimately bounded. Furthermore, because of satisfying Assumption 1, the controller is designed with initial set $S_1(r_1) = B^1([r_{1x}, 0]^T, \epsilon_{1x}) \times B([r_{1z}, 0]^T, \epsilon_{1z}) \times S_{in}$ where $r_1 \in \mathcal{R}_1 = \mathbb{R}^2$, $\epsilon_{1x}, \epsilon_{1z} > 0$ and $S_{in} \subseteq (-\pi/2, \pi/2) \times \mathbb{R}^3$ such that for $x(t_0) \in S_1(r_1)$ then

$$\begin{cases} \|e_{1x}(t)\| \le M_{1x} \exp(-\alpha_{1x}t)(\|e_{1x}(t_0)\| + \delta_{1inx}), \\ \|e_{1z}(t)\| \le M_{1z} \exp(-\alpha_{1z}t)(\|e_{1z}(t_0)\| + \delta_{1inz}), \quad \text{and} \\ x_{in} \in X_{in}, \ \forall t_0 \le t < t_0 + T_1; \end{cases} \begin{cases} \|e_{1x}(t)\| \le \delta_{1x}, \\ \|e_{1z}(t)\| \le \delta_{1z}, \\ x_{in} \in S_{in}, \ \forall t \ge t_0 + T_1 \end{cases}$$

$$(5.1)$$

---

[1] $B(r, \epsilon) = \{\eta | \ \|\eta - r\| < \epsilon\}$.

for some T_1 M_{1x}, M_{1z}, α_{1x}, α_{1z}, δ_{1inx}, δ_{1inz}, δ_{1x}, $\delta_{1z} > 0$. In above, $e_{1x} = [p_x - r_{1x}, \dot{p}_x]^T$, $e_{1z} = [p_z - r_{1z}, \dot{p}_z]^T$, and $x_{in} = [\theta, \dot{\theta}, T_M, a_M]^T$. Equation (5.1) explicitly over specifies the reachable set of the mode q_1 by examing the stability property. For other modes, although the control designs are slightly modified for tracking different outputs, the reachable sets of other modes are similarly computed. In Figure 4, we show the inital sets of all the control modes by

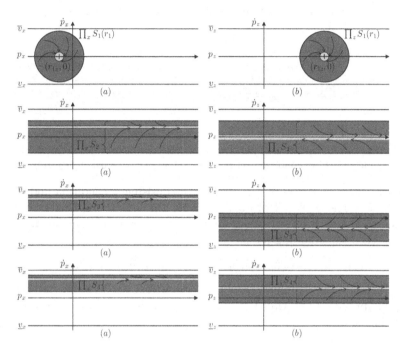

Fig. 4. Projection of $S_1(r_1)$, $S_2(r_2)$, $S_3(r_3)$, and $S_4(r_4)$ onto: (a) $p_x - \dot{p}_x$ plane; (b) $p_z - \dot{p}_z$ plane

projecting them onto $p_x - \dot{p}_x$ plane and $p_z - \dot{p}_z$ plane where the projection operator is defined as $\Pi_i : x_{ex} \mapsto (p_i, \dot{p}_i)$ for $i \in \{x, z\}$. In summary, the control modes can be specified by

Control Mode	Trajectory Set	Initial Set
q_1	$\mathcal{R}_1 = \mathbb{R}^2$	$S_1 = B(0,4) \times B(0,4) \times S_{in}$
q_2	$\mathcal{R}_2 = [-3,3] \times \{0\}$	$S_2 = \mathbb{R} \times (-3.5, 3.5) \times (-3.5, 3.5) \times S_{in}$
q_3	$\mathcal{R}_3 = [2,4] \times [-3,0]$	$S_3 = \mathbb{R} \times (1.5, 4.5) \times (-3.5, 0.5) \times S_{in}$
q_4	$\mathcal{R}_4 = [2,4] \times [0,3]$	$S_4 = \mathbb{R} \times (1.5, 4.5) \times (-0.5, 3.5) \times S_{in}$

where $S_{in} = B(0, 0.2)$, $X_{in} = (-\pi/2, \pi/2) \times \mathbb{R}^3$ and the associated parameters are defined as $\underline{v}_x = -6$, $\underline{v}^{cr} = 1$, $\overline{v}_x = 6$, $\underline{v}_z = -6$, $\overline{v}_z^{as} = 1$, $\underline{v}_z^{de} = -1$, $\overline{v}_z = 6$.

Given the set of control modes, we generated the consistent control mode graph by applying Algorithm 1. In Figure 5, we illustrate the idea of computing the reachable sets on $p_x - \dot{p}_x$ plan. One can easily see the advantage of using feedback, since it is straight forward not only to check the consistent mode switching condition but also to determine the feasible range of trajectory, that is compute the sets $\mathcal{R}^{ij}$. In particular consider the pair (q_1, q_2), that is the transition from hover to cruise. As can be seen from the left side of Figure 5, the consistency condition is trivially satisfied since the ball $S_1(r_1)$ will *eventually* shrink towards the setpoint $(r_{1x}, 0)$, and as a result, will be totally contained inside $S_2(r_2)$ for any r_2. Therefore, in this case $\mathcal{R}^{12} = \mathcal{R}_1 \times \mathcal{R}_2$. Therefore,

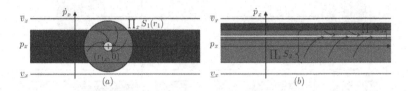

Fig. 5. Graphical illustration of performing reachability computation for checking consistent mode switching condition on $p_x - \dot{p}_x$ plane: (a) $q_1 \rightarrow q_2$; (b) $q_2 \rightarrow q_3$

feedback allows us to check very easily the consistency condition and compute the sets $\mathcal{R}^{ij}$. The right side of Figure 5 shows the similar graphical computation for the mode transition (q_2, q_3), from cruise to ascend. In a similar manner, we have checked the following pairs,

$$\{(q_1, q_2), (q_2, q_2), (q_2, q_3), (q_2, q_4), (q_3, q_2), (q_3, q_3), (q_3, q_4), (q_4, q_2), (q_4, q_3), (q_4, q_4)\}$$

All of the above reachability computations were extremely simple to check. The result of applying Algorithm 1 is summarized in the control mode graph that is shown in Figure 2.

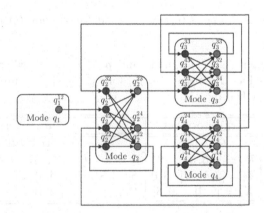

Fig. 6. Consistent control mode graph for the multi-modal helicopter control example

Recall the *high-altitude takeoff* task, which is the task of having the Hover mode q_1 as an initial mode and ask for a finite control mode sequence to reach the Ascend mode q_3. We can now see that from Figure 2 that q_1 has $\{q_1^{12}\}$ as a submode, and $q_3 = \{q_3^{23}, q_3^{43}, q_3^{32}, q_3^{34}\}$, and there exit many paths which are feasible for achieving the task. However, $q_1^{12} q_2^{12} q_2^{23} q_3^{23}$ gives a solution to the task with the minimum number of mode switches, $i.e.$, $q_1 \rightarrow q_2 \rightarrow q_3$. Given a cost function with respect to the continuous variables, the performance of the sequence can now be optimized with respect to the feasible trajectories. We have therefore decoupled the problem in a purely discrete graph search problem, and a collection of continuous designs within each mode.

Simulation results of the controlled system based on the selected sequence are shown in Figure 2. In the simulation, we can choose $r_1 = [0\ 0]^T \in \mathcal{R}_1^{12}$, $r_2 = [2\ 0]^T \in \mathcal{R}_2^{12} \cap \mathcal{R}_2^{23}$ and $r_3 = [3\ -1]^T \in \mathcal{R}_3^{23}$. The initial conditions of the outer system are $p_x(0) = -2$, $\dot{p}_x(0) = -0.2$, $p_z(0) = 1$, $\dot{p}_z(0) = 0.5$. The initial condition of the inner system, $x_{in}(0) \in S_{in}$. Mode switchings occur at $t = 20$ for $q_1 \rightarrow q_2$ and at $t = 45$ for $q_2 \rightarrow q_3$.

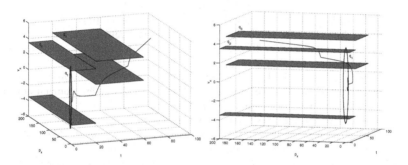

Fig. 7. Projected trajectories of the helicopter along with the initial sets of the next control modes from different view angles are shown. Notice that immediate transition $q_2 \rightarrow q_3$ after $q_1 \rightarrow q_2$ is not allowed until $x(t)$ enters the initial set $S_3(r_3)$.

6   Conclusion

In this paper, we have considered the mode switching problem among a collection of output tracking controllers for nonlinear systems. Our approach consists of extracting a finite graph which refines the original collections of modes, but is consistent with the physical system. Extracting a finite graph critically depends on the fact the closed loop, output tracking controllers reduce the complexity of the model to the complexity of the output trajectories.

Even though, our framework reduces the continuous complexity so that many of the computations can be done by hand, obtaining a consistent mode graph for a large scale helicopter or aircraft (a Boeing 747 has approximately 500 modes) will clearly require the development of a computational tool. Such a mode switching tool can be used off-line for synthesizing the mode switching logic every time a new mode is designed. The control mode graph can then be used on-line for efficient and dependable real-time mode switching.

Acknowledgments. The authors would like to thank Paulo Tabuada for extremely intense discussions on the subject. This work is partially supported by the DARPA SEC grant, F33615-98-C-3614, DARPA MoBIES grant F33615-00-C-1707, DARPA JFACC grant N66001-99-C-8510, and the University of Pennsylvania Research Foundation.

References

1. A. Balluchi, L. Benvenuti, M.D. Di Benedetto, C. Pinello, and A.L. Sangiovanni-Vincentelli, Automotive engine control and hybrid systems: challenges and opportunities, *Proceedings of the IEEE*, 88(7):888 -912, July 2000.
2. T. J. Koo, S. Sastry. Output Tracking Control Design of a Helicopter Model Based on Approximate Linearization. In *Proceedings of the 37th Conference on Decision and Control*, pp.3635-40, Tampa, Florida, December 1998.
3. T. J. Koo, B. Sinopoli, A. Sangiovanni-Vincentelli, and S. Sastry. A Formal Approach to Reactive System Design: A UAV Flight Management System Design Example. In *Proceedings of IEEE International symposium on Computer-Aided Control System Design* Kohala Coast, Hawaii. September 1999.
4. J. Liu, X. Liu, T. J. Koo, B. Sinopoli, S. S. Sastry, and E. A. Lee. Hierarchical Hybrid System Simulation. In *Proceedings of the 38th Conference on Decision and Control*, Phoenix, Arizona. December 1999.
5. O. Shakernia, Y. Ma, T. J. Koo, and S. Sastry, *Landing an Umanned Air Vehicle: Vision Based Motion Estimation and Nonlinear Control*, Asian Journal of Control, Vol. 1, No.3, pp. 128-145, September 1999.
6. Omid Shakernia, George J. Pappas, Shankar Sastry, *Decidable Controller Synthesis for Classes of Linear Systems*, Hybrid Systems : Computation and Control, Lecture Notes in Computer Science, volume 1790, pages 407-420, 2000.
7. J. Lygeros, C. Tomlin, S. Sastry. Controllers for Reachability Specifications for Hybrid Systems, Automatica, Volume 35, Number 3, March 1999.
8. R. Milner. Communication and Concurrency, Prentice Hall, 1989.
9. G. Lafferriere, G.J. Pappas, S. Yovine. Reachability Computation for Linear Hybrid Systems, In Proceedings of the 14th IFAC World Congress, volume E, pages 7-12, Beijing, 1999.
10. G. Lafferriere, G.J. Pappas, and S. Yovine. Symbolic Reachability Computations for Families of Linear Vector Fields, Journal of Symbolic Computation, To appear.
11. A.B. Kurzhanski, P.Varaiya, Ellipsoidal Techniques for Reachability Analysis, Hybrid Systems : Computation and Control, Lecture Notes in Computer Science, 2000.
12. E. Asarin, O. Bournez, T. Dang, O. Maler, and A. Pnueli, Effective Synthesis of Switching Controllers for Linear Systems, Proceedings of the IEEE, 88(2):1011-1025.
13. A. Chutinan, B.H. Krogh, Verification of polyhedral-invariant hybrid systems using polygonal flow pipe approximations, Hybrid Systems : Computation and Control, Lecture Notes in Computer Science, 1999.
14. I. Kolmanovsky, E. G. Gilbert. Multimode Regulators for Systems with State & Control Constraints and Disturbance Inputs. In *Lecture Notes in Control and Information Sciences 222, Control Using Logic-Based Switching*, A. Stephen Morse(Ed.),pp. 104-117, Springer-Verlag, London, 1997.
15. S. Sastry. *Nonlinear Systems: Analysis, Stability, and Control*. Springer-Verlag, New York, 1999.

Characterization of Stabilizing Switching Sequences in Switched Linear Systems Using Piecewise Linear Lyapunov Functions*

Xenofon D. Koutsoukos[1] and Panos J. Antsaklis[2]

[1] Xerox Palo Alto Research Center
3333 Coyote Hill Road, Palo Alto, CA 94304, USA
koutsouk@parc.xerox.com
[2] Department of Electrical Engineering
University of Notre Dame, Notre Dame, IN 46556, USA
antsaklis.1@nd.edu

Abstract. In this paper, the stability of switched linear systems is investigated using piecewise linear Lyapunov functions. Given a switched linear system, we present a systematic methodology for computing switching laws that guarantee stability based on the matrices of the system. We assume that each individual subsystem is stable and admits a piecewise linear Lyapunov function. Based on these Lyapunov functions, we compose "global" Lyapunov functions that guarantee stability of the switched linear system. A large class of stabilizing switching sequences for switched linear systems is characterized by computing conic partitions of the state space. The approach is applied to both discrete-time and continuous-time switched linear systems.

1   Introduction

In this paper, we study the stability of continuous and discrete-time switched linear systems using piecewise linear Lyapunov functions and we *identify classes of switching sequences that result in stable trajectories*. The main motivation behind this problem is that it is often easier to find switching controllers than to find a fixed controller. In the case when we have multiple control objectives, we may design a continuous controller for each control objective, and control the behavior of the plant by switching between different controllers. For example, in the control of the longitudinal dynamics of an aircraft with constrained angle of attack, the control objective is twofold: track the pilot's reference normal acceleration while maintaining a safety constraint in the angle of attack [8]. A continuous feedback control law can be easily designed for each control objective resulting in two asymptotically stable subsystems and a switching mechanism can be used to simultaneously achieve both objectives. Such a switching system might become unstable for certain switching sequences, even if all the individual

---

* The partial financial support of the National Science Foundation (ECS99-12458) and the Army Research Office (DAAG55-98-1-0199) is gratefully acknowledged.

M.D. Di Benedetto, A. Sangiovanni-Vincentelli (Eds.): HSCC 2001, LNCS 2034, pp. 347–360, 2001.

subsystem are stable (see for example [8]). For such problems, it is important to characterize switching sequences that result in stable trajectories.

Stability of switched systems has been studied extensively in the literature; see for example [8,16,17] and the references therein. Sufficient conditions for uniform stability, uniform asymptotic stability, exponential stability and instability were established in [22]. Necessary conditions (converse theorems) for some of the above stability results have also been established. Analysis tools for switched and hybrid systems based on multiple Lyapunov functions were presented in [5]. Stability analysis of switched systems is usually carried out using a Lyapunov-like function for each subsystem [8]. These Lyapunov functions are pieced together in some manner in order to compose a Lyapunov function that guarantees that the energy of the overall system decreases to zero along the state trajectories of the system. The application of the theoretical results to practical hybrid systems is accomplished usually using a linear matrix inequality (LMI) problem formulation for constructing a set of quadratic Lyapunov-like functions [12,21]. Existence of a solution to the LMI problem guarantees that the hybrid system is stable. However, in order to formulate the LMI problem, a partition of the state space and therefore a switching law must be known a priori. Usually, such a partition consists of a set of ellipsoidal regions derived by exploiting the physical insight for the particular application. Although, the LMI approach for hybrid system stability is computationally efficient, it is based only on sufficient conditions and more importantly, it relies on a particular partition chosen by the designer.

In order to investigate the stability properties of practical hybrid systems, there is an important need to characterize partitions of the state space that lead to stable trajectories based on the system parameters. Such partitions can be used very efficiently for the design of switching control laws that guarantee stability of the overall system. In our approach, we characterize a large class of switching sequences that result in stable trajectories. Given a switched linear system, we present a systematic methodology for computing switching laws based on the system parameters that guarantee stability. We assume that each individual subsystem is stable and admits a piecewise linear Lyapunov function. Based on these Lyapunov functions, we compose "global" Lyapunov functions that guarantee stability of the switched linear system. The main contribution of this work is that based on the piecewise linear Lyapunov functions we construct a conic partition of the state space that is used to characterize a large class of switching laws that result in stable trajectories.

It should be noted that the problem considered in this paper has been addressed using multiple Lyapunov function tools under the assumption that switching among stable systems is slow enough [8,16]. Here, we consider piecewise linear Lyapunov functions and we develop a systematic approach to characterize stabilizing switching sequence that offers a significant advantage. Individual piecewise linear Lyapunov functions are "pieced together" in a systematic way and they result in a conic partition of the state space that can be used very efficiently for the design of the switching control law. Note that the paper reports results from [14] and that early results for the discrete-time case have been reported in [15].

The paper is organized as follows. In Section 2, the problem of identifying stabilizing switching sequences is described. Section 3 presents the necessary background for piecewise linear Lyapunov functions. The emphasis is put on computational methods for constructing such Lyapunov functions. The technical results for the characterization of stabilizing switching sequences are presented in Section 4. The application of the methodology to continuous-time switched linear systems is presented in Section 5. Finally, concluding remarks are presented in Section 6.

2   Problem Statement

In this section, we consider discrete-time switched linear systems described by

$$x(t+1) = A_q x(t), \quad q \in Q = \{1, \ldots, N\} \tag{1}$$

where $x(t) \in \Re^n, t \in \mathbf{Z}^+$ (the set of nonnegative integers) and $A_q \in \Re^{n \times n}$.

The mathematical model described by (1) represents the continuous (state) portion of a piecewise linear hybrid dynamical system. The particular mode q at any given time instant may be selected by a decision-making process. In this paper, we represent such a decision-making process by a switching law of the form

$$q(t+1) = \delta(q(t), x(t)). \tag{2}$$

Given $x(t)$, the next state is computed using the mode $q(t)$, that is $x(t+1) = A_{q(t)} x(t)$. The function $\delta : Q \times \Re^n \to \Re^n$ is discontinuous with respect to x. A switching law is defined here using a partition of the state space.

Our objective is to investigate the stability of the switched linear system (1) under the switching law (2). Note that the origin $x_e = 0$ is an equilibrium for the system (1). Furthermore, for a particular switching law, the switched system (1) can be viewed as a special case of a time-varying linear system, and therefore the usual definitions of stability can be used; see for example [1].

3   Piecewise Linear Lyapunov Functions

In this section, we briefly present some background material necessary for the stability analysis of switched linear systems presented later in this paper. We consider the discrete-time linear system

$$x(t+1) = Ax(t) \tag{3}$$

where $x(t) \in \Re^n$ and $A \in \Re^{n \times n}$.

Definition 1. *A nonempty set $P \subset \Re^n$ is said to be (positively) invariant for the system (3) if $x(0) \in P$ implies that $x(t) \in P$ for every $t \in (\mathbf{Z}^+) \mathbf{Z}$.*

In the case when the system admits a positively invariant polyhedral set P containing the origin a Lyapunov function can be constructed by considering the *Minkowski functional (gauge function)* of P; see for example [3]. For bounded invariant polyhedral sets this is accomplished as follows (the extension to unbounded polyhedral sets is straightforward):

Let F_i be a face of a polytope and consider the corresponding hyperplane H_i as shown in Fig. 1. The hyperplane can be described (perhaps after normalization) by $H_i = \{x \in \Re^n : \langle x, w_i \rangle = 1\}$. where $w_i \in \Re^n$ is the gradient vector of the hyperplane and $\langle \cdot, \cdot \rangle$ denotes the inner product.

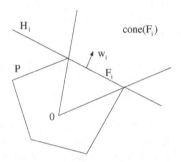

Fig. 1. A polytope P, a face F_i and its corresponding hyperplane H_i.

Since the set P includes an open neighborhood of the origin, $\Re^n$ can be partitioned into a finite number of cones defined as follows. Each face F of the polytope can be described as the convex hull of its extreme points $f_j \in \Re^n$, $j = 1, \ldots, r$. A finitely generated cone can be defined for the face F by

$$\mathrm{cone}(F) = \{x \in \Re^n : x = \sum_{j-1}^{r} \alpha_j f_j, \ \alpha_j > 0, \ j = 1, \ldots, r\}. \tag{4}$$

Consider a polytope $P \subset \Re^n$ and assume that $0 \in \mathrm{int}(P)$. The Minkowski functional of P is defined by

$$V(x) = \inf\{\rho > 0 | x \in \rho P\} \tag{5}$$

where $\rho P = \{\rho x | x \in P\}$. Consider a particular face F_i and the corresponding cone. Since $F_i \in \partial P$ there exist unique $\rho > 0$ and $\hat{x} \in F_i$ such that for any $x \in \mathrm{cone}(F_i)$ we have $x = \rho \hat{x}$ and the Minkowski functional can be computed by

$$V(x) = \frac{\|x\|_2}{\|\hat{x}\|_2} = \rho = \rho \langle \hat{x}, w_i \rangle = \langle x, w_i \rangle \tag{6}$$

since $\langle \hat{x}, w_i \rangle = 1$. Therefore, for $x \in \mathrm{cone}(F_i)$, the Lyapunov function induced by the set P can be written as $V(x) = \langle x, w_i \rangle$. Consequently, the Lyapunov function induced by P can be computed for $x \in \Re^n$ by

$$V(x) = \max_{1 \le i \le m} \langle x, w_i \rangle. \tag{7}$$

A special case of piecewise linear Lyapunov functions arise when the positively invariant set P of Definition 1 is centrally symmetric. In this case, the Lyapunov function $V(x)$ can be represented using the infinity norm. Furthermore, there exists a class of linear systems for which such a Lyapunov function can be computed very efficiently. Consider the following Lyapunov function candidate $V(x) = \|Wx\|_\infty$ where $W \in \Re^{m \times n}$ and $\| \cdot \|_\infty$ denotes the infinity norm defined by $\|x\|_\infty = \max_{1 \le i \le n} |x_i|$.

Theorem 1. *[2] $V(x) = \|Wx\|_\infty$ is a Lyapunov function for the system (3) if and only if there exist a matrix $Q \in \Re^{m \times m}$ such that $WA - QW = 0$ and $\|Q\|_\infty < 1$.*

It should be noted that similar results have been established for differential and difference inclusions in [19].

3.1   Computation of Piecewise Linear Lyapunov Functions

In order to study the stability properties of the switched linear system (1) we assume that each individual subsystem admits such a piecewise linear Lyapunov function. The efficient computation of each Lyapunov function is very important for the application of the proposed methodology to practical hybrid systems. In the previous section, we described a class of piecewise linear functions induced by polyhedral sets that contain the origin. A Lyapunov function for each individual subsystem can be defined by computing a positively invariant polyhedral set for the subsystem. In the following, we briefly give the necessary background for the computation of these piecewise linear Lyapunov functions. First, we briefly describe an important class of systems for which positively invariant polyhedral sets and the corresponding Lyapunov functions can be computed by a similarity transformation [2]. In this case, the Lyapunov functions can be described using the infinity norm. Second, we outline an algorithm [6,7] which can be used for the computation of general positively invariant polyhedral sets.

A class of linear systems for which such a Lyapunov function can be computed very efficiently is presented in [2]. Consider the system $x(t+1) = Ax(t)$ where the eigenvalues of the matrix A are located in the complex plane within the square defined by the vertices $(1,0)$, $(0,i)$, $(-1,0)$, and $(0,-i)$. Then, the following result is shown.

Corollary 1. *[2]. If all the eigenvalues $\lambda_i = \mu_i \pm \sigma_i$ of the nth order linear system $x(t+1) = Ax(t)$ are in the open square $|\mu_i| + |\sigma_i| < 1$, then there exists a matrix $W \in \Re^{n \times n}$ with $rankW = n$ such that the polyhedral set $P = \{x \in \Re^n : \|Wx\|_\infty < 1\}$ is a positively invariant set for the system.*

The matrix W can be computed as the solution to the matrix equation

$$WA - QW = 0 \tag{8}$$

with the condition $\|Qx\|_\infty < 1$. It is well known [10] that if the matrices A and Q do not have common eigenvalues then (8) has only the trivial solution $W = 0$.

The important assumption in Corollary 1 is that $W \in \Re^{n \times n}$ with rank$W = n$. In this case, W can be computed as the similarity transformation matrix by which A is transformed to the *Real Jordan Canonical Form* [10].

We presented a class of discrete-time linear systems for which positively invariant polyhedral sets are described by the Lyapunov function $V(x) = \|Wx\|_\infty$ and can be computed very efficiently. However, it should be noted that in our stability analysis for switched linear systems, it is not necessary for the individual invariant polyhedral sets to be centrally symmetric. Positively invariant polyhedral sets for stable discrete-time systems can be determined using *computer generated Lyapunov functions* [6]. The class of computer generated Lyapunov functions has been used for stability analysis of nonlinear systems in [6,7,18,20]. The main idea is to construct a Lyapunov function that guarantees the stability of a set of matrices that is determined by applying Euler's discretization method to a system of nonlinear differential equations.

Our approach here is to use a computer generated Lyapunov function for each individual subsystem. Consider the matrix $A \in \Re^{n \times n}$ and let $P_0 \subset \Re^n$ be a bounded polyhedral region of the origin. We denote the convex hull of P by conv(P). Following [6] we define

$$P_k = \text{conv}\left(\bigcup_{i=0}^{\infty} A^i P_{k-1}\right) \tag{9}$$

and

$$P^* = \bigcup_{i=0}^{\infty} P_i. \tag{10}$$

The following results may be found in [6]: First, the matrix A is stable if and only if P^* is bounded. Second, if A is stable then each set P_k can be computed by P_{k-1} using finitely many iterations. Furthermore, it is shown in [7] that if there exists constant $K \in \Re$ such that the eigenvalues of A satisfy the condition $|\lambda_i| \leq K < 1$, then the set P^* is finitely computable. In this case the set P^* is polyhedral as the convex hull of finitely many points. Furthermore, P^* is a positively invariant set of the system. Then, a piecewise linear Lypunov function can be defined as the Lypunov function induced by the set P^*.

4   Stabilizing Switching Sequences

In this section, we present an approach based on multiple Lyapunov functions for the stability analysis of the switched system (1). The main contribution is an efficient characterization of a class of switching laws of the form (2) which guarantee the stability of the system. We assume that each individual subsystem admits a positively invariant polyhedral set that contains the origin which is described by

$$P_q = \{x \in \Re^n : W^q x < \bar{1}\} \tag{11}$$

where $W^q \in \Re^{m_q \times n}$ and $\bar{1} = [1, \ldots, 1]^T \in \Re^n$. In view of the above results, such a polyhedral set can be computed if the there exists constant $K \in \Re$ such that the eigenvalues of A_q satisfy the condition $|\lambda_i| \leq K < 1$. We denote the rows of the matrix W^q by $w_i^q \in \Re^n$, $i = 1, \ldots, m_q$. The Lyapunov function induced by the set P_q can be described by

$$V_q(x) = \max_{1 \leq i \leq m_q} \langle x, w_i^q \rangle. \tag{12}$$

We consider a class S of switching sequences that can be described by $s = (q_0, t_0), (q_1, t_1), \ldots, (q_j, t_j), \ldots, \ x(t_0) = x_0$. It is assumed that if s is finite then $t_{j+1} = \infty$ and that $q_j \neq q_{j+1}$. Such a sequence can be generated by the switching law $q_j(t_j + 1) = \delta(q_{j-1}(t_j), x(t_j))$, $j = 1, 2, \ldots$.

Proposition 1. *Consider a switching sequence* $s \in S$. *If* $V_{q_j}[x(t_j + 1)] \leq V_{q_{j-1}}[x(t_j)]$, $j = 1, 2, \ldots$, *then the switched system* $x(t + 1) = A_q x(t)$ *is stable in the sense of Lyapunov.*

Proof. Consider the multiple Lyapunov function defined by

$$V[x(t)] = V_{q_j}[x(t)], \ \ t_j < t \leq t_{j+1} \tag{13}$$

then by the definition of V_{q_j} we have that for every $t > t_0$, $t \in \mathbf{Z}^+$

$$DV(x) = V[x(t + 1)] - V[x(t)] \leq 0. \tag{14}$$

Note that the switched system for a fixed switching sequence s can be viewed as a time-varying system. Since $V(x)$ is positive definite and radially unbounded, and DV negative semidefinite, the system is stable in the sense of Lyapunov; see for example [1].

A multiple Lyapunov function composed by piecewise linear Lyapunov functions of the individual subsystems offers a significant advantage. It allows the characterization of the switching sequences that satisfy the condition of Proposition 1 by computing a conic partition of the state space.

First, we briefly describe the necessary notions and notation from convex analysis in order to construct the conic partition. Given a polytope $P \in \Re^n$, then a face of dimension k is denoted as $k-$face F. The hyperplane that corresponds to a $k-$face F is defined by the affine hull of F and is denoted by aff(F). Each $(n-1)-$face corresponds to a hyperplane that is defined by aff$(F_i) = \{x \in \Re^n : \langle x, w_i \rangle = 1\}$ where $w_i \in \Re^n$ is the corresponding gradient vector. The set of vertices of F can be found as vert$(F) = $ vert$(P) \cap$ aff(F) where vert(P) is the set of vertices of the polytope P. Finally, we denote the cone generated by the vertices of F by cone(F). Consider a pair of subsystems with matrices A_{q_1} and A_{q_2}. We want to compute the region $\Omega_{q_1}^{q_2} = \{x \in \Re^n : V_{q_2}(x) \leq V_{q_1}(x)\}$. Consider the faces $F_{i_1}^{q_1}$ and $F_{i_2}^{q_2}$ of the polytopes P_{q_1} and P_{q_2} respectively and assume that $C = $ cone$(F_{i_1}^{q_1}) \cap$ cone$(F_{i_2}^{q_2}) \neq \emptyset$. Next, we define the halfspace $H_{q_1}^{q_2} = \{x \in \Re^n : \langle x, w_{i_2}^{q_2} - w_{i_1}^{q_1} \rangle \leq 0\}$ and the set $\Omega = C \cap H_{q_1}^{q_2}$. It is shown in the following lemma that the multiple Lyapunov function defined in Proposition 1 is decreasing if the system switches from q_1 to q_2 while $x \in \Omega$.

Lemma 1. *For every $x \in \Omega$ we have that $V_{q_2}(x) \leq V_{q_1}(x)$.*

Proof. For every $x \in C$ the Lyapunov functions for the subsystems are given by $V_{q_1}(x) = \langle x, w_{i_1}^{q_1} \rangle$ and $V_{q_2}(x) = \langle x, w_{i_2}^{q_2} \rangle$ respectively. If $x \in \Omega$ we have that $\langle x, w_{i_2}^{q_2} - w_{i_1}^{q_1} \rangle \leq 0$ since $x \in H_{q_1}^{q_2}$, and therefore $V_{q_2}(x) \leq V_{q_1}(x)$.

Since $0 \in H_{q_1}^{q_2}$, the set Ω is a clearly a polyhedral cone as the intersection of cones with a common apex $(x = 0)$ as shown in Fig. 2. The set $\Omega_{q_1}^{q_2}$ can be computed as the union of polyhedral cones by repeating the above procedure for all the pairs $(F_{i_1}^{q_1}, F_{i_2}^{q_2})$ of $(n-1)$–faces of the polytope P as shown in the following algorithm.

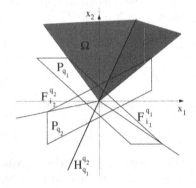

Fig. 2. The conic partition of the state space.

Algorithm for the computation of $\Omega_{q_1}^{q_2}$

INPUT: W^{q_1}, W^{q_2};
for $i_1 = 1, \ldots, m_{q_1}$
    for $i_2 = 1, \ldots, m_{q_2}$
        $C = \text{cone}(F_{i_1}^{q_1}) \cap \text{cone}(F_{i_2}^{q_2})$;
        if $C \neq \emptyset$ then
            $H_{q_1}^{q_2} = \{x \in \Re^n : \langle x, w_{i_2}^{q_2} - w_{i_1}^{q_1} \rangle \leq 0\}$
            $\Omega = C \cap H_{q_1}^{q_2}$;
            $\Omega_{q_1}^{q_2} = \Omega_{q_1}^{q_2} \cup \Omega$;
        end
    end
end

The above procedure can be repeated for every pair of subsystems to identify a class of stabilizing switching signals for the switched linear system. The class of switching sequences is characterized by the following result. Note that a numerical example that illustrates the approach may be found in [15].

Theorem 2. *Consider the class of switching sequences S defined by*

$$q_j(t_j + 1) = \delta(q_{j-1}(t_j), x(t_j)) \tag{15}$$

$$x(t_j) \in \Omega_{q_{j-1}}^{q_j} \neq \emptyset \tag{16}$$

for $j = 1, 2, \ldots$. The switched linear system $x(t+1) = A_q x(t)$ is stable in the sense of Lyapunov for every switching sequence $s \in S$.

Proof. By induction, we have that if $s = (q_0, t_0)$ then the system is stable since A_{q_0} is stable. Assume that the switched system is stable for the switching sequence $s = (q_0, t_0), (q_1, t_1), \ldots, (q_{j-1}, t_{j-1})$ and consider the sequence $s' = (q_0, t_0), (q_1, t_1), \ldots, (q_{j-1}, t_{j-1}), (q_j, t_j)$. Since $x(t_j) \in \Omega_{q_{j-1}}^{q_j}$, we have that $V_{q_j}[x(t_j)] \leq V_{q_{j-1}}[x(t_j)]$. Therefore, the multiple Lyapunov function defined by $V[x(t)] = V_{q_j}[x(t)]$, $t_j < t \leq t_{j+1}$ is decreasing for every t and the system is stable in the sense of Lyapunov.

5   Continuous-Time Switched Linear Systems

In this section, a characterization of stabilizing switching sequences for continuous-time switched linear systems is presented. The set of stabilizing switching sequences is characterized by computing a conic partition of the state space similarly to the discrete-time case. We consider the switched linear system

$$\dot{x}(t) = A_q x(t), \quad q \in Q\{1, \ldots, N\} \tag{17}$$

where $x(t) \in \Re^n$ and $A_q \in \Re^{n \times n}$. The switching law is described by

$$q(t^+) = \delta(q(t), x(t)). \tag{18}$$

where $t^+ = \lim_{\tau \to t, \, \tau > t} \tau$. The problem is to identify classes of switching signals generated by (18) for which the system (17) is stable. Note that in the following it is assumed that only finitely many switchings can occur in a finite time interval.

5.1   Background Material

In order to study the stability properties of the switched linear system (17), we assume that each individual subsystem admits a piecewise linear Lyapunov function induced by a positively invariant polyhedral set. Next, we summarize some results from [13] for the computation of piecewise linear Lyapunov functions for a class of continuous-time linear systems. Consider the continuous-time linear system $\dot{x}(t) = Ax(t)$ where $x(t) \in \Re^n$ and $A \in \Re^{n \times n}$.

Similarly to the discrete-time case, there exists a class of continuous linear systems for which a positively invariant polyhedral set can be computed very efficiently. If the eigenvalues λ_i of the linear system satisfy the condition $|\text{Im}\{\lambda_i\}| < |\text{Re}\{\lambda_i\}|$ then a Lyapunov function $V(x) = \|Wx\|_\infty$ can be constructed using a similarity transformation [13].

The use of piecewise linear Lyapunov functions for the stability of linear systems is based on the following result [11]. Assume that there exists a function $V(x)$ such that V is positive definite and radially unbounded, and the *upper right Dini derivative* [4] of V satisfies the condition

$$DV = \lim_{\Delta t \to 0} \sup \frac{V[x(t + \Delta t)] - V[x(t)]}{\Delta t} < 0. \tag{19}$$

Then, the equilibrium $x = 0$ is globally asymptotically stable.

The conditions for $V(x) = \|Wx\|_\infty$ to be a Lyapunov function for the system $\dot{x}(t) = Ax(t)$ can be stated using the logarithmic norm induced by the infinity norm. The logarithmic norm μ_∞ of a matrix $Q \in \Re^{n \times n}$ is defined as [9]

$$\mu_\infty = \lim_{\alpha \to 0+} \frac{\|I - \alpha Q\|_\infty - 1}{\alpha} \tag{20}$$

$$= \max_i \{ q_{ii} + \sum_{j=1, j \neq i} |q_{ij}| \}. \tag{21}$$

Theorem 3. *[13] $V(x) = \|Wx\|_\infty$ is a Lyapunov function for the system $\dot{x} = Ax(t)$ if and only if there exists $Q \in \Re^{n \times n}$ such that $WA - QW = 0$ and $\mu_\infty(Q) < 0$.*

Corollary 2. *[13] If all the eigenvalues $\lambda_i = \mu_i \pm \sigma_i$ of the nth order system $\dot{x} = Ax(t)$ satisfy the condition $|\mu_i| \leq |\sigma_i|$, then there exists $W \in \Re^{n \times n}$ with rankW $= n$ such that the polyhedral set $P = \{ x \in \Re^n : \|Wx\|_\infty < 1 \}$ is a positively invariant set for the system.*

The above corollary is a consequence of the fact that the matrix equation $WA - QA = 0$ has a solution W with rankW $= n$ if and only if the eigenvalues of A are identical with the eigenvalues of Q [10]. The matrix W can be computed as the similarity transformation matrix by which A is transformed to the real Jordan canonical form similar to the discrete-time case.

5.2 Stabilizing Switching Sequences

In this section, we present an approach based on multiple Lyapunov functions for the stability analysis of the switched system (17). We assume that each individual subsystem admits a piecewise linear Lyapunov function described by the infinity norm. The main contribution is an efficient characterization of a class of switching laws of the form (2) which guarantee the stability of the system. Similar results can be developed for more general piecewise linear Lyapunov functions as in the discrete-time case in Section 4. We assume that each individual subsystem admits a positively invariant polyhedral set that contains the origin which is described by

$$P_q = \{ x \in \Re^n : \|W^q x\|_\infty < 1 \} \tag{22}$$

where $W^q \in \Re^{n \times n}$. We denote the rows of the matrix W^q by $w_i^q \in \Re^n$, $i = 1, \ldots, n$. We consider a class S of switching sequences that are described by $s = (q_0, t_0), (q_1, t_1), \ldots, (q_j, t_j), \ldots,\ \ x(t_0) = x_0$ where $t_j \in \Re^n, j = 0, 1, \ldots$. It is assumed that the sequence of switching instants $t_0, t_1, \ldots, t_j, \ldots$ is divergent in the sense that there are no infinitely many switchings in a finite time interval. Similarly to the discrete-time case, it is assumed that $q_j \neq q_{j+1}$. A sequence s can be generated by the switching law $q_j(t_j^+) = \delta(q_{j-1}(t_j), x(t_j))$, $j = 1, 2, \ldots$.

Proposition 2. *Consider a switching sequence $s \in S$. If $V_{q_j}[x(t_j^+)] \leq V_{q_{j-1}}[x(t_j)]$, $j = 1, 2, \ldots$, then the switched system $\dot{x} = A_q x(t)$ is stable in the sense of Lyapunov.*

Proof. Consider the multiple Lyapunov function defined by

$$V[x(t)] = V_{q_j}[x(t)], \quad t_j < t \leq t_{j+1}. \tag{23}$$

Then, we have

$$DV = \lim_{\Delta t \to 0} \sup \frac{V[x(t + \Delta t)] - V[x(t)]}{\Delta t} \leq 0. \tag{24}$$

for every $t \in \Re^n$ and therefore, the equilibrium $x = 0$ is stable in the sense of Lyapunov; see for example [11].

A conic partition of the state space can be used to characterize a class of switching sequences that satisfy the condition of Proposition 2. Consider a pair of subsystems with matrices A_{q_1} and A_{q_2}. The region $\Omega_{q_1}^{q_2} = \{x \in \Re^n : V_{q_2}(x) \leq V_{q_1}(x)\}$ can be computed as a union of finitely generated cones and can be computed by the algorithm presented in Section 4 similarly to the discrete-time case. The class of stabilizing switching sequences is characterized by the following result.

Theorem 4. *Consider the class of switching sequences S defined by*

$$q_j(t_j^+) = \delta(q_{j-1}(t_j), x(t_j)) \tag{25}$$
$$x(t_j) \in \Omega_{q_{j-1}}^{q_j} \neq \emptyset \tag{26}$$

for $j = 1, 2, \ldots$. The switched linear system $\dot{x} = A_q x(t)$ is stable in the sense of Lyapunov for every switching sequence $s \in S$.

Proof. Similar to the proof of Theorem 2.

Example 1. Consider the switched discrete-time linear system

$$\dot{x} = A_q x(t), \quad q \in \{1, 2\} \tag{27}$$

where

$$A_1 = \begin{bmatrix} 1.7 & 1.8 \\ -4.5 & -3.7 \end{bmatrix} \text{ and } A_2 = \begin{bmatrix} 0.7 & -1 \\ 1.6 & -1.7 \end{bmatrix}. \tag{28}$$

The eigenvalues of the matrices A_1 and A_2 are $\lambda = -1 \pm .9j$ amd $\lambda = -.5 \pm .4j$. The real Jordan canonical form can be computed by the following similarity transformations.

$$Q_1 = W^1 A_1 (W^1)^{-1} = \begin{bmatrix} -1 & 0.9 \\ -0.9 & -1 \end{bmatrix} \text{ where } W^1 = \begin{bmatrix} 2 & 1 \\ 1 & 1 \end{bmatrix} \tag{29}$$

and

$$Q_2 = W^2 A_2 (W^2)^{-1} = \begin{bmatrix} -0.5 & 0.4 \\ -0.4 & -0.5 \end{bmatrix} \text{ where } W^2 = \begin{bmatrix} -1 & 1 \\ 1 & -0.5 \end{bmatrix}. \tag{30}$$

We have that $\mu_\infty(Q_1) = -0.1 < 0$ and therefore, $V_1(x) = \|W^1 x\|_\infty$ is a Lyapunov function for the subsystem A_1. Similarly, $\mu_\infty(Q_2) = -0.1 < 0$ and $V_2(x) = \|W^2 x\|_\infty$ is a Lyapunov function for the subsystem A_2. The functions V_1 and V_2 correspond to the positively invariant polyhedral sets

$$P_1 = \{x \in \Re^2 : \|W^1 x\|_\infty \leq 1\} \text{ and } P_2 = \{x \in \Re^2 : \|W^2 x\|_\infty \leq 1\} \tag{31}$$

shown in Fig. 3(i).

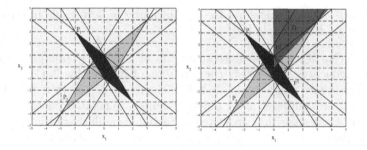

Fig. 3. (i) Positively invariant polyhedral sets, (ii) The region Ω.

Consider the faces F^1 and F^2 shown in Fig. 3(ii). For every $x \in \text{cone}(F^1) \cap \text{cone}(F^2)$ we have that $V_1(x) = \langle x, w^1 \rangle$ and $V_2(x) = \langle x, w^2 \rangle$ with $w^1 = [2, 1]$ and $w^2 = [-1, 1]$ respectively. We consider the halfspace

$$H_1^2 = \{x \in \Re^2 : \langle x, w^2 - w^1 \rangle \leq 0\} \tag{32}$$
$$= \{x \in \Re^2 : x_1 \geq 0\}. \tag{33}$$

Therefore, for every $x \in \Omega = \text{cone}(F^1) \cap \text{cone}(F^2) \cup H_1^2$ we have that $V_2(x) \leq V_1(x)$.

By repeating the procedure for all the pairs of faces for the polytopes P_1 and P_2 the we compute the region

$$\Omega_{q_1}^{q_2} = \{x \in \Re^2 : V_{q_2}(x) < V_{q_1}(x)\} \tag{34}$$
$$= \{x \in \Re^2 : x_1 > 0\}. \tag{35}$$

Similarly we have that

$$\Omega_{q_2}^{q_1} = \{x \in \Re^2 : V_{q_1}(x) < V_{q_2}(x)\} \tag{36}$$

$$= \{x \in \Re^2 : x_1 < 0\}. \tag{37}$$

Therefore, for any switching sequence s given by the switching law

$$q_2(t^+) = \delta(q_1(t), x(t)) \tag{38}$$

$$x(t) \in \Omega_{q_1}^{q_2} \tag{39}$$

and

$$q_1(t^+) = \delta(q_2(t), x(t)) \tag{40}$$

$$x(t) \in \Omega_{q_2}^{q_1} \tag{41}$$

the switched system is stable. A stable trajectory is shown in Fig. 4(i).

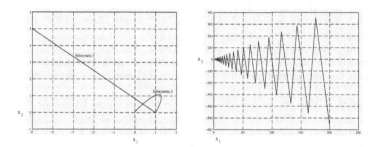

Fig. 4. (i) A stable trajectory. (ii) An unstable trajectory.

The characterization of the stabilizing switching sequences is based on sufficient conditions. Therefore, for a switching sequence s that does not satisfy the formulated conditions, the switched system is not necessarily unstable. However, the switched system (27) can generate unstable trajectories as shown in Fig. 4(ii). An unstable trajectory can be generated by requiring that the system will keep switching indefinitely and that the Lyapunov function is increasing at every switching.

6   Conclusions

In this paper, a class of stabilizing switching sequences for switched linear systems is characterized by computing conic partitions of the state space. The main advantage of the approach is that the methodology for computing switching laws that guarantee stability is based on the parameters of the system and so, trajectories for particular initial conditions do not need to be calculated. Therefore, the proposed approach can be used very efficiently to investigate the stability properties of practical hybrid systems.

References

1. P. Antsaklis and A. Michel. *Linear Systems*. McGraw-Hill, 1997.
2. G. Bitsoris. Positively invariant polyhedral sets of discrete-time linear systems. *International Journal of Control*, 47(6):1713–1726, 1988.
3. F. Blanchini. Nonquadratic Lyapunov functions for robust control. *Automatica*, 31(3):451–461, 1995.
4. F. Blanchini. Set invariance in control. *Automatica*, 35(11):1747–1767, 1999.
5. M. Branicky. Multiple Lyapunov functions and other analysis tools for switched and hybrid systems. *IEEE Trans. on Automatic Control*, 43(4):475–482, 1998.
6. R. Brayton and C. Tong. Stability of dynamical systems: A constructive approach. *IEEE Trans. on Circuits and Systems*, CAS-26(4):224–234, 1979.
7. R. Brayton and C. Tong. Constructive stability and asymptotic stability of dynamical systems. *IEEE Trans. on Circuits and Systems*, CAS-27(11):1121–1130, 1980.
8. R. DeCarlo, M. Branicky, S. Pettersson, and B. Lennartson. Perspectives and results on the stability and stabilizability of hybrid systems. *Proceedings of IEEE*, 88(7):1069–1082, July 2000.
9. V. Desoer and H. Haneda. The measure of a matrix as a tool to analyze computer algorithms for circuit analysis. *IEEE Trans. on Circuit Theory*, 19(5):480–486, 1972.
10. F. Gantmacher. *Matrix Theory*. Chelsea, 1959.
11. W. Hahn. *Stability of Motion*. Springer-Verlag, 1967.
12. M. Johansson and A. Rantzer. Computation of piecewise quadratic Lyapunov functions for hybrid systems. *IEEE Trans. on Automatic Control*, 43(4):555–559, 1998.
13. H. Kiendl, J. Adamy, and P. Stelzner. Vector norms as Lyapunov functions for linear systems. *IEEE Trans. on Automatic Control*, 37(6):839–1842, 1992.
14. X. Koutsoukos. *Analysis and Design of Piecewise Linear Hybrid Dynamical Systems*. PhD thesis, Department of Electrical Engineering, University of Notre Dame, Notre Dame, IN, 2000.
15. X. Koutsoukos and P. Antsaklis. Stabilizing supervisory control of hybrid systems based on piecewise linear Lyapunov functions. In *Proceedings of the 8th IEEE Mediterranean Conference on Control and Automation*, Rio, Greece, July 2000.
16. D. Liberzon and A. Morse. Basic problems in stability and design of switched systems. *IEEE Control Systems Magazine*, 19(5):59–70, October 1999.
17. A. Michel. Recent trends in the stability analysis of hybrid dynamical systems. *IEEE Trans. on Circuits and Systems I*, 46(1):120–134, 1999.
18. A. Michel, B. Nam, and V. Vittal. Computer generated Lyapunov functions for interconnected systems: Improved results with applications to power systems. *IEEE Trans. on Circuits and Systems*, CAS-31(2):189–198, 1984.
19. A. Molchanov and Y. Pyatnitskiy. Criteria of asymptotic stability of differential and difference inclusions encountered in control theory. *Systems & Control Letters*, 13:59–64, 1989.
20. Y. Ohta, H. Imanishi, L. Gong, and H. Haneda. Computer generated Lyapunov functions for a class of nonlinear systems. *IEEE Trans. on Circuits and Systems-I: Fundamental Theory and Applications*, 40(5):428–433, 1993.
21. S. Pettersson and B. Lennartson. Stability and robustness of hybrid systems. In *Proceedings of the 35th IEEE Conference on Decision and Control*, pages 1202–1207, Kobe, Japan, December 1996.
22. H. Ye, A. Michel, and L. Hou. Stability theory for hybrid dynamical systems. *IEEE Trans. on Automatic Control*, 43(4):461–474, 1998.

On a Novel Class of Bifurcations in Hybrid Dynamical Systems

The Case of Relay Feedback Systems

P. Kowalczyk and M. di Bernardo

Department of Engineering Mathematics,
University of Bristol, Bristol BS8 1TR, U.K.,
{P.Kowalczyk, M.diBernardo}@bristol.ac.uk

Abstract. Our study is concerned with a particular class of hybrid dynamical systems, namely systems with discontinuous vector fields. We will show that such systems can exhibit a novel class of bifurcations which are not observed in smooth dynamical systems. Particularly, we concentrate on bifurcations which arise due to the existence of so-called sliding motion. Using appropriate discrete mappings we show the possible existence of complex transitions which we term sliding, multisliding and grazing-sliding bifurcations. Relay feedback systems are used as a representative example.

Keywords: Hybrid Systems, Bifurcations, Sliding motion

1 Overview

Hybrid control strategies are increasingly used in applications. The resulting dynamical systems are characterised by a combination of continuous and discrete dynamics which can give rise to a unique class of phase space transitions. A particularly interesting class of hybrid systems of relevance in applications is that of switched dynamical systems. Examples include systems with dry friction [1][2], systems with impacts (impact oscillators, vibroimpact systems) [3] and relay feedback systems [4].

Under certain conditions these systems can exhibit solutions lying within their discontinuity set or *sliding*. Numerical and experimental evidence of dynamical transitions involving sliding was recently reported in the literature. Examples include the formation of "chattering orbits" in parallel resonant power electronics converters [5], the onset of stick-slip motion in friction oscillators [6] and the the occurence of fast switching periodic solutions in relay feedback systems [4]. These transitions can be consistently classified in terms of the bifurcation scenarios introduced in this paper. Their occurrence can be explained in terms of the interaction between the system Ω-limit set and the phase-space manifold where sliding is possible,.

In what follows, we will focus our attention on linear systems with a relay feedback element. Although, systems with a relay feedback have been studied for

M.D. Di Benedetto, A. Sangiovanni-Vincentelli (Eds.): HSCC 2001, LNCS 2034, pp. 361–374, 2001.

a long time [7], [8] the dynamics of these systems is not fully understood. Even low-order relay feedback systems can exhibit complex self oscillations, which include periodic solutions with segments of sliding motion [9], [10], [11]. The aim of this paper is to use relay feedback systems as a representative example to describe a novel class of bifurcations involving sliding which can be observed in a wider class of switched and hybrid dynamical systems [12].

The outline of the paper is the following. The general form of systems with a relay feedback under investigation is introduced in section 2 and appropriate maps used for numerical investigation are defined. Section 3 illustrates the four possible cases of novel bifurcations caused by the interaction of the system Ω-limit set with the region where sliding is possible. Then, in section 4 the detailed analysis of a third-order representative example is presented. Evidence of chaotic attractors are given and appropriate one-dimensional mappings are derived to study their nature. Finally, in section 5 after drawing some conclusions, we give suggestions for further work.

2   Background

In what follows, we consider a class of systems with discontinuous vector field corresponding to single-input, single-output, linear time-invariant (LTI) systems with unit negative feedback of the output variable. The systems under investigation have the following general form:

$$\dot{x} = Ax + Bu, \qquad (1)$$
$$y = Cx, \qquad (2)$$
$$u = -\text{sgn}(y), \qquad (3)$$

where $A \in R^{n \times n}, B \in R^{n \times 1}$ and $C \in R^{1 \times n}$ are constant matrices. The input u and output y of the linear part are scalar functions, while x, the state vector, has $n \geq 1$ components. The " sgn" function (which is the non-linear term in the system equations) is defined as $\text{sgn}(y) = 1$, if $y > 0$, $\text{sgn}(y) = -1$, if $y < 0$ and $\text{sgn}(y) \in (-1, 1)$, if $y = 0$.

It is assumed that the system matrices are given in observer canonical form, i.e.:

$$A = \begin{pmatrix} -a_1 & 1 & 0 & \cdots & 0 \\ -a_2 & 0 & 1 & \cdots & 0 \\ \vdots & & & \ddots & \vdots \\ -a_{n-1} & 0 & 0 & 0 & 1 \\ -a_n & 0 & 0 & 0 & 0 \end{pmatrix}, \quad B = \begin{pmatrix} b_1 \\ b_2 \\ \vdots \\ b_4 \\ b_5 \end{pmatrix}, \quad C = \begin{pmatrix} 1 \\ 0 \\ \vdots \\ 0 \\ 0 \end{pmatrix}^T. \qquad (4)$$

The above matrices correspond to the following transfer function:

$$G(s) = C(sI - A)^{-1}B = \frac{b_1 s^{n-1} + b_2 s^{n-2} + \cdots + b_{n-1}s + b_n}{s^n + a_1 s^{n-1} + a_2 s^{n-2} + \cdots + a_{n-1}s + a_n}. \qquad (5)$$

The system trajectory generated by the vector field characterized by equations (1)-(3) is smooth and continuous in the two subspaces, H_1 and H_2 defined as:

$$H_1 = \{x \in R^n : Cx > 0\}, \tag{6}$$

$$H_2 = \{x \in R^n : Cx < 0\}. \tag{7}$$

System (1)-(3) switches from one (LTI) region (H_1 or H_2) to the other whenever the system trajectory crosses the switching hyperplane S defined as:

$$S = \{x \in R^n : Cx = 0\}. \tag{8}$$

For all initial conditions outside S, the system trajectory will ultimately cross S assuming positive and stable steady-state gain $G(0)$ [9]. Note that the system under investigation is symmetric with respect to the origin.

2.1   Sliding Motion

Systems such as (1)-(3) can exhibit a very peculiar type of motion termed *sliding*. This corresponds to a solution lying within the system discontinuity set S. Heuristically, sliding can be seen as characterised by an infinite number of switchings between the two subspaces H_1 and H_2. Sliding motion is only possible when the vector field points towards the switching manifold S in both regions H_1 and H_2 (see fig. 1). Thus by studying the direction of the vector field in a neighborhood of the switching manifold, it is possible to identify a set $S_3 \subset S$ where sliding is possible. We term S_3 as the sliding region. Any trajectory hitting the switching manifold in S_3 is constrained to evolve on it until the trajectory reaches the point where the vector field changes its direction on the boundary of the sliding region (see figure 1). Using the equivalent control method presented in [13], we can obtain the dynamical system describing the motion of a trajectory within the region S_3. The equivalent control input $u_{eq} \in (-1, 1)$ is defined as the

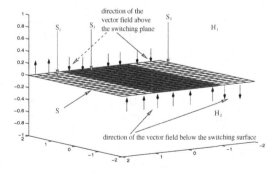

Fig. 1. Schematic representation of the phase space topology in the case $n = 3$

controller that keeps the trajectory on the switching hyperplane, i.e. the control input that guarantees $\dot{y} = 0$ and $y = 0$. Using (1)-(3), it can be shown that for the system under investigation such control input is given by:

$$u_{eq} = -(CB)^{-1}CAx. \tag{9}$$

By substituting (9) into (1) we obtain the set of equations describing the system dynamics within the sliding region, which is given by:

$$\dot{x} = \hat{A}x, \tag{10}$$

where $\hat{A} = [I - (CB)^{-1}BC]A$ and I denotes the $n \times n$ identity matrix.

According to the direction of the vector field, we can define regions on the hypersurface S where $\dot{y} = 0$, $\dot{y} > 0$ and $\dot{y} < 0$ respectively. Namely, we define $S_1 = \{x \in R^n : CAx > CB\}$, $S_2 = \{x \in R^n : CAx < -CB\}$, $S_3 = \{x \in R^n : |CAx| < CB\}$.

Additionally, we define the boundary between S_3 and S_1 which we denote as ∂S_{31}, and the boundary between S_3 and S_2 which we denote as ∂S_{32}, as: $\partial S_{31} = \{x \in R^n : CAx = CB\}$, $\partial S_{32} = \{x \in R^n : CAx = -CB\}$. Note that sliding is only possible when the sliding set S_3 is non-empty i.e. when $CB > 0$, in (13).

2.2   Self Oscillations and Poincaré Maps

Typically, a system with relay feedback has self-oscillations [14]. This corresponds to the periodic switching of the system trajectory between H_1 and H_2 (an example for a third-order system is presented in figure 2). The dark region in the figure indicates the region on the switching manifold S where the trajectory of the system slides (the region denoted as S_3 in figure 1).

As shown, in [10] using the system explicit solutions we can characterise the system evolution by using an appropriate set of discrete-time maps. Namely we can define, the upper switching map $\Pi^+ : \bar{S}_1 \mapsto S$ as the mapping which describes the dynamics from $x_0 \in S_1$ to $x_1 \in S$ (see figure 3). We also define the lower switching map $\Pi^- : \bar{S}_2 : S_2 \mapsto S$ as the map which describes the system dynamics from a point $x_1 \in S_2$ to $x_2 \in S$. Finally, we define the overall switching map Π as the composition of Π^+ and Π^-: $\Pi = \Pi^+ \circ \Pi^-$. The map Π can be used to analyze simple periodic orbits.

As discussed in [10] sliding sections can become part of an orbit. To investigate the behaviour of orbits with a section lying in the sliding surface we introduce a map Σ which maps the points in region S_3 to its boundary $\partial S_3 := \partial S_{31} \cup \partial S_{32}$. Once the trajectory reaches the boundary of the sliding section, it leaves the switching region. We define Σ as the mapping which takes a point, $\hat{x}$, from region S_3 to a point x_1 on its boundary, i.e. $\Sigma : R^2 \to R^1 : S_3 \mapsto \partial S_3$. The simplest symmetric orbit with sliding is depicted in figure 3. Note the existence of two sliding segments per period (the orbit is symmetric). Stable asymmetric orbits are also possible [16].

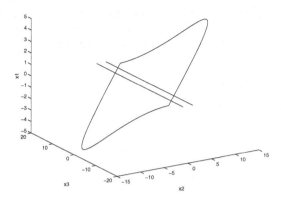

Fig. 2. Typical trajectory (corresponding to the self-oscillations) of the system with relay feedback (1)-(3)

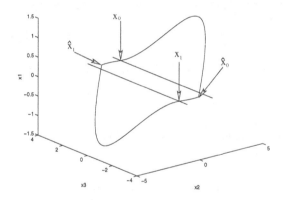

Fig. 3. The simple symmetric orbit with two sliding segments

The orbit depicted in figure 3 can be described by the composition of mappings Π^+, Π^- and Σ. Orbits with higher number of sliding sections and asymmetric orbits can be defined by an appropriate composition of the mappings Π^+, Π^- and Σ (see [10] for further details).

3   Bifurcation Scenarios Involving Sliding Section

We now introduce the possible bifurcation scenarios involving the interaction between trajectories of the system and the sliding region S_3. These scenarios were identified after careful numerical and analytical investigation and were partly reported independently for the first time in [10] and [15].

We distinguish four possible cases of such bifurcations involving sliding, which we will term generically as sliding bifurcations (see figure 4). Without loss of generality, we assume that such local bifurcations involve sections of trajectories belonging to some periodic orbit of the system. Figure 4(a) depicts the so-called

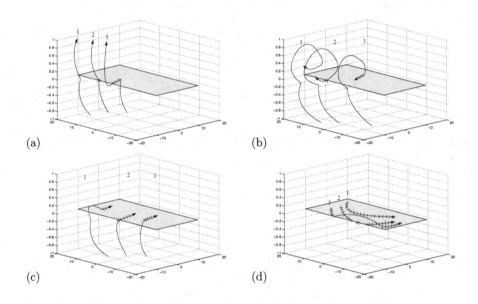

(a)   (b)

(c)   (d)

Fig. 4. The four possible bifurcation scenarios involving collision of a segment of the trajectory with the boundary of the sliding region ∂S_3

sliding bifurcation of type A. This corresponds to the following scenario. When a control parameter is varied the trajectory hits transversally the boundary of the sliding strip ∂S_3 (trajectory 2 in figure 4(a)). Further variation of the parameter, make the trajectory enter the sliding region S_3, thus causing the onset of sliding motion. Note, that the trajectory leaves the sliding strip tangentially (i.e $\dot{y} = 0$).

In the case presented in figure 4(b), instead, the trajectory grazes tangentially the boundary of the sliding strip, ∂S_3, from the subspace H_1 (or H_2). Again, this causes the formation of a section of sliding motion. We term this transition as a **grazing-sliding bifurcation**.

The third scenario depicted in figure 4(c) is somehow similar to a sliding bifurcation (case 4(a)). In case 4(a), though, the trajectory zooms off the switching manifold S at the bifurcation point while in case 4(c) it stays within the sliding region. Specifically, these two bifurcation events differ by the sign of $\ddot{y}$ at the boundary of the sliding strip (∂S_3). We call case 4(c), a **switching-sliding bifurcation**, or **sliding bifurcation type B**.

The last case is termed a **multisliding bifurcation** and is depicted in figure 4(d). It differs from the scenarios presented above since the segment of the trajectory which undergoes the bifurcation lies entirely in the sliding region S_3. Namely, through the variation of some parameters, a sliding segment hits tangentially the boundary of the sliding strip. Further variations of the parameter, cause such sliding segment to "fall" off the sliding region causing the formation of an additional segment of the trajectory lying in the H_1 or H_2 subspace.

We now give analytical conditions for each of these bifurcations in terms of the properties of the system output, y, at the bifurcation point, say, $\bar{x}$. Similar conditions were also reported independently in the Russian Literature in [15].

3.1 Analytical Conditions for Sliding Bifurcations

For each case of the four scenarios reported above, the following conditions must hold at the bifurcation point, say $\bar{x}$:

1. $Cx = 0$,
2. $CA\bar{x} = CB$.

Condition 1 ensures that at the bifurcation point the trajectory lies on the switching manifold. Condition 2 corresponds to the fact that the bifurcation point belongs to the boundary of the sliding strip. Note, that condition 2 also implies that $\dot{y} = CAx - CB = 0$ i.e. the trajectory must leave S_3 tangentially. Additional conditions involiving higher order derivatives of y can be given for each of the scenarios. Namely we have the following extra conditions.

Sliding bifurcation type A. (figure 4(a))
In addition to conditions 1 and 2 we note that in this case the trajectory moves toward the boundary of S_3 at the bifurcation point $\bar{x}$. Thus, we have $\ddot{y} > 0$, i.e.

$$CA^2x - CAB > 0. \tag{11}$$

Grazing while sliding bifurcation. (figure 4(b))
As in the previous case, the trajectory moves away from the sliding region S_3 at a grazing-sliding bifurcation point, $\bar{x}$. Hence, in addition to the two general conditions 1 and 2, we also require condition (11) to hold.

Multisliding bifurcation. (figure 4(c))
In this case the bifurcating trajectory hits the boundary of the sliding strip tangentially. Thus, at $\bar{x}$ we must have $\ddot{y} = 0, \dddot{y} > 0$, i.e.

$$CA^2x - CAB = 0 \tag{12}$$
$$CA^3x - CA^2B > 0 \tag{13}$$

Switching sliding, sliding type B bifurcation. (figure 4(d))
Finally, in this case, the trajectory moves towards the interior of S_3 (away from ∂S_{31}) at the bifurcation point, $\bar{x}$, thus $\ddot{y} < 0$ and we have

$$CA^2 x - CAB < 0. \tag{14}$$

Similar conditions can be given if intersections with ∂S_{32} are considered. A generalization of these conditions to the case of n-dimensional PWS systems of the form:

$$\dot{x} = \begin{cases} F_1(x) & \text{if } H(x) > 0, \\ F_2(x) & \text{if } H(x) < 0 \end{cases}$$

where $x \in R^n$, $F_1, F_2 : R^n \mapsto R^n$ are sufficiently smooth in the region ofinterest and $H : R^n \mapsto R$ is a scalar function of the system states. can be found in [12].

4   Numerical Analysis of a Third Order Representative Example

The state space representation of the third-order relay feedback system, which will serve as a representative example is characterised by the matrices:

$$A = \begin{pmatrix} -(2\zeta\omega + \lambda) & 1 & 0 \\ -(2\zeta\omega\lambda + \omega^2) & 0 & 1 \\ -\lambda\omega^2 & 0 & 0 \end{pmatrix}, \quad B = \begin{pmatrix} k \\ 2k\rho\sigma \\ k\rho^2 \end{pmatrix} \quad C = \begin{pmatrix} 1 \\ 0 \\ 0 \end{pmatrix}^T. \tag{15}$$

The above state-space representation corresponds to the following transfer function:

$$G(s) = k\frac{s^2 + 2\sigma\rho s + \rho^2}{(s^2 + 2\zeta\omega s + \omega^2)(s + \lambda)}. \tag{16}$$

The parameters ω and ζ denote the natural frequency and the damping of the complex pair of poles while ρ and σ represent the corresponding quantities for the complex pair of zeros, $-\lambda$ is the location of the real pole and $\frac{k\rho^2}{\omega^2\lambda}$ is the steady-state gain.

4.1   Sliding Bifurcation

As mentioned in the previous section, we can observe the transition from a generic orbit to an orbit with sliding by varying the system parameters. We present examples of these "sliding bifurcations" for the third order relay system (15) according to the four distinct scenarios introduced above.

Figure 5(a) represents a stable symmetric orbit (before its transition to an orbit with sliding) for the following values of the parameters, $\zeta = \omega = \lambda = -\sigma = k = 1$. Here ρ is varied in a neighborhood of $\rho_0 = 3$.

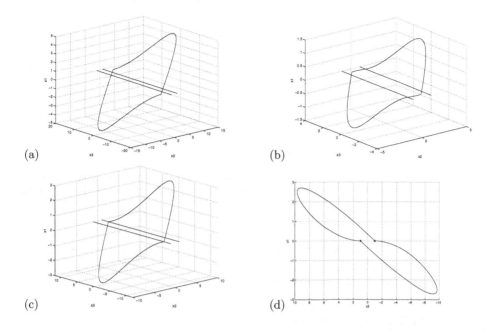

Fig. 5. The scenario of sliding bifurcations of the simple orbit for the parameter values: $-\sigma = \lambda = k = \zeta\omega = 1$, ρ is a varied parameter with subsequent values $\rho = 3$ fig.(a), $\rho = 2.1$ fig.(b) and $\rho = 1$ for fig(c), (d) projection of the trajectory on the x_1, x_2 plane showing that the orbit does intersect the boundary of the sliding strip at the bifurcation point

As the parameter ρ is decreased, this simple orbit hits the boundary of the sliding segment ∂S_3 transversally (see figures 5-(a) and (b)). Through this sliding bifurcation of type A, variation of the parameter ρ , cause the formation of a sliding orbit. To investigate the stability of the orbits which undergo sliding bifurcation the eigenvalues of a the point mappings Π^+ and $\Sigma \circ \Pi^+$ were computed. The orbits presented in figures 4(a) - 4(d) are symmetric orbits. Thus, it suffices to compute the eigenvalues of the fixed points associated to these solutions using either the lower or the upper switching map, Π^- or Π^+ (appropriately composed with Σ when sliding orbits are considered). Figs. 6(a) and 6(b) show the two significant eigenvalues of a fixed point (corresponding to a symmetric orbit).

The region denoted as 2 in figures 6(a), 6(b) corresponds to the fixed point associated with a simple symmetric orbit. The region labeled as 1 in figures 6(a), 6(b) corresponds to the fixed point associated with a sliding orbit. Note the apparent piecewise smoothness in the value of eigenvalues of the fixed points of orbits before and after the sliding bifurcation. One eigenvalue becomes identically zero at the sliding bifurcation point (fig. 6(b)). Hence, there is only one significant

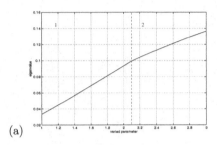   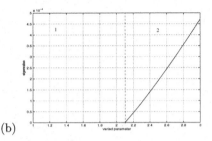

(a)   (b)

Fig. 6. absolute values of eigenvalues of a map Π^+ and $\Pi^+ \circ \Sigma$ before (part of graph 6(a), 6(b) denoted as 2 and after sliding bifurcations part of the graph 6(a), 6(b) denoted by 1

eigenvalue characterising sliding orbits in these three-dimensional system. These orbits can be analyzed using the map $\Theta : \partial S_3 \mapsto \partial S_3$ defined above which in this case is indeed one-dimensional.

4.2   Multisliding Bifurcation

In this subsection, we consider the bifurcation scenario which we termed multisliding (see figure 4(a)). Let us denote, by A an orbit before the multisliding bifurcation and B an orbit after its occurience (thus both orbits differ by the number of sliding segments). We also assume that upper case denotes stable orbits and lower case unstable ones. Close to a multisliding bifurcation point (fig. 4(d)) we can observe two type of transitions $A \to B$ or $A, b \to \{\phi\}$. The transition $A \to B$ corresponds to a transcritical-like bifurcation scenario where a new sliding orbit with a different number of sliding segments is born at the bifurcation point. The other case $A, b \to \{\phi\}$ corresponds to the case when two orbits, one stable and the other unstable, collide and disappear on the boundary. The transcritical-like transition, $A \to B$, of a multisliding orbit is shown in figure 7. The parameters have the following values: $\zeta = 0.05, \rho = -\sigma = k = \lambda = 1$. The parameter ω is varied and takes the value 10.14 in fig. 7(a), 10.24 in fig. 7(b) and 10.74 in figure 7(c). It was mentioned in section 2 that the orbits with sliding section(s) can be analyzed using appropriate one-dimensional mappings from the line ∂S_3 back to itself. Fig. 7(d) shows the one-dimensional map obtained by varying the x_3 coordinate on the line $x_2 = 1$ ($x_1 = 0$) and applying the maps Π^+, Σ and Π^-. The proper composition of these maps drives the point from the line $x_2 = 1(x_1 = 0)$ back to itself. Note, the existence of a kink in figure 7(d). This is the effect of the multisliding bifurcation. The multisliding transition of type $0 \to A, b$ and the corresponding one-dimensional map from the line ∂S_3 back to itself is shown in fig. 8. Here, the orbit was obtained for the following parameter values: $-\sigma = \rho = k = 1, \lambda = 0.05, \omega = 10$; while ζ is varied in a neighborhood of $\zeta_0 = 0.0395$.

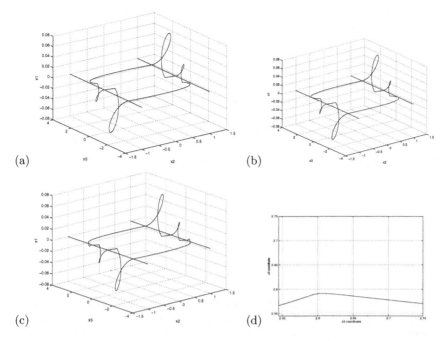

(a)   (b)

(c)   (d)

Fig. 7. Figures 7(a)-7(c) represent the scenario of multisliding bifurcation. Note the tangency of the orbit 7(b) to the boundary of the sliding segment ∂S_3. Figure 7(d) represents the map from the line ∂S_{31} back to itself for the parameter values corresponding to the orbit depicted in figure 7(b)

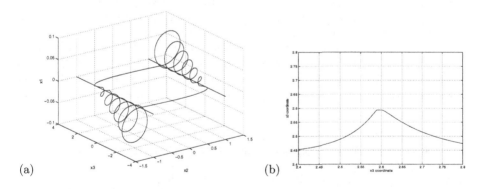

(a)   (b)

Fig. 8. Symmetric orbit with multiple amount of sliding sections (a) and corresponding 1-dimensional map (b)

4.3 Grazing while Sliding Bifurcation

We now present numerical evidence for the so-called grazing-sliding bifurcation - figure 4(b). A trajectory undergoes the grazing-sliding transition when a segment of the trajectory touches tangentially the boundary ∂S_3 of the sliding segment

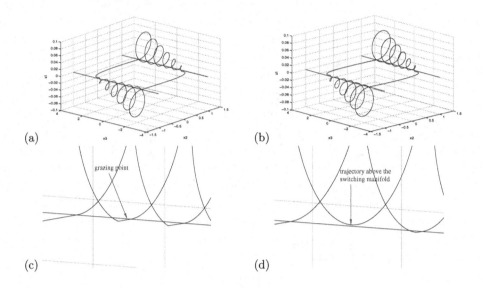

Fig. 9. Symmetric orbit with multiple amount of sliding sections before (a) and after (b) grazing while sliding bifurcations, (c)(d) close up of the region where part of the trajectory graze the boundary of the sliding strip - accordingly before and after bifurcation

from the subspace H_1 or H_2. After this bifurcation, the trajectory contains an additional sliding segment (figures 4(a)-4(c)). In the case presented here, as the parameter ζ is increased, one of the loops making up the orbit (figure 9(a)) changes its shape. This in turn causes (with further variation of the control parameter ζ) the loop to touch the boundary of the sliding strip from above (and below - note the symmetry of the transition scenario) and enter the sliding strip. (figure 9(b)). The parameter values for which the transition described was detected take the following values:$\lambda = 0.05, k = -\sigma = \rho = 1, \omega = 10$. ζ is varied between 0.025 and 0.032.

4.4   Switching Sliding Bifurcation, Sliding Type B

Despite several attempts switching-sliding bifurcations of stable periodic solutions were not detected for the third-order system under investigation. Evidence of their occurence in a second-order friction oscillator can be found in [15].

4.5   Chaos

The seemingly simple system which serves us as an example is also found to exhibit chaotic behaviour. The chaotic attractor depicted in fig. 10 is obtained for the following parameter values: $\zeta = -0.08, \omega = 10, k = \rho = -\sigma = 1$ and $\lambda = 0.05$. Applying the idea of 1-dimensional point mappings from the line

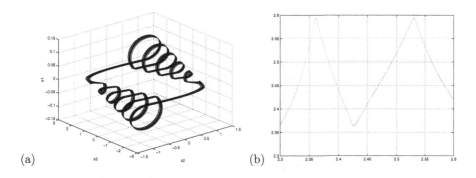

(a)   (b)

Fig. 10. Chaotic attractor and corresponding 1-dimensional map

∂S_{31} back to itself one can study this chaotic evolution by considering the one-dimensional map which presented in figure 10(b). Note the characteristic shape of the kinks of the map due to near-multisliding events in the trajectory.

The map shown in figure 10(b) has interesting dynamics, similar to those of the double iteration of the tent map [17]. Thus, the occurence of chaos in the system can be explained as resulting from the merging of two asymmetric chaotic attractors. It is relevant to point out that the formation of the attractor is organized by the occurence of the sliding bifurcations presented in the paper (see [16]).

5   Conclusions and Future Work

It has been shown by means of a representative example that very complex dynamics can be observed in systems with discontinuous vector field. Evidence of novel bifurcations was given , namely sliding, multisliding and grazing-sliding bifurcations. Our numerical analysis details their occurrence in a third-order relay feedback system. We show that these novel transitions lead to the formation of the chaotic attractor presented in fig. 10.

All these novel bifurcations can be studied analytically by means of the Poincaré maps we introduced. Current work to be presented elsewhere [12] is aimed at carrying out the analytical investigation of these transitions for a general class of n-dimensional PWS systems while deriving appropriate normal form maps in a neighborhood of the bifurcation point. This will allow a classification of all possible bifurcation scenarios following one of the transitions presented in this paper.

We conjecture that the bifurcations described in this paper are common in applications involving a wider class of switched dynamical systems with sliding. Moreover, we anticipate that they are an important mechanism leading to the formation of deterministic chaos and other complex behaviour in hybrid dynamical systems.

References

1. Ugo Galvanetto and Steven R. Bishop. Dynamics of a simple damped oscillator undergoing stick-slip vibrations. *Meccanica 34*, pages 337–347, 1999.
2. K. Popp N. Hinrichs, M. Oestereich. On the modelling of friction oscillators. *Journal of sound and Vibration*, 216, 1998.
3. B. Broglietto. *Non smooth Mechanics*. Springer Verlag, 1999.
4. A. Rantzer K. H. Johansson. Global analysis of third-order relay feedback systems. *Proceedings 13th IFAC World Congress*, E, 1996.
5. Robert Pique Enric Fossas. The parallel resonant converter. a dynamical system approach. *Proceedings of European Power Electronics Conference (EPE95)*, 1995.
6. Dick. H. van Campen Remco. I. Leine. Bifurcations in nonlinear discontinouos systems. *Nonlinear dynamics*, 23:105–164, October 2000.
7. I. Flugge-Lotz. *Discontinuous automatic control*. Princenton University Press, 1953.
8. A. Andronow, S. E. Khaikin, and A. A. Vitt. *Theory of oscillators*. Pergamon Press, Oxford, 1965.
9. Karl Henrik Johansson. *Relay feedback and Multivariable Control*. Department of Automatic Control, Lund Institute of Technology, 1997.
10. Mario di Bernardo, Karl Henrik Johansson, and Francesco Vasca. Self-oscillations and sliding in relay feedback systems: Symmetry and bifurcations. *International Journal of Bifurcation and Chaos*, to appear Vol. 11, no. 4, April 2001.
11. T. T. Georgiou S. Varigonda. Dynamics of relay relaxation oscillators. *to appear in IEEE, Transactions on Automatic Control*, January 2001.
12. M. diBernardo A. Nordmark, P. Kowlaczyk. Bifurcations of dynamical systems with sliding. *In preparation*, 2001.
13. V. I. Utkin. *Sliding Modes in Control Optimization*. Springer-Verlag, Berlin, 1992.
14. Ya. Z. Tsypkin. *Relay Control Systems,*. Cambridge University Press, Cambridge, U.K, 1984.
15. M. Feigin. *Forced oscillation in systems with discontinuous nonlinearities*. Nauka Moscow, 1994 (*in Russian*).
16. M. diBernardo P. Kowlaczyk. On the existance of stable asymmetric limit cycles and chaos in unforced symmetric relay feedback systems. *submitted to the European Control Conference*, Lisbone 2001.
17. P. G. Drazin. *Nonlinear systems*. Cambridge University Press, 1992.

Global Controllability of Hybrid Systems with Controlled and Autonomous Switchings[*]

Ekaterina S. Lemch[1], Shankar Sastry[1], and Peter E. Caines[2]

[1] Dept. of Electrical Engineering and Computer Sciences
275 Cory Hall 1774
University of California at Berkeley
Berkeley, CA, 94720-1774, U.S.A.
{lemch,sastry}@eecs.berkeley.edu
[2] Department of Electrical and Computer Engineering
McGill University
3480 University Street, Montreal
Quebec, Canada H3A 2A7
peterc@cim.mcgill.ca

Abstract. In this paper we investigate the question of the global controllability posed for control hybrid systems with autounomous and controlled swithchings. The main tool for our analysis is the notion of the *controlled hybrifold*. New sufficient conditions for the global controllability are obtained in terms of the so-called *hybrid fountains*.

1 Introduction

In this paper we consider systems which have a hybrid nature, in the sense that the dynamics of the system combines continuous and discrete components. We model *control hybrid systems* as a tuple consisting of a state space, a set of admissible continuous and discrete controls, a family of controlled vector fields assigned to each discrete state, a collection of autonomous and controlled switching surfaces, and a collection of the correspondint reset maps.

The main question investigated in the paper is the controllability of control hybrid systems. This issue has been addressed in [1,5,12,13]. In particular, in [12], the notion of controllability for hybrid systems is formalized by continuity of system functions. In [1], the authors derive a necessary and sufficient algebraic condition for a certain subclass of piecewise affine hybrid systems. In [13], a sufficient condition for controllability of hybrid systems is formulated in terms of the so-called *arrival sets*.

Because of the complexity of the problem of the global controllability, its unlikely to find uniform sufficient conditions for general hybrid systems. Thus, we restrict our study to a special subclass of control hybrid systems, namely, the systems that can be represented as *hybrifolds*. The notion of the hybrifold

[*] The work is supported by DARPA under F33615-98-C-3614 and NSERC grant number OGP 0001329.

M.D. Di Benedetto, A. Sangiovanni-Vincentelli (Eds.): HSCC 2001, LNCS 2034, pp. 375–386, 2001.

was originally introduced in [14] and extended to control hybrid systems with autonomous switchings in [9] (see also [6], where the hybrifold notion is used in problems of optimal control for hybrid systems). In this paper we generalize the results formulated in [9] to systems that admit both autonomous and controlled switchings. New sufficient conditions for the global controllability are obtained in terms of the so called *hybrid fountains*. The advantage of the approach proposed in this paper is in the fact, that the fountain property can be verified at each particular state and, hence, there is no need to invoke a dynamic programming-like procedure to determine arrival sets of the system.

The paper is organized as follows. In Section 2, we formally define the class of control hybrid systems H under our consideration and specify the standard assumptions on the continuous and discrete parts of the dynamics of H. In Section 3, we generalize the notion of the *hybrifold* to control hybrid systems with controlled and autonomous switchings and define a controlled flow on the hybrifold. Section 4 relates the global controllability of H to the global controllability of the associated controlled hybrifold. In Section 5, we introduce the notion of a *hybrid fountain* and provide new sufficient conditions for the global controllability of control hybrid systems.

2   Regular Control Hybrid Systems: Standing Assumptions

We consider *control hybrid systems* which in this paper are taken to be of the following form.

Definition 1. An *n-dimensional control hybrid systems* H is a 6-tuple

$$H = \{Q, \mathcal{D}, \mathcal{S}, \mathcal{R}, \Sigma, \mathcal{F}\}, \tag{1}$$

where

$Q = \{1, \cdots, k\}$, $1 \leq k < \infty$, is a set of discrete states (which are called *control locations*);

$\mathcal{D} = \{D_i; \ i \in Q, D_i \subset \mathbb{R}^n\}$ is a collection of *domains* of H;

$\mathcal{S} = \mathcal{S}_a \cup \mathcal{S}_c$ is a collection of autonomous and controlled *switching surfaces*;

$\mathcal{R} = \mathcal{R}_a \cup \mathcal{R}_c$ is a collection of autonomous and control *resets*.

$\Sigma = \Sigma_c \cup \Sigma_d$ is the set of admissible continuous and discrete *controls*;

$\mathcal{F} = \{f_i; \ i \in Q, f_i : D_i \times \mathbb{R}^{n_u} \to \mathbb{R}^n\}$ is a collection of control vector fields assigned to each location;

□

Each of these components shall be further specified in the next part of the section.

The collections of autonomous swithching surfaces (called *guards*) and autonomous resets

$$\mathcal{S}_a = \{S_a^{ij}; \ (i,j) \in E_a\} \qquad \mathcal{R}_a = \{R_a^{ij}; \ (i,j) \in E_a\},$$

where $E_a \subset Q \times Q$, are such that each guard S_a^{ij} is a subset of D_i and each autonomous reset R_a^{ij} is a continuous injective map acting from S_a^{ij} to D_j.

Similarly, for controlled switching surfaces and resets we have:

$$\mathcal{S}_c = \{S_c^{ij}; \ (i,j) \ \epsilon \ E_c\} \qquad \mathcal{R}_c = \{R_c^{ij}; \ (i,j) \ \epsilon \ E_c\},$$

where $E_c \subset Q \times Q$, each controlled switching surface S_c^{ij} is a subset of D_i, and each controlled reset R_c^{ij} is a continuous injective map acting from S_c^{ij} to D_j.

The set of discrete controls Σ_d is taken to be $\{\sigma_{ij}; \ (i,j) \ \epsilon \ E_c\}$, where each σ_{ij} is a discrete control that can be applied at (and only at) states $x \ \epsilon \ S_c^{ij}$.

Take an arbitrary initial state (i, x_0) which does not lie on any of the switching surfaces. Then, for any control $u \ \epsilon \ \Sigma_c$, the systems evolves according to the ODE

$$\dot{x} = f_i(x, u), \qquad x(0) = x_0$$

until it hits (at some point $\bar{x}$) either (i) a guard S_a^{ij} or (ii) a controlled switching surface S_c^{ik}.

In the former case (i), the system necessarily switches to the discrete location j and the continuous component of the states resets to $R_a^{ij}(\bar{x})$. Next, the system evolves according to the dynamics f_j in the domain D_j.

In the latter case (ii), we distinguish two possibilities.

(ii.a) The discrete control σ_{ik} is applied at $\bar{x}$; then the system switches to the location k and the continuous component of the state resets to $R_c^{ik}(\bar{x})$. Next, the system evolves according to f_k in D_k.

(ii.b) The discrete control σ_{ik} is not applied; the system continues evolving according to f_i in D_i.

The following definition of a hybrid time trajectory is based on [10,11].

Definition 2 (Forward Hybrid Time Trajectory).
A *(forward) hybrid time trajectory* is a sequence of semi-closed intervals

$$\tau = \{[\tau_i, \tau_{i+1}); \ 1 \leq i \leq N \leq \infty, \tau_i < \tau_{i+1}\}.$$

We shall use the symbol $N(\tau)$ to denote the size of the time trajectory (i.e. the number of semi-intervals in the sequence τ), the symbol $\langle \tau \rangle$ to denote the set $\{1, 2, \cdots, N(\tau)\}$, and the symbol τ_∞ to denote the *execution time*, which, for a finite $N(\tau)$, is defined to be $\tau_\infty \ \underline{\Delta} \ \tau_{N(\tau)+1} - \tau_1$. $\qquad \square$

Based on the above description of the evolution of H, for any control pair (u, σ), where u is a continuous control in Σ_c and σ is a sequence of discrete controls $\{v_1, v_2, \cdots, v_k; \ v_i \ \epsilon \ \Sigma_d\}$, we can define the notion of the control execution $\chi = \{\tau, q, \phi\}$ of H starting at the initial state $p \ \epsilon \ D$, where

(i) τ is a hybrid time trajectory that contains the sequence of the switching times;

(ii) $q : \langle \tau \rangle \rightarrow Q$ is a map that contains the sequence of discrete locations visited by the hybrid trajectory;

(iii) $\phi = \{\phi_j; j \in \langle \tau \rangle\}$ is the collection of continuously differentiable maps of t that satisfies the corresponding ODEs and the switching conditions as described above.

As in [14], we shall restrict ourselves to the study of hybrid systems that are subject to the following assumptions.

A1 The control hybrid system H_w is deterministic and non-blocking, for any control pair $w = (u, \sigma)$.

A2 For each $i \in Q$, D_i is assumed to be a non-empty, closed, contractible n-dimensional sub-manifold of $\mathbb{R}^n$, with a piecewise smooth boundary.

A3 For each $e \in E_a$ and $\tilde{e} \in E_c$, the guard S_a^e and the controlled switching surface $S_c^{\tilde{e}}$ are closed $(n-1)$-dimensional submanifolds with a piecewise smooth boundary. These sets have finite number of connected components.

A4 All resets maps are continuous and injective.

A5 None of the autonomous transition sets (i.e. $\{S_a^e, R_a^e(S_a^e); \quad e \in E_a\}$; denoted $ATrans$) have intersections with the controlled transition sets (i.e. $\{S_c^{\tilde{e}}, R_c^{\tilde{e}}(S_c^{\tilde{e}}); \quad \tilde{e} \in E_c\}$; denoted $CTrans$). Further, for any two (autonomous or controlled) transition sets B_1, B_2 (denoted $Trans$), we have

$$B_1 \cap B_2 \neq \emptyset \Rightarrow B_1 = S_c^{ij_1} = B_2 = S_c^{ij_2},$$

for some $i, j_1, j_2 \in Q$.

Remark 1. We note that the restriction $S_a^e \cap S_c^{\tilde{e}} = \emptyset$ comes from the fact that H is assumed to be deterministic. The rest of the restrictions of $A5$ can be somewhat relaxed. We impose $A5$ to avoid cumbersome technical details, while illustrating the point that certain hybrid systems can be represented as manifolds (termed *hybrifolds*), and thus, results on the global controllability formulated for manifolds can be transformed to hybrid systems.   □

Next we list the assumptions on the continuous part of the dynamics of H.

B1 For each $i \in Q$, $X_i \in C^r(D_i \times U; \mathbb{R}^n)$, $r \in \{1, 2, \cdots, \infty, \omega\}$, where C^ω denotes the class of analytic functions.

B2 The set of *admissible control functions*

$$\Sigma_c = \Sigma_c{}^s(\mathbb{R}; \mathbb{R}^{n_u}), s \in \{1, 2, \cdots, \infty\},$$

is the set of all $\mathbb{R}^{n_u}$-valued bounded piecewise $C^s(\mathbb{R}; \mathbb{R}^{n_u})$ functions of time with limits from the right. Hence any $u \in \Sigma_c$, defined on some $[T_1, T_2)$, $T_2 < \infty$, is C^s on $[T_1, T_2)$ with the exception of a finite number of points.

For the results formulated in this paper we shall need $r = 1$, $s = 1$.

Definition 3. A control hybrid system satisfying assumptions A1-A5 and B1-B2 is called a *regular* control hybrid system with controlled and autonomous switchings.   □

Finally, it shall be assumed that the system H is *non-Zeno* in the sense that in finite time only a finite number of discrete transitions may be generated.

Lemma 1. Let H be a regular control hybrid system. For any control pair (u, σ) and any $p \in D$, there exists a unique control execution of H starting at p. □

3   Controlled Hybrifold

In [14], a set M_H (called the *hybrifold*) is constructed from a hybrid system with autonomous switchings H. In this section we generalize this procedure to hybrid systems with autonomous and controlled switchings, prove that the resulting set M_H is a manifold and, finally, define the *controlled hybrid flow* on M_H.

The basic idea in the construction of the hybrifold is to *glue* together each switching surface to the image of the corresponding reset map by identifying any state $p \in S_s^e$, where $e \in E_s$, $s = a, c$, with the corresponding image $R_s^e(p)$. So an equivalence relation $\sim$ on $D \overset{\Delta}{=} \bigcup_{i=1}^{\|Q\|} D_i$ is generated by

$$p \sim R_s^e(p),$$

for all $e \in E_s$ and $p \in S_s^e$. This relation gives rise to the quotient space

$$M_H = D/\sim,$$

where each equivalence class is collapsed to a point.

Let π be the natural projection map

$$\pi : D \to M_H$$

which assigns to each p its equivalence class. We put the quotient topology on M_H, i.e. the smallest topology in which $V \subset M_H$ is open if and only if $\pi^{-1}(V) \subset D$ is open (in the relative topology of D).

Definition 4. The set M_H with the quotient topology defined on it is called the *controlled hybrifold* associated with H. □

The following result is based on [14].

Theorem 1. M_H is a topological n-manifold with boundary. □

Henceforth we shall deal not with the original domains D_i but rather with the hybrifold M_H. We shall assume, without loss of generality, that M_H is embedded in $\mathbb{R}^m$, for some $n \leq m < \infty$.

Definition 5 (Hybrid Control Flow). Take an arbitrary continuous control $u \in \Sigma_c$ defined on some $[T_1, T_2)$, $T_2 < \infty$, a sequence of discrete controls σ, and a state $x \in M_H$. Let $p \in \pi^{-1}(x)$.

As follows from Lemma 1, there exists a unique control execution $\chi = \{\tau, q, \phi\}$ of H starting at p which corresponds to the control pair (u, σ).

We shall use the symbol $\Psi^H(t, x, u, \sigma)$, $t \in [T_1, T_2)$, to denote the *controlled hybrid flow* on M_H. $\Psi^H(t, x, u, \sigma)$ is defined as follows:

$$\Psi^H(t, x, u, \sigma) \triangleq \pi(\phi_i(t)), \text{ for any } i \in \langle \tau \rangle \text{ and } t \in [\tau_i, \tau_{i+1}).$$

In particular, we have $\Psi^H(\tau_1, x, u, \sigma) = \pi(\phi_1(\tau_1)) = \pi(p) = x$.   □

Remark 2. We note that, as follows from the Assumption A5, the definition of the control flow on M_H does not depend on the choice of the representative p in the equivalence class x.   □

Lemma 2. For any control u, the controlled hybrid flow $\Psi^H(\cdot, x, u, \sigma)$ is continuous on M_H with respect to the argument t.

Proof: This follows from the fact that all points of discontinuity of the control hybrid execution are removed by identifying them with their images under the corresponding reset maps.   □

4   The Global Controllability of Hybrid Systems

Let H be an arbitrary regular control hybrid system and M_H its controlled hybrifold. In this section we relate the global controllability of the total domain D of H with the global controllability of M_H.

Definition 6 (Accessible sets of the control hybrid system H).
Let $p \in D$. We shall say that a state $p' \in D$ is *accessible from p (with respect to $V \subset D$)* if there exists a continuous control $u \in \Sigma_c$, defined on some $[T_1, T_2)$, $T_2 < \infty$, and a sequence of discrete controls $\sigma = \{v_1, \cdots, v_k\}$ such that the corresponding control execution $\chi = (\tau, q, \phi)$ of H starting at p satisfies

(i) $\phi_{N(\tau)}(T) = p'$, for some $T \in [\tau_{N(\tau)}; \tau_{N(\tau)+1})$; and
(ii) for any $j \in \langle \tau \rangle$ and $t \in [\tau_j; \tau_{j+1})$, $\phi_j(t) \in V$.

The set of all states in D accessible from p (with respect to V) shall be denoted by $A_D^V(p)$. In the case $V = D$, we shall write $A_D(p)$.   □

Thus we assumed that an accessible state p' can be reached from p in finite time using a finite number of switching (or *jumps*) between control locations.

Remark 3. We observe that, as follows from the definition of the control execution of H, $R_s^e(p) \in A_D(p)$, for any state $p \in S_s^e$, $e \in E_s$, $s = a, c$.   □

Similarly, we can define the accessible states using the dynamics of the controlled hybrifold M_H.

Definition 7 (Accessible sets of the controlled hybrifold M_H).
Let $x \, \epsilon \, M_H \subset \mathbb{R}^m$. We shall say that a state $x' \, \epsilon \, M_H$ is *accessible from x (with respect to $V \subset M_H$)* if there exists a continuous control $u \, \epsilon \, \Sigma_c$ defined on some $[T_1, T_2)$, $T_2 < \infty$, and a sequence of discrete controls $\sigma = \{v_1, \cdots, v_k\}$ such that

(i) $x' = \Psi^H(T, x, u, \sigma)$, for some $T \, \epsilon \, [T_1, T_2)$; and
(ii) for any $T_1 \leq t \leq T$, $\Psi^H(t, x, u, \sigma) \, \epsilon \, V$.

The set of all states in M_H accessible from x (with respect to V) shall be denoted by $A^V(x)$. In the case $V = M_H$, we shall write $A(x)$. □

The set of all states *co-accessible* to p (to x), with respect to $V \subset D$ (with respect to $V \subset M_H$), in H (in M_H) is defined dually and shall be denoted as $CA_D^V(p)$ (as $CA^W(x)$).

Remark 4. We observe that for any $p \, \epsilon \, D$ and any neighborhood V of p in D, we have

$$\pi(A_D^V(p)) \subset A^{\pi(V)}(\pi(p)), \tag{2}$$

where $\pi : D \longrightarrow M_H$ is the natural projection map. This is because any orbit in D is projected by π onto an orbit in M_H.

On the other hand, let $p, p' \, \epsilon \, D$ and let $\pi(p') \, \epsilon \, A^V(\pi(p))$. Then there exist some $y, y' \, \epsilon \, D$ such that (i) $p \sim y$, $p' \sim y'$ and (ii) $y' \, \epsilon \, A_D^{\pi^{-1}(V)}(y)$. In other words, the existence of a trajectory from $\pi(p)$ to $\pi(p')$ in M_H does not necessarily imply the existence of a control execution connecting p to p'; it only implies the existence of a control execution from some $y \, \epsilon \, D$ to some $y' \, \epsilon \, D$, where $y \sim p$ and $y' \sim p'$.

This is particularly easy to see in the situation, where at some controlled switching surface S_c^{ij} at least two discrete controlled σ_{ij_1}, σ_{ij_2} can be applied. Take $x \, \epsilon \, S_c^{ij}$ and consider $y_1 = R_c^{ij_1}(x)$ and $y_2 = R_c^{ij_2}(x)$. Then x, y_1, y_2 lie in the same equivalence class (they are glued together in M_H) and, hence, $\pi(y_1)$ and $\pi(y_2)$ are mutually accessible in M_H. At the same time y_1 and y_2 are not necessarily mutually accessible in D.

Hence in general, we do not have the reverse to (2) inclusion and we can only guarantee that for any $x \, \epsilon \, M_H$ and $V \subset M_H$,

$$A^V(x) \subset \pi \left\{ \bigcup_{p \epsilon \pi^{-1}(x)} A_D^{\pi^{-1}(V)}(p) \right\}. \tag{3}$$

□

Definition 8. We say that a set $D_1 \subset D$ is *controllable with respect to $D_2 \subset D$* for the control hybrid system H if $A_D^{D_2}(p) = D_1$, for all $p \, \epsilon \, D_1$.

In the particular case when $D_1 = D$, $D_2 = D$, and $A_D(p) = D$, for all $p \, \epsilon \, D$, we shall say that the total domain D is *globally controllable* for H.

Similarly, we shall say that a set $C_1 \subset M_H$ is *controllable with respect to $C_2 \subset M_H$* if $A^{C_2}(x) = C_1$, for all $x \, \epsilon \, C_1$. M_H is *globally controllable* if $A(x) = M_H$, for all $x \, \epsilon \, M_H$. □

Theorem 2. Let H be a regular control hybrid system. Then the total domain D is globally controllable if and only if the associated hybrifold M_H is globally controllable.

Proof:
$\implies$ Let D be globally controllable. Then, using Remark 4 (2), we obtain for any $x \in M_H$,

$$M_H = \pi(D) = \pi(A_D(p)) \subset A^{\pi(D)}(\pi(p)) = A(x) \subset M_H,$$

where p is an arbitrary point in the set $\pi^{-1}(x) \subset D$. Hence $A(x) = M_H$, for any $x \in M_H$, and M_H is globally controllable.

$\impliedby$ Conversely, let M_H be globally controllable. Take any $p, p' \in D$. Each of them could lie in any of the sets

$$CTrans, ATrans, \tilde{D} \triangleq D - Trans,$$

i.e. there are 9 possible cases.

Consider, for instance, the case when $p \in R_c^e(S_c^e)$ and $p' \in R_c^{e'}(S_c^{e'})$, for some $e = (i,j), e' = (i,j') \in E_c$. Take the inverse image $y' = \{R_c^{e'}\}^{-1}(p')$. As follows from the description of the hybrid executions given in Section 2, there exist states $z \in D_j \cap \tilde{D}$ and $z' \in D_i \cap \tilde{D}$ such that z is accessible from y and z' is co-accessible to y'. Next note, that since $z, z' \in D - Trans$ and π is 1 to 1 on $\tilde{D}$, from the existence of an orbit connecting $\pi(z)$ to $\pi(z')$ in M_H follows the existence of a control execution that drives z to z'. Finally, combining all the accessibility relations for p, z, z', y', p' we conclude that $p' \in A_D(p)$.

The rest of the cases can be considered in an analogous manner. Thus $A_D(p) = D$, for any $p \in D$, and D is globally controllable. $\qquad\square$

The above result allows us to use the hybrifold and the continuous controlled hybrid flow defined on it in order to study the global controllability of the original control hybrid system. The advantage of this approach is in the fact that the controllability results formulated for differential control systems acting on subsets or sub-manifolds of $\mathbb{R}^n$ can be transformed to control hybrid systems. This shall be demonstrated in the next section.

5   Hybrid Fountains

In this section we introduce the notion of a *hybrid fountain* which we shall use as the main hypothesis in our controllability result. Henceforth the symbol $B_\delta(x)$, where $x \in M_H$, $0 < \delta \in \mathbb{R}^1$, shall denote the m-dimensional ball with the center x and the radius δ. The sets $A^{B_\delta(p)}(p)$ and $CA^{B_\delta(p)}(p)$ shall be denoted as $A^\delta(p)$ and $CA^\delta(p)$, respectively.

Definition 9. A state $x \in M_H$ is called a *hybrid fountain* if

$$\exists\, \mu > 0 \; \forall\, \delta,\; 0 < \delta < \mu,\; A^\delta(x) - \{x\} \text{ and } CA^\delta(x) - \{x\}$$
$$\text{are non-empty, open sets.} \tag{4}$$

If the function $\rho \triangleq \sup\{\mu;$ such that the condition (4) holds$\}$ is continuous at x, we shall say that x is a *continuous* hybrid fountain. If ρ is unbounded at x we consider it to be continuous at x. □

The reader is referred to [2,3,7] for applications of the fountain condition to the study of ordinary differential systems acting on subsets of $\mathbb{R}^n$. See also [8], where a set of algebraic conditions for verification of the fountain property is presented, and [4] where applications to *hierarchical hybrid control theory* are outlined.

Henceforth we shall use the term *controlled closed orbit* in the sense of *controlled loop*.

Theorem 3. Let each $x \in M_H$ be a continuous hybrid fountain and let for each $x \in M_H$ there exist a control $u \in \Sigma_c$ such that x lies on a nontrivial (controlled under u) closed orbit in M_H. Then each connected component of $[M_H]^\circ$ is controllable with respect to M_H.

Proof: Let C denote one of (the finite number of) the connected components of $[M_H]^\circ$. For any two states x, x' in C we define a relation $\sim_o$ in such a way that $x \sim_o x'$ if and only if there exists a (controlled) nontrivial closed orbit in M_H passing through both x and x', i.e. there exists a control pair u, σ defined on some $[T_1, T_2)$, $T_2 < \infty$, such that

(i) $\exists T, \ T_1 < T < T_2, \ \Psi(T_1, x, u, \sigma) = \Psi(T, x, u, \sigma)$; and
(ii) $\exists \bar{t}, \ T_1 < \bar{t} \leq T, \ \Psi(\bar{t}, p, u, \sigma) = p'$.

Clearly, the relation $\sim_o$ is reflexive (since each state in M_H lies on a nontrivial orbit), symmetric and transitive. Hence there exists a partition of C on the equivalence classes of $\sim_o$. Let $[x]$, for an arbitrary $x \in C$, denote the equivalence class containing x. We **claim** that $[x]$ is an open subset in C.

Indeed, take any $z \in [x]$. Let u and $0 \leq t < \infty$ be such that $z = \Psi(t, x, u, \sigma)$. Define $a = \Psi(t - \Delta, x, u, \sigma)$ and $b = \Psi(t + \Delta, x, u, \sigma)$, $\Delta > 0$. Then, since a and b are hybrid fountains, the sets $A^\delta(a) - \{a\}$ and $CA^\delta(b) - \{b\}$ are open, for sufficiently small $\delta > 0$. Choose Δ so small that $z \in A^\delta(a)$ and $z \in CA^\delta(b)$ (this is possible since a, b are *continuous* hybrid fountains). Then there exists an open neighborhood $N(z)$ of z which lie in the intersection $(A^\delta(a) - \{a\}) \cap (CA^\delta(b) - \{b\})$. Each state $z' \in N(z)$ is accessible from a and co-accessible to b. Moreover, since $a, b \in [x]$, we conclude that z' lies on a non-trivial orbit passing through x. This is true for all $z' \in N(z)$, hence $N(z) \subset [x]$ and $[x]$ is open, as **claimed**.

For any $x, x' \in C$ we have $[x] \cap [x'] \neq \emptyset \implies [x] = [x']$, so any two equivalence classes are either disjoint or coincide. Thus the set C can be represented as the disjoint union $C = A \cup B$, where $A \triangleq [x]$, for some $x \in C$, and $B \triangleq \bigcup_{\substack{x' \in C \\ x' \notin [x]}} [x']$.

A and B are open and disjoint. Since C is connected, we conclude that B is empty, i.e. any $x' \in C$ is such that $x \sim_o x'$. In other words, any two states in C lie on a nontrivial controlled orbit in M_H and hence, C is controllable with respect to M_H. □

Remark 5. We note at this point that weaker recurrence conditions can be used instead of the existence of closed orbits. Also, for the proof of the above result, the continuous hybrid fountain condition (4) can be relaxed to

$$\rho(x) \triangleq \sup\{\mu > 0; A^\mu(x) - \{x\}, CA^\mu(x) - \{x\} \text{ are non-empty, open sets}\}$$

is continuous, for all $x \in M_H$.   □

Theorem 4. Assume that the hybrifold M_H is connected and the conditions of Theorem 3 are satisfied. Then M_H is globally controllable.

Proof: As has been shown in [14], M_H is n-dimensional manifold (possibly with boundary). This implies, by definition, that for any boundary state in ∂M_H there exists a neighborhood which is homeomorphic to $\mathbb{R}^n_+$. Hence $[M_H]^\circ$ and M_H have the same number of connected components; in particular, $[M_H]^\circ$ is connected if and only if M_H is connected.

Take any boundary state $x \in \partial M_H$. Then, since x is a hybrid fountain, the sets $A^\delta(x) - \{x\}$ and $CA^\delta(x) - \{x\}$ are non-empty and open, for sufficiently small $\delta > 0$. Hence there exist $a \in (A^\delta(x) - \{x\}) \cap [M_H]^\circ$ and $b \in (CA^\delta(x) - \{x\}) \cap [M_H]^\circ$.

For any state $p' \in [M_H]^\circ$ we can find a control $u \in \Sigma_c$ which would drive a p' and a control $u' \in \Sigma_c$ which would drive p' to b. This is because a, b, p' lie in $[M_H]^\circ$ and, as follows from Theorem 3, $[M_H]^\circ$ is controllable. We conclude that arbitrary $p \in \partial M_H$ and $p' \in [M_H]^\circ$, and thus arbitrary $p, p' \in M_H$, are mutually accessible. Hence M_H is globally controllable.   □

Consider the *directed graph* Γ of H which has vertices Q and edges E. We can treat it as a finite state machine, by defining the transition function $\Phi : Q \to Q$ in such a way that for any $i, j \in Q$, $\Phi(i) = j$ if and only if $(i, j) \in E$ or $i = j$.

Theorem 5. Assume that the conditions of Theorem 3 are satisfied. Then M_H is globally controllable if and only if the graph $\Gamma = \{Q, E\}$ is controllable as a finite state machine.

Proof:

$\Longrightarrow$ Assume that M_H is globally controllable. Then for any $i, j \in Q$, $i \neq j$, take some states $p \in D_i$ and $p' \in D_j$. There exists a trajectory ψ from p to p' in M_H. Let the sequence $i = r_1, r_2, \cdots, r_\ell = j$, $\ell > 1$, be such that ψ switches consecutively from the domain D_{r_s} to the domain $D_{r_{s+1}}$, where $s = 1, 2, \cdots, \ell-1$, using the corresponding guards and the images of the reset maps. Hence each consecutive pair (r_s, r_{s+1}) belongs to E and hence, there exists a trajectory from the state i to the state j in the graph Γ. Since this holds for an arbitrary pair $(i, j) \in Q$, we conclude that Γ is controllable as a finite state machine.

$\Longleftarrow$ Conversely, assume that Γ is controllable as a finite state machine. Then for any two states $p, p' \in D$ take i and j such that $p \in D_i$ and $p' \in D_j$. If $i \neq j$, find a trajectory $i = r_1, r_2, \cdots, r_\ell = j$, $\ell > 1$, in the graph Γ. Since each consecutive pair (r_s, r_{s+1}) belongs to E, there exists a guard $G_{(r_s, r_{s+1})}$ in the domain D_{r_s} which is identified with the image of the reset map $R_{(r_s, r_{s+1})}$ in the domain $D_{r_{s+1}}$. Hence the domains D_{r_s} and $D_{r_{s+1}}$, and thus D_i and D_j, lie in one connected component of M_H. This can be shown for all $i, j \in Q$. Hence M_H is connected and, as follows from Theorem 4, M_H is globally controllable.   □

An application of the obtained results can be illustrated on a two water tank system example, which, for the lack of space, shall be described briefly. The water can be added to the system at some rate $w > 0$ (where we treat the parameter w as control) in two different modes:

1: the water is added (exclusively) via tank 1;
2: the water is added (exclusively) via tank 2.

In addition to that, the water is removed from tank i, $i = 1, 2$, at some constant rate $v_i > 0$. The two tank system can be modeled as a control hybrid system in the following way. We shall distinguish two control locations - each corresponds to one of the modes, i.e. $Q = \{1, 2\}$. The continuous dynamics at the locations are as:

$$q = 1: \quad \begin{cases} \dot{x} = w - v_1 \\ \dot{y} = -v_2 \end{cases} \quad (x, y) \in D_1 \triangleq \{[l_1, \infty) \times [l_2, \infty)\},$$

$$q = 2: \quad \begin{cases} \dot{x} = -v_1 \\ \dot{y} = w - v_2 \end{cases} \quad (x, y) \in D_2 \triangleq \{[l_1, \infty) \times [l_2, \infty)\},$$

where x, y denote the levels of water in the tanks 1 and 2, respectively.
The class of control functions is taken to be the set of all functions taking values in $\Re$ and satisfying B_2.
The guards are defined as

$$G_{(1,2)} = 1 \times \{(x, y) \in D_1; \ y = l_2\}, \quad G_{(2,1)} = 2 \times \{(x, y) \in D_2; \ x = l_1\}.$$

The resets are defined in such a way that when hitting a guard in one domain the system switches to the other control location, without changing the continuous part of the state, i.e.

$$R_{(1,2)}(1; x, l_2) = (2; x, l_2), \quad R_{(2,1)}(2; l_1, y) = (1; l_1, y).$$

Furthermore, assume that for some level $y = l$, $l \geq l_2$, in the first tank, a discrete switching to the second tank is allowed.
To construct the corresponding controlled hybrifold we identify (via the identity reset maps) the $x = l_1$, $y = l_2$, $y = l$ axes of D_1 with the $x = l_1$, $y = l_2$, $y = l$ axes of D_2, respectively.

Using the obtained results, it can be verified that each state of the hybrifold is a hybrid fountain lying on a closed orbit. Hence, the two water tank system can be shown to be globally controllable.

Remark 6. In conclusion we note that algebraic conditions for verification of the fountain property at each state $x \in M_H$ shall be presented in a future version of the paper.

References

1. A.Bemporad, G. Ferrari-Trecate, and R. Morari. Observability and controllability of piecewise affine and hybrid systems. In *Proceedings of the 38th IEEE Control Systems Society Conference on Decision and Control*, pages 3966–3971, Phoenix, AZ., Phoenix, AZ, 1999.
2. P.E. Caines and E.S. Lemch. On the global controllability of Hamiltonian and other nonlinear systems: fountains and recurrence. In *Proceedings of the 37th IEEE Control Systems Society Conference on Decision and Control*, pages 3575–3580, Tampa, FL, 1998.
3. P.E. Caines and E.S. Lemch. On the global controllability of nonlinear systems: fountains, recurrence, and application to Hamiltonian systems. *Submitted to SIAM J. on Control and Optimization*, 2000.
4. P.E. Caines and E.S. Lemch. *Hierarchical hybrid systems: geometry, controllability and applications to air traffic control*. Proceedings of 14th World IFAC, volume E, Beijing, China, July, 1999.
5. J. Ezzine and A.H. Haddad. Controllability and observability of hybrid systems. *Int. J. Control*, 49(6):2045–2055, 1989.
6. Ekaterina S. Lemch, Jianghai Hu, and Shankar Sastry. Approximation techniques in optimal control problems for a class of hybrid systems. *Hybrid Systems: Computation and Control, Third International Workshop*, 2001.
7. E.S. Lemch. Nonlinear and hierarchical hybrid control systems. *Ph.D. thesis, McGill University, Canada*, August, 1999.
8. E.S. Lemch and P.E. Caines. On the global controllability of nonlinear systems: algebraic conditions for the existence of fountains. *Fourteenth International Symposium on Mathematical Theory of Networks and Systems*, June, 19-23, 2000.
9. E.S. Lemch, S. Sastry, and P.E. Caines. On the global controllability of hybrid systems: Hybrifolds and fountains. In *To Appear in Proceedings of the 39th IEEE Control Systems Society Conference on Decision and Control*, Sydney, Australia, Sydney, Australia, 2000.
10. J. Lygeros, K.H. Johansson, S. Sastry, and M. Egerstedt. On the existence of executions of hybrid automata. In *Proceedings of the 38th IEEE Control Systems Society Conference on Decision and Control*. Phoenix, AZ, Phoenix, AZ, 1999.
11. J. Lygeros, C. Tomlin, and S. Sastry. Controllers for reachability specifications for hybrid systems. *Automatica*, 35(3), March, 1999.
12. A. Nerode and W. Kohn. Models for hybrid systems: automata topologies, controllability, observability. *Hybrid Systems*, pages 317–356, Berlin, Germany, 10-12 October, 1991.
13. J.H. Schuppen. A sufficient condition for controllability of a class of hybrid systems. *Hybrid Systems: Computation and Control, First International Workshop*, Berkeley, CA, April, 1998.
14. S.N. Simić, K.H. Johansson, S. Sastry, and J. Lygeros. Towards a geometric theory of hybrid systems. *Hybrid Systems: Computation and Control, Third International Workshop*, Pittsburgh, PA, 2000.

Modeling of Continuous-Discrete Processes

Vishal Bahl and Andreas A. Linninger

Department of Chemical Engineering, University of Illinois at Chicago, USA.
810 S. Clinton Street, Chicago, IL, U.S.A, 60607.
{vbahl1, linninge}@uic.edu,
http://vienna.che.uic.edu

Abstract. Models of industrial processes often contain discrete phenomena superimposed on the continuous system behavior. Simulation
of batch processes, start-up and shutdown procedures, fault diagnosis
and alarms fall under this category. Models for such processes require a
mathematical framework for both its continuous and discrete state transitions. A key problem in hybrid simulation lies in the detection and exact location of discontinuities that delineate state changes. Hence, hybrid
systems require special numerical procedures, which are not available in
conventional integration methods. In this paper, important issues pertaining to the numerical aspects in hybrid simulation will be discussed.
We will demonstrate a new approach to event handling. The main target
of this new approach is enhanced computational performance without
loss of rigor. The authors anticipate the significance of high speed in the
advent of new challenges in optimal control and dynamic optimization
problems. The improvements are due to the exploiting local monotonicity
and smooth function properties observed in varaible step-size integration
algorithms.

1   Introduction

The mathematical model for a physical process expresses mass, energy and momentum balances by means of differential equations. These solutions to the conservation equations lead to continuous trajectories of the state variables. In in-
dustrially relevant process models, however, discrete actions or discontinuities
may interrupt the continuous evolution of state variables. As an example, consider the cyclic operation of a batch unit under logical control. Each batch cycle
is composed of different stages or steps, e.g. fill, heat, react, etc. The system
dynamics in each state is governed by differential equations, and switching conditions that cause the transition from one stage to the next. The state transitions
of a process model could reflect physical discontinuities such as hysteresis or saturation. Otherwise, they may be externally imposed on the process by logical
controller actions or forcing function. Systems with discontinuities superimposed
on the continuous system behavior are termed continuous-discrete or hybrid systems. The dynamics of hybrid systems falls between two extremes: (i) Systems
are driven by continuous dynamics, if the number of discontinuities is small,
e.g. batch operations. (ii) In event-driven systems, discontinuities dominate the

M.D. Di Benedetto, A. Sangiovanni-Vincentelli (Eds.): HSCC 2001, LNCS 2034, pp. 387–402, 2001.

process dynamics, e.g. digital control system (DCS). Hence, continuous and the discrete sub-models could be viewed as either super-systems or sub-systems of each other. Standard numerical treatment of hybrid systems via 'continuous' integration methods breaks down at sufficiently abrupt discontinuities. Equally, discrete simulation techniques such as Petri-Nets fail to express continuous dynamics. Hence, a mathematical framework for addressing both continuous as well as discrete process dynamics effectively is needed. Recently, new challenges in optimal control and dynamic optimization involve discrete-continuous models for constraints in non-linear optimization functions [1]. The sensitivity function evaluations of gradient-based search techniques require repeated calls to the hybrid system equations. In the light of these repeated computations, the efficiency of the hybrid algorithm is crucial [2].

A concise presentation of effective algorithms for hybrid systems simulation, their strengths and weaknesses is the main goal of this article. Section 2 reviews and assesses prior work in hybrid simulation. Section 3 develops the mathematical framework for a new approach to efficient continuous-discrete simulation. It will present a hierarchical procedure based on statistical observations, yielding a desired performance increase. Section 4 discusses some of the advanced topic issues in hybrid simulation, e.g. multiple and simultaneous discontinuities in an interval. It also analyzes step-size control and recommends solver tolerances for the algorithm. Finally, an application in section 5 quantifies the performance of the new algorithm using benchmark case studies, and compares the proposed methodology with existing approaches.

2   Background

A hybrid system is characterized by three important elements (i) a continuous part (ii) a discrete part and (iii) state transitions [3]. The continuous dynamics of a physical process can be modeled by sets of differential equations. Transient balance equations lead to time-dependent trajectories of the state variables, i.e. the continuous part. The evolution of state variables may be interrupted by a discrete-time discontinuity called *'events'* , i.e. the discrete part. Events may involve discontinuous changes in the state variable values or their derivatives, a switch in the underlying model equation or both. After an event, the system traverses into a new state, i.e. state transition.

Each state of a continuous-discrete process can be associated to distinct mode, ξ. The *'continuous'* dynamics of each mode, ξ, involves a set of differential equations given by equation (1).

$$f_\xi(x, y, \dot{y}, u(t), t) = 0, t \in [t_n, t_{n+1}] \tag{1}$$

In (1), $f_\xi : R^{m_\xi} \times R^{n_\xi} \times R^{n_\xi} \times R^{l_\xi} \times R \mapsto R^{(n+m+1)_\xi}$ is a vector function; $x \in \Re^{m_\xi}$ and $y \in \Re^{n_\xi}$ denote the algebraic and differential variables respectively. $u(t) \in \Re^{l_\xi}$ are the known system inputs. The number and the type of model equations, f_ξ, are specific to the current mode ξ.

The cause for a transition into a new mode can be expressed mathematically by an event function. More precisely a switch occurs when the function, $z_{\xi\psi}$, crosses a threshold value of zero. The customary normalization to the right-hand-side zero explains its alias as z-function as given by equation (2).

$$z_{\xi\psi}(x, y, \dot{y}, t) = 0 \qquad (2)$$

In equation (2), $z_{\xi\psi}$, is termed the event function associated with the transition of mode ξ to mode ψ. It is a function of the state variable and the independent variable time. The state transition takes place at the exact time instant, t^*, at which the conditional, $z_{\xi\psi}$, becomes zero. This time, t^*, terminates the validity of the old mode ξ. The new mode ψ starts exactly at this same instant, giving rise to two sets of state variables values associated with time t^*. Each set corresponds to one mode ξ and ψ respectively.

In principle, hybrid systems of equation (1) and switching function (2) can be numerically integrated via integration routines combined with logical if-statements to check for transitions [4]. Gear [5], has shown that such a brute force approach with multi-step integration methods leads to gross losses in speed and accuracy. In the worst case, discontinuities may cause floating-point errors and a subsequent crash of the solver algorithm. A robust hybrid simulation algorithm should first identify whether events have occurred, locate their exact time, and execute the appropriate actions pertaining to the event. This approach usually involves a technique called discontinuity locking.

2.1   Discontinuity Locking

Multi-step integration routines solve systems of differential equations via repeated computations executed in small intervals with step-size h. In discontinuity locking, the validity of current state ξ is enforced throughout the entire length of the current integration step with a small step-size. Hence, the state variable trajectories are computed smoothly throughout the small interval using equations (1). Then, the trajectories of z-functions (equation 2) are examined for any possible zero-crossings in the current interval. This first phase is called *event detection*. A zero penetration, which must necessarily lie within the bounds of the current interval, h, indicate the occurrence of an event. This changeover is triggered for a zero penetration from both the negative or the positive side. The event with the earliest zero-crossing t^* is called the active event. The precise value of this event time, t^*, the corresponding values of all state variable values must be computed by adequate means such as interpolation. This second phase is termed *event location*. After locating the event time, the system switches into the new state as directed by the actions associated with the state transition. Possible conflicts among multiple and competing events have to be handled here also. Therefore this last stage is called *step completion*.

Discintinuity locking requires the ability to extrapolate into the undefined region smoothly. Therefore discontinuity locking may fail for systems bordering a numerical singularity such as logarithmic functions. Nevertheless, this approach has been incorporated in most of the algorithms ([6], [7], [8]).

2.2   Review of Existing Algorithms

Several algorithms have been developed earlier for detecting and locating discontinuities in a dynamic simulation problem. The algorithms vary in their approach to the event detection and location phases.

Carver [6] developed an event-handling algorithm for systems of ordinary differential equations. State transitions were modeled via algebraic discontinuity or event functions, cf. equation (2). Their differentials were appended to the systems' set of differential equations. The combined augmented system of differential equations was integrated using a modified Hindmarsh-Gear method. Events were identified by tracking sign changes of the event function in each integration step. Events were located by solving a qth order polynomial for a zero crossing. Hay and Griffin [9] used a similar approach based on an augmented system including the derivatives of the discontinuity functions, and sign changes of the event function. For event location, they deployed linear and quadratic interpolation with a reduced step size.

Joglekar and Reklaitis [7] detected events by checking for threshold crossing of event function. The event time was found by solving a qth order interpolation polynomial by means of a Newton's iteration scheme. However, their approach did not explicitly solve for the exact event time and was therefore prone to inaccuracy.

Birta et. al [10] approximated the event conditional by a cubic polynomial and considered all possible configurations of the polynomial for event detection. Events were located by a Regula-Falsi method and a Newton's iteration scheme. Shampine et al. [11] uses a Sturm sequence to determine the zero of a linear event conditional and locates the event time by using a bisection method in conjunction with a Sturm sequence.

Pantelides [12] directly integrated the algebraic event functions alongside the system differential equations. Zero crossings in the trajectories of this differential-algebraic system indicated events. Events were located using bisection method. Preston and Berzins [13] developed an event-handling algorithm for a particular class of dynamic simulation problems pertaining to valve operations. A discontinuity was detected through the use of a switch function that changed sign when the valve opens or closes. To find the time at which a discontinuity occurred, backward interpolation on the switch function was used.

Park [8] developed a rigorous event-handling algorithm with superior performance of the root exclusion than the one proposed by Shampine. It employed an interval arithmetic technique for event detection. The root finding procedure consisted of two steps (i) a root exclusion test and (ii) Newton's method with recursive interval bisection. The root exclusion test used interval arithmetic to obtain an interval enclosure. An interval enclosure of a function with one argument captures the largest and lowest values the function can assume. Functions with enclosures not containing zero cannot have a root in the interval of interest. Enclosures with zero may or may not exhibit a real root. Consequently, an interval Newton Method combined with interval bisection was deployed to analyze intervals with enclosures containing a zero.

The algorithms discussed above broadly fall into two categories: Type I algorithms only detect events that have a single zero crossing within the integration step. Type II algorithms can identify most events with multiple zero-crossings. The first category of algorithms is based on the conventional approach to event handling and detect a discontinuity by checking for a sign change in the event function ([6],[7],[9],[13]). While type I algorithms are fast, they are unreliable since they may miss situations with multiple roots in the interval. Many of the algorithms of this category also suffer from a phenomenon termed *discontinuity sticking*, first described by Park and Barton [8]. Small inaccuracies in the event function cause repeated firing of the same event in the subsequent integration steps. This undesirable effect is due to renewed zero crossing caused by small time drifts due to the double precision arithmetic of event location. Nevertheless, they are adequate for modeling physical systems with linear discontinuity functions.

Type II algorithms deploy more rigorous root exclusion tests for detection of discontinuities ([8], [11]). The root exclusion test eliminates state variable trajectories without zeros in the interval. The algorithms belonging to this category consume more manipulations than type I algorithms. In [8], a root exclusion test is based on a Sturm sequence [8]. In this approach, it is necessary to construct a Sturm sequence for an nth order polynomial which required $(n+1)(n+2)/2$ multiplications. On the other hand, Barton's root exclusion test uses a cleverly normalized interval arithmetic (IA) technique requiring just n evaluations [8]. However, the IA fails to identify a zero with multiplicity greater than one, because of singularity in the Interval Jacobian matrix. Moreover, the interval arithmetic is typically twice as expensive as conventional algebra. While IA methods are excellent for systems with a small number of events, they may not be optimal for event-driven systems.

In the following section a new algorithm with a more efficient root exclusion test is presented. A hierarchical approach to event detection based on the statistical evidence of event occurrence will be discussed. The improvements are mainly targeted at improved performance as required in the context of dynamic optimization ([1],[2]). A detailed discussion of the algorithm follows.

3   Hierarchical Approach to Discontinuity Handling in Event-Driven Processes

The main thrust of the new algorithm lies in providing a simple and yet rigorous root exclusion test for high-order numerical multi-step integrators with adaptable step-size control. Two avenues for performance improvements will be offered. Numerical experiments show that within an integration step, most variable trajectories are locally monotonic. This observation can be attributed to the step-size control mechanism, which discards trajectories with inflection points or non-smooth behavior. This property holds specifically true for most event conditionals of physical processes. A second issue exploits the fact that in most intervals no events occur. We will show in the next section how these two properties can be used advantageously for developing an efficient hybrid simulation algorithm.

Fig. 1 outlines the information flow of the variable step-size integrator with event-handling. White boxes demarcate the stages of standard high-order integrators; grayed fields underscore additional steps required for event handling. The event handling part traverses through the usual three stages: (i) event detection (ii) event location and (iii) step completion. The objective of event detection phase aims at examining whether any event function in the present mode had become zero in the current integration step. Step completion executes the actions associated with the state transition.

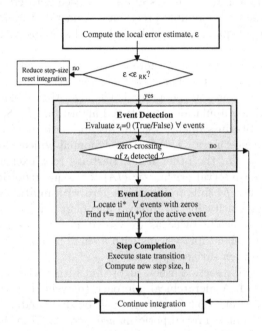

Fig. 1. Information flow diagram for integration with event-handling

3.1   Event Detection

For event detection, the event functions in equation (2) are examined. Statistical observations on monotonicity as well as events frequency led us to conceive a hierarchical procedure composed of three layers depicted in Figure 2. The top layer handles intervals with the highest likelihood of occurrence. Lower layers are necessary to safeguard rigor with increasing effort. Typically the lowest nesting levels are only reached in rare occasions such as the tough benchmark case studies in section 5.

Locally monotonic intervals. Local montonicity follows from same-signed gradients at the support points in high-order integrators. In case of a fifth order Runge-Kutta (RK) method [14], there are four gradients available at no additional effort. Hence, the montonicity test costs but a simple boolean operations for a sign change in the first derivatives. In most integration steps no events occur, and those with a zero crossing are likely to exhibit monotonic trajectory. For locally monotonic event functions, a sign-change corresponding to the beginning and the end of the integration interval, suffices for detecting an event. The adverse outcome of the monotonicity test indicates a rare non-monotonic interval.

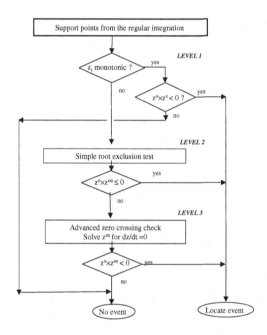

Fig. 2. Information flow diagram for hierarchical event detection

Locally non-monotonic intervals. For locally non-monotonic trajectories the second level of Fig. 2 is reached. We are especially interested in cheaply excluding non-monotonic intervals without zeros to avoid rigorous root search. For most intervals, a simple over-estimator or under-estimator to the event function is adequate, see figure 3 (i) and 3 (ii). The first order estimator, z^{ou}, requires the initial function and its gradients information as indicated by equation (3). Note that this test applies only for non-monotonic intervals where there is at least one zero in the first order. Therefore, the interval has to exhibit at least one extremal point. Hence z^{ou} should enclose the maxima or minima (see figure 3(i) and 3(ii))

$$z^{ou} = z^o + (\dot{z} \times h) \tag{3}$$

In the above equation, z^0 is the event conditional at the initial point in the interval, z its derivative, and h is current step size. Figure 3(iii) shows an instance in which the over/under-estimator envelope fails. Although these situations are possible in theory, the step-size control mechanism of figure 1 rejects such trajec-tories. A formal proof of this property based on principles of flexibility analysis is being developed, and will be discusses in [16].

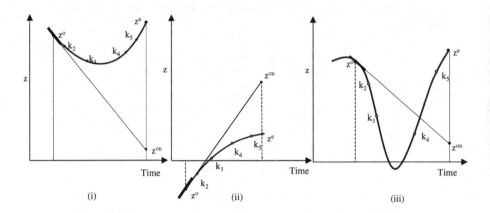

Fig. 3. estimators to the true function (i) under-estimator (ii) over-estimator to the function and (iii) case where root exclusion fails

Simple Root Exclusion Test. The simple root exclusion test, i.e. $z^{ou}z^0 > 0$, excludes the possibility of zero crossing in an integration step. In this case, the integration is continued without a state transition.

Advanced Root Exclusion Test. z^{ou} and z^0 lying on opposite sides of the abscissa, i.e. $z^{ou}z^0 \leq 0$, indicates a necessary, but not a sufficient criterion for an event. This branch leads to level three analysis in figure 2. Two stages are involved:

Examine Support Points: In each integration step, the discrete support points, $k_i, i = 2, 3, ..., 5$ are examined for a sign change. If two support points have an opposite sign, then a zero crossing has been identified (figure 3(ii)).

Exact Interpolation using Lagrangian Polynomials: If the is no sign change between two support points k_i and k_{i+1}, then there may be a zero crossing as shown in figure 4(iii). In that situation, a Lagrangian polynomial is constructed using the support points of the current interval. The extreme point, z^{ex}, cor-responds to a maximum or minumum with zero in its first dervative, $dz/dt = 0$. The assocaited time instant, t^*, is found using a Newton's Raphson method. The extremum, z^{ex} and the initial value z^0 are again checked for a sign change.

It should be noted that decisions high the hierarchy are less expensive than the tests performed in subsequent lower layers. In most physical systems, simple root exclusions suffices for most of the integration steps. Typically 99.9 % of the intervals have no discontinuities at all. Hence, the performance of root exclusion test often determines the speed of the entire algorithm.

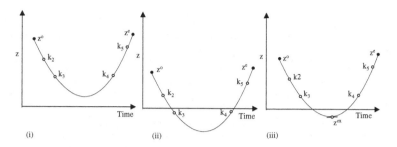

Fig. 4. Different types of non-monotonic event functions (i) no zero crossing (ii) zero crossing with a sign change in the value between the support points (iii) zero crossing with no change in sign of the gradients for support points

3.2   Event Location

For every event function with a root in the interval, the exact event time needs to be computed in the event location phase. Since time is the independent variable, exact points of the discontinuity cannot be obtained directly from equation (4) and (5).

$$f_\xi(x, y, \dot{y}, u(t), t) = 0, t \in [t_n, t_{n+1}] \tag{4}$$

$$z_{\xi\psi}(x^*, y^*, t^*) \pm \varepsilon_{\text{event}} = 0 \tag{5}$$

In the above equations (4) and (5), x are the algebraic variable values, y are the differential variable values and u(t) are known forcing functions. The star indicated their value at the event time, t^*.

Event Location via implicit Euler's method and function evaluation (method 1): In order to compute the exact event time, the differential equations in (4) are discretised using a first-order implicit Euler's method. Discretization renders algebraic equations parameterized in the formerly independent time, t, see Equation (6). Together with the event condition of equation (5), the system can be solved for the unknown event time. A small tolerance, ε_{event}, added to the event function in equation (6) ensures sufficient zero penetration. For a positive approach to a root, the value of the tolerance is positive. The discretized system is solved simultaneously using Newton's method to obtain the unknown event time. In addition, we obtain the corresponding state variable values at the event time (x^*, y^*, u^*). The iteration converges rapidly due to extremely good guesses of the initial values. This methodology also offers an opportunity for controlling the sign and precision of the event conditionals, which is paramount for general-purpose hybrid simulation.

$$y^* = y^o + h^*(\dot{y}|_{t=t^*}) \tag{6}$$

High-order approximations: Simulations using higher order implicit discretization techniques were examined in order to assess the precision of event location. The second-order semi-implicit method leads to the set of equation (7). Note that the Jacobian is computed only once using the values at the beginning of the interval.

$$y^* = y^o + (R_1 k_1 + R_2 k_2) \tag{7}$$

Where,
$$k_1 = h[I - haJ(y^o)]^{-1} f(y^o)$$
$$k_2 = h[I - haJ(y^o)]^{-1} f(y^o + b_2 k_1)$$
$$a = 0.435, b_2 = 3/4, R_1 = 1.0358, R_2 = 0.8349$$

This second-order semi-implicit approach requires more than twice the number of unknowns and more function evaluations as compared to first order Euler's method. In our experience and in the simulation runs for Craver's benchmark case studies, the event location times obtained using first and second order discretisation were almost identical. We conclude from these experiments that first order implicit Euler's method is acceptable for most practical cases.

Event Location via interpolation (method 2): The second methodology avoids repeated function re-evaluations altogether by interpolation of the all trajectories between the discrete support points. This approach was proposed by Barton [8] for differential algebraic systems (DAE). An interpolation in time for the state and event functions, e.g. $z_I(t)$, can be obtained advantageously via Lagrangian polynomials, $l_i(t)$ given in equation (8). It is worth mentioning that the interpolation completely decouples the variables in the system described by equation (1). Hence, the event time can be computed using a one-dimensional Newton Raphson method to solve for time t^* only. With the exact event time, the computation of the state variable value reduces to a mere function evaluation of its corresponding interpolation polynomial, one at a time.

$$z_I(t) = \sum_{i=1}^{n+1} z_i l_i(t), l_i = \prod_{j=1, j\neq i}^{n+1} \frac{t - t_j}{t_i - t_j} \tag{8}$$

$$z_I(t^*) \pm \varepsilon_{\text{event}} = 0 \tag{9}$$

Although method 1 assures accurate event location, repeated function calls to compute the derivative of the state variables can be less effective. This situation holds especially true in large systems with a small number of event conditionals. For process models loaded with involved physical property procedures, method 2 for event location is superior to method 1. However, method 1 tends to be more accurate since it maintains variable dependencies in the local neighborhood of an event. Method 1 may also be superior in event-driven systems that involve large numbers of event functions.

3.3   Step Completion

After a discontinuity has been located precisely, the consistent state transition must be implemented. Hence, step completion executes all actions consequent to the active event. The actions may entail: (a) discontinuous changes in the state variables (b) a changeover to a new set of describing equations or (c) triggering of another event. After step completion, control returns to the regular drive routine of the integrator. Integration resumes involving a new cycle of event handling in subsequent intervals.

4 Advanced Issues in Hybrid Simulation

4.1 Multiple/Simultaneous Discontinuities in Integration Step

Note that there maybe more than one z-function that has a root in the interval. In this situation, the exact location of the event times, t_i^*, allows to deduce the *active* event. The *active* event is characterized by the earliest event time, t_{active}^*, which is the smallest of all event times t_i^*. Therefore, for each candidate event, the exact location of roots must be found. Only the state transition of the active event is executed. After *firing* the active event, integration resumes. The handling of all other events is delegated to subsequent integration steps.

A situation often omitted in hybrid simulation deals with *synchronous events*. It concerns models with two or more events occurring with little or no time delay. In a practice, this occurs frequently when modeling multiple digital controllers, which samples at same time instant. Without special treatment, closeness of the two events could lead to singularity in the integration method or failure to detect the events at all [15]. Our algorithm handles such types of events by examining for simultaneity or near simultaneity of the events. The approach considers all events occurring within a time interval, Δh_{sim}, as simultaneous. All instances of simultaneous events fire.

4.2 Step Size Selection after a Discontinuity

Smoothness of the trajectories is ensured by the step-size control mechanism. Therefore, it is important that step acceptance is performed prior to event handling. After location of a discontinuity, the integration should move away from the discontinuity with large strides in the interest of the overall efficiency. This goal is antagonistic to the objective of small integration error. Three options for selecting an appropriate step size, h_{next}, after location of a discontinuity are discussed.

One choice of the new step could be derived from the step size, h_{event}, obtained in the event location phase. It corresponds to arbitrary location of an event time vis-à-vis the bounds of the associated integration step. Consequently, the value of h_{event} could be arbitrarily small. Since it does not correlate with the system time constants at all, it is an infeasible choice for a new step-size.

A better option is to maintain the step size, $h_{current}$, before an event was detected. This approach is suitable for systems where the time constants remain unaltered between states. If the describing equations change, the new initial value problem may commence with multiple step-size reduction. This behavior is certainly undesirable.

A third approach deploys a fixed initial step-size, $h_{initial}$, adopted at the start time of the integration. Usually this choice involves very small values constituting a very conservative approach. However, this option gives users direct control allowing them to adopt a problem-specific trade-off between economy and computational accuracy. The latter method was used in the case studies of section 5.

4.3   Selection of Tolerances

State-of-the-art algorithms avert error propagation in numerical integration by means of adaptive step-size control. This technique compares the differences in numerical solutions obtained by variable orders to achieve a fixed relative accuracy, ε_{RK}. The step-size is increased rapidly when entering a smooth region. If the local truncation error leaves the desired tolerance limits, the step-size is reduced in the subsequent step. If the truncation error violates its limit, the step is rejected and re-evaluated with a smaller step-size. Event detection involves a set of new tolerances and adjustable parameters. For optimal performance of the entire procedure, the tolerances of the integrator and the event handling must be concerted.

The tolerance $\pm\varepsilon_{event}$ ensures sufficient zero penetration as given by equations (5) and (9). Its magnitude is chosen large enough to avoid discontinuity sticking, while avoiding unacceptable offsets from the exact event boundary. The value of $\pm\varepsilon_{event}$ must be chosen larger than the tolerance, TOLMIN, which bounds the residual equations in the Newton Raphson (NR) Method. The second tolerance in NR gauges the break-off for function evaluation, TOLF, is set to $2\varepsilon_{event}$. Δh_{sim} is the tolerance for delineating simultaneous events. The selected tolerance values are shown in Table 1.

Table 1. Solver parameters for the algorithm

Solver parameter	Value
ε_{RK}	$1.0e^{-6}$
ε_{event}	$10\varepsilon_{RK}$
TOLMIN	ε_{RK}
TOLF	$2\varepsilon_{RK}$
$h_{initial}$	$10\varepsilon_{RK}$
Δh_{sim}	ε_{RK}

5   Application and Results

The efficiency of the new algorithm was tested against benchmark case studies. Specifics and problem descriptions can be found in [6]. A more detailed discussion of the third benchmark example is presented in subsection 5.1. Section 5.2 summarizes the results of the performance tests.

5.1   A Rectifier Circuit - Carvers Example 3

This example concerns a rectifier circuit as depicted in figure 5(i). It consists of two diodes D1 and D2, two AC sources U1 and U2, three resistances R1 - R3 and three inductors L1 - L3. The balances for currents and voltages are given by equations (10) and (11).

$$i_3 = i_1 + i_2 \tag{10}$$

$$\nu_3 = R_3(i_1 + i_2) + L_3(i_1' + i_2') \tag{11}$$

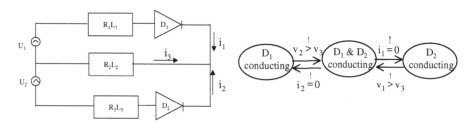

Fig. 5. Curcuit and state transition diagrams for Carver's example 3

Table 2. States for the rectifier circuit

State	State transitions	Differential Equations
D_1 conducting	$(i_1 > 0$ or $v_1 > v_3)$ and $(i_2 = 0$ and $v_2 \leq v_3)$	$i_1' = (v_1 - i_1 a_1)/a_2$ $i_2' = i_2 = 0$
Both D_1 and D_2 conducting	$(i_1 > 0$ or $v_1 > v_3)$ and $(i_2 > 0$ and $v_2 > v_3)$	$i_1' = (a_5 v_1 + a_6 v_2) + a_7 i_1 + a_8 i_2)$ $i_2' = (a_9 v_1 + a_{10} v_2) + a_{11} i_1 + a_{12} i_2)$
Only D_2 conducting	$(i_2 > 0$ or $v_2 > v_3)$ and $(i_1 = 0$ and $v_1 \leq v_3)$	$i_1' = i_1 = 0$ $i_2' = (v_2 - i_2 a_3)/a_4$
The constants are given as: $R_1 = R_2 = 2, R_3 = 10, L_1 = L_2 = 0.04, L_3 = 0.2, v_1 = -v_2 = 100 sin(100\pi t)$ $a_i = (12, 0.24, 12, 0.24, 13.64, -11.64, -50, 0, -11.64, 13.64, 0, -50$		

The values for i_1 and i_2 differ depending upon three distinct states: (i) diode D_1 is conducting, (ii) diode D_2 is conducting, and (iii) both D_1 and D_2 are conducting. In effect, the system toggles between three states as prescribed in table 2. The three states correspond to four event functions depicted in Fig. 5(ii). Equations (12) describes the four event functions that actually cause state transitions. The event-triggering state transitions can be obtained by careful examination of the expressions in the second column of table 2. Complex nested event conditionals required in this case study could be expressed by means of a high-level modeling language. A description of the hybrid simulation environment and its high-level language is beyond the scope of this paper and has been described elsewhere [16]. Figure 6 (i) shows the current profiles obtained while figure 6(ii) shows the voltage changes for v1, v2 and v3 in time.

$$z_1 = i_1, z_2 = i_2, z_3 = v_1 - v_3, z_4 = v_2 - v_3 \qquad (12)$$

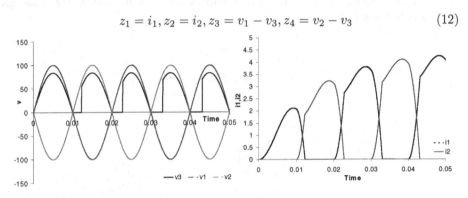

Fig. 6. (i) current profiles and (ii) voltage variations in the circuit problem

5.2   Discussion of the Performance Results

Table 4 shows the performance evaluation for the new algorithm applied to three Carvers benchmark case studies. The three examples clearly illustrate the strength of the new root exclusion test. It detected all events in strict time order without discontinuity sticking. It can also be seen that in most integration intervals we have no root at all (92.80-99.95 %). Hence, the overall efficiency of the algorithm is governed by the afficacy of the root exclusion test. The ratio of non-monotonic intervals to monotonic intervals is typically small. This holds especially true for most of the physical systems with discontinuities. In Carver's example 2 4.65 % of the intervals were non-monotonic. This number is high since Carver deployed periodic functions with atleast two non-montonic intervals per period. The algorithm successfully eliminated all the non-monotonic intervals without a root.

The performance of the algorithm was also compared to a Type I algorithms, see Table 4. Our implementation of a type I algorithm deployed quadratic interpolation for event location. The experiments further show that Type I algorithms failed to detect all the events for Carver's example 3. This drastic breakdown can be explained by the reliance of type I algorithms on function evaluation performed at the bounds of each step. Hence, zero-crossings in the middle of an interval are lost. In terms of function evaluations, type I and our new method is equivalent. However, only the new algorithm proved robust on all examples with an execution speed comparable to the fast type I algorithms.

The performance of the algorithm was also compared to the interval arithmetic techniques. The results are shown in table 5. Our root exclusion test is slightly better than the one involving the interval arithmetic techniques. However, there is a substantial improvement in the rigorous root finding phase of

Table 3. Performance Evaluation of the new algorithm

Case Study	Monotonic intervals	Non-monotonic intervals	Intervals with no events	Intervals excluded	Events	Evaluations for root excl.
Carvers example 1	39	3	92.80	3	3	6
Carvers example 2	164	8	95.90	8	7	16
Carvers example 3	22157	23	99.95	23	10	46

Table 4. Performance comparison of the new approach with a Type I algorithm

Example	Problem parameters		Type I algorithm		New algorithm	
	Equations	Events	Functions	Residuals	Functions	Residuals
Carvers example 1	2	1	739	2217	589	1898
Carvers example 2	3	2	883	2649	914	2930
Carvers example 3	6	4	fails	fails	1753	4888

Table 5. Comparison of the event detection phase of the new approach with interval arithmetic

Event Detection	Algebraic evaluations (New Algorithm)	Algebraic evaluations (Interval Arithmetic)
Root exclusion test	3	5
Rigorous event detection phase	19	56

event detection. This enhanced improvement in performance is essential for event-driven hybrid systems such as simulation of digital regulatory control of a physical process.

6   Conclusions

A fast and simple method for hybrid system integration by means of a multi-step integration algorithm with step-size control was presented. Our approach is statistically motivated leading to a hierarchical event detection procedure. The improvements are due to the exploiting local monotonicity and smooth function properties observed in algorithms with step-size control. A three-layered hierarchy of event exclusion tests with increasing complexity safeguards the rigor of the method, while upholding the performance. A cheap root exclusion test excludes roots of event functions fast. Even the most expensive test in the inner nesting level is faster than existing approach based on interval arithmetic. Phenomena not detected by popular bisection methods such as same-signed non-monotonic event functions with zero crossing are handled effectively. The method lays the foundation for rapid simulation algorithms as required in new types of dynamic optimization and optimal control problems.

Acknowledgements. Financial support from VAI, Austria, is gratefully acknowledged. Typesetting of this paper with LATEXwas generously assisted by Prof. L. Nitsche and C. Singaravapu.

References

1. Abel, O., and Marquardt, W. Scenario-integrated Modeling and Optimization of Dynamic Systems. *AIChE*, Journal, Vol. 46.,No. 4. pages 803–821. 2000.
2. Galan, S. and Barton, P.I. Dynamic Optimization of Hybrid Systems. *Comp. Chem. Eng*, Vol. 22., pages S183–S190. 1998.
3. Fahrland, D.A. Combined discrete event continuous system simulation. *Simulation*, Vol. 14.,pages 61–72. 1970.
4. Brennan, K.E, Campbell, S.L. and Petzold, L.R. Numerical Solution of Initial value problems in Differential Algebraic Equations. *North-Holland*, Vol. 14.,New York, U.S.A., 1989.
5. Gear, C.W and Osterby, O. Solving ordinary differential equations with discontinuities. Report UIUCDCS, Dept. Comput. Sci. University of Illinois, pages 81–1064,1980.
6. Carver, M.B. Efficient Integration over discontinuities in ordinary differential equation simulations. *Math.Comp.Sim*, Vol. XX, pages 190–196. 1978.
7. Joglekar, G.S. and Reklaitis, G.V. A simulator for batch and semi-continuous processes. *Comp. Chem. Eng*, Vol. 8., pages 315–327. 1984.
8. Park, T. and Barton, P.I. State Event Location in Differential Algebraic Models. *ACM Trans.Comp.Sim.*, Vol. 6.,pages 137–165. 1996.
9. Hay, J.L. and Griffin, A.W.J. Simulation of discontinuous dynamical systems. *Proc. 9th IMAC Conference on Simulation of Systems.*, pages 79-97, Italy,1979.
10. Birta, L.G., Oren, T.I, and Kettenis, D.L. A robust procedure for discontinuity handling in continuous system simulation. *Trans.Soc.Comput.Sim*, Vol. 2., No. 3, pages 189–205. 1985.
11. Shampine, L.F., Gladwell, I., and Brankin, R.W. Reliable solution of special event location problems for ODEs. *Numerical Analysis Report 138.*, Dept. of Mathematics, University of Manchester. England. 1987.
12. Pantelides, C.C., Gritsis, D., Morison, K.R., and Sargent, R.W.H. The mathematical modeling of transient system using differential-algebraic equations. *Comp.Chem.Eng*, Vol. 12. No. 5 (1988) 449-454.
13. Preston, A. J. and Berzins, M.: Algorithms for location of discontinuities in dynamic simulation problem. *Comp.Chem.Eng*, Vol.15. No. 10 pages 701–713. 1991.
14. Cash, J.R and Karp, A.H. A Variable Runge-Kutta Method for initial Value Problems with Rapidly varying right-hand Sides. *ACM Transactions on Mathematical Software*, Vol. 16. No. 3. pages 201–222. 1990.
15. Bahl, V. and Linninger, A. Hybrid Simulation of Continuous-Discrete Systems", in Computer-Aided Chemical Engineering, S. Pierrucci (eds), pp. 163-168, Elsevier, Amsterdam, 2000.
16. Bahl, V. Continuous-discrete simulation: MS Thesis (in preparation), University of Illinois at Chicago, 2001.

Hybrid I/O Automata Revisited

Nancy Lynch[1]*, Roberto Segala[2]**, and Frits Vaandrager[3]***

[1] MIT Laboratory for Computer Science, Cambridge, MA 02139, USA,
lynch@theory.lcs.mit.edu
[2] Dipartimento di Matematica, Università di Bologna, Piazza di Porta San Donato 5,
40127 Bologna, Italy, segala@cs.unibo.it
[3] Computing Science Institute, University of Nijmegen, P.O. Box 9010,
6500 GL Nijmegen, The Netherlands, fvaan@cs.kun.nl

Abstract. In earlier work, we developed a mathematical *hybrid I/O automaton (HIOA)* modeling framework, capable of describing both discrete and continuous behavior. This framework has been used to analyze examples of automated transportation systems, intelligent vehicle highway systems, air traffic control systems, and consumer electronics applications. Here, we reconsider the basic definitions of the HIOA framework, in particular, the dual use of external variables for discrete and continuous communication. We present a new HIOA model that is simpler than the earlier model, due to a clearer separation between discrete and continuous activity.

1 Introduction

Recent years have seen a rapid growth of interest in *hybrid systems*—systems that contain both discrete and continuous components, typically computers interacting with the physical world. Such systems are used in many application domains, including automated transportation, avionics, automotive control, process control, robotics, and consumer electronics. Motivated by a desire to describe and reason carefully about such applications, we are continuing our efforts to adapt techniques from computer science to the setting of hybrid systems.

In our previous work in this area, we developed a mathematical *hybrid I/O automaton* modeling framework [15,16]. This framework supports description and analysis of hybrid systems using powerful methods of *parallel composition* and *levels of abstraction*. We also proved sufficient conditions for hybrid I/O automata to be *receptive*, which means that they allow time to advance to infinity independently of the input provided by the environment. We and others have used this framework to analyze examples of automated transportation systems [18,13,23,22,14,10], intelligent vehicle highway systems [6,12], air traffic control systems [11,9], and consumer electronics systems [4].

* Supported by AFOSR F49620-00-1-0097, F49620-97-1-0337; NTT MIT9904-12; NSF ACI-9876931, CCR-9909114, CCR-9804665; PATH 1784-18454LD.
** Supported by MURST project TOSCA.
*** Supported by Esprit Project 26270, Verification of Hybrid Systems (VHS).

M.D. Di Benedetto, A. Sangiovanni-Vincentelli (Eds.): HSCC 2001, LNCS 2034, pp. 403–417, 2001.
© Springer-Verlag Berlin Heidelberg 2001

In this paper, we present a *new hybrid I/O automaton model* that is considerably simpler than the earlier model, yet supports similar description and analysis methods and similar receptivity theorems. The main simplification is a clearer separation between the notions of discrete and continuous communication. We arrived at this separation as a result of reconsidering the relationship between the computer science notion of shared variable communication and the control theory notion of continuous flow across component boundaries.

Levels of abstraction, compositionality, and receptiveness for hybrid systems have also been addressed by Alur and Henzinger [2,3] in their work on reactive modules. However, reactive modules communicate only via shared variables, and not via shared actions. In [3], a definition of receptiveness similar to the one in [15,16] is proposed, and is shown to be preserved by composition. However, in [3], no circular dependencies ("feedback loops") are allowed among the continuous variables of the components, a restriction that greatly simplifies the analysis.

The rest of this paper is organized as follows. Section 2 defines notions that are useful for describing the behavior of hybrid systems: trajectories and hybrid sequences. Section 3 contains the theory for the *hybrid automaton (HA)* model, which has all of the structure of the HIOA model except for the division of external actions and variables into inputs and outputs. Section 4 introduces inputs and outputs, and presents the basic theory for HIOAs. Section 5 presents the new theory of receptiveness, including the main theorem, Theorem 7, stating that receptiveness is preserved by composition under certain compatibility conditions. Section 6 describes sufficient conditions for these compatibility conditions to hold, and in particular, describes Lipschitz automata.

2   Describing Hybrid Behavior

In this section, we give basic definitions that are useful for describing discrete and continuous system behavior, including discrete and continuous state changes, and discrete and continuous flow of information over component boundaries. Throughout this paper, we fix a *time axis* T, which is a compact subgroup of $(R, +)$, the real numbers with addition.

2.1   Static and Dynamic Types

We assume a universal set V of *variables*. A variable represents either a location within the state of a system component, or a location where information flows from one system component to another. For each variable, we assume both a *(static) type*, which gives the set of values it may assume, and a *dynamic type*, which gives the set of trajectories it may follow. Our motivation for introducing dynamic types is that this allows us to define input enabling for hybrid I/O automata: if v is an input variable of HIOA A then, roughly speaking, we require that A accepts each input signal on v, as long as it respects the dynamic type of v. Since we are in a hybrid setting where discrete transitions may change the state at any time, elements of a dynamic type may contain (countably many) "discontinuities". Formally, we assume for each variable v:

- *type*(v), the *(static) type* of v. This is a set of values.
- *dtype*(v), the *dynamic type* of v. This is a set of functions from left-closed intervals of T to *type*(v) that is closed under the following operations:
  1. (Time shift) For each $f \in dtype(v)$ and $t \in T$, $f + t \in dtype(v)$. Here $f + t$ is the function given by $(f + t)(t') = f(t' - t)$.
  2. (Subinterval) For each $f \in dtype(v)$ and each left-closed interval $J \subseteq dom(f)$, $f \lceil J \in dtype(v)$. Here $f \lceil J$ is the function obtained by restricting the domain of f to J.
  3. (Pasting) For each sequence $f_0, f_1, f_2, \ldots$ of functions in $dtype(v)$ such that (a) the domain of each f_i, except possibly for the last one, is right-closed, (b) for each nonfinal index i, $\max(dom(f_i)) = \min(dom(f_{i+1}))$, the function f given by $f(t) \triangleq f_i(t)$, where i is the smallest index with $t \in dom(f_i)$, is in $dtype(v)$.

Example 1. For any variable v, the set C of constant functions from a left-closed interval to *type*(v) is closed under time shift and subintervals. If the dynamic type of v is obtained by closing C under the pasting operation, then v is called a *discrete* variable, as in [19]. If we take T = R and *type*(v) = R, then other examples of dynamic types can be obtained by taking the pasting closure of the set of continuous or smooth functions, the set of integrable functions, or the set of measurable locally essentially bounded functions. The set of all functions from left-closed intervals of R to R is also a dynamic type.

In practice, dynamic types are often defined via pasting closure of a class of continuous functions. In these cases the elements of dynamic types are continuous from the left. Elsewhere in the literature on hybrid systems one often encounters functions that are continuous from the right (see, e.g., [8]). To some extent, the choice of how to define function values at discontinuities is arbitrary. An advantage of our choice is a nice correspondence between concatenation and prefix ordering of trajectories (see Lemma 2). In the rest of this paper, when we say that the dynamic type of a variable v equals S, we actually mean that the dynamic type of v is obtained by applying the above closure operations to S.

2.2   Trajectories

In this subsection, we define the notion of a *trajectory*, define operations on trajectories, and prove simple properties of trajectories and their operations. A trajectory is used to model the evolution of a collection of variables over an interval of time.

Basic Definitions. Let V be a set of variables, that is, a subset of V. A *valuation* **v** for V is a function that associates to each variable $v \in V$ a value in *type*(v). We write *val*(V) for the set of valuations for V. Let J be a left-closed interval of T with left endpoint equal to 0. Then a *J-trajectory* for V is a function

$\tau : J \rightarrow val(V)$, such that for each $v \in V$, $\tau \downarrow v \in dtype(v)$. Here $\tau \downarrow v$ is the function with domain J defined by $(\tau \downarrow v)(t) = \tau(t)(v)$.

We say that a J-trajectory is *finite* if J is a finite interval, *closed* if J is a (finite) closed interval, and *full* if $J = \mathsf{T}^{\geq 0}$. A *trajectory* for V is a J-trajectory for V, for any J. We write $trajs(V)$ for the set of all trajectories for V. For T a set of trajectories, $finite(T)$, $closed(T)$ and $full(T)$ denote the subsets of finite, closed and full trajectories in T, respectively. A trajectory with domain $[0, 0]$ is called a *point* trajectory. If $\mathbf{v}$ is a valuation then $\wp(\mathbf{v})$ denotes the point trajectory that maps 0 to $\mathbf{v}$.

If τ is a trajectory then $\tau.ltime$, the *limit time* of τ, is the supremum of $dom(\tau)$. Similarly, we define $\tau.fval$, the *first valuation* of τ, to be $\tau(0)$, and if τ is closed, we define $\tau.lval$, the *last valuation* of τ, to be $\tau(\tau.ltime)$. For τ a trajectory and $t \in \mathsf{T}^{\geq 0}$, we define $\tau \trianglelefteq t \stackrel{\Delta}{=} \tau \lceil [0, t]$, $\tau \triangleleft t \stackrel{\Delta}{=} \tau \lceil [0, t)$, and $\tau \trianglerighteq t \stackrel{\Delta}{=} (\tau \lceil [t, \infty)) - t$. Note that the result of applying the above operations is always a trajectory, except when the result is a function with an empty domain. By convention, $\tau \trianglelefteq \infty \stackrel{\Delta}{=} \tau$ and $\tau \triangleleft \infty \stackrel{\Delta}{=} \tau$.

Prefix Ordering. Trajectory τ is a *prefix* of trajectory υ, denoted by $\tau \leq \upsilon$, if τ can be obtained by restricting υ to a non-empty, downward closed subset of its domain. Formally, $\tau \leq \upsilon$ iff $\tau = \upsilon \lceil dom(\tau)$. For T a set of trajectories for V, $pref(T)$ denotes the *prefix closure* of T. We say that T is *prefix closed* if $T = pref(T)$.

The following lemma gives a simple domain theoretic characterization of the set of trajectories over a given set V. (See [7] for basic definitions and results on complete partially ordered sets, (cpo's)).

Lemma 1. *Let V be a set of variables. Then the set $trajs(V)$ of trajectories for V, together with the prefix ordering $\leq$, is an algebraic cpo whose compact elements are the closed trajectories.*

Concatenation. The concatenation of two trajectories is obtained by taking the union of the first trajectory and the function obtained by shifting the domain of the second trajectory until the start time agrees with the limit time of the first trajectory; the last valuation of the first trajectory, which may not be the same as the first valuation of the second trajectory, is the one that appears in the concatenation. Formally, let τ, υ be trajectories, with τ closed. Then the *concatenation* is the function given by $\tau \frown \upsilon \stackrel{\Delta}{=} \tau \cup (\upsilon \lceil (0, \infty) + \tau.ltime)$. Using the closure of dynamic types under time shift and pasting, it follows that $\tau \frown \upsilon$ is a trajectory. Observe that $\tau \frown \upsilon$ is finite (resp. closed, full) iff υ is finite (resp. closed, full). Observe also that concatenation is associative.

The following lemma, which is easy to prove, shows the close connection between concatenation and the prefix ordering.

Lemma 2. *Let τ, υ be trajectories with τ closed. Then $\tau \leq \upsilon$ iff there exists a trajectory τ' such that $\tau \frown \tau'$.*

Note that if $\tau \le \upsilon$, then the trajectory τ' such that $\upsilon = \tau \frown \tau'$ is unique except that it has an arbitrary value for $\tau'.fval$. Note also that the "$\Leftarrow$" implication would not hold if the first valuation of the second argument, rather than the last valuation of the first argument, were used in the concatenation.

Using a limit construction, we can generalize the definition of concatenation for any (finite or countably infinite) number of arguments. Let $\tau_0, \tau_1, \tau_2, \ldots$ be a (finite or infinite) sequence of trajectories, such that τ_i is closed for each nonfinal index i. Define trajectories $\tau'_0, \tau'_1, \tau'_2, \ldots$ by $\tau'_i \triangleq \tau_0 \frown \tau_1 \frown \cdots \frown \tau_i$. We define the *concatenation* $\tau_0 \frown \tau_1 \frown \tau_2 \ldots$ to be $\lim_{i \to \infty} \tau'_i$. It is easy to prove that $\tau_0 \frown \tau_1 \frown \tau_2 \ldots$ is a trajectory.

2.3   Hybrid Sequences

In this subsection, we introduce the notion of a *hybrid sequence*, which is used to model a combination of changes that occur instantaneously and changes that occur over intervals of time. Our definition is parameterized by a set A of *actions*, which are used to model instantaneous changes and instantaneous synchronization with the environment, and a set V of *variables*, which are used to model changes over intervals and continuous interaction. We also define some special kinds of hybrid sequences and operations on hybrid sequences.

Basic Definitions. An (A, V)-*sequence* is a finite or infinite alternating sequence $\alpha = \tau_0 \, a_1 \, \tau_1 \, a_2 \, \tau_2 \cdots$, where (1) each τ_i is a trajectory in $trajs(V)$, (2) each a_i is an action in A, (3) if α is a finite sequence then it ends with a trajectory, and (4) if τ_i is not the last trajectory in α then $dom(\tau_i)$ is closed. We define a *hybrid sequence* to be an (A, V)-sequence for some A and V.

Since the trajectories in a hybrid sequence can be point trajectories, our notion of hybrid sequence allows a sequence of discrete actions to occur at the same real time, with corresponding changes of state.

If α is a hybrid sequence, with notation as above, then we define the *first valuation* of α, $\alpha.fval$, to be $\tau_0.fval$, and we define the *limit time* of α, $\alpha.ltime$, to be $\sum_i \tau_i.ltime$. A hybrid sequence α is defined to be:

- *time-bounded* if $\alpha.ltime$ is finite.
- *admissible* if $\alpha.ltime = \infty$.
- *closed* if α is a finite sequence and the domain of its final trajectory is a closed interval. In this case we define the *last valuation* of α, $\alpha.lval$, to be $last(\alpha).lval$.
- *Zeno* if α is neither closed nor admissible, that is, if α is time-bounded and is either an infinite sequence, or else a finite sequence ending with a trajectory whose domain is right-open.

Prefix Ordering. We say that (A, V)-sequence $\alpha = \tau_0 \, a_1 \, \tau_1 \ldots$ is a *prefix* of (A, V)-sequence $\alpha' = \tau'_0 \, a'_1 \, \tau'_1 \ldots$, denoted by $\alpha \le \alpha'$, if either $\alpha = \alpha'$, or α is a finite sequence ending in some τ_k; $\tau_i = \tau'_i$, and $a_{i+1} = a'_{i+1}$ for every i, $0 \le i < k$;

and $\tau_k \leq \tau'_k$. Like the set of trajectories over V, the set of (A, V)-sequences is a cpo.

Lemma 3. *The set of (A, V)-sequences together with the prefix ordering $\leq$ is an algebraic cpo with as compact elements the set of closed (A, V)-sequences.*

Restriction. Let A, A' be sets of actions and V, V' sets of variables. The (A', V')-restriction of an (A, V)-sequence is obtained by projecting the trajectories on the variables in V', removing the actions not in A', and concatenating the adjacent trajectories.

Lemma 4. *Restriction is a continuous operation with respect to prefix ordering.*

Concatenation. Suppose α and α' are (A, V)-sequences, with α closed. Then the *concatenation* is the (A, V)-sequence given by

$$\alpha \frown \alpha' \triangleq init(\alpha) \, (last(\alpha) \frown head(\alpha')) \, tail(\alpha').$$

(If σ is a nonempty sequence then $head(\sigma)$ denotes the first element of σ and $tail(\sigma)$ denotes σ with its first element removed; if σ is finite, then $last(\sigma)$ denotes the last element of σ and $init(\sigma)$ denotes σ with its last element removed.)

Lemma 5. *Let α, α' be (A, V)-sequences with α closed. Then $\alpha \leq \alpha'$ iff there exists and (A, V)-sequence α'' such that $\alpha' = \alpha \frown \alpha''$.*

Note that if $\alpha \leq \alpha'$, then the (A, V)-sequence α'' such that $\alpha' = \alpha \frown \alpha''$ is unique except that it has an arbitrary value in $val(V)$ for $\alpha''.fval$.

Based on Lemma 5 and Lemma 3, we can extend concatenation to infinitely many (A, V)-sequences as follows. Let $\alpha_1, \alpha_2, \ldots$ be an infinite sequence of closed (A, V)-sequences. Then define the *concatenation* $\alpha_1 \frown \alpha_2 \frown \cdots$ to be $\lim_{i \to \infty} \alpha'_i$, where $\alpha'_i = \alpha_1 \frown \alpha_2 \frown \cdots \frown \alpha_i$.

3 Hybrid Automata

As a preliminary step toward defining hybrid I/O automata, we first define a slightly more general *hybrid automaton* model. Hybrid automata classify actions as external and internal, but do not further subdivide the external actions into input and output actions. Likewise, they classify variables as external and internal. The input/output distinction is added in Section 4. In addition to defining hybrid automata, we here define an implementation relation between hybrid automata and a composition operation.

3.1   Definition of Hybrid Automata

A *hybrid automaton (HA)* $\mathcal{A} = (W, X, \Theta, E, H, \mathcal{D}, \mathcal{T})$ consists of:

- A set W of *external variables* and a set X of *internal variables*, disjoint from each other. We call a valuation $\mathbf{x}$ for X a *state*, and we refer to $val(X)$ as the set of states of $\mathcal{A}$. We write $V \triangleq W \cup X$. Given a valuation $\mathbf{v}$ for V, we denote by $state(\mathbf{v})$ the state $\mathbf{v} \lceil X$.
- A nonempty set $\Theta \subseteq val(X)$ of *start states*.
- A set E of *external actions* and a set H of *internal actions*, disjoint from each other. We write $A \triangleq E \cup H$ and let $a, b, \ldots$ range over A.
- A set $\mathcal{D} \subseteq val(X) \times A \times val(X)$ of *discrete transitions*. We use $\mathbf{x} \xrightarrow{a}_{\mathcal{A}} \mathbf{x}'$ as shorthand for $(\mathbf{x}, a, \mathbf{x}') \in \mathcal{D}$. We sometimes drop the subscript, and write $\mathbf{x} \xrightarrow{a} \mathbf{x}'$, when $\mathcal{A}$ should be clear from the context.
- A set $\mathcal{T}$ of trajectories for V. Given a trajectory $\tau \in \mathcal{T}$ we denote $\tau.fval \lceil X$ by $\tau.fstate$, and, if τ is closed, $\tau.lval \lceil X$ by $\tau.lstate$. We require that the following axioms hold:
  - **T1** (Prefix closure) For every $\tau \in \mathcal{T}$ and every $\tau' \leq \tau$, $\tau' \in \mathcal{T}$.
  - **T2** (Suffix closure) For every $\tau \in \mathcal{T}$ and every $t \in dom(\tau)$, $\tau \trianglerighteq t \in \mathcal{T}$.
  - **T3** (Concatenation closure) Let $\tau_0, \tau_1, \tau_2, \ldots$ be a sequence of trajectories in $\mathcal{T}$ such that, for each nonfinal index i, τ_i is closed and $\tau_i.lstate = \tau_{i+1}.fstate$. Then $\tau_0 \frown \tau_1 \frown \tau_2 \ldots \in \mathcal{T}$.

Axioms **T1-3** express some natural closure properties on the set of trajectories that we need for our results about parallel composition. In a composed system, any trajectory of any component may be interrupted at any moment by a discrete transition of another component. Axiom **T1** ensures that the part of the trajectory up to the discrete transition is a trajectory, and axiom **T2** ensures the remainder is a trajectory. Axiom **T3** is required because the environment of a hybrid automaton, as a result of internal discrete transitions, may change its continuous dynamics repeatedly, and the automaton must be able to follow this behavior. Even without performing discrete transitions itself, a hybrid automaton must be able to follow this type of behavior of its environment. In the earlier definition of hybrid automata presented in [15,16], we used a special stuttering action e in place of axiom **T3**; this gave rise to technical complications.

Another major difference between our new definition and the earlier one is that the external variables are no longer considered to be part of the state; thus, for instance, the discrete transitions do not depend on the values of these variables. Analogous to the way in which external actions can be used to model synchronization of discrete transitions of different components, external variables allow us to model synchronization of continuous activity ("flow") between components. Because the external actions and external variables are not part of the state, we think of them as "ephemeral".

We often denote the components of a HA $\mathcal{A}$ by $W_{\mathcal{A}}$, $X_{\mathcal{A}}$, $\Theta_{\mathcal{A}}$, $E_{\mathcal{A}}$, etc, and the components of a HA $\mathcal{A}_i$ by W_i, X_i, Θ_i, E_i, etc. We sometimes omit these subscripts, where no confusion seems likely.

3.2   Executions and Traces

We now define execution fragments, executions, trace fragments, and traces, which are used to describe automaton behavior.

An *execution fragment* of a HA $\mathcal{A}$ is an (A, V)-sequence $\alpha = \tau_0\, a_1\, \tau_1\, a_2\, \tau_2 \cdots$, where (1) each τ_i is a trajectory in $\mathcal{T}$, and (2) if τ_i is not the last trajectory in α then $\tau_i.lstate \overset{a_{i+1}}{\to} \tau_{i+1}.fstate$. An execution fragment records all the instantaneous, discrete state changes that occur during a specific evolution of a system, as well as the state changes and external variable changes that occur while time advances. We write $frags_{\mathcal{A}}$ for the set of all execution fragments of $\mathcal{A}$.

If α is an execution fragment, with notation as above, then we define the *first state* of α, $\alpha.fstate$, to be $state(\alpha.fval)$, or equivalently, $\tau_0.fstate$. An execution fragment α is defined to be an *execution* if $\alpha.fstate$ is a start state, that is, is in Θ. We write $execs_{\mathcal{A}}$ for the set of all executions of $\mathcal{A}$.

If α is a closed execution fragment then we define the *last state* of α, $\alpha.lstate$, to be $state(\alpha.lval)$, or equivalently, $last(\alpha).lstate$. A state of $\mathcal{A}$ is *reachable* if it is the last state of some closed execution of $\mathcal{A}$.

Lemma 6. *Let α and α' be execution fragments of $\mathcal{A}$ with α closed, and such that $\alpha.lstate = \alpha'.fstate$. Then $\alpha ^\frown \alpha'$ is an execution fragment of $\mathcal{A}$.*

Lemma 7. *Let α and α' be execution fragments of $\mathcal{A}$ with α closed. Then $\alpha \le \alpha'$ iff there is an execution fragment α'' such that $\alpha' = \alpha ^\frown \alpha''$.*

The trace of an execution fragment records the external actions and the evolution of external variables. Formally, if α is an execution fragment, then the *trace* of α, denoted by $trace(\alpha)$, is the (E, W)-restriction of α. A *trace fragment* of a hybrid automaton $\mathcal{A}$ *from* a state $\mathbf{x}$ of $\mathcal{A}$ is a trace that arises from an execution fragment of $\mathcal{A}$ whose first state is $\mathbf{x}$. We write $tracefrags_{\mathcal{A}}(\mathbf{x})$ for the set of trace fragments of $\mathcal{A}$ from $\mathbf{x}$. Also, we define a *trace* of $\mathcal{A}$ to be a trace fragment from an initial state, that is, a trace that arises from an execution of $\mathcal{A}$, and write $traces_{\mathcal{A}}$ for the set of traces of $\mathcal{A}$.

Hybrid automata $\mathcal{A}_1$ and $\mathcal{A}_2$ are *comparable* if they have the same external actions and variables, that is, if $W_1 = W_2$ and $E_1 = E_2$. If $\mathcal{A}_1$ and $\mathcal{A}_2$ are comparable then we say that $\mathcal{A}_1$ *implements* $\mathcal{A}_2$, denoted by $\mathcal{A}_1 \le \mathcal{A}_2$, if the traces of $\mathcal{A}_1$ are included among those of $\mathcal{A}_2$, that is, if $traces_{\mathcal{A}_1} \subseteq traces_{\mathcal{A}_2}$.

3.3   Simulation Relations

Let $\mathcal{A}$ and $\mathcal{B}$ be comparable HAs. A *simulation* from $\mathcal{A}$ to $\mathcal{B}$ is a relation $R \subseteq val(X_{\mathcal{A}}) \times val(X_{\mathcal{B}})$ satisfying the following conditions, for all states $\mathbf{x}_A$ and $\mathbf{x}_B$ of $\mathcal{A}$ and $\mathcal{B}$, respectively:

1. If $\mathbf{x}_A \in \Theta_A$ then there exists a state $\mathbf{x}_B \in \Theta_B$ such that $\mathbf{x}_A\, R\, \mathbf{x}_B$.
2. If $\mathbf{x}_A\, R\, \mathbf{x}_B$, $\mathbf{x}_A \overset{a}{\to}_A \mathbf{x}'_A$ and $\tau = trace(\wp(\mathbf{x}_A)\, a\, \wp(\mathbf{x}'_A))$, then $\mathcal{B}$ has a closed execution fragment α with $\alpha.fstate = \mathbf{x}_B$, $trace(\alpha) = trace(\tau)$, and $\mathbf{x}'_A\, R\, \alpha.lstate$.

3. If $\mathbf{x}_A \; R \; \mathbf{x}_B$ and τ is a closed trajectory of $\mathcal{A}$ with $\mathbf{x}_A = \tau.fstate$ and $\mathbf{x}'_A = \tau.lstate$, then $\mathcal{B}$ has a closed execution fragment α with $\alpha.fstate = \mathbf{x}_B$, $trace(\alpha) = trace(\tau)$, and $\mathbf{x}'_A \; R \; \alpha.lstate$.

Lemma 8. *Let $\mathcal{A}$ and $\mathcal{B}$ be comparable HAs, and let R be a simulation from $\mathcal{A}$ to $\mathcal{B}$. Let $\mathbf{x}_A$ and $\mathbf{x}_B$ be states of $\mathcal{A}$ and $\mathcal{B}$, respectively, such that $\mathbf{x}_A \; R \; \mathbf{x}_B$. Then $tracefrags_\mathcal{A}(\mathbf{x}_A) \subseteq tracefrags_\mathcal{B}(\mathbf{x}_B)$.*

Theorem 1. *Let $\mathcal{A}$ and $\mathcal{B}$ be comparable HAs, and let R be a simulation from $\mathcal{A}$ to $\mathcal{B}$. Then $traces_\mathcal{A} \subseteq traces_\mathcal{B}$.*

3.4 Composition

We now introduce the operation of composition for hybrid automata, which allows an automaton representing a complex system to be constructed by composing automata representing individual system components. We prove that the composition operation respects our implementation relationship (inclusion of sets of traces). Our composition operation identifies actions and variables with the same name in different component automata. When any component automaton performs a step involving an action a, so do all component automata that have a in their signatures. Common variables are shared among the components.

We define composition as a partial, binary operation on hybrid automata. Since internal actions of an automaton $\mathcal{A}_1$ are intended to be unobservable by any other automaton $\mathcal{A}_2$, we do not allow $\mathcal{A}_1$ to be composed with $\mathcal{A}_2$ unless the internal actions of $\mathcal{A}_1$ are disjoint from the actions of $\mathcal{A}_2$. Also, we require disjointness of the internal variables of $\mathcal{A}_1$ and the variables of $\mathcal{A}_2$. Formally, we say that hybrid automata $\mathcal{A}_1$ and $\mathcal{A}_2$ are *compatible* if for $i \neq j$, $X_i \cap V_j = H_i \cap A_j = \emptyset$. If $\mathcal{A}_1$ and $\mathcal{A}_2$ are compatible then their *composition* $\mathcal{A}_1 \| \mathcal{A}_2$ is defined to be the structure $\mathcal{A} = (W, X, \Theta, E, H, \mathcal{D}, \mathcal{T})$ where

- $W = W_1 \cup W_2$, $X = X_1 \cup X_2$, $E = E_1 \cup E_2$, $H = H_1 \cup H_2$.
- $\Theta = \{\mathbf{x} \in val(X) \mid \mathbf{x} \lceil X_1 \in \Theta_1 \wedge \mathbf{x} \lceil X_2 \in \Theta_2\}$.
- For each $\mathbf{x}, \mathbf{x}' \in val(X)$ and each $a \in A$, $\mathbf{x} \xrightarrow{a}_\mathcal{A} \mathbf{x}'$ iff for $i = 1, 2$, either (1) $a \in A_i$ and $\mathbf{x} \lceil X_i \xrightarrow{a}_i \mathbf{x}' \lceil X_i$, or (2) $a \notin A_i$ and $\mathbf{x} \lceil X_i = \mathbf{x}' \lceil X_i$.
- $\mathcal{T} \subseteq trajs(V)$ is given by $\tau \in \mathcal{T} \Leftrightarrow \tau \downarrow V_1 \in \mathcal{T}_1 \wedge \tau \downarrow V_2 \in \mathcal{T}_2$.

Proposition 1. *$\mathcal{A}_1 \| \mathcal{A}_2$ is a hybrid automaton.*

Theorem 2. *Suppose $\mathcal{A}_1, \mathcal{A}_2$ and $\mathcal{B}$ are HAs with $\mathcal{A}_1 \leq \mathcal{A}_2$, and suppose that each of $\mathcal{A}_1$ and $\mathcal{A}_2$ is compatible with $\mathcal{B}$. Then $\mathcal{A}_1 \| \mathcal{B} \leq \mathcal{A}_2 \| \mathcal{B}$.*

In the full version of this paper, we define two natural hiding operations on HAs, which hide external actions and external variables, respectively, and prove that these operations also respect the implementation preorder.

4 Hybrid I/O Automata

In this section we specialize the hybrid automaton model of Section 3 by adding a distinction between input and output.

4.1 Definition of Hybrid I/O Automata

A *hybrid I/O automaton (HIOA)* $\mathcal{A}$ is a tuple $(\mathcal{H}, U, Y, I, O)$ where

- $\mathcal{H} = (W, X, \Theta, E, H, \mathcal{D}, \mathcal{T})$ is a hybrid automaton.
- U and Y partition W into *input* and *output* variables, respectively. Variables in $Z \stackrel{\triangle}{=} X \cup Y$ are called *locally controlled*; as before we write $V \stackrel{\triangle}{=} W \cup X$.
- I and O partition E into *input* and *output actions*, respectively. Actions in $L \stackrel{\triangle}{=} H \cup O$ are called *locally controlled*; as before we write $A \stackrel{\triangle}{=} E \cup H$.
- The following additional axioms are satisfied:

  E1 (Input action enabling)

  For all $\mathbf{x} \in val(X)$ and all $a \in I$ there exists $\mathbf{x}'$ such that $\mathbf{x} \stackrel{a}{\rightarrow} \mathbf{x}'$.

  E2 (Input flow enabling)

  For all $\mathbf{x} \in val(X)$ and $\upsilon \in trajs(U)$, there exists $\tau \in \mathcal{T}$ such that $\tau.fstate = \mathbf{x}, \tau \downarrow U \leq \upsilon$, and either

  1. $\tau \downarrow U = \upsilon$, or
  2. there exist $t \in dom(\tau)$ and $l \in L$ such that l is enabled from $\tau(t)$.

Input action enabling is the input enabling condition of ordinary I/O automata. Input flow enabling is a new corresponding condition for continuous interaction. It says that an HIOA should be able to accept any continuous input flow, either by letting time advance for the entire duration of the input flow, or by reacting with a locally controlled action after some part of the input flow has occurred.

An *execution* of an HIOA $\mathcal{A}$ is an execution of $\mathcal{H}_{\mathcal{A}}$. Similarly, a *trace* of $\mathcal{A}$ is a trace of $\mathcal{H}_{\mathcal{A}}$. Two HIOAs $\mathcal{A}_1$ and $\mathcal{A}_2$ are *comparable* if their inputs and outputs coincide, that is, if $I_1 = I_2$, $O_1 = O_2$, $U_1 = U_2$, and $Y_1 = Y_2$. If $\mathcal{A}_1$ and $\mathcal{A}_2$ are comparable, then $\mathcal{A}_1 \leq \mathcal{A}_2$ is defined to mean that the traces of $\mathcal{A}_1$ are included among those of $\mathcal{A}_2$: $\mathcal{A}_1 \leq \mathcal{A}_2 \stackrel{\triangle}{=} traces_{\mathcal{A}_1} \subseteq traces_{\mathcal{A}_2}$. If $\mathcal{A}_1$ and $\mathcal{A}_2$ are comparable HIOAs then $\mathcal{H}_1$ and $\mathcal{H}_2$ are comparable and $\mathcal{A}_1 \leq \mathcal{A}_2$ iff $\mathcal{H}_1 \leq \mathcal{H}_2$.

The definition of simulation for HIOAs is the same as for HAs, and the soundness result carries over immediately to the enriched setting.

4.2 Composition

The definition of composition for HIOAs builds on the corresponding definition for HAs, but also takes the input/output structure into account. Just as in the definition of compatibility for HAs, we do not allow an HIOA $\mathcal{A}_1$ to be composed with an HIOA $\mathcal{A}_2$ unless the internal actions and variables of $\mathcal{A}_1$ are disjoint from the actions and variables, respectively, of $\mathcal{A}_2$. In addition, in order that the composition operation might satisfy nice properties (such as Theorem 7), we require that at most one component automaton "controls" any given action or variable; that is, we do not allow $\mathcal{A}_1$ and $\mathcal{A}_2$ to be composed unless the sets of output actions of $\mathcal{A}_1$ and $\mathcal{A}_2$ are disjoint and the sets of output variables of $\mathcal{A}_1$ and $\mathcal{A}_2$ are disjoint.

If $\mathcal{A}_1$ and $\mathcal{A}_2$ are compatible then their *composition* $\mathcal{A}_1 \| \mathcal{A}_2$ is defined to be the tuple $\mathcal{A} = (\mathcal{H}, U, Y, I, O)$ where $\mathcal{H} = \mathcal{H}_1 \| \mathcal{H}_2$, $U = (U_1 \cup U_2) - (Y_1 \cup Y_2)$, $Y = Y_1 \cup Y_2$, $I = (I_1 \cup I_2) - (O_1 \cup O_2)$, and $O = O_1 \cup O_2$.

The definition of compatibility given above is not quite strong enough to imply that the composition of two HIOAs is actually an HIOA. Thus, we define a stronger notion and say that compatible HIOAs $\mathcal{A}_1$ and $\mathcal{A}_2$ are *strongly compatible* if $\mathcal{A}_1 \| \mathcal{A}_2$ satisfies axiom **E2**. Strong compatibility implies that the reaction of the composed automaton to any input flow v must be the result of a deliberate reaction by either $\mathcal{A}_1$ or $\mathcal{A}_2$. That is, either both $\mathcal{A}_1$ and $\mathcal{A}_2$ accept v in its entirety, or one of the two reacts with a locally controlled action. No "time deadlock" is allowed due to incompatible reactions of $\mathcal{A}_1$ and $\mathcal{A}_2$.

Proposition 2. *The composition of two strongly compatible HIOAs is an HIOA.*

Theorem 3. *Suppose $\mathcal{A}_1, \mathcal{A}_2$ and $\mathcal{B}$ are HIOAs with $\mathcal{A}_1 \leq \mathcal{A}_2$, and each of $\mathcal{A}_1$ and $\mathcal{A}_2$ is strongly compatible with $\mathcal{B}$. Then $\mathcal{A}_1 \| \mathcal{B} \leq \mathcal{A}_2 \| \mathcal{B}$.*

5   Receptive Hybrid I/O Automata

In this section we adapt the notion of receptiveness [20] to our new framework. Informally speaking, a system is receptive provided that it admits a strategy for resolving its nondeterministic choices that never generates infinitely many locally controlled actions in finite time. An important consequence of this definition is that a receptive HIOA has some response defined for any sequence of discrete and continuous input. We show that receptiveness is closed under composition. Because of the improvements in our new model, the treatment of receptiveness in this paper is simpler than that in [20]; however, we only address admissibility here, and not general liveness properties as in [20].

An execution fragment of an HIOA is *locally-Zeno* if it is Zeno and contains infinitely many locally controlled actions. An HIOA $\mathcal{A}$ is *locally-Zeno* if it has at least one locally-Zeno execution fragment. In the rest of the paper we will be interested mainly in *non-locally-Zeno* HIOAs, that is, HIOAs that are not locally-Zeno. We use non-locally-Zeno HIOAs as the basis for defining receptiveness.

Theorem 4. *Let $\mathcal{A}_1$, $\mathcal{A}_2$ be strongly compatible non-locally-Zeno HIOAs. Then $\mathcal{A}_1 \| \mathcal{A}_2$ is also non-locally-Zeno.*

Theorem 5. *Let $\mathcal{A}$ be a non-locally-Zeno HIOA. Then, for each (I, U)-sequence β and each state $\mathbf{x}$, there is an execution fragment α of $\mathcal{A}$ such that (1) $\alpha.fstate = \mathbf{x}$, (2) $\alpha \lceil (I, U) = \beta$.*

The property stated in Theorem 5 is known in the literature as *I/O feasibility* [17]; it implies that any finite execution can be extended to an admissible execution, no matter what the environment does.

A *strategy* for an HIOA $\mathcal{A}$ is an HIOA $\mathcal{A}'$ that differs from $\mathcal{A}$ only in that $\mathcal{D}' \subseteq \mathcal{D}$ and $\mathcal{T}' \subseteq \mathcal{T}$. A strategy $\mathcal{A}'$ for an HIOA $\mathcal{A}$ can be viewed as a nondeterministic memoryless strategy in the sense of [5,20] that chooses some of the evolutions that are possible from each of the states of $\mathcal{A}$. The fact that the states of $\mathcal{A}$ and $\mathcal{A}'$ are the same ensures that $\mathcal{A}'$ chooses evolutions for every state $\mathbf{x}$ of $\mathcal{A}$.

We say that an HIOA is *receptive* if it has a non-locally-Zeno strategy.

Theorem 6. *A receptive HIOA is I/O feasible.*

Theorem 7. *Let $\mathcal{A}_1$ and $\mathcal{A}_2$ be two compatible receptive HIOAs with two strongly compatible non-locally-Zeno strategies $\mathcal{A}_1'$ and $\mathcal{A}_2'$, respectively. Then $\mathcal{A}_1 \| \mathcal{A}_2$ is a receptive HIOA with non-locally-Zeno strategy $\mathcal{A}_1' \| \mathcal{A}_2'$.*

6   Sufficient Conditions for Strong Compatibility

In order to apply Theorem 7, one has to establish that two strategies are strongly compatible. This is difficult in general since it requires checking compatibility between the continuous dynamics of two systems. However, for certain restricted classes of HIOAs, strong compatibility follows directly from compatibility.

6.1   HIOAs with Restrictions on Input Variables

Our first example is the class of HIOAs without input variables. It is routine to verify that two HIOAs without input variables are strongly compatible iff they are compatible. From the perspective of classical control theory a system without input variables is uninteresting because it cannot be controlled; in a hybrid setting, however, a system without input variables can still interact with its environment via discrete input actions. *Linear hybrid automata* [1], for instance, have no input variables.

Another example is the class of *autistic* HIOAs—those for which the values of output variables do not depend on the values of input variables. Formally, an HIOA $\mathcal{A}$ is called *autistic* if for all $\tau \in \mathcal{T}$ and all $\upsilon \in trajs(U)$ such that $dom(\tau) = dom(\upsilon)$ there exists $\tau' \in \mathcal{T}$ such that $\tau' \downarrow U = \upsilon$ and $\tau' \downarrow Y = \tau \downarrow Y$.

6.2   Lipschitz HIOAs

In this section, we define *Lipschitz HIOAs*, based on systems of differential equations using Lipschitz functions. We give examples of conditions on classes of Lipschitz HIOAs that imply strong compatibility. The ideas are derived from methods in the literature on control theory [21]. In control theory, continuous system behavior is typically defined using differential equations of the form:

$$D \triangleq \begin{cases} \dot{x} = f(x, u) \\ y = g(x) \end{cases}$$

where u, y, and x are the vectors of input, output, and state variables, respectively, together with a starting condition of the form $x(0) = x_0$.

To ensure that the system's behavior is defined, the differential equations must admit a solution for each possible starting condition. The following theorem from calculus gives sufficient conditions for a solution to exist.

Theorem 8 (Local existence). *If f is globally Lipschitz and u is C^1, then for each starting condition $x(0) = x_0$ there is a unique solution to the equations of D, defined on a maximal neighborhood of 0, such that $x(0) = x_0$.*

Observe that, since the set of globally Lipschitz functions is closed under composition, the local existence theorem is valid also when the variables u are the result of a globally Lipschitz function applied to a C^1 function.

Suppose two interacting systems are described by sets of equations D_1 and D_2 of the form given above. Then their combined behavior can be described by the union of the sets of equations D_1 and D_2. It is easy to show that, if the functions occurring in D_1 and D_2 are globally Lipschitz, and D_1 and D_2 do not have any common output and state variables, then the union of these two sets of equations is expressible in the same form with functions that are globally Lipschitz. Thus, in this case no additional machinery is needed to prove that the behavior of the interacting systems is well defined. We define a set D of equations to be Lipschitz if functions f and g are globally Lipschitz.

To extend the above ideas to the hybrid case we define the notion of a Lipschitz HIOA. An HIOA $\mathcal{A}$ is *Lipschitz* if there is a subset M of its state variables (we call these the *mode variables*) such that:

L1 The dynamic type of each variable in M is piecewise constant.

L2 The dynamic type of each variable not in M is a subset of the set of real-valued functions defined on left-closed intervals of the reals that can be expressed in the form $h(c(\cdot))$ where h is a globally Lipschitz function and c is a C^1 function, closed under pasting.

L3 The values of the M variables are constant in each trajectory of $\mathcal{T}$.

L4 For each valuation $\mathbf{m}$ of M there is a Lipschitz system of equations $D_\mathbf{m}$ with input variables U, output variables Y, and state variables $X - M$ such that the following holds: If trajectory τ of $\mathcal{T}$ starts from a state $\mathbf{x}$ with $\mathbf{x} \lceil M = \mathbf{m}$, then $\tau \lceil V - M$ is expressible as the concatenation of countably many trajectories $\tau_0, \tau_1, \ldots$, where each τ_i is a solution to $D_\mathbf{m}$.

Define a Lipschitz HIOA to be *input bounded* if for each input variable u there exists a positive real value B such that every function in the dynamic type of u has range in $[-B, B]$.

Lemma 9. *Compatible input-bounded Lipschitz HIOAs are strongly compatible.*

Theorem 9. *The composition of two compatible input-bounded Lipschitz HIOAs is a Lipschitz HIOA.*

Theorem 10. *Let A_1 and A_2 be compatible receptive HIOAs with non-locally-Zeno, input-bounded, Lipschitz strategies. Then $A_1 \| A_2$ is a receptive HIOA with a non-locally-Zeno input-bounded Lipschitz strategy.*

Theorem 11. *The composition of two compatible receptive input-bounded Lipschitz HIOAs is a receptive input-bounded Lipschitz HIOA.*

The conclusion that we derive from Theorem 11 is that compatibility implies strong compatibility if we describe the continuous behaviors of HIOAs by means of differential equations of the form of D with functions f and g globally Lipschitz. In general, any choice of conditions on f, g, and u that guarantees local existence of unique solutions, continuity of solutions, and that is preserved by interaction between systems, can be used to define a class of automata for which strong compatibility follows from compatibility.

References

1. R. Alur, C. Courcoubetis, N. Halbwachs, T.A. Henzinger, P.-H. Ho, X. Nicollin, A. Olivero, J.Sifakis, and S. Yovine. The algorithmic analysis of hybrid systems. *Theoretical Computer Science*, 138:3–34, 1995.
2. R. Alur and T.A. Henzinger. Reactive modules. *Proc. LICS'96*, pp. 207–218, 1996.
3. R. Alur and T.A. Henzinger. Modularity for timed and hybrid systems. In *Proc. of CONCUR'97*, LNCS 1243, pp. 74–88, 1997.
4. D.J.B. Bosscher, I. Polak, and F.W. Vaandrager. Verification of an audio control protocol. In *Proc. of FTRTFT'94*, LNCS 863, pp. 170–192, 1994.
5. D. Dill. *Trace Theory for Automatic Hierarchical Verification of Speed-Independent Circuits*. ACM Distinguished Dissertations. MIT Press, 1988.
6. E. Dolginova and N.A. Lynch. Safety verification for automated platoon maneuvers: A case study. *Proc. of HART'97*, LNCS 1201, pp. 154–170, 1997.
7. C.A. Gunter. *Semantics of Programming Languages: Structures and Techniques*. MIT Press, Cambridge, Massachusetts, 1992.
8. A. Kapur, T.A. Henzinger, Z. Manna, and A. Pnueli. Proving safety properties of hybrid systems. In *Proc. of FTRTFT'94*, LNCS 863, pp. 431–454, 1994.
9. C. Livadas, J. Lygeros, and N.A. Lynch. High-level modelling and analysis of TCAS. In *Proc. of RTSS'99*, 1999.
10. C. Livadas and N.A. Lynch. Formal verification of safety-critical hybrid systems. In *Proc. of HSCC'98*, LNCS 1386, pp. 253–272, 1998.
11. J. Lygeros and N.A. Lynch. On the formal verification of the TCAS conflict resolution algorithms. In *Proc. of 36th IEEE Conference on Decision and Control*, pp. 1829–1834, 1997. Extended abstract.
12. J. Lygeros and N.A. Lynch. Strings of vehicles: Modeling and safety conditions. In *Proc. of HSCC'98*, LNCS 1386, pp. 273–288, 1998.
13. N.A. Lynch. Modelling and verification of automated transit systems, using timed automata, invariants and simulations. In *Hybrid Systems III*, LNCS 1066, 1996.
14. N.A. Lynch. A three-level analysis of a simple acceleration maneuver, with uncertainties. *Proc. of 3rd AMAST Workshop on Real-Time Systems*, pp. 1–22, 1996.
15. N.A. Lynch, R. Segala, F.W. Vaandrager, and H.B. Weinberg. Hybrid I/O automata. In *Hybrid Systems III*, LNCS 1066, pp. 496–510, 1996.

16. N.A. Lynch, R. Segala, F.W. Vaandrager, and H.B. Weinberg. Hybrid I/O automata. Report CSI-R9907, Computing Science Institute, Univ. of Nijmegen, 1999.
17. N.A. Lynch and F.W. Vaandrager. Action transducers and timed automata. *Formal Aspects of Computing*, 8(5):499–538, 1996.
18. N.A. Lynch and H.B. Weinberg. Proving correctness of a vehicle maneuver: Deceleration. *Proc. 2nd European Workshop on Real-Time and Hybrid Systems*, 1995.
19. O. Maler, Z. Manna, and A. Pnueli. From timed to hybrid systems. In *Proc. REX Workshop on Real-Time: Theory in Practice*, LNCS 600, pp. 447–484, 1992.
20. R. Segala, R. Gawlick, J.F. Søgaard-Andersen, and N.A. Lynch. Liveness in timed and untimed systems. *Information and Computation*, 141(2):119–171, March 1998.
21. E.D. Sontag. *Mathematical Control Theory — Deterministic Finite Dimensional Systems*, volume 6 of *Texts in Applied Mathematics*. Springer-Verlag, 1990.
22. H.B. Weinberg and N.A. Lynch. Correctness of vehicle control systems: A case study. In *Proc. RTSS'96*, pp. 62–72, 1996.
23. H.B. Weinberg, N.A. Lynch, and N. Delisle. Verification of automated vehicle protection systems. In *Hybrid Systems III*, LNCS 1066, pp. 101–113,1996.

Validating a Hamilton-Jacobi Approximation to Hybrid System Reachable Sets*

Ian Mitchell[1]**, Alexandre M. Bayen[2], and Claire J. Tomlin[2]

[1] Scientific Computing and Computational Mathematics Program,
Gates 2B, Stanford University, Stanford, CA, 94305, USA
mitchell@sccm.stanford.edu
[2] Department of Aeronautics and Astronautics,
Durand 250, Stanford University, Stanford, CA, 94305, USA
{bayen,tomlin}@stanford.edu

Abstract. We develop a general framework for solving the hybrid system reachability problem, and indicate how several published techniques fit into this framework. The key unresolved need of any hybrid system reachability algorithm is the computation of continuous reachable sets; consequently, we present new results on techniques for calculating numerical approximations of such sets evolving under general nonlinear dynamics with inputs. Our tool is based on a local level set procedure for boundary propagation in continuous state space, and has been implemented using numerical schemes of varying orders of accuracy. We demonstrate the numerical convergence of these schemes to the viscosity solution of the Hamilton-Jacobi equation, which was shown in earlier work to be the exact representation of the boundary of the reachable set. We then describe and solve a new benchmark example in nonlinear hybrid systems: an auto-lander for a commercial aircraft in which the switching logic and continuous control laws are designed to maximize the safe operating region across the hybrid state space.

1 Introduction

The focus of this paper is the development and numerical validation of a computational tool to perform as exact as possible reachability computation and controller synthesis for nonlinear hybrid systems. As such, we draw on our previous work in which we characterized the boundary of the reachable set of a hybrid system as the zero level set of the viscosity solution of a particular Hamilton-Jacobi equation [1], and in which we showed that it was feasible to compute this zero level set using so-called "level set methods" [2]. The current paper reflects our progress in the development of a general purpose tool for this reachable

* Research supported by DARPA under the Software Enabled Control Program (AFRL contract F33615-99-C-3014), by a Frederick E. Terman Faculty Award, and by a graduate fellowship provided by the Délégation Générale pour l'Armement in France.
** corresponding author

M.D. Di Benedetto, A. Sangiovanni-Vincentelli (Eds.): HSCC 2001, LNCS 2034, pp. 418–432, 2001.
© Springer-Verlag Berlin Heidelberg 2001

set computation—the core of which is a new variant of a "local level set" algorithm that more efficiently computes a more accurate representation of the reachable set boundary. In addition, we demonstrate the numerical convergence of our computation by analyzing the results as the continuous state space grid is made finer, a standard method of validation for scientific computing codes. In this way, we show that high accuracy can be achieved at the cost of increased computational time and space. We illustrate our tool on a single mode aircraft conflict resolution example [2,3], as well as on a new benchmark example of a six mode commercial aircraft auto-lander, which exhibits nondeterminism and cycles in its discrete behavior.

Our motivation for this project stems from the belief that for many applications of hybrid systems, it is important to be able to accurately represent the reachable set. We have dealt primarily in the safety verification of avionic systems, where accurate representation of the safe region of operation translates into the ability to operate the system closer to the boundaries of that region, at a higher performance level than previously allowed. For very high dimensional state spaces, additional logic (such as projection operators) or new techniques (such as convex overapproximations) will be needed; however, our results in this paper show that it is feasible to do exacting computation for hybrid systems with nonlinear continuous dynamics in three continuous state dimensions and six discrete modes, and we believe it will be feasible to extend this up to five continuous dimensions and large numbers of discrete modes.

2   Reachability for Hybrid Systems

Assuming that tools for discrete and continuous reachability are available—we postpone to subsequent sections the problems of creating such tools—computing reachable sets for hybrid systems requires keeping track of the interplay between these discrete and continuous tools. In this section we summarize the general framework for handling this interaction (following [1]), and we show how various hybrid system reachability algorithms described in the literature fit into this framework.

Fundamentally, reachability analysis in discrete, continuous or hybrid systems seeks to partition states into two categories: those that are reachable from the initial conditions, and those that are not. We will label these two sets of states G and $E = G^c$ respectively.

Any inputs to the hybrid automata are assumed to lie in bounded sets and to have the goal of locally maximizing or minimizing the reachable set: at each iteration, the reachability algorithm chooses values for inputs ξ_G that maximize the size of G and values for inputs ξ_E that minimize the size of G (and hence maximize the size of E). Any nondeterminism in the transition relation is also utilized to consistently maximize or minimize G, depending on the goal of the reachability computation. For hybrid automata, the discrete inputs σ and continuous inputs ν can be assigned to the two categories $\xi_G = (\sigma_G, \nu_G)$ and $\xi_E = (\sigma_E, \nu_E)$ according to whether they seek to maximize or minimize G.

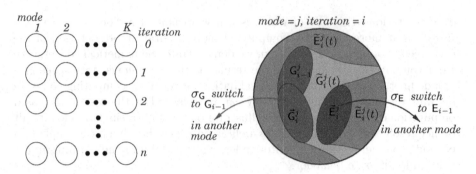

Fig. 1. Iterative Reachability Algorithm: Showing detail of iteration for discrete mode k at iteration i.

The reachability computation follows an iterative, two stage algorithm shown graphically in Figure 1. The outer iteration computes reachability over the discrete switches, producing iterates G_i and E_i at iteration $i = 1, 2, \ldots$. The inner iteration runs a separate continuous reachability problem in each of the discrete modes $j = 1, 2, \ldots K$ to compute the estimates G_i^j and E_i^j. We define the "switch" sets

- $\vec{G}_i^j$ contains all states in mode j from which a discrete transition to a state in G_{i-1} (typically a state in another mode) can be forced to occur through the application of a discrete input σ_G; these states will be defined by the invariant of mode j and the guards of the transitions from mode j.
- $\vec{E}_i^j$ contains all states from which a discrete transition to a state in E_{i-1} can be forced to occur through the application of a discrete input σ_E; these states are also defined by the invariant of mode j and the guards of transitions from mode j.

Then the goal of the continuous reachability tool is to identify the "flow" sets

- $\widetilde{G}_i^j(t)$ contains states from which for all ν_E there exists ν_G that will force the resulting trajectory to flow into $G_{i-1}^j \cup \vec{G}_i^j$ within time t.
- $\widetilde{E}_i^j(t)$ contains states from which there exists ν_E that for all ν_G will force the resulting trajectories to flow into $\vec{E}_i^j$ within time t or to stay outside of $G_{i-1}^j \cup \vec{G}_i^j$ for at least time t.

Note that in some problems the order of the existential and universal quantifiers in the definition above must be reversed. Given these sets,

$$G_i^j = \lim_{t \to \infty} \widetilde{G}_i^j(t), \qquad G_i = \bigcup_{j=1}^{K} G_i^j, \qquad G = \lim_{i \to \infty} G_i,$$

$$E_i^j = \lim_{t \to \infty} \widetilde{E}_i^j(t), \qquad E_i = \bigcup_{j=1}^{K} E_i^j, \qquad E = \lim_{i \to \infty} E_i,$$

where G_0^j is the set of initial conditions of the reachability problem and $E_0^j = (G_0^j)^c$. Simple modifications of this algorithm suffice to solve finite time reachability problems.

The procedure described above, developed in [1,3], was motivated by the work of [4,5] for reachability computation and controller synthesis on timed automata, and that of [6] for controller synthesis on linear hybrid automata. In that development the reachability problem's objective was to determine E—the largest controllable invariant subset of the state space—by computing the set of states G which were reachable in backwards time from the set of predefined unsafe states. In terms of the definitions above, control inputs from this problem lie in ξ_E and disturbance inputs in ξ_G. For safety, any model nondeterminism would be used to maximize the unsafe set G.

Other hybrid system reachability algorithms fall within this framework; the differences lie in their discrete and continuous reachability solvers and the types of initial conditions, inputs, invariants and guards that they admit. Most are described as running forwards in time from a set of safe initial conditions, in which case G is computed as the smallest controllable invariant set. For example, in [7,8] reachability is run with ξ_G as the controlled inputs and ξ_E as the disturbance inputs with the resulting safe set as G. The *CheckMate* tool [9] deals with threshold event-driven hybrid systems—meaning that switches are both enabled and forced only at hyperplanes in the continuous state space—so there is no equivalent to σ_E and thus $\bar{E}_i^j = \emptyset$. Because *VeriSHIFT*'s algorithm [10] is designed for bounded time, decidability can be proven for certain hybrid automata. If we are willing to forgo decidability then its extension to infinite time is straightforward and produces a reachability procedure similar in expressive capacity to *CheckMate*, albeit for different continuous representations.

3   Continuous Reachability with Level Sets

While practical algorithms for computing discrete reachability over many thousands of states have been designed and implemented, determination of continuous reachability for even low dimensional systems is still an open problem. The continuous portion of a hybrid reachability problem requires methods of performing four key operations on sets: unions, intersections, tests of equality, and evolution according to the discrete mode's continuous flow field. The choice of representation for sets dictates the complexity and accuracy of these operations; consequently, continuous reachability algorithms can be classified according to how they represent sets.

Polygonal representations have proven the most popular. The tool **d/dt** [7, 11] tracks the motion of convex polyhedra under linear flow, collecting the nonconvex union of this result into "orthogonal polyhedra" [12]. The developers of *CheckMate* describe optimization based methods of tracking convex polyhedra under general flows, including specializations for the affine case [13,14]. Projectagons [15] is the term used to describe the idea of storing nonconvex high dimensional polyhedra as the intersection of two dimensional projections, which are evolved under affine overapproximations of general flows using linear programming. *VeriSHIFT* [10] uses ellipsoidal representation of reach sets for linear flows with linear input; it implements techniques developed in [16].

3.1   The Hamilton-Jacobi Partial Differential Equation

For our representation scheme, we characterize the set being tracked implicitly by defining a "level set function" $J(x,t)$ throughout the continuous state space which is negative inside the set, zero on its boundary, and positive outside, and which encodes the initial data in $J(x,0)$. The intersection of two such sets is simply the maximum of their level set functions at each point in state space, and the union is the minimum; a variety of easily implemented equality tests are possible. Evolution of a level set under a nonlinear flow field is governed by the Hamilton-Jacobi (HJ) partial differential equation (PDE) (see, for example, [2])

$$-\frac{\partial J(x,t)}{\partial t} = \max_{\nu_{\min}} \min_{\nu_{\max}} f(x, \nu_{\min}, \nu_{\max})^T \nabla J(x,t), \tag{1}$$

$$= H(x, \nabla J(x,t)). \tag{2}$$

where $\nu_{\min}$ are those continuous inputs trying to minimize the size of the set being tracked, and $\nu_{\max}$ are those inputs trying to maximize its size. The order of the optimization must be chosen appropriately for the situation. The implicit representation has a number of advantages when compared with the explicit representations that other researchers are pursuing, including a conceptually simple representation of very general sets and a size which is independent of the complexity of the set (although it grows exponentially with dimension). In addition, a set of sophisticated numerical techniques to accurately solve PDEs may be drawn upon for computation. In the remainder of this section, we focus on the representation (2), and assume that the modeler can compute the appropriate optimization over inputs in (1) if given x and $\nabla J(x,t)$.

3.2   Solving the Hamilton-Jacobi PDE

The HJ PDE (2) is well known to have complex behavior. Even with smooth initial data $J(x,0)$ and continuous Hamiltonian $H(x, \nabla J)$, the solution $J(x,t)$ can develop discontinuous derivatives in finite time; consequently, classical infinite time solutions to the PDE are generally not possible. In the quest for a unique weak solution Crandall and Lions introduced the concept of the viscosity solution [17], which has since been shown to be the appropriate weak solution for Hamilton-Jacobi-Bellman type control problems such as (1) (see, for example, [18]). For most problems of interest, finding the analytic viscosity solution is not possible, and so we seek a numerical solution.

Floating point arithmetic and the truncation required by finite series expansions conspire to ensure that any numerical approximation of the solution of a differential equation will contain errors. The algorithms presented in [7]–[16] seek guaranteed overapproximations (and in some cases, underapproximations) of the system's reachable sets. Numerical methods for solving PDEs, on the other hand, have traditionally aimed for convergent approximations: those approximations that will become exact as some parameter of the method—the grid spacing Δx, for example—goes to zero. While guaranteed overapproximation has its pros and cons for use in reachability applications, we have decided to focus first on convergent approximations of (2) in order to take advantage of existing schemes and numerical analyses [19,20,21,22,23]. We can develop confidence in a convergent approximation's accuracy by successive refinement of Δx.

If we are willing to pursue convergent numerical approximations of (2), a reasonable question is whether it would be simpler and as reliable to solve for the optimal trajectories starting from points on the boundary of the initial set, and thereby approximate the boundary of the reachable set. This technique, however, is equivalent to solving the PDE by the characteristic method, and the characteristics of the Hamilton-Jacobi equation are known to collide and/or separate [18], which would make for an incorrectly represented reachable set.[1]

Returning to methods of solving (2) numerically, the state space over which we compute reachability is topologically simple, and so we approximate the solution of (2) on a Cartesian grid of nodes. Three terms in the equation must be approximated at each node, based on the values of the level set function at that node and its neighbors: the gradient ∇J, the Hamiltonian H, and the time derivative $\frac{\partial J(x,t)}{\partial t}$. We discuss each of these separately.

In each dimension at each grid point there exist both left and right approximations of the gradient ∇J, depending on which neighboring grid points' values are used in the finite difference calculation. We label the vector of left approximations ∇J^-, the vector of right approximations ∇J^+, and will see below that ∇J^-, ∇J^+ or some combination of the two will be used to compute the numerical Hamiltonian $\hat{H}$. The accuracy of a derivative approximation is measured in terms of the order of its local truncation error; an order p method has error $\|\nabla J - \nabla J^\pm\| = \mathcal{O}(\Delta x^p)$. At the current time, we have implemented the basic first order accurate approximation for speed [21] and a weighted, essentially non-oscillatory fifth order accurate approximation for high fidelity [20,22]. "Non-oscillatory" in this context indicates that near discontinuities in the level set derivative, a scheme may revert to lower order accuracy so as to avoid introducing spurious numerical oscillations into the solution. Technically, therefore, all schemes are globally first order accurate, but in practice the higher order accuracy in the smooth parts of the solution produces better global results. This property is sometimes called "high resolution" to distinguish it from true high order accuracy.

We have chosen to use the well studied Lax-Friedrichs numerical Hamiltonian approximation $\hat{H}$ [20,24]

$$\hat{H}(x, \nabla J^-, \nabla J^+) = H(x, \tfrac{\nabla J^- + \nabla J^+}{2}) - \tfrac{1}{2}\alpha^T(\nabla J^+ - \nabla J^-), \qquad (3)$$

---

[1] For example, it turns out that much of the helical bulge of the reach set computed in Section 3.4 lies on a collection of optimal trajectories fanning out from a single point on the boundary of the problem's initial conditions.

where $H(x, \nabla J)$ is given by (2) and the term containing the vector coefficient α is a high order numerical dissipation added to damp out spurious oscillations in the solution. Upwinded numerical Hamiltonians were considered; but although they do not require the artificial dissipation of Lax-Friedrichs, they cannot easily deal with the ∇J dependent flow appearing in (2).

The time derivative of the PDE is handled by the method of lines: the value of the level set function J at each node is treated as an ODE $\frac{dJ}{dt} = \hat{H}$, with $\hat{H}$ given by (3). General ODE solvers, such as Runge-Kutta (RK) schemes, can then be applied. The explicit nature of these techniques, however, limits the size of the timestep to some flow speed dependent multiple of the grid spacing—typically a small fraction—called the Courant-Friedrichs-Lewy (CFL) number. Standard RK iterations lead to very small CFL values and can introduce spurious oscillations into a numerical Hamilton-Jacobi solution; therefore, we use total variation diminishing (TVD) versions of Runge-Kutta (see, for example, [19,23]). We have currently implemented TVD RK schemes which are first and second order accurate in time. Due to CFL restrictions the timestep is usually much smaller than the grid spacing, so it is possible to use lower order accuracy in time than in space without noticeable loss of solution quality.

3.3 Localizing Computation

The Hamilton-Jacobi equation (2) describes the evolution of the level set function over all of space. But we are only interested in its zero level set; thus, we can restrict our computational updates to nodes near the boundary between positive and negative $J(x, t)$—an idea variously called "local level sets" [25] or "narrowbanding" [21]. We have implemented a new variant of this method in our code.

Because the boundary is of one dimension less than the state space, considerable savings are available for two and three dimensional problems. If the number of nodes in each dimension is n (proportional to Δx^{-1}) and the dimension d, the total number of nodes is $\mathcal{O}(n^d)$; the CFL restriction on timestep means that total computational cost is $\mathcal{O}(n^{d+1})$. With local level sets, we reduce computational costs back down to $\mathcal{O}(n^d)$.

3.4 Numerical Validation of Aircraft Collision Avoidance

The numerical schemes mentioned above for solving the Hamilton-Jacobi equation are complicated; therefore, it is not surprising that theoretical proofs of convergence to the viscosity solution are available for only the very simplest low order accuracy methods [24]. High resolution methods have instead been subjected to "numerical validation": comparison to known analytic solutions and lower order accurate approximations of an extensive collection of examples for a broad range of grid sizes [20], from which can be drawn encouraging conclusions regarding their accuracy.

In this section we present a similar validation of our implementation on the single mode, three dimensional aircraft collision avoidance example (see [3,2] for

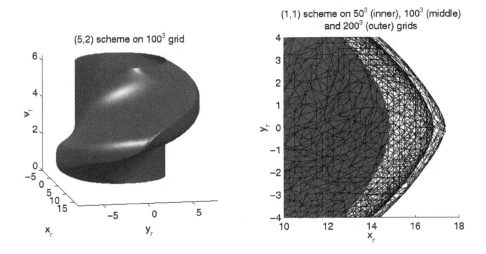

Fig. 2. Reachable Set for Aircraft Collision Avoidance Example

details). The example features a control aircraft trying to avoid collision with a disturbance aircraft, where both aircraft have fixed and equal altitude, speed and turning radius—they may only choose which direction they will turn:

$$\dot{x}_r = -v_u + v_d \cos \psi_r + u y_r, \qquad \dot{y}_r = v_d \sin \psi_r - u x_r, \qquad \dot{\psi}_r = d - u,$$

where $v_u = v_d = 5$ are the aircraft speeds, x_r and y_r are the relative planar location of the aircraft and ψ_r is their relative heading. The inputs $|u| \leq 1$ and $|d| \leq 1$ are the control's and disturbance's respective turn rates. The initial unsafe set $J(x, 0)$ is the interior of the radius five cylinder centered on the ψ_r axis. Choosing optimal inputs according to (1) with $\nu_G = \nu_{\max} = d$ and $\nu_E = \nu_{\min} = u$, we get the optimal Hamiltonian:

$$H(x, p) = -p_1 v_u + p_1 v_d \cos \psi_r + p_2 v_d \sin \psi_r + |p_1 y_r - p_2 x_r - p_3| - |p_3|.$$

Using our new C++ implementation, grid sizes corresponding to 50, 70, 100, 140, and 200 nodes in each dimension were tried with a low order accurate scheme (first order space and time, hereafter referred to as the "(1,1)" scheme) and a high resolution scheme (fifth order space and second order time, hereafter the "(5,2)" scheme). On the eight million node finest grid—only around 10% of which is being actively updated on any one timestep by the local level set algorithm—execution time for the (5,2) scheme was about eighteen hours on a Sun UltraSparc II with lots of memory. Reducing the grid size in half results in the expected eightfold savings in memory and time; hence, the coarsest grid takes only fifteen minutes with the (5,2) scheme.

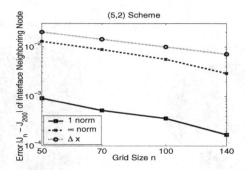

Fig. 3. Convergence of (5,2) Scheme to Finest Grid Solution (J_n is the solution $J(x,t)$ on a grid size of n)

Results are visualized[2] by the zero level isosurface of the unsafe reachable set G, shown in Figure 2. On the left is a head-on view of the (5,2) solution. On the right is a zoomed overhead view of the point of the bulge computed by the (1,1) scheme for several grid sizes. The fact that the solutions grow closer together as the grid is refined provides visual evidence of convergence.

The solutions produced by the (5,2) scheme are visually identical for all grids, and to show quantitative convergence as the grid is refined we require a suitable error metric. Comparing the value of $J(x,t)$ over the entire domain is inappropriate, since our algorithms assume that we seek only an accurate computation of its zero level set. Instead, we consider just the nodes neighboring the zero level set—those nodes which have at least one adjacent node whose J value is of opposite sign. We compare solutions on the four coarser grids to the solution on the finest grid, using linear interpolation on the finest grid if necessary. Figure 3 demonstrates that the scheme is converging to the finest grid's solution of (2) at approximately a linear rate in both average error and pointwise maximum error. We cannot expect to show a higher order convergence rate because of the linear interpolation used to evaluate the error and, as explained in Section 3.2, the scheme is truly high order accurate only in smooth portions of the solution.

Two conclusions can be drawn from Figures 2 and 3. First, low order schemes are not at all competitive in terms of accuracy with the (5,2) scheme. Thus, while our previously reported best results [2] took only an hour to run in Matlab, because they used a (slightly different) first order scheme, our new (5,2) implementation can produce more accurate results in about fifteen minutes using only the coarsest grid. Second, the pointwise maximum error of the (5,2) scheme is always less than the grid spacing, so if a $50^{-1} = 2\%$ error is tolerable for this application, only this fastest, coarsest grid need ever be run.

---

[2] Figure 2 and Figure 6 visualize some level set surfaces as triangular meshes; these are not the meshes on which the Hamilton-Jacobi PDE was solved, but rather an artifact of three dimensional Matlab visualization techniques.

4 Aircraft Landing Example

Once a method of determining continuous reachability is available, the discrete iteration of the algorithm described in Section 2 is relatively straightforward. In fact, for discrete transition graphs with no cycles it is possible to order the continuous reachability problems such that no discrete iteration is required (e.g. the three mode example presented in [2]). In order to examine the complications induced by discrete cycles—such as how to avoid zenoness, in what order to execute the continuous reachability problems, and how to determine which switches are active—a new example has been developed, which exhibits those difficulties and has real life applications: the landing of a civilian airliner.

Physical model: A simple point mass model for aircraft vertical navigation is used, which accounts for lift L, drag D, thrust T, and gravity mg (see [3] and references therein). State variables are aircraft height z, horizontal position x, velocity $V = \sqrt{\dot{x}^2 + \dot{z}^2}$ and flight path angle $\gamma = \tan^{-1}(\frac{\dot{z}}{\dot{x}})$. Inputs are thrust T and angle of attack α, where aircraft pitch $\theta = \gamma + \alpha$ (see the left side of Figure 4). The equations of motion can be expressed as follows:

$$\frac{d}{dt}\begin{bmatrix} V \\ \gamma \\ x \\ z \end{bmatrix} = \begin{bmatrix} \frac{1}{m}[T\cos\alpha - D(\alpha, V) - mg\sin\gamma] \\ \frac{1}{mV}[T\sin\alpha + L(\alpha, V) - mg\cos\gamma] \\ V\cos\gamma \\ V\sin\gamma \end{bmatrix} \tag{4}$$

The functions $L(\alpha, V)$ and $D(\alpha, V)$ are modelled based on empirical data [26] and Prandtl's lifting line theory [27]:

$$L(\alpha, V) = \tfrac{1}{2}\rho S V^2 C_L(\alpha), \qquad D(\alpha, V) = \tfrac{1}{2}\rho S V^2 C_D(\alpha),$$

where ρ is the density of air, S is wing area, and $C_L(\alpha)$ and $C_D(\alpha)$ are the dimensionless lift and drag coefficients.

In determining $C_L(\alpha)$ we will follow standard auto-lander design and assume that the aircraft switches between three fixed flap deflections $\delta = 0°$, $\delta = 25°$ and $\delta = 50°$ (with slats either extended or retracted), thus constituting a hybrid system with different nonlinear dynamics in each mode. This model is representative of current aircraft technology; for example, in Airbus cockpits the pilot uses a lever to select among four predefined flap deflection settings. We assume a linear form for the lift coefficient $C_L(\alpha) = h_\delta + 4.2\alpha$, where parameters $h_{0°} = 0.2$, $h_{25°} = 0.8$ and $h_{50°} = 1.2$ are determined from experimental data for a DC9-30 [26]. The value of α at which the vehicle stalls decreases with increasing flap deflection: $\alpha_{0°}^{\max} = 16°$, $\alpha_{25°}^{\max} = 13°$, $\alpha_{50°}^{\max} = 11°$; slat deflection adds $7°$ to the $\alpha^{\max}$ in each mode. The right side of Figure 4 gives a graphical summary of the possible configurations. The drag coefficient is computed from the lift coefficient as [27] $C_D(\alpha) = 0.041 + 0.045C_L^2(\alpha)$ and includes flap deflection, slat extension and gear deployment corrections. So for a DC9-30 landing at sea level and for all $\alpha \in [-5°, \alpha_\delta^{\max}]$, the lift and drag terms in (4) are given by

$$L(\alpha, V) = 68.6\,(h_\delta + 4.2\alpha)V^2 \qquad D(\alpha, V) = (2.81 + 3.09\,(h_\delta + 4.2\alpha)^2)V^2 \tag{5}$$

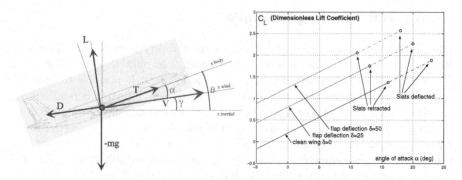

Fig. 4. Left: Force diagram for the point mass approximation of the aircraft. Right: lift coefficient $C_L(\alpha)$ model for the DC9-30 [26]. Circles located at $(\alpha_\delta^{\max}, C_L(\alpha_\delta^{\max}))$ indicate the stall angle and the corresponding lift coefficient in each mode.

Flap deflection dynamics model: In reality, the decision to move from one deflection setting to another can occur at any time, but approximately 10 seconds are required for a 25° degree change in flap deflection. A five state model of this situation is shown on the left side of Figure 5, where the system is in state R if the flaps are retracting and state D if the flaps are deflecting. The system is zeno because instantaneous switches are allowed between any modes.

Current implementation: For our preliminary implementation, we have chosen to ignore the continuous dynamics associated with discrete mode switching, allowing the flaps and slats to move instantly to their commanded positions. However, if such instantaneous controlled switches were always enabled then the system would be zeno; therefore, we introduce transition modes $0t$, $25t$ and $50t$, which use the envelopes and flight dynamics of the regular modes $0u$, $25d$ and $50d$ (the discrete automaton is shown on the right side of Figure 5). A regular mode may make a controlled switch to a transition mode, so flight dynamics can be changed instantly. Transition modes have only a timed switch at $t = t_{\text{delay}}$, so controlled switches will be separated by at least t_{delay} time units and the system is nonzeno. For the executions shown below, $t_{\text{delay}} = 0.5$ seconds.

Landing: Extensive descriptions of the final stage of landing, when aircraft height is below 50 feet, exist (see, for example, [26,28]). Restrictions on the flight path angle, aircraft velocity and touchdown (TD) speed are used to determine the initial safe set E_0:

$$
\begin{cases}
z \leq 0 & \text{landing or has landed} \\
V > V_\delta^{\text{stall}} & \text{faster than stall speed} \\
V < V^{\max} & \text{slower than limit speed} \\
V \sin\gamma \geq \dot{z}_0 & \text{limited TD speed} \\
\gamma \leq 0 & \text{monotonic descent}
\end{cases}
\cup
\begin{cases}
z > 0 & \text{aircraft in the air} \\
V > V_\delta^{\text{stall}} & \text{faster than stall speed} \\
V < V^{\max} & \text{slower than limit speed} \\
\gamma > -3° & \text{limited descent flight path} \\
\gamma \leq 0 & \text{monotonic descent}
\end{cases}
\tag{6}
$$

We again draw on numerical values for a DC9-30 [26]: stall speeds $V_{0u}^{\text{stall}} = 78$ m/s, $V_{25d}^{\text{stall}} = 61$ m/s, $V_{50d}^{\text{stall}} = 58$ m/s, maximal touchdown speed $\dot{z}_0 = 0.9144$

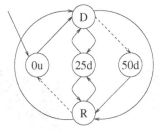 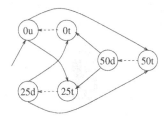

Fig. 5. Discrete transition graph of slat and flap settings. The left graph shows the model with flap deflection dynamics and the right graph shows the currently implemented model. Solid lines are controlled switches (σ_E in this version of the reachability problem) and dashed lines are uncontrolled switches (σ_G).

m/s, and maximal velocity $V^{\max} = 83$ m/s. For passenger comfort, the aircraft's input range is restricted to $T \in [0 \text{ kN}, 160 \text{ kN}]$ and $\alpha \in [0°, 10°]$.

The interior of the surface shown in the first row of Figure 6 represents E_0 for each mode. The second row of the figure shows the safe envelope E when there is no mode switching. Portions of E_0 are excluded from E for two reasons. States near $z = 0$ correspond to low altitudes and are too close to the ground at steep flight path angles to allow control inputs time to prevent the plane from crashing. States close to the stall velocity correspond to low speeds where there is insufficient lift and the flight path angle becomes steeper than that allowed by the flight envelope. This latter condition holds throughout the very narrow range of speeds allowed in mode $0u$, with the result that only post-touchdown states $(z \leq 0)$ are controllable in this mode. The third row shows how E can be increased if switches are permitted (for example, mode $0u$ becomes completely controllable). Mode $50d$ is the best to be in for landing and there is no difference in E with or without switching enabled. The fourth row shows slices of the set in the third row, taken at $z = 3$ meters. The light grey regions are unsafe G and the dark grey are safe E. The figure shows that modes $0u$ and $25d$ are safe only because there exists a discrete switch to a safe state in another mode.

We have presented and numerically validated a tool for determining accurate approximations of reachable sets for hybrid systems with nonlinear continuous dynamics and adversarial continuous and discrete inputs. By developing convergent approximations of such complex systems, we will be better able to synthesize aggressive but safe controllers. As an example, the six mode auto-lander shows that for envelope protection purposes the safest control decisions are to switch directly to full flap deflection, but to maintain airspeed until touchdown. With the summary data from the reachability analysis, such decisions can be made based on local state information; without it the auto-lander may not detect that low speeds—while still within the flight envelope—lead inevitably to unsafe flight path angles.

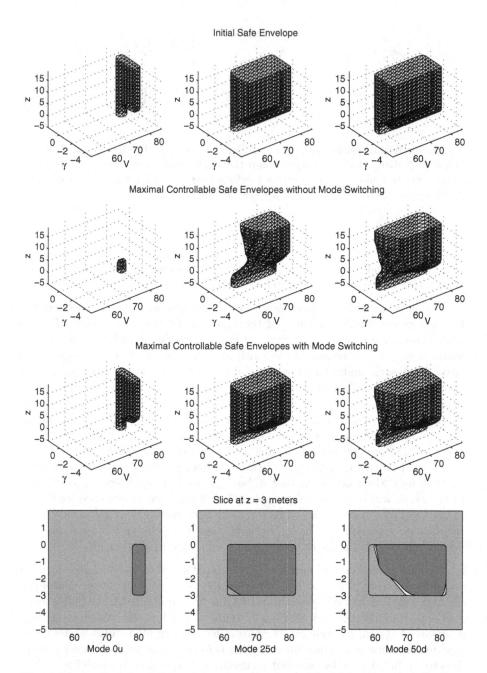

Fig. 6. Maximally controllable safe envelopes for the multimode landing example. From left to right the columns represent modes $0u$, $25d$ and $50d$.

Our current work includes further validation of our numeric algorithm, extending our implementation to four continuous dimensions in order to capture the full landing example dynamics, projections to capture higher dimensional dynamics, schemes for overapproximating the solution of the HJ PDE, automation of the discrete algorithm, and parallel implementations.

Acknowledgements. We would like to thank Professors Ron Fedkiw and Stanley Osher for extensive discussions about the details of numerical schemes for solving the Hamilton-Jacobi PDE. Professor Fedkiw is also responsible for some key ideas in our new variant for localizing the level set computation. In addition, we would like to thank Professor Ilan Kroo for discussions about flight dynamics and for his help in the design of the auto-lander example.

References

1. C. Tomlin, J. Lygeros, and S. Sastry, "Controller design for hybrid systems," *Proceedings of the IEEE*, vol. 88, no. 7, July 2000.
2. I. Mitchell and C. Tomlin, "Level set methods for computation in hybrid systems," in *Hybrid Systems: Computation and Control* (B. Krogh and N. Lynch, eds.), LNCS 1790, pp. 310–323, Springer Verlag, 2000.
3. C. J. Tomlin, *Hybrid Control of Air Traffic Management Systems*. PhD thesis, Department of Electrical Engineering, University of California, Berkeley, 1998.
4. O. Maler, A. Pnueli, and J. Sifakis, "On the synthesis of discrete controllers for timed systems," in *STACS 95: Theoretical Aspects of Computer Science* (E. W. Mayr and C. Puech, eds.), no. 900 in LNCS, pp. 229–242, Munich: Springer Verlag, 1995.
5. E. Asarin, O. Maler, and A. Pnueli, "Symbolic controller synthesis for discrete and timed systems," in *Proceedings of Hybrid Systems II, Volume 999 of LNCS* (P. Antsaklis, W. Kohn, A. Nerode, and S. Sastry, eds.), Cambridge: Springer Verlag, 1995.
6. H. Wong-Toi, "The synthesis of controllers for linear hybrid automata," in *Proceedings of the IEEE Conference on Decision and Control*, (San Diego, CA), 1997.
7. T. Dang, *Vérification et synthèse des systèmes hybrides*. PhD thesis, Institut National Polytechnique de Grenoble (Verimag), 2000.
8. E. Asarin, O. Bournez, T. Dang, O. Maler, and A. Pnueli, "Effective synthesis of switching controllers for linear systems," *Proceedings of the IEEE*, vol. 88, no. 7, pp. 1011–1025, July 2000.
9. B. Silva and B. H. Krogh, "Formal verification of hybrid systems using *CheckMate*: A case study," in *Proceedings of the American Control Conference*, (Chicago, IL), pp. 1679–1683, 2000.
10. O. Botchkarev and S. Tripakis, "Verification of hybrid systems with linear differential inclusions using ellipsoidal approximations," in *Hybrid Systems: Computation and Control* (B. Krogh and N. Lynch, eds.), LNCS 1790, pp. 73–88, Springer Verlag, 2000.
11. E. Asarin, O. Bournez, T. Dang, and O. Maler, "Approximate reachability analysis of piecewise-linear dynamical systems," in *Hybrid Systems: Computation and Control* (N. Lynch and B. Krogh, eds.), no. 1790 in LNCS, pp. 21–31, Springer Verlag, 2000.

12. O. Bournez, O. Maler, and A. Pnueli, "Orthogonal polyhedra: Representation and computation," in *Hybrid Systems: Computation and Control* (F. Vaandrager and J. van Schuppen, eds.), no. 1569 in LNCS, pp. 46–60, Springer Verlag, 1999.

13. A. Chutinan and B. H. Krogh, "Verification of polyhedral-invariant hybrid automata using polygonal flow pipe approximations," in *Hybrid Systems: Computation and Control* (F. Vaandrager and J. H. van Schuppen, eds.), no. 1569 in LNCS, pp. 76–90, New York: Springer Verlag, 1999.

14. A. Chutinan and B. H. Krogh, "Approximating quotient transition systems for hybrid systems," in *Proceedings of the American Control Conference*, (Chicago, IL), pp. 1689–1693, 2000.

15. M. Greenstreet and I. Mitchell, "Reachability analysis using polygonal projections," in *Hybrid Systems: Computation and Control* (F. Vaandrager and J. van Schuppen, eds.), no. 1569 in LNCS, pp. 103–116, Springer Verlag, 1999.

16. A. B. Kurzhanski and P. Varaiya, "Ellipsoidal techniques for reachability analysis," in *Hybrid Systems: Computation and Control* (B. Krogh and N. Lynch, eds.), LNCS 1790, pp. 202–214, Springer Verlag, 2000.

17. M. G. Crandall, L. C. Evans, and P.-L. Lions, "Some properties of viscosity solutions of Hamilton-Jacobi equations," *Transactions of the American Mathematical Society*, vol. 282, no. 2, pp. 487–502, 1984.

18. L. Evans, *Partial Differential Equations*. Providence, Rhode Island: American Mathematical Society, 1998.

19. C.-W. Shu and S. Osher, "Efficient implementation of essentially non-oscillatory shock-capturing schemes," *Journal of Computational Physics*, vol. 77, pp. 439–471, 1988.

20. S. Osher and C.-W. Shu, "High-order essentially nonoscillatory schemes for Hamilton-Jacobi equations," *SIAM Journal on Numerical Analysis*, vol. 28, no. 4, pp. 907–922, 1991.

21. J. A. Sethian, *Level Set Methods and Fast Marching Methods*. New York: Cambridge University Press, 1999.

22. R. Fedkiw, T. Aslam, B. Merriman, and S. Osher, "A non-oscillatory Eulerian approach to interfaces in multimaterial flows (the ghost fluid method)," *Journal of Computational Physics*, vol. 152, pp. 457–492, 1999.

23. M. Kang, R. Fedkiw, and X.-D. Liu, "A boundary condition capturing method for multiphase incompressible flow," *Journal of Computational Physics*, 2000. Submitted.

24. M. G. Crandall and P.-L. Lions, "Two approximations of solutions of Hamilton-Jacobi equations," *Mathematics of Computation*, vol. 43, no. 167, pp. 1–19, 1984.

25. D. Peng, B. Merriman, S. Osher, H. Zhao, and M. Kang, "A PDE based fast local level set method," *Journal of Computational Physics*, vol. 165, pp. 410–438, 1999.

26. I. M. Kroo, *Aircraft Design: Synthesis and Analysis*. Stanford, California: Desktop Aeronautics Inc., 1999.

27. J. Anderson, *Fundamentals of Aerodynamics*. New York: McGraw Hill Inc., 1991.

28. United States Federal Aviation Administration, *Federal Aviation Regulations*, 1990. Section 25.125 (landing).

Robust Controller Synthesis for Hybrid Systems Using Modal Logic*

Thomas Moor and J.M. Davoren

Research School of Information Sciences and Engineering
Australian National University
Canberra ACT 0200 AUSTRALIA
{thomas.moor, j.m.davoren}@anu.edu.au

Abstract. In this paper, we formulate and robustly solve a quite general class of hybrid controller synthesis problems. The type of controller we investigate is the switching control mechanism of a hybrid automaton (via guard and mode invariant sets), and the robustness result is with respect to variations in the right hand sides of the differential equations that depend continuously on a parameter. We present a novel methodology for controller design and synthesis which uses modal logic as a formalism for reasoning about sets of plant states, and various operators on sets arising from the differential equations and from metric tolerance relations on the state space.

1   Introduction

In general terms, a hybrid system H can be said to satisfy a performance specification *robustly* if every system H' in some nominated *variation class* around H also satisfies that specification. Likewise, a synthesis procedure for a class of control problems can be called robust if the nominal closed-loop hybrid system obtained from the solution controller can be shown to robustly satisfy each of the specifications of the problem, with respect to some nominated variation class. Robustness in hybrid control systems is an under-explored topic. A starting point is given in [10], which proposes a range of variation classes for hybrid automata, including near relatives of those in the present work and its predecessor [6]. Robustness issues for hybrid controller design, for a variety of different control settings and problems, are also investigated in [3,8,19,21].

In this paper we find a robust solution to a rather general switching control problem for hybrid systems. The plant consists of a finite number of continuous systems, given by differential equations over a common state space; the controller steers the plant state by determining when to discretely switch between the various differential equations; and the closed-loop trajectories correspond to those of (a subclass of) the widely accepted hybrid automaton model. In addition to the well-studied classes of *safety* (reachability or invariance) and

---

* Research partially supported by US Office of Naval Research, Grant N 00014-98-1-0535.

M.D. Di Benedetto, A. Sangiovanni-Vincentelli (Eds.): HSCC 2001, LNCS 2034, pp. 433–446, 2001.

liveness (non-blocking and non-Zeno) performance specifications, we deal with a class of *event sequence specifications*, requiring that trajectories traverse in prescribed sequences through the blocks of a given finite partition of the plant state space. This gives a general-purpose way of specifying the attainment of local goals along hybrid trajectories, and integrating the type of event sequence specifications examined in DES approaches to hybrid systems [5,12,17].

In [6], we develop an abstract algorithm which solves this controller synthesis problem for arbitrary differential equations with unique solutions, with a proof of finite termination derived from an assumption of compactness of the sets given in the data of the specifications. In that work, we consider one type of variation class that is motivated by considerations of *sensor and actuator imprecision*, and is obtained by allowing a metric tolerance or "margin of error" around the guard sets and in the reset relations; we have shown that our synthesis procedure is robust with respect to that class. In the present paper, we turn our attention to the more traditional control-theoretic perspective on robustness in terms of *parameter uncertainty*; i.e. variations in the right hand sides of the differential equations that depend continuously on a parameter. While these two variation classes are quite distinct, a key technical tool for both cases are *metric tolerance relations*, which are put to use in different ways.

This paper also demonstrates the flexibility and adaptability of our novel methodology for hybrid controller synthesis based on *modal logic*, first developed in [6,7]. For our purposes, modal logic is best viewed as a formalism for reasoning about *sets of states* and *operators on sets* arising from relations on the state space. Considered as a family of logics, modal logic includes the temporal logics more commonly used in formal verification of hybrid systems. More precisely, we work with a *polymodal fusion* of several *normal monomodal logics* [20]. The main benefits our methodology are the following.

- Modal logic provides us with a uniform framework for investigating not only the widely used pre- and post-image operators induced by continuous flows, but also operators induced by metric tolerance relations, and the latter are essential in the context of robustness. As distinct from temporal logics, we reason about the *component parts* of hybrid trajectories, and this is essential for synthesis as opposed to analysis of hybrid systems.

- We use modal logic not merely as a convenient notation, but also draw on the power of *deductive proof systems*. In the course of proving the correctness of our synthesis algorithm, we show that certain key modal formulas are formally deducible from the statement of the algorithm together with explicit assumptions; this appeals to the soundness of a suitable Hilbert proof system w.r.t. the Kripke (transition system) semantics. In future work we will employ automated reasoning tools based on the decidability of the logical consequence and validity problems for modal logics, utilising tableaux proof systems [9].

- In our use of modal logic, we make a clean separation between (i) determining *what* sets need to be computed in order to solve the synthesis problem, and (ii) *how and when* such computations can be performed effectively. Issue (i) is resolved by the our synthesis algorithm below. Issue (ii) is essentially the standard *model checking problem* for hybrid systems, and any model checking tools — either *exact* [1,2,14,15] or *approximate* [4,13,16] — can be used to implement our synthesis algorithm.

In this short paper, we restrict our focus to the core ingredients, and to those aspects of the work that are crucial for plant parameter robustness. Consult [6] for a more detailed account of our framework based on modal logic.

The body of the paper is organised as follows. In Section 2, we briefly review hybrid automata, define plant parameter variation classes, and give a key result on parameterised vector fields. In Section 3, we formally state the controller synthesis problem. Section 4 is a terse review of modal logic applied to hybrid systems, and in Section 5, we give our abstract synthesis algorithm, formalised in the language of modal logic. In Section 6, we outline the proof of the main result of robust correctness. The concluding Section 7 includes a brief discussion of effective implementations of the procedure.

2   Hybrid Automata

We work with the standard and widely accepted hybrid automaton model of Alur, Henzinger *et al.* [1,2].

Definition 1. *A* hybrid automaton *is a system*

$$H = (\, Q, E, X, \{F_q, Inv_q\}_{q \in Q}, \{r_{q,q'}, Grd_{q,q'}\}_{(q,q') \in E} \,)\,, \tag{1}$$

where: Q *is a finite set of* discrete control modes; $E \subseteq Q \times Q$ *is the* discrete transition relation; $X \subseteq \mathbb{R}^n$ *is the* continuous state space; *for each* $q \in Q$, $F_q : X \to \mathbb{R}^n$ *is a vector field, and* $Inv_q \subseteq X$; *and for each* $(q, q') \in E$, $r_{q,q'} \subseteq X \times X$ *is a reset relation, and* $Grd_{q,q'} = \mathrm{dom}(r_{q,q'})$.

In order to ensure that closed-loop trajectories are well-defined, we assume that the vector fields F_q are locally Lipschitz continuous, and the state space X is open. Then from each initial condition $x_0 \in X$, each differential equation $\dot{x} = F_q(x)$ has a unique maximal integral curve in X on a well defined maximal interval of time $[0, T_q(x_0))$, where $T_q(x_0) \in \mathbb{R}^+ \cup \{\infty\}$. We denote this maximal curve by

$$\Phi_q(x_0, \, \cdot \,) \colon [0, \, T_q(x_0)) \to X\,. \tag{2}$$

In the case of $T_q(x_0) < \infty$, it is well known that $\Phi_q(x_0, \, \cdot \,)$ escapes from any *bounded* subset of X at some time less than or equal to $T_q(x_0)$. For the scope of this paper, we can restrict attention to bounded invariant sets Inv_q. Then maximal curves from $x_0 \in Inv_q$ either leave Inv_q within finite time or stay within Inv_q forever with $T_q(x_0) = \infty$. Closed-loop trajectories are then defined as follows.

Definition 2. *A* trajectory *of a hybrid automaton* H *is a finite or infinite sequence* $\eta = (\Delta_i, q_i, \gamma_i)_{i \in I}$ *such that for each* $i \in I$:

- *the duration $\Delta_i \in \mathbb{R}^+ \cup \{\infty\}$, with $\Delta_i = \infty$ only if I is finite and $i = \max(I)$;*
- *the discrete state $q_i \in Q$;*
- *the continuous curve $\gamma_i : [0, \Delta_i] \to X$ satisfies $\gamma_i(t) = \Phi_{q_i}(\gamma_i(0), t)$ and $\gamma_i(t) \in Inv_{q_i}$ for all $t \in [0, \Delta_i]$, with the convention that $[0, \Delta_i]$ is $[0, \infty)$ if $\Delta_i = \infty$;*
- *if $i < \sup(I)$, then $(q_i, q_{i+1}) \in E$ and $\gamma_i(\Delta_i) \xrightarrow{r_{q_i, q_{i+1}}} \gamma_{i+1}(0)$.*

A trajectory will be called: step-infinite *if it makes infinitely many switches;* time-infinite *if the sum over all durations is unbounded; and* full *if it is either step-infinite or time-infinite or else it is blocked, in the sense that it cannot be extended to reach any further guard region.*

A broad framework of variation classes for hybrid automata is proposed in [10]. Our interest here is in parameter variations in the vector fields.

Definition 3. *Given a hybrid automaton H as in Eq. (1), let $F_q^v : X \to \mathbb{R}^n$ be a family of vector fields parameterised by the discrete modes $q \in Q$ and an uncertainty parameter $v \in V \subseteq \mathbb{R}^m$, where $\mathbf{0} \in V$ and $F_q^{\mathbf{0}} \equiv F_q$. Then*

$$H^v = (Q, E, X, \{F_q^v, Inv_q\}_{q \in Q}, \{r_{q,q'}, Grd_{q,q'}\}_{(q,q') \in E}), \tag{3}$$
$$\mathcal{H}^\varepsilon = \{H^v \mid \|v\| < \varepsilon\} \tag{4}$$

defines a parameterised variation class around the nominal model $H^{\mathbf{0}} = H$ with variation bound ε.

In correspondence with the nominal model, we denote the maximal integral curves of the vector field F_q^v by $\Phi_q^v(x_0, \cdot) : [0, T_q^v(x_0)) \to X$ where $T_q^v(x_0) \in \mathbb{R}^+ \cup \{\infty\}$. The following assumptions on the vector fields are to ensure that the flow $\Phi_q^v(x_0, t)$ is continuous in v and x_0.

(A0) The parameter set V is open. The vector field $F_q^v(x)$ is continuous in both x and v. Furthermore, $F_q^v(x)$ is locally Lipschitz continuous in x uniformly in v; i.e. there exists a Lipschitz constant which may depend on x but not on v.

In particular, assumption **(A0)** ensures that for any given finite time interval and any given *open tube* around the nominal integral curve $\Phi_q(x_0, t)$, all variations $\Phi_q^v(x_0, t)$ evolve within that tube – provided that the variation is sufficiently small; e.g. [11], Theorem 2.6. In the hybrid setting, we need to examine continuous parameter dependency w.r.t. a given domain D in the state space, rather than w.r.t. a given interval on the time axis. That is, we are interested in the dependency of $\Phi_q^v(x_0, t)$ in v as long as that curve evolves within an invariant set Inv_q. We formalise these ideas in terms of metric tolerance relations, and in so doing, set up the link to modal logics.

Definition 4. *Given a metric d on the state space X, the δ-ball $B_\delta(x)$ of radius $\delta > 0$ with centre $x \in X$ is defined by*

$$B_\delta(x) \stackrel{\text{def}}{=} \{y \in X \mid d(x,y) < \delta\}. \tag{5}$$

For a set $A \subseteq X$, we call the set $B_\delta(A) \overset{\text{def}}{=} \{x \in X \mid B_\delta(x) \cap A \neq \emptyset\}$ the δ-expansion of A. We also call the (reflexive and symmetric) relation $B_\delta \subseteq X \times X$ a metric tolerance relation. For the scope of this paper, d is assumed to be a metric that induces the standard Euclidean topology on X.

For a set $A \subseteq X$, let

$$T_q^v(A, x_0) = \sup\{\tau < T_q^v(x_0) \mid (\forall s \in [0, \tau)) \, \Phi_q^v(x_0, s) \in A\} \qquad (6)$$

denote the time at which $\Phi_q^v(x_0, \cdot)$ escapes from A, so $T_q^v(x_0) = T_q^v(X, x_0)$.

Proposition 1. *Let D be a compact set with $B_{4\delta}(D) \subseteq X$ for a given metric tolerance $\delta > 0$. Furthermore, assume $T_q(B_{3\delta}(D), x_0) < \infty$ for all $x_0 \in D$. Then there exits a variation bound $\varepsilon > 0$ such that $T_q^v(D, x_0) \leq T_q(B_{2\delta}(D), x_0) \leq T_q^v(x_0)$ and $\Phi_q^v(x_0, t) \in B_{2\delta}(\Phi_q(x_0, t))$ for all $t \leq T_q(B_{2\delta}(D), x_0)$, all $x_0 \in D$ and all $v, \|v\| < \varepsilon$.*

Proof. Apply [11], Theorem 2.6, together with a standard compactness argument.

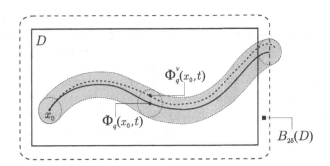

Fig. 1. Illustration of Proposition 1

Figure 1 illustrates a perturbed integral curve lying within a 2δ-tube around the nominal curve from a point $x_0 \in D$, as given by Proposition 1. When a hybrid automaton with bounded invariant sets is designed so that when an integral curve leaves its invariant set, it does so by some uniform minimum distance, Proposition 1 provides an elementary robustness property for this continuous evolution in between any two successive discrete control switches. However, even small variations in the parameter may have the effect that a perturbed trajectory runs into a different guard set than the corresponding nominal trajectory. In turn, such a perturbed trajectory may switch to a different vector field and thus may potentially stray far away from the nominal trajectory. The avoidance of this phenomenon motivates several of the design choices in formulating a robust solution to our target control problem.

3   Control Problem Statement

A hybrid automaton can be seen as the closed-loop feedback system resulting from the inter-connection of a switched continuous plant and a discrete switching controller. See [6] for a more detailed analysis of this control-theoretic content of a hybrid automaton. For the controller synthesis problem under investigation, the plant is given by a finite family of vector fields $F_c : X \to \mathbb{R}^n$ indexed by a *control alphabet* $c \in C$. We then ask for a synthesis procedure that constructs a closed-loop hybrid automaton H by building the missing entities that form the switching control mechanism, namely Q, E, Inv_q, and $Grd_{q,q'}$, where the reset relation is required to be *elementary*; i.e.

$$r_{q,q'} = test.Grd_{q,q'} \;\stackrel{\text{def}}{=}\; \{\, (x, x') \in X \times X \mid x \in Grd_{q,q'} \text{ and } x' = x \,\}. \quad (7)$$

As Q is not known in advance, the synthesis procedure also needs to allocate a particular control $c \in C$ (indexing a vector field) to each discrete mode $q \in Q$.

The control goal is to satisfy the following closed-loop performance specifications.

(S1) *Safety*: given a proscribed set $Bad \subseteq X$, construct a set $Good \subseteq X - Bad$ with the property that every H-trajectory starting in $Good$ always remains outside Bad.

(S2) *Event sequence behaviour with δ-overlaps*: given a finite partition $\{E_k\}_{k \in K}$ of $X - Bad$, a relation $next \subseteq K \times K$, and a metric parameter $\delta > 0$, let $A_k = B_\delta(E_k)$ be the δ-expansion of the partition block E_k, for each $k \in K$; the requirement is that for every full H-trajectory starting in $Good$, whenever it enters one of the sets A_k, it remains there until it crosses into $A_{k'} - A_k$, for some $k' \in next(k)$.

(S3) *Liveness I*: every full H-trajectory starting in $Good$ shall be step-infinite.

(S4) *Liveness II*: every full H-trajectory starting in $Good$ shall be time-infinite.

The specification **(S1)** is the classic form of a safety property, while **(S3)** and **(S4)** are, respectively, the *non-blocking* and the *non-Zeno* forms of liveness properties. The specification **(S2)** prescribes an order of traversal through the δ-expanded partition blocks. Formally, switches from one such block to another are identified as events from the finite alphabet K and **(S2)** requires the closed-loop to generate a sublanguage of $\{(k_i)_{i \in I} \mid \forall i < \sup(I) : k_{i+1} \in next(k_i)\}$. The metric tolerance δ ensures that the event sequence specification refers to overlapping regions $A_k \cap A_{k'}$ rather than the common boundaries $bd(E_k) \cap bd(E_{k'})$ of partition blocks. In particular, the overlaps are full dimensional and allow for some "wiggle room" which is essential for our robustness results. A more detailed motivation of **(S2)** is given in [6].

Our synthesis procedure is subject to the following further assumptions.

(A1) The set $X - Bad$ is compact (with respect to the standard Euclidean topology).

(A2) The map $next \subseteq K \times K$ is *total*, so for each $k \in K$, there is at least one $k' \in next(k)$.

(A3) For all $k, k' \in K$ such that $k \xrightarrow{next} k'$, the partition blocks E_k and $E_{k'}$ are contiguous in the sense that $bd(E_k) \cap bd(E_{k'}) \neq \varnothing$.

(A4) For each $k \in K$, the block E_k has a non-empty δ-*contraction*; i.e. the set $\{x \in X \mid B_\delta(x) \subseteq E_k\}$ is non-empty.

(A5) For all $k, k', k'' \in K$ such that $k \xrightarrow{next} k' \xrightarrow{next} k''$, the infimum of the metric distance between points in the set $bd(E_k) \cap bd(E_{k'})$ and points in the set $bd(E_{k'}) \cap bd(E_{k''})$ is at least 3δ.

By **(A1)**, the relevant portion of the state space is required to be compact; this is used in applying Proposition 1 and in proving finite termination of our algorithm. Assumptions **(A2)**, **(A3)** and **(A4)** are non-triviality conditions. The assumption **(A5)** gives a foundation for non-Zeno-ness by ensuring that closed-loop trajectories must traverse some minimum spatial distance when fulfilling the event sequence specification.

4 Modal Logics for Hybrid Systems

This section sets out only the bare details of modal logics and their application to hybrid systems. For a more substantial account, the reader is referred to [7] and also to [6]. The handbook chapter [18] gives a broader introduction to the family of modal and temporal logics.

A *modal signature* is a pair (Rel, Prp), where Rel is an alphabet of atomic relation labels, and Prp is an alphabet of atomic propositions. The set $\mathcal{L}(\text{Rel}, \text{Prp})$ of *modal formulas* φ of signature (Rel, Prp) is generated by the grammar:

$$\varphi ::= p \mid \neg\varphi \mid \varphi_1 \vee \varphi_2 \mid \langle a \rangle \, \varphi \tag{8}$$

where $p \in \text{Prp}$ and $a \in \text{Rel}$. The other Boolean connectives are definable, e.g. $\varphi_1 \wedge \varphi_2 \overset{\text{def}}{=} \neg(\neg\varphi_1 \vee \neg\varphi_2)$, $\varphi_1 \rightarrow \varphi_2 \overset{\text{def}}{=} (\neg\varphi_1 \vee \varphi_2)$, as are the dual modal operators: $[a]\varphi \overset{\text{def}}{=} \neg\langle a \rangle \neg\varphi$.

The formal semantics of modal (and temporal) logics are given with respect to *labeled transition systems*, also called *LTS models* or *generalized Kripke models*. An LTS model of signature (Rel, Prp) is a structure:

$$\mathfrak{M} = (S, \{a^{\mathfrak{M}}\}_{a \in \text{Rel}}, \{\llbracket p \rrbracket^{\mathfrak{M}}\}_{p \in \text{Prp}}) \,. \tag{9}$$

where: $S \neq \varnothing$ is the state space, of arbitrary cardinality; for each $a \in \text{Rel}$, $a^{\mathfrak{M}} \subseteq S \times S$ is a relation; and for each $p \in \text{Prp}$, $\llbracket p \rrbracket^{\mathfrak{M}} \subseteq S$ is a subset of states. For formulas $\varphi \in \mathcal{L}(\text{Rel}, \text{Prp})$, the *denotation set* $\llbracket \varphi \rrbracket^{\mathfrak{M}} \subseteq S$ is defined by induction, starting with the sets $\llbracket p \rrbracket^{\mathfrak{M}}$ denoting atomic propositions $p \in \text{Prp}$. For compound formulas:

$$\llbracket \neg\varphi \rrbracket^{\mathfrak{M}} \overset{\text{def}}{=} S - \llbracket \varphi \rrbracket^{\mathfrak{M}} \,, \tag{10}$$

$$\llbracket \langle a \rangle \varphi \rrbracket^{\mathfrak{M}} \overset{\text{def}}{=} \text{Pre}^{\exists}(a^{\mathfrak{M}})(\llbracket \varphi \rrbracket^{\mathfrak{M}}) \quad \text{for } a \in \text{Rel} \,, \tag{11}$$

$$\llbracket \varphi_1 \vee \varphi_2 \rrbracket^{\mathfrak{M}} \overset{\text{def}}{=} \llbracket \varphi_1 \rrbracket^{\mathfrak{M}} \cup \llbracket \varphi_2 \rrbracket^{\mathfrak{M}} \,, \tag{12}$$

where the *existential pre-image operator* $\text{Pre}^{\exists}(r) : \mathcal{P}(S) \rightarrow \mathcal{P}(S)$ of a relation $r \subseteq S \times S$ is:

$$\text{Pre}^{\exists}(r)(A) \overset{\text{def}}{=} \{x \in S \mid (\exists y \in S)[\, x \xrightarrow{r} y \wedge y \in A]\} \,. \tag{13}$$

For formulas $\varphi \in \mathcal{L}(\text{Rel}, \text{Prp})$ and models $\mathfrak{M}$ of signature (Rel, Prp), we say: φ is *satisfied* at state s in $\mathfrak{M}$, written $\mathfrak{M}, s \vDash \varphi$, if $s \in [\![\varphi]\!]^{\mathfrak{M}}$; and φ is *true* in $\mathfrak{M}$, or $\mathfrak{M}$ *satisfies* φ, written $\mathfrak{M} \vDash \varphi$, if $[\![\varphi]\!]^{\mathfrak{M}} = S$.

In encoding the control problem and input data in modal logic, we work in an LTS model $\mathfrak{M}_0$ over the plant state space $S := X \subseteq \mathbb{R}^n$. The set of atomic proposition symbols is $\text{Prp}_0 = \{\mathbf{Bad}\} \cup \{\mathbf{E}_k \mid k \in K\}$, with the self-evident denotation sets. The alphabet Rel_0 of relation symbols will grow dynamically in the course of the synthesis algorithm (but will still be finite, due to finite termination). The relation symbols divide into four sorts, which we indicate by consistently using the same letters, adorned with subscripts and superscripts when needed. We will have relation symbols $\mathbf{e}$ for *evolution relations* and $\mathbf{f}$ for *flow* (or *orbit*) *relations*; symbols $\mathbf{r}$ for *reset relations*; and symbols $\boldsymbol{\delta}$ for *metric tolerance relations*.

Definition 5. *Given a flow* $\Phi : X \times \mathbb{R}^+ \to X$ *(possibly a partial function) and any set* $A \subseteq X \subseteq \mathbb{R}^n$, *define a relation* $e(A, \Phi) \subseteq X \times X$ *of evolution along* Φ *restricted within* A, *by:*

$$x \xrightarrow{e(A,\Phi)} x' \stackrel{\text{def}}{\Leftrightarrow} (\exists t \in \mathbb{R}^+)[\, x' = \Phi(x, t) \,\wedge\, (\forall s \in [0, t])\, \Phi(x, s) \in A\,]. \quad (14)$$

The unrestricted orbit relation $f(\Phi) \subseteq X \times X$ *is the special case:* $f(\Phi) = e(X, \Phi)$.

This precisely captures the notion of a hybrid trajectory segment, taking $A = Inv_q$ and $\Phi = \Phi_q$ for each control mode $q \in Q$. For $\mathbf{e}^{\mathfrak{M}_0} = e(A, \Phi)$, a formula $\langle \mathbf{e} \rangle \varphi$ denotes the subset of states in A from which there is a curve along Φ that reaches *some* φ-state, and stays within A at all intermediate points; this is the standard notion of backwards reachability extensively used in the hybrid systems literature. The dual $[\mathbf{e}]$ operator expresses invariance, since $[\mathbf{e}]\varphi$ denotes the set of points *all* of whose e-successors are φ-states. The compound $\mathbf{A} \wedge [\mathbf{e}]\langle \mathbf{e} \rangle \varphi$ denotes the set of states in A all of whose e-successors have a further e-successor which satisfies φ, and so captures the notion of *inevitably* reaching a φ-state. This compound construct is an essential ingredient of our synthesis algorithm, where in addressing the event sequence requirement **(S2)**, we need to identify states that are inevitably driven to certain local goal regions. Figure 2 illustrates the difference between the inevitability formula $\mathbf{A} \wedge [\mathbf{e}]\langle \mathbf{e} \rangle \mathbf{G}$ and the backwards reachability formula $\langle \mathbf{e} \rangle \mathbf{G}$, where $\mathbf{G}$ denotes a local goal.

The reset relations under study are elementary, so $(\mathbf{r}_{q,q'})^{\mathfrak{M}_0} = test.\mathbf{Grd}_{q,q'}$. In this case, the modal operators $\langle \mathbf{r}_{q,q'} \rangle$ and $[\mathbf{r}_{q,q'}]$ can be eliminated:

$$\langle \mathbf{r}_{q,q'} \rangle \varphi \;\leftrightarrow\; (\mathbf{Grd}_{q,q'} \wedge \varphi) \quad \text{and} \quad [\mathbf{r}_{q,q'}]\varphi \;\leftrightarrow\; (\mathbf{Grd}_{q,q'} \to \varphi). \quad (15)$$

For metric tolerance relations $\boldsymbol{\delta}^{\mathfrak{M}_0} = B_\delta$, a formula $\langle \boldsymbol{\delta} \rangle \varphi$ denotes the δ-*expansion* of the set of φ-states, since $B_\delta(A) = \text{Pre}^{\exists}(B_\delta)(A)$. The dual box formula $[\boldsymbol{\delta}]\varphi$ denotes the δ-*contraction* of the set of φ-states, meaning the set of points in $[\![\varphi]\!]^{\mathfrak{M}_0}$ around which one can fit a δ-ball wholly inside $[\![\varphi]\!]^{\mathfrak{M}_0}$.

An axiomatic Hilbert-style proof system capturing basic properties of the modal operators of evolution, flow and metric tolerance relations is given in [6], Section 5. These axioms also may form a basis for employing automated reasoning tools, e.g. tableaux proof systems [9].

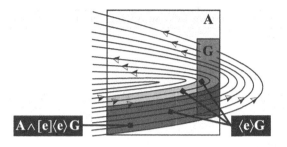

Fig. 2. Denotation of inevitability and backwards reachability formulas

5   Abstract Algorithm of Synthesis Procedure

Our solution to the control problem consists of two parts. First, we strategically construct a finite number of subsets of X, defined in terms of the input data F_c, Bad, E_k, $next$ and δ. Formally, this construction is given as an abstract algorithm where the sets of states are defined by modal logic formulas. The algorithm is a fine-tuned variation of the one presented in [6]. In particular, the proof of finite termination as given in [6] carries over without change. The algorithm may either terminate with failure or indicating success. In the former case it produces some diagnostic output, as described below. In the case of successful termination, the second part of our solution procedure uses the constructed sets of states to assemble our nominal closed-loop hybrid automaton H and the set $Good$. The pair $(H,\ Good)$ then is guaranteed to fulfill the performance specifications **(S1)**-**(S4)**. It is in this second part that the present work departs essentially from [6] and extends the scope of our method to the plant parameter variation class $\mathcal{H}^{\varepsilon}$.

The first part of our procedure is given in Algorithm 1; see [6] for a more detailed exposition including graphical output for a nontrivial example. Given the page constraints on this short paper, we are restricted to a brief discussion of the individual steps of the algorithm. We begin by taking the given metric parameter δ and decomposing it as a sum $\delta = 2\delta_1 + 2\delta_2$, with $\delta_1 > \delta_2 > 0$. Roughly speaking, δ_1 is used as "wiggle room" in order to cope with parameter variations in the vector fields, while δ_2 gives some extra allowance required for an implementation based on approximated evaluation of the modal operators. In the initialisation phase, the formula **Danger**$_k$ denotes the states that are dangerous from the viewpoint of the block E_k: the outright Bad states and the relative bad states in blocks $E_{k'}$ with k' not $next$-related to k. The formula $\mathbf{A}_{k,0}^{(0)}$ denotes A_k, the initial δ-expansion of E_k. The formula **Goal**$_{k,0}^{(0)}$ denotes the states that are *well inside* $E_{k'}$, in the $(\delta - \delta_2)$-contraction of $E_{k'}$, for some $k' \in next(k)$.

The main routine consists of an outer j-iteration which runs the core routine for successive j and each $k \in K$. The purpose of the core routine is to identify states in $\mathbf{A}_{k,0}^{(j)}$ that can be safely driven into the **Goal**$_{k,0}^{(j)}$. The iteration in i is with respect to the number of control switches required to achieve this local

Algorithm 1 Abstract algorithm for computing sets for synthesis procedure

1: % INITIALISATION %

2: $j := 0$ and $i := 0$

3: **FOR ALL** $k \in K$ **DO**

4:     $\mathbf{Danger}_k \overset{\text{def}}{=} \langle \delta_1 \rangle \mathbf{Bad} \lor \bigvee_{k' \notin next(k) \cup \{k\}} \mathbf{E}_{k'}$ $\qquad\qquad$ $\mathbf{A}_{k,0}^{(0)} \overset{\text{def}}{=} \langle \delta \rangle \mathbf{E}_k$

5:     $\mathbf{Goal}_{k,0}^{(0)} \overset{\text{def}}{=} \bigvee_{k' \in next(k)} [\delta - \delta_2] \mathbf{E}_{k'}$ $\qquad$ $\mathbf{Drop}_k^{(0)} \overset{\text{def}}{=} \mathbf{A}_{k,0}^{(0)} \land \mathbf{Goal}_{k,0}^{(0)}$

6: % MAIN-ROUTINE %

7: **REPEAT** % FOR $j = 0, 1, \ldots$ %

8:     % CORE-ROUTINE(k, j) for $k \in K$ %

9:     **FOR ALL** $k \in K$ **DO**

10:         **REPEAT** % FOR $i = 0, 1, \ldots$ %

11:             **FOR ALL** $c \in C$ **DO**

12:                 $(\mathbf{e}_{k,i,c}^{(j)})^{\mathfrak{M}_0} \overset{\text{def}}{=} e([\![\mathbf{A}_{k,i}^{(j)}]\!]^{\mathfrak{M}_0}, \Phi_c)$

13:                 $\mathbf{Sure}_{k,i,c}^{(j)} \overset{\text{def}}{=} \mathbf{A}_{k,i}^{(j)} \land [\mathbf{e}_{k,i,c}^{(j)}] \neg \mathbf{Danger}_k$

14:                 $\mathbf{Success}_{k,i,c}^{(j)} \overset{\text{def}}{=} \mathbf{A}_{k,i}^{(j)} \land [\mathbf{e}_{k,i,c}^{(j)}] \langle \mathbf{e}_{k,i,c}^{(j)} \rangle (\mathbf{A}_{k,i}^{(j)} \land \mathbf{Goal}_{k,i}^{(j)}) \land \langle \mathbf{f}_c \rangle \neg \langle \delta_1 \rangle \mathbf{A}_{k,i}^{(j)}$

15:                 $\mathbf{Fine}_{k,i,c}^{(j)} \overset{\text{def}}{=} \mathbf{Sure}_{k,i,c}^{(j)} \land \mathbf{Success}_{k,i,c}^{(j)}$

16:             $\mathbf{Goal}_{k,i+1}^{(j)} \overset{\text{def}}{=} \mathbf{Goal}_{k,i}^{(j)} \lor (\bigvee_{c \in C} [2\delta_1 + \delta_2] \mathbf{Fine}_{k,i,c}^{(j)})$

17:             $\mathbf{A}_{k,i+1}^{(j)} \overset{\text{def}}{=} \mathbf{A}_{k,i}^{(j)} \land \neg [2\delta_1 + \delta_2] \mathbf{Goal}_{k,i+1}^{(j)}$

18:             $i := i + 1$

19:         **UNTIL** $\mathfrak{M}_0 \vDash \neg [\delta_2] (\mathbf{Goal}_{k,i}^{(j)} \land \neg \mathbf{Goal}_{k,i-1}^{(j)})$

20:         $last(k, j) := i - 1$

21:     % j-th ATTEMPT AT $next$ COMPATIBILITY %

22:     **FOR ALL** $k \in K$ **DO**

23:         $\mathbf{Pick}_k^{(j)} \overset{\text{def}}{=} \bigvee_{k' \in next(k)} (\mathbf{A}_{k,0}^{(0)} \land \mathbf{Goal}_{k',last(k',j)}^{(j)})$

24:         $\mathbf{Drop}_k^{(j+1)} \overset{\text{def}}{=} \mathbf{Drop}_k^{(j)} \land \neg \langle \delta_2 \rangle (\mathbf{Drop}_k^{(j)} \land \neg \mathbf{Pick}_k^{(j)})$

25:         $\mathbf{A}_{k,0}^{(j+1)} \overset{\text{def}}{=} \mathbf{A}_{k,0}^{(0)}$ $\qquad$ $\mathbf{Goal}_{k,0}^{(j+1)} \overset{\text{def}}{=} \mathbf{Drop}_k^{(j+1)}$

26:     $j := j + 1$ and $i := 0$

27: **UNTIL** $\mathfrak{M}_0 \vDash \bigwedge_{k \in K} (\mathbf{Drop}_k^{(j-1)} \to \mathbf{Pick}_k^{(j-1)})$

28: % FINAL CLEAN-UP %

29: **IF** $[\![\mathbf{Drop}_k^{(j-1)}]\!]^{\mathfrak{M}_0} = \varnothing$ for some $k \in K$ **THEN**

30:     terminate & report incompatibility between k and its $next$-successors

31: **ELSE**

32:     $final := j - 1$

33:     **FOR ALL** $k \in K$ and $i \in I_k \overset{\text{def}}{=} \{0, \cdots, last(k, final)\}$ and $c \in C$ **DO**

34:         $\mathbf{A}_{k,i} \overset{\text{def}}{=} \mathbf{A}_{k,i}^{(final)}$ $\qquad$ $(\mathbf{e}_{k,i,c})^{\mathfrak{M}_0} \overset{\text{def}}{=} (\mathbf{e}_{k,i,c}^{(final)})^{\mathfrak{M}_0}$

35:         $\mathbf{Goal}_{k,i} \overset{\text{def}}{=} \mathbf{Goal}_{k,i}^{(final)}$ $\qquad$ $\mathbf{Fine}_{k,i,c} \overset{\text{def}}{=} \mathbf{Fine}_{k,i,c}^{(final)}$

36:     terminate with success

goal. In the iteration, $\mathbf{Goal}_{k,i}^{(j)}$ accumulates the states that can be driven to the initial $\mathbf{Goal}_{k,0}^{(j)}$ by at most i switches, while $\mathbf{A}_{k,i+1}^{(j)}$ denotes states which have been not resolved so far. The formula $\mathbf{Fine}_{k,i,c}^{(j)}$ identifies the states in $\mathbf{A}_{k,i}^{(j)}$ which can be driven to $\mathbf{Goal}_{k,i}^{(j)}$ using control c, and done so safely by being kept out of $\mathbf{Danger}_k$. Note that the recursive definition of $\mathbf{A}_{k,i+1}^{(j)}$ in line 17 involves the terms $\mathbf{A}_{k,i}^{(j)}$ and $\mathbf{Goal}_{k,i}^{(j)}$ within the scope of an odd number of negations. Thus it cannot be coded as a μ-calculus formula, and in particular the inner i-iteration is essentially different from fixed point iterations of maximal invariant sets as used in game-theoretic approaches to safety problems for hybrid systems [19].

While the core routine works on solving the problem locally, within the individual A_k, the outer j-loop checks that these local solutions can be merged to form a global controller. Within each A_k, the region where the local solution finally "drops-off" states is denoted by $\mathbf{Drop}_k^{(j)}$. The region where such states can be "picked-up" by adjacent local solutions is identified by $\mathbf{Pick}_k^{(j)}$; for compatibility between local solutions, $\mathbf{Pick}_k^{(j)}$ is required to contain $\mathbf{Drop}_k^{(j)}$. If this is not the case, local goals are suitably reduced.

Suppose Algorithm 1 terminates with success. Then, the nominal closed-loop system H and initial states $Good$ are defined as:

- $Q := \{ (k,i,c) \in K \times \mathbb{N} \times C \mid i \in I_k \text{ and } [\![\mathbf{Fine}_{k,i,c}]\!]^{\mathfrak{M}_0} \neq \varnothing \}$
- $F_{(k,i,c)} := F_c$ for all $(k,i,c) \in Q$
- for each $q = (k,i,c) \in Q$, set
  $Inv_q := [\![\langle\boldsymbol{\delta_1}\rangle\mathbf{A}_{k,i}]\!]^{\mathfrak{M}_0} \cap int\big([\![\neg\langle\boldsymbol{\delta_1}\rangle(\mathbf{A}_{k,i} \wedge \mathbf{Goal}_{k,i})]\!]^{\mathfrak{M}_0}\big)$
- $E := \{ ((k,i,c),(k',i',c')) \in Q \times Q \mid k' \in next(k) \text{ or } (k'=k \text{ and } i' < i)\}$
- for each $(q,q') = ((k,i,c),(k',i',c')) \in E$ set
  $Grd_{q,q'} := Inv_q \cap [\![\langle\boldsymbol{2\delta_1}\rangle(\mathbf{A}_{k,i} \wedge \mathbf{Goal}_{k,i}) \wedge \mathbf{Fine}_{k',i',c'}]\!]^{\mathfrak{M}_0}$
- $r_{q,q'} := test.Grd_{q,q'}$.
- $Good = \cup_{(k,i,c)\in Q}(Inv_{(k,i,c)} \cap [\![\mathbf{Fine}_{k,i,c}]\!]^{\mathfrak{M}_0})$

6   Correctness and Robustness of Synthesis Procedure

Theorem 1. *Let $F_c^v : X \rightarrow \mathbb{R}^n$, $c \in C$, $v \in V \subseteq \mathbb{R}^m$ be a finite family of parameter dependent vector fields, where the nominal case is denoted by $F_c = F_c^0$, $c \in C$. For given specification data $Bad \subset X$, $\{E_k\}_{k\in K}$, $next \subseteq K \times K$ and $\delta > 0$, subject to assumptions $(\mathbf{A0})$–$(\mathbf{A5})$, suppose Algorithm 1 terminates with success, and H is the nominal closed-loop hybrid automaton as above. Then there exists a parameter bound $\varepsilon > 0$ such that for every H^v in the variation class $\mathcal{H}^\varepsilon$, the pair $(H^v, Good)$ satisfies each of the performance specifications $(\mathbf{S1})$–$(\mathbf{S4})$.*

The proof of Theorem 1 follows the same general line of argumentation as in [6]. In this outline, we focus on the extra challenges of the variation class $\mathcal{H}^\varepsilon$.

We begin by choosing a variation bound $\varepsilon > 0$ such that perturbed integral curves must remain within a δ_1-tube around the nominal curve. This is done by applying Proposition 1 for each $q = (k,i,c) \in Q$, with $D = cl([\![\mathbf{Fine}_q \wedge \mathbf{Inv}_q]\!]^{\mathfrak{M}_0})$ and a metric tolerance of $\frac{1}{2}\delta_1$. From the construction of $\mathbf{Success}_q$ (see Alg. 1, line 14) we conclude that any nominal curve starting in $\mathbf{Fine}_q$ leaves $\langle \delta_1 \rangle \, \mathbf{A}_{k,i}$ via $\mathbf{A}_{k,i} \wedge \mathbf{Goal}_{k,i}$. Then, by the definition of Inv_q, each nominal curve starting in D leaves $B_{\delta_1}(D)$. The requirements of Proposition 1 are fulfilled and we get a variation bound $\varepsilon(q) > 0$ dependent on q. We choose $\varepsilon := \min\{\varepsilon(q) \mid q \in Q\}$ as a witness of the bound claimed by Theorem 1. In what follows, fix an arbitrary $H^v \in \mathcal{H}^\varepsilon$.

The high level strategy is to identify a list of modal logic formulas whose truth in $\mathfrak{M}_0$ provides sufficient conditions for the specifications **(S1)**–**(S4)** to be satisfied by any H^v in $\mathcal{H}^\varepsilon$. The crucial modal formulas **(T1)**–**(T4)** are analogs of those in [6], and are required for each $q = (k, i, c) \in Q$, $(q, q') \in E$ and for the perturbed flow relations $e_q^v := e(Inv_q, \Phi_c^v)$, for $q \in Q$.

(T1) $\big(\mathbf{Inv}_q \wedge \mathbf{Fine}_q \big) \quad \rightarrow \quad [e_q^v] \, \langle \delta_1 \rangle \, \mathbf{Fine}_q$

(T2) $\big(\mathbf{Inv}_q \wedge \mathbf{Fine}_q \big) \quad \rightarrow \quad [\mathbf{test.Grd}_{q,q'}] \, \mathbf{Fine}_{q'}$

(T3) $\big(\mathbf{Inv}_q \wedge \mathbf{Fine}_q \big) \quad \rightarrow \quad [e_q^v] \, \langle e_q^v \rangle \, \big(\bigvee_{q' \in E(q)} \mathbf{Grd}_{q,q'} \big)$

(T4) $\big(\mathbf{Inv}_q \wedge \mathbf{Fine}_q \big) \quad \rightarrow \quad \langle f_c^v \rangle \, \neg \mathbf{Inv}_q$

In [6], the corresponding formulas are derived directly from the statement of the algorithm together with the explicit assumptions. Here, we are proving correctness of a variant H^v and therefore need to exploit the relationship between the perturbed modal operators and their nominal counterparts in which the algorithm is formalised; that is, $\langle e_q^v \rangle$ and its relationship to $\langle e_q \rangle$.

From Proposition 1 and our choice of ε, we can derive the following relational inclusion:

$$test.Inv_q \circ test.Fine_q \circ e_q^v \quad \subseteq \quad e_q \circ B_{\delta_1} \,, \tag{16}$$

where $\circ$ is relational composition, which we write in left-to-right word order. This in turn implies the truth in $\mathfrak{M}_0$ of the formula:

$$\big(\mathbf{Inv}_q \wedge \mathbf{Fine}_q \wedge [e_q][\delta_1] \, \varphi \big) \quad \rightarrow \quad [e_q^v] \, \varphi \tag{17}$$

for any $\varphi \in \mathcal{L}(\mathrm{Rel}_0, \mathrm{Prp}_0)$. Then, **(T1)** can be deduced from $\mathbf{Fine}_q \rightarrow [e_q] \mathbf{Fine}_q$ (see [6], Lemma 7.2) together with formula (17), while **(T2)** is an immediate consequence of the definitions. Formulas **(T1)** and **(T2)** are used to establish the safety specification.

From Proposition 1 and assumption **(A0)**, we can derive the more sophisticated modal fact:

$$\big(\mathbf{Inv}_q \wedge \mathbf{Fine}_q \big) \quad \rightarrow \quad \big([e_q^v] \, \langle e_q^v \rangle \, \langle 2\delta_1 \rangle \, \mathbf{Goal}_q \wedge \langle f_c^v \rangle \, \neg \mathbf{Inv}_q \big) . \tag{18}$$

Formula (18) expresses the essential properties of the construct $\mathbf{Success}_q$ (Alg. 1, line 14) but now referring to the perturbed relations e_q^v rather than the nominal e_q. In particular, we use (18) to deduce **(T3)**, and **(T4)** is an immediate consequence. Formulas **(T3)** and **(T4)** are used to verify step-infinite liveness and the event sequence specification.

Having deduced the modal conditions **(T1)–(T4)**, from this point on, we can largely mimic the proof in [6] to establish that H^v and *Good* satisfy each of the specifications **(S1)–(S4)**.

7   Discussion and Conclusion

This paper addresses a basic hybrid control problem, namely the design of a switching control mechanism via guard and invariant sets. We use a novel methodology based on modal logic to solve this problem for a significant list of performance specifications, and we do so in a manner that is robust w.r.t. parameter uncertainty in the differential equations.

A significant issue to be investigated in future work is the question of *completeness* of the algorithm; i.e. whether there exists a parameterised plant and specification data such that there is a robust solution to the control problem but the algorithm terminates with failure due to *next* incompatibility. In general one may expect such incompleteness to occur. So the question arises as to what additional conditions on the input data could ensure completeness. A full treatment of this issue necessitates the development of more mathematical tools for analysing the space of all possible solutions to our control problem, leading to an appropriate notion of switching controllability.

As discussed in the introduction, our synthesis algorithm can be implemented on any available model checking tool. There are two main approaches: *exact symbolic computation*, representing sets of states by first-order logic formulas (e.g. [1,2,14,15]), and *approximated representation*, whereby sets are under- or over-approximated as finite unions of cells (e.g. [4,13,16]). We have developed a prototype software implementation of our synthesis algorithm based on an approximation using boxes generated by a regular grid, and it is applicable to arbitrary linear differential equations. The software runs on a massively parallel cluster effectively employing 96 CPUs, and has been tested on several non-trivial examples. This work on approximation based model checking is to be presented in a separate paper.

Acknowledgements. We thank our colleagues for useful discussions: Brian Anderson, Thomas Brinsmead, Raj Goré, Gerardo Lafferriere, George Pappas, and Matthew Smith.

References

1. R. Alur, C. Courcoubetis, N. Halbwachs, T.A. Henzinger, P.-H. Ho, X. Nicollin, A. Olivero, J. Sifakis, and S. Yovine. The algorithmic analysis of hybrid systems. *Theoretical Computer Science*, 138:3–34, 1995.
2. R. Alur, T.A. Henzinger, G. Lafferriere, and G. Pappas. Discrete abstractions of hybrid systems. *Proceedings of the IEEE*, 88:971–984, July 2000.
3. B.D.O. Anderson, F. de Bruyne, S. Dey, and K. Wong. Ensuring robustness in hybrid control systems. Technical report, Dept. Systems Engineering, RSISE, Australian National University, April 1999.

4. E. Asarin, O. Bournez, T. Dang, and O. Maler. Approximate reachability analysis of piecewise-linear dynamical systems. In N. Lynch and B. Krogh, editors, *Hybrid Systems: Computation and Control (HSCC'00)*, LNCS 1790, pages 20–31. Springer-Verlag, 2000.

5. J.E.R. Cury, B.A. Krogh, and T. Niinomi. Synthesis of supervisory controllers for hybrid systems based on approximating automata. *IEEE Transactions on Automatic Control*, 43:564–568, 1998.

6. J.M. Davoren and T. Moor. Logic-based design and synthesis of controllers for hybrid systems. Technical report, Dept. Systems Engineering, RSISE, Australian National University, July 2000.
   `http://arp.anu.edu.au/~davoren/hybrid_control/hybrid_control.html`, submitted for publication.

7. J.M. Davoren and A. Nerode. Logics for hybrid systems. *Proceedings of the IEEE*, 88:985–1010, July 2000.

8. E. Frazzoli, M.A. Dahleh, and E. Feron. Robust hybrid control for autonomous vehicle motion planning. Technical report, LIDS-P-2468, Laboratory for Information and Decision Systems (LIDS), Massachusetts Institute of Technology, May 2000.

9. R. Goré. Tableaux methods for modal and temporal logics. In M. D'Agostino *et al.*, editors, *Handbook of Tableaux Methods*, pages 297–396. Kluwer, 1999.

10. C. Horn and P.J. Ramadge. Robustness issues for hybrid systems. In *Proceedings of the 34th International Conference on Decision and Control, CDC'95*, pages 1467–1472. IEEE Press, 1995.

11. H.K. Khalil. *Nonlinear Systems*. Prentice-Hall, 1996. Second edition.

12. X. Koutsoukos, P.J. Antsaklis, J.A. Stiver, and M.D. Lemmon. Supervisory control of hybrid systems. *Proceedings of the IEEE*, 88:1026–1049, July 2000.

13. A.B. Kurzhanski and P. Varaiya. Ellipsoidal techniques for reachability analysis. In N. Lynch and B. Krogh, editors, *Hybrid Systems: Computation and Control (HSCC'00)*, LNCS 1790, pages 202–214. Springer-Verlag, 2000.

14. G. Lafferriere, G.J. Pappas, and S. Sastry. O-minimal hybrid systems. *Mathematics of Control, Signals, and Systems*, 13:1–21, 2000.

15. G. Lafferriere, G.J. Pappas, and S. Yovine. A new class of decidable hybrid systems. In F.W. Vaandrager and J.H. van Schuppen, editors, *Hybrid Systems: Computation and Control (HSCC'99)*, LNCS 1569, pages 137–151. Springer-Verlag, 1999.

16. T. Moor and J. Raisch. Discrete control of switched linear systems. In *Proceedings of the European Control Conference 1999*, 1999.

17. T. Moor and J. Raisch. Supervisory control of hybrid systems within a behavioural framework. *Systems and Control Letters*, 38:157–166, 1999.

18. C. Stirling. Modal and temporal logics. In S. Abramsky, D.M. Gabbay, and T. Maibaum, editors, *Handbook of Logic in Computer Science*, volume 2, pages 477–563. Oxford University Press, Clarendon Press, Oxford, 1992.

19. C. Tomlin, J. Lygeros, and S. Sastry. A game-theoretic approach to controller design for hybrid systems. *Proceedings of the IEEE*, 88:949–970, July 2000.

20. F. Wolter. *Decision Problems for Combined Modal Logics*. Habilitationsschrift. Institut für Informatik, Universität Leipzig, 1999.

21. C.A. Yfoulis, A. Muir, P.E. Wellstead, and N.B.O.L. Pettit. Stabilization of orthogonal piecewise linear systems: Robustness analysis and design. In F.W. Vaandrager and J.H. van Schuppen, editors, *Hybrid Systems: Computation and Control (HSCC'99)*, LNCS 1569, pages 256–270. Springer-Verlag, 1999.

Diagnosis of Physical Systems with Hybrid Models Using Parametrized Causality

Pieter J. Mosterman*

Institute of Robotics and Mechatronics, DLR Oberpfaffenhofen
P.O. Box 1116, D-82230 Wessling, Germany
Pieter.J.Mosterman@dlr.de
http://www.op.dlr.de/~pjm

Abstract. Efficient algorithms exist for fault detection and isolation of physical systems based on functional redundancy. In a qualitative approach, this redundancy can be captured by a temporal causal graph (TCG), a directed graph that may include temporal information. However, in a detailed continuous model, time constants may be present that are beyond the bandwidth of the data acquisition system, which leads to incorrect fault isolation because of a difference in observed and modeled behavior. To solve this, the modeled time constants can be taken to be infinitely small, which results in a model with mixed continuous/discrete, *hybrid* behavior that is difficult to analyze because the causality of the directed graph may change. In this paper, to avoid the combinatorial explosion when using a bank of TCGs in parallel, causal paths are parametrized by the state of local switches. The result is a hybrid model that produces parametrized predictions that can be efficiently matched against observed behavior.

1 Introduction

To reduce cost, improve performance, and to manage the complexity of large engineered systems, functional redundancy can be employed in fault detection and isolation (FDI). In this approach, a system model links measured variables by their functional relations, facilitating the computation of redundant values for selected system variables. In general, the system model can be of a continuous or discrete nature. In case of a continuous model, often parameter and state estimation techniques based on a state space model of the system are used for FDI [1,4]. In case of a discrete event approach, models that capture failure modes and transition sequences are applied [5,15,16]. Both these methods have proven themselves successful in their respective applications.

Previous work [8,9] has focused on qualitative parameter estimation of continuous system models. These models are represented by a temporal causal graph (TCG) that is automatically derived from a bond graph model of a physical system [8,11]. This work revealed the importance to design the model in harmony

* Pieter J. Mosterman is supported by a grant from the DFG Schwerpunktprogramm KONDISK.

M.D. Di Benedetto, A. Sangiovanni-Vincentelli (Eds.): HSCC 2001, LNCS 2034, pp. 447–458, 2001.

with the data acquisition system, i.e., behavior that is beyond the bandwidth of the data acquisition system should not be included in the model as it leads to incorrect fault isolation [2].

Removing large and small parameters from the system model causes the following model characteristics that complicate the FDI task:

- Algebraic loops may emerge. Because of the passive behavior of physical processes, these algebraic loops have negative gain, and, therefore, any qualitative ± deviation is reversed when propagated around the loop. This, in turn, leads to many unknown values of system variables in a qualitative sense.
- In case of abrupt faults that cause mode changes, higher index systems may arise with algebraic constraints between time derivative behavior. These systems may exhibit impulsive behavior.
- The direction of the computational causality in the model may change. When abrupt faults cause component parameter changes to values that are taken to be infinitely large or small, they are effectively removed from the model, which changes the model configuration, and, in effect, the model becomes of a switched continuous, hybrid, nature.

Other work [3,12], addresses the first two issues whereas this paper focuses on the hybrid diagnosis problem.

In order to deal with the change of causality, the TCG can be derived for each possible system configuration or *mode*. However, in case of many locally acting switches, the combinatorial explosion quickly leads to an intractable problem. These problems can be mitigated to some extent by dynamically generating the TCG of each possible system mode in response to a failure. This may still result in a problem with large computational complexity which can be further reduced by measuring system variables that indicate specifically which local switches may have occurred [13] and predictions for each of the variables that determine different causal assignments are required to be made and analyzed. Once a set of possible TCGs is available, Gaussian decision techniques have been applied to compute the most likely mode of continuous behavior [7].

Recent attention to hybrid diagnosis [7,14] concentrates on efficiently processing a set of TCGs. This paper describes how a hybrid model can be made amenable to the diagnosis algorithms that were developed in previous work [8,9] by systematically generating one parametrized TCG. In this graph, the directed links are enabled by conditionals that correspond to the mode in which these links are present. The result is a set of predictions that are parametrized by the state of the local switches and the diagnosis problem then becomes one of constraint satisfaction [17]. The solution to this constraint satisfaction problem contains the possible parameter changes (i.e., the faults) and the effect on the system mode that this is required to have.

2   Preliminaries

This section reviews the qualitative FDI approach developed in previous work [8, 9]. Instead of a temporal causal graph, though, the model representation format and processing will be in qualitative matrix algebra, which is easier to represent and to extend with the required notions.

Consider the one-tank hydraulic system in Fig. 1. The functional relation for flow, f_R, through the outflow pipe is given by $f_R = \frac{p_R}{R}$, where p_R is the pressure drop across the pipe and R is the pipe resistance to flow. The pressure p_R depends on the pressure at the bottom of the tank, p_C, according to $p_R = p_C$ (i.e., the ambient pressure is assumed to be 0). The rate of change in the pressure, $\dot{p}_C$, at the bottom of the tank is given by $\dot{p}_C = \frac{1}{C} f_C$, where $f_C = f_{in} - f_R$ and f_{in} is the flow into the tank and C is the tank capacity.

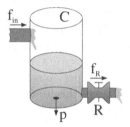

Fig. 1. A tank with in- and outflow.

To derive qualitative predictions, the system is written as a directed graph that captures the causal (directed) relations between system variables. For the one-tank system, the preferred (integral) causality model description is

$$\begin{bmatrix} 1 & 0 & 0 & 0 \\ 0 & 1 & 0 & 0 \\ 0 & 0 & 1 & 0 \\ 0 & 0 & 0 & 1 \end{bmatrix} \begin{bmatrix} p_C \\ f_C \\ f_R \\ p_R \end{bmatrix} = \begin{bmatrix} 0 & \lambda^{-1}C^{-1} & 0 & 0 \\ 0 & 0 & -1 & 0 \\ 0 & 0 & 0 & R^{-1} \\ 1 & 0 & 0 & 0 \end{bmatrix} \begin{bmatrix} p_C \\ f_C \\ f_R \\ p_R \end{bmatrix} + \begin{bmatrix} 0 \\ f_{in} \\ 0 \\ 0 \end{bmatrix} \tag{1}$$

where λ represents the time differentiation operator and λ^{-1} indicates integration over time. The corresponding temporal causal graph (TCG) is given in Fig. 2.

The TCG can be represented by a weighted adjacency matrix where the columns are cause and rows are the effect variables and the entries capture the parameters on the graph edges. This is called the temporal causal matrix (TCM), that is

$$\begin{bmatrix} 1 & \lambda^{-1}C^{-1} & 0 & 0 \\ 0 & 1 & -1 & 0 \\ 0 & 0 & 1 & R^{-1} \\ 1 & 0 & 0 & 1 \end{bmatrix} \begin{bmatrix} p_C \\ f_C \\ f_R \\ p_R \end{bmatrix} \tag{2}$$

for the TCG in Fig. 2.

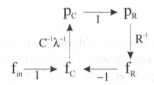

Fig. 2. TCG of the one-tank system.

Our diagnosis engine TRANSCEND [6] relies on qualitative information to achieve diagnosis. In this framework, only the three values $-$, 0, $+$ are used to indicate values that are too low, normal, and too high, with respect to some nominal value, respectively. For example, a value of a model variable that is measured to be above its nominal value is marked $+$. In case the outflow of the tank system in Fig. 1 is too high, this is represented by f_R^+.

Note that in a qualitative representation, the parameters R and C correspond to direct relations between variables, and, therefore, they can be replaced by value 1. This results in a qualitative system where 1 and -1 represent direct and reverse relations, respectively.

To find parameter deviations, in previous work a backpropagation algorithm is used. In qualitative matrix algebra this is equivalent to repeated multiplication of the initial deviation with the transpose TCM. Here, for f_R^+ this results in the sequence of vectors

$$\begin{bmatrix} 0 \\ 0 \\ 1 \\ 0 \end{bmatrix}, \begin{bmatrix} 0 \\ 0 \\ 1 \\ R^{-1} \end{bmatrix}, \begin{bmatrix} 1 \\ 0 \\ 1 \\ 1 \end{bmatrix}, \begin{bmatrix} 1 \\ C^{-1} \\ 1 \\ 1 \end{bmatrix}, \begin{bmatrix} 1 \\ 1 \\ ? \\ 1 \end{bmatrix}, \begin{bmatrix} 1 \\ 1 \\ ? \\ ? \end{bmatrix}, \begin{bmatrix} ? \\ 1 \\ ? \\ ? \end{bmatrix}, \begin{bmatrix} ? \\ ? \\ ? \\ ? \end{bmatrix}. \tag{3}$$

The parameters R^{-1} and C^{-1} are fault hypotheses and replaced by 1 after they are generated because R and C are positive parameters, and, therefore, in a qualitative framework they represent direct relations. Also, qualitatively $1 - 1$ is unknown, "?". Once all variables are unknown, no further parameter deviations can be hypothesized (the remaining candidates that are not generated in Eq. (3) are $-R^{-1}$ and $-C^{-1}$). The resulting set of possible faults is, therefore, R^{-1} or C^{-1} too high, i.e., $\{R^-, C^-\}$ (the remaining candidates are $\{R^+, C^+\}$). Physically, these fault candidates correspond to, e.g., leakage in the outflow pipe (R^-) or an object that has fallen into the tank (C^-).

Next, predictions of future system behavior are generated for each of the possible parameter deviations, R^- and C^-. From the TCM, their initial deviations are found to be

$$R^- \rightarrow \begin{bmatrix} 0 \\ 0 \\ 1 \\ 0 \end{bmatrix}, C^- \rightarrow \begin{bmatrix} 1 \\ 0 \\ 0 \\ 0 \end{bmatrix}. \tag{4}$$

To achieve a suffiently high order prediction for the measured variable, f_R, the initial deviation is repeatedly multiplied with the TCM. Here, a second order prediction requires eight such multiplications and for R^- this yields

$$\begin{bmatrix} p_C \\ f_C \\ f_R \\ p_R \end{bmatrix} = \begin{bmatrix} 1 & \lambda^{-1} & 0 & 0 \\ 0 & 1 & -1 & 0 \\ 0 & 0 & 1 & 1 \\ 1 & 0 & 0 & 1 \end{bmatrix}^8 \begin{bmatrix} 0 \\ 0 \\ 1 \\ 0 \end{bmatrix} = \begin{bmatrix} -\lambda^{-1} + \lambda^{-2} \\ -1 + \lambda^{-1} \\ 1 - \lambda^{-1} + \lambda^{-2} \\ -\lambda^{-1} + \lambda^{-2} \end{bmatrix}. \tag{5}$$

The TCM raised to the power 8 can be computed off-line to be

$$\begin{bmatrix} 1 & \lambda^{-1} & 0 & 0 \\ 0 & 1 & -1 & 0 \\ 0 & 0 & 1 & 1 \\ 1 & 0 & 0 & 1 \end{bmatrix}^8 = \begin{bmatrix} 1 - \lambda^{-1} + \lambda^{-2} & \lambda^{-1} - \lambda^{-2} & -\lambda^{-1} + \lambda^{-2} & -\lambda^{-1} + \lambda^{-2} \\ -1 + \lambda^{-1} & 1 - \lambda^{-1} + \lambda^{-2} & -1 + \lambda^{-1} & -1 + \lambda^{-1} \\ 1 - \lambda^{-1} & \lambda^{-1} - \lambda^{-2} & 1 - \lambda^{-1} + \lambda^{-2} & 1 - \lambda^{-1} \\ 1 - \lambda^{-1} & \lambda^{-1} - \lambda^{-2} & -\lambda^{-1} + \lambda^{-2} & 1 - \lambda^{-1} + \lambda^{-2} \end{bmatrix} \tag{6}$$

and can be used for efficiently generating predictions for other fault candidates.

The polynomials in λ are equal to the qualitative signatures generated in previous work [8,9]. For this example, the signature for the measured variable is f_R^{+-+}, where the superscripts indicate the qualitative values of the time derivative behavior with increasing order from left to right, i.e., there is a positive discontinuous change with negative slope that increases. For the pressure at the bottom of the tank, the prediction is p_C^{0-+}, i.e., no discontinuous change in pressure occurs and the pressure is decreasing.

This method works well if the system of equations that describes continuous behavior is fixed. However, in case discrete switches cause changes in the continuous model, signatures for each mode have to be generated. This quickly becomes intractable, and, therefore, for these system models a parametrized formulation is advantageous.

3   Hybrid Models for FDI

For the qualitative FDI approach to be effective, it is imperative that the modeled time constants are observable, i.e., within the bandwidth of the data acquisition system. If a parameter that models an abrupt fault changes to a very large or small value, it may correspond to a time constant that cannot be observed, and, therefore, this behavior needs to be abstracted from the model. This causes the model to be of a switched continuous, hybrid nature.

In general, modeled discontinuities result in causal changes. Therefore, the TCM may take several different forms and so do the corresponding predictions of future behavior, depending on whether a mode change occurs. Consider for example a valve that controls the outflow in Fig. 1 in a binary manner, i.e., either there is an outflow determined by the Bernoulli resistance ($\alpha_1 = 1$) or there is no outflow ($\alpha_1 = 0$). When the switch is modeled as a discontinuous change, the corresponding model includes a change in causality when the control valve switches its state. If it is open, the pressure p_C determines the outflow f_R and if it is closed, $f_R = 0$, which determines the pressure drop across the pipe to be $p_R = f_R R = 0$. To handle the change in TCM, the causal relations can be parametrized to make them dependent on the mode of operation.

To this end, first the system is described in a noncausal form by using implicit equations. An implicit model of the one tank consists of the following equations

$$0 = C\dot{p}_C - f_C \tag{7}$$
$$0 = f_C - f_{in} + f_R \tag{8}$$
$$0 = Rf_R - p_R \tag{9}$$
$$0 = \alpha_1(p_R - p_C) + (1 - \alpha_1)f_R \tag{10}$$

From Eq. (10), in case the control valve is open, $\alpha_1 = 1$, and $p_R = p_C$, when the control valve is closed, $\alpha_1 = 0$, and $f_R = 0$.

The TCM for this system of equations contains the relations between each of the variables. For example, Eq. (7) embodies a temporal relation between p_C and f_C and Eq. (10) a direct relation between p_C and p_R that is only active when $\alpha_1 \neq 0$. The TCM then becomes

$$\begin{bmatrix} 1 & \lambda^{-1}C^{-1} & 0 & \alpha_1 \\ \lambda C & 1 & -1 & 0 \\ 0 & -1 & 1 & R^{-1} \\ \alpha_1 & 0 & R & 1 \end{bmatrix} \begin{bmatrix} p_C \\ f_C \\ f_R \\ p_R \end{bmatrix} \tag{11}$$

and causal links from p_C to p_R and from p_R to p_C are only active when the system is in mode α_1. A special case arises for $\alpha_1 = 0$ which implies $f_R = 0$. This effect is not present in the TCM because it is not a relation between variables. However, it contains essential diagnostic information about system behavior that can be included by an input vector

$$\begin{bmatrix} 0 \\ 0 \\ -(1 - \alpha_1) \\ 0 \end{bmatrix} \tag{12}$$

where the $-$ sign is because the flow, f_R, is positive during normal operation, and, therefore, its deviation is $-$ when the valve closes (possibly inadvertently).

Diagnosis now proceeds to predict future behavior, y_f, for each hypothesized fault, f, and both possible configurations ($\alpha_1 = 0$ and $\alpha_1 = 1$). To this end, the TCM, A, raised to a sufficiently high power, n, operates on the sum of the input vector, u, and each of the initial deviations, d_f, generated from the hypothesized faults,

$$y_f = A^n(d_f + u) \tag{13}$$

These predictions are then compared against actual observations to prune the fault hypotheses and find the correct fault.

Note that, to facilitate a qualitative algebra, the $(1 - \alpha)$ construct with $\alpha \in \{0, 1\}$ cannot be used to (de)activate relations because in a qualitative sense $(1 - \alpha)$ is unknown instead of 0. Therefore, $\neg\alpha$ is used to indicate a quantitative evaluation of $(1 - \alpha)$ so that $\neg\alpha$ produces a value $\{0, 1\}$.

For the initial deviation that corresponds to R^- in Eq. (4) and the input vector in Eq. (12), after multiplying with the TCM five times, the prediction becomes

$$\begin{bmatrix} \alpha_1 - \lambda^{-1} \\ \alpha_1\lambda - 1 + \alpha_1\lambda^{-1} \\ -\alpha_1\lambda + 1 - \alpha_1\lambda^{-1} \\ -\alpha_1\lambda + 1 - \alpha_1\lambda^{-1} \end{bmatrix} (1 - \neg\alpha_1) \tag{14}$$

Compared with the prediction derived from the explicit system in Section 2 this shows impulsive behavior because of the positive powers of λ and other spurious behavior because *all* possible relations are present in the TCM. In other words, for a given causal assignment all other relations are present as well even though these may not be consistent with the given causal assignment.

To demonstrate that such an extensive set of relations quickly leads to contradiction, consider an implicit relation $0 = x_1 + x_2 + x_3$ with TCM

$$\begin{bmatrix} 1 & -1 & -1 \\ -1 & 1 & -1 \\ -1 & -1 & 1 \end{bmatrix} \begin{bmatrix} x_1 \\ x_2 \\ x_3 \end{bmatrix} \tag{15}$$

Because in a qualitative sense $1-1$ is unknown, this leads to unknown predictions as soon as the TCM is raised to a power > 1 (e.g., $x_1^+ \rightarrow x_2^- \rightarrow x_3^+ \rightarrow x_1^-$, and x_1 is unknown). This problem can be circumvented by committing to one causal assignment only. In matrix form, this is achieved by using binary selection variables, $k_i \in \{0, 1\}$,

$$\begin{bmatrix} 1 & -k_1 k_2 & -k_1 k_2 \\ -k_1 \neg k_2 & 1 & -k_1 \neg k_2 \\ -k_2 \neg k_1 & -k_2 \neg k_1 & 1 \end{bmatrix} \tag{16}$$

and the matrix is invariant under multiplication.

In summary, to design an approach for diagnosis based on hybrid models, the TCM is derived from an implicit model formulation that includes mode selection parameters, α_i, to switch between equations. The possible causal assignments of ternary and higher relations are then made mutually exclusive by introducing selection parameters, k_i. If possible, the parameters α_i can be related to k_i and the TCM contains only mode selection parameters, α_i, and, therefore, produces fault hypotheses and predictions that are parametrized by α_i only.

4   A Case Study

To make the implicit approach suitable for diagnosis, it must deal with additional causal paths and the possible conflicts. Consider the two tank system in Fig. 3 with externally controlled outflow valves on the left and right and a pressure controlled valve between the left and right tank. An implicit quantitative model of this system could look like

$$\begin{aligned}
0 &= -f_{in} + f_{C_1} + f_{R_{b1}} + f_{R_{12}} \\
0 &= \alpha_1(-p_{C_1} + p_{R_{12}} + p_{C_2}) + (1 - \alpha_1)f_{R_{12}} \\
0 &= \alpha_2(p_{C_1} - p_{R_{b1}}) + (1 - \alpha_2)f_{R_{b1}} \\
0 &= \alpha_3(p_{C_2} - p_{R_{b2}}) + (1 - \alpha_3)f_{R_{b2}} \\
0 &= f_{C_2} + f_{R_{b2}} - f_{R_{12}} \\
0 &= C_1\dot{p}_{C_1} - f_{C_1} \\
0 &= C_2\dot{p}_{C_2} - f_{C_2} \\
0 &= p_{R_{b1}} - R_{b1}f_{R_{b1}} \\
0 &= p_{R_{b2}} - R_{b2}f_{R_{b2}} \\
0 &= p_{R_{12}} - R_{12}f_{R_{12}}
\end{aligned} \tag{17}$$

where α_i are mode selection parameters and α_1, α_2, and α_3 correspond to the state of the middle, left, and right valves in Fig. 3, respectively, where $\alpha_i = 0$ implies the valve is closed and $\alpha_i = 1$ that the valve is open.

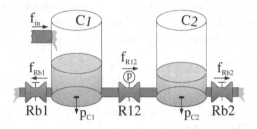

Fig. 3. Two tanks with outflow valves and a pressure controlled connecting valve.

This model contains a number of ternary relations (input variables are not considered as fault candidates) and when a deviation is propagated, multiple possible paths are taken. To prevent this, the paths can be parametrized as demonstrated in Section 3 (the binary relations are mutually consistent),

$$
\begin{bmatrix}
1 & -k_1 k_2 & -k_1 k_2 & 0 & 0 & \lambda C_1 & 0 & 0 & 0 & 0 \\
-k_1 \neg k_2 & 1 & -k_1 \neg k_2 & 0 & 0 & 0 & 0 & 0 & R_{b1}^{-1} & 0 \\
-k_2 \neg k_1 & -k_2 \neg k_1 & 1 & k_3 k_4 & k_3 k_4 & 0 & R_{12}^{-1} & 0 & 0 & 0 \\
0 & 0 & k_3 \neg k_4 & 1 & -k_3 \neg k_4 & 0 & 0 & \lambda C_2 & 0 & 0 \\
0 & 0 & k_4 \neg k_3 & -k_4 \neg k_3 & 1 & 0 & 0 & 0 & 0 & R_{b2}^{-1} \\
\lambda^{-1} C_1^{-1} & 0 & 0 & 0 & 0 & 1 & \alpha_1 k_5 k_6 & \alpha_1 k_5 k_6 & \alpha_2 & 0 \\
0 & 0 & R_{12} & 0 & 0 & \alpha_1 k_6 \neg k_5 & 1 & -\alpha_1 k_6 \neg k_5 & 0 & 0 \\
0 & 0 & 0 & \lambda^{-1} C_2^{-1} & 0 & \alpha_1 k_5 \neg k_6 & -\alpha_1 k_5 \neg k_6 & 1 & 0 & \alpha_3 \\
0 & R_{b1} & 0 & 0 & 0 & \alpha_2 & 0 & 0 & 1 & 0 \\
0 & 0 & 0 & 0 & R_{b2} & 0 & 0 & \alpha_3 & 0 & 1
\end{bmatrix}
\begin{bmatrix}
f_{C_1} \\
f_{R_{b1}} \\
f_{R_{12}} \\
f_{C_2} \\
f_{R_{b2}} \\
p_{C_1} \\
p_{R_{12}} \\
p_{C_2} \\
p_{R_{b1}} \\
p_{R_{b2}}
\end{bmatrix}
\tag{18}
$$

For this model, the causality of some of the binary relations is fixed for each possible mode and incorporating this *a priori* knowledge leads to a more constrained model. For example, the relation $0 = \alpha_2(p_{C_1} - p_{R_{b1}})$ leads to two entries in the TCM, one for $p_{C_1} \overset{\alpha_2}{\to} p_{R_{b1}}$ and one for $p_{R_{b1}} \overset{\alpha_2}{\to} p_{C_1}$. Analysis reveals that the latter causal relation is never used for any configuration of valve states, and, therefore, the corresponding entry in the TCM can be removed. The matrix entries in Eq. (18) that vanish because of pre-processing are marked by a bounding box.

The causality of the ternary relations can be analyzed exhaustively because it only involves a limited number of local constraints. Causal analysis of the system of equations shows that although the causality of the ternary equations may change, the changed causality corresponds to the vanishing (deactivating) of an edge. For example, the causality of $0 = \alpha_1(-p_{C_1} + p_{R_{12}} + p_{C_2})$ changes when α_1 changes its value. But, for the state $\neg\alpha_1$, the equation is not active anymore. Therefore, this need not be explicitly modeled, and the relation between the α_i and k_i degrades to the fixed values $k_1 = 1$, $k_2 = 1$, $k_3 = 1$, $k_4 = 0$, $k_5 = 0$, and $k_6 = 1$.

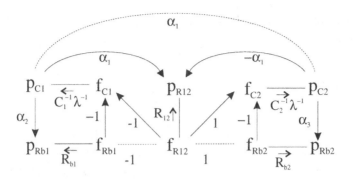

Fig. 4. The temporal causal graph of the two-tank system.

In Fig. 4 the temporal graph of the TCM is shown to clarify the relations between system variables. The dashed edges are those that are present in the original implicit formulation because of ternary relations but that are removed based on a mode dependent causal analysis. The undirected edges are implicit binary relations and can be decomposed into two edges with opposite direction (corresponding to the two entries in the TCM) to be compatible with the temporal causal graph format used in previous work [8,9]. Note that in many cases, graph propagation is more efficient than matrix multiplication, especially in case of sparse matrices.

After replacing the parameters with their qualitative equivalent, the resulting TCM is given by

$$
\begin{bmatrix}
1 & -1 & -1 & 0 & 0 & 0 & 0 & 0 & 0 & 0 \\
0 & 1 & 0 & 0 & 0 & 0 & 0 & 0 & \boxed{1} & 0 \\
0 & 0 & 1 & 0 & 0 & 0 & \boxed{1} & 0 & 0 & 0 \\
0 & 0 & 1 & 1 & -1 & 0 & 0 & 0 & 0 & 0 \\
0 & 0 & 0 & 0 & 1 & 0 & 0 & 0 & 0 & \boxed{1} \\
\lambda^{-1} & 0 & 0 & 0 & 0 & 1 & 0 & 0 & 0 & 0 \\
0 & 0 & \boxed{1} & 0 & 0 & \alpha_1 & 1 & -\alpha_1 & 0 & 0 \\
0 & 0 & 0 & \lambda^{-1} & 0 & 0 & 0 & 1 & 0 & 0 \\
0 & \boxed{1} & 0 & 0 & 0 & \alpha_2 & 0 & 0 & 1 & 0 \\
0 & 0 & 0 & 0 & \boxed{1} & 0 & 0 & \alpha_3 & 0 & 1
\end{bmatrix}
\begin{bmatrix}
f_{C_1} \\ f_{R_{b1}} \\ f_{R_{12}} \\ f_{C_2} \\ f_{R_{b2}} \\ p_{C_1} \\ p_{R_{12}} \\ p_{C_2} \\ p_{R_{b1}} \\ p_{R_{b2}}
\end{bmatrix}
\tag{19}
$$

where the boxed entries are those that correspond to bidirectional, non-causal, edges (in this particular case, these could still be made mode-dependent, where the entries above the diagonal become α_i and below become $\neg\alpha_i$).

The predictions of the TCM are parametrized by the active mode. This leads to more efficient diagnosis compared to the use of a bank of TCMs, which, in this case of three switches, would consist of eight TCMs that need to be processed separately. For example, in case of a measurement $f_{R_{b2}}^{+}$, R_{b2}^{-} is one of the fault hypotheses that results in the prediction

$$
\begin{bmatrix}
-\alpha_1\lambda^{-1} + \alpha_1\lambda^{-2} \\
-\alpha_1\alpha_2\lambda^{-2} \\
\alpha_1\lambda^{-1} - \alpha_1\lambda^{-2} \\
-1 + \alpha_1\lambda^{-1} + \alpha_3\lambda^{-1} - \alpha_1\lambda^{-2} \\
1 - \alpha_3\lambda^{-1} + \alpha_3\lambda^{-2} \\
-\alpha_1\lambda^{-2} \\
\alpha_1\lambda^{-1} - \alpha_1\lambda^{-2} \\
-\lambda^{-1} + \alpha_3\lambda^{-2} \\
-\alpha_1\alpha_2\lambda^{-2} \\
1 - \alpha_3\lambda^{-1} + \alpha_3\lambda^{-2}
\end{bmatrix}.
\tag{20}
$$

In addition, the input vectors for $\neg\alpha_1$, $\neg\alpha_2$ and $\neg\alpha_3$ are determined to be

$$
\neg\alpha_1 \rightarrow
\begin{bmatrix} 0 \\ 0 \\ -1 \\ 0 \\ 0 \\ 0 \\ 0 \\ 0 \\ 0 \end{bmatrix},
\neg\alpha_2 \rightarrow
\begin{bmatrix} 0 \\ -1 \\ 0 \\ 0 \\ 0 \\ 0 \\ 0 \\ 0 \\ 0 \end{bmatrix},
\neg\alpha_3 \rightarrow
\begin{bmatrix} 0 \\ 0 \\ 0 \\ 0 \\ -1 \\ 0 \\ 0 \\ 0 \\ 0 \end{bmatrix},
\tag{21}
$$

and their effect is propagated as well. For $\neg\alpha_1$, this leads to the prediction for p_{C_1} to be $\neg\alpha_1\lambda^{-1} - \neg\alpha_1\alpha_2\lambda^{-2} - \neg\alpha_1\alpha_1\lambda^{-2}$, or $\neg\alpha_1\lambda^{-1} - \neg\alpha_1\alpha_2\lambda^{-2}$. The combined prediction for p_{C_1} becomes

$$
\neg\alpha_1\lambda^{-1} - \neg\alpha_1\alpha_2\lambda^{-2} - \alpha_1\lambda^{-2}
\tag{22}
$$

The parametrized predictions can be matched against further measurements (e.g., $p_{C_1}^{0+}$, where the second order derivative is not measured). In case α_1, i.e., the pressure controlled connecting valve remains open, the prediction for p_{C1} is $-\lambda^{-2}$, a falling level of liquid in C_1 with second order behavior. This is inconsistent with the $p_{C_1}^{0+}$ observation and the fault $R_{b_2}^-[\alpha_1]$ is rejected as a possible explanation of the anomalous system behavior. If the new pressure in C_2 causes the connecting valve to close, the predicted behavior of p_{C_1} changes. This can be derived by evaluating the prediction with $\neg\alpha_1$, which yields $\lambda^{-1} - \alpha_2\lambda^{-2}$, i.e., the liquid level in C_1 rises. In case the left outflow valve remains open, α_2, the rate of increase decreases but if this outflow valve closes, the level continues to rise. It is easily verified that the predictions of both fault hypotheses ($R_{b_2}^-[\neg\alpha_1\alpha_2]$ and $R_{b_2}^-[\neg\alpha_1\neg\alpha_2]$) are consistent with the $p_{C_1}^{0+}$ measurement, and, therefore, possible causes of the observed anomalous behavior. Further measurements are needed to prune this set of candidates, as described in detail elsewhere [8,9].

5   Conclusions

Algorithms and hybrid models for diagnosis of physical systems are required to deal with configuration changes between modes of operation but the combinatorial explosion prohibits a global enumeration approach. This papers shows that mode changes can be modeled by locally activating and deactivating relations between system variables. When relations are (de)activated, the causal effect between system variables may change. This is handled by including all possible relations between system variables. Because of the presence of relations not describing system behavior in a given mode, the model may foster conflicting relations, which is solved by introducing parameters to enforce mutual exclusion between different causal assignments on individual relations. Performing local analyses establishes the relation between these parameters and mode selection parameters. The resulting method generates conditional predictions that depend on the mode of the system which allows for efficient execution of the diagnosis algorithms.

The presented method allows for a declarative prediction of future system behavior. It has not taken yet taken into account imperative mode switching functionality (e.g., a switching constraint such as $p_1 > p_2$ causes $\alpha_2 = 1$). Including this may constrain possible mode changes, and, therefore, further prune the set of hypothesized candidates.

Note that the analysis of interacting local switches is automated in HYBRSIM [10] based on analysis of *causal areas* in a bond graph. This forms the basis for future research into automatically performing the pre-processing of the relations between mode selection parameters and those that ensure mutual exclusion of different causal assignments. This should facilitate scaling the approach, because the complexity increases exponentially only with interacting switches within one causal area. So, e.g., for k causal areas with m switches, instead of 2^{km} modes, $k2^m$ modes have to be analyzed, and typically if a hybrid bond graph modeling approach is useful, the number of switches that interact directly, i.e., without dynamic behavior, is low.

References

1. R.N. Clark, P.M. Frank, and R.J. Patton. Introduction. In Ron Patton, Paul Frank, and Robert Clark, editors, *Fault Diagnosis in Dynamic Systems: Theory and Applications*, chapter 1, pages 1–19. Prentice-Hall, UK, 1989.
2. Philippus J. Feenstra, Eric J. Manders, Pieter J. Mosterman, Gautam Biswas, and Joel Barnett. Modeling and instrumentation for fault detection and isolation of a cooling system. In *Proceedings of the IEEE Southeastern Conference 2000*, pages 365–372, Nashville, TN, April 2000.
3. Philippus J. Feenstra, Pieter J. Mosterman, Gautam Biswas, and Peter C. Breedveld. Bond graph modeling procedures for fault detection and isolation of complex flow processes. In *International Conference on Bond Graph Modeling and Simulation (ICBGM '01)*, pages 77–82, Phoenix, AZ, January 2001.
4. Paul Frank. Fault diagnosis: A survey and some new results. *Automatica: IFAC Journal*, 26(3):459–474, 1990.
5. Jan Lunze. Diagnosis of quantised systems by means of timed discrete-event representations. In Nancy Lynch and Bruce H. Krogh, editors, *Lecture Notes in Computer Science, Hybrid Systems: Computation and Control*, pages 258–271, Berlin, 2000. Springer-Verlag.

6. Eric Jan Manders, Pieter J. Mosterman, and Gautam Biswas. Signal to Symbol Transformation Techniques for Robust Diagnosis in TRANSCEND In *Tenth International Workshop on Principles of Diagnosis*, pages 155–165, Lock Awe Hotel, Scotland, June 1999.
7. Sheila McIlraith, Gautam Biswas, Dan Clancy, and Vineet Gupta. Hybrid systems diagnosis. In Nancy Lynch and Bruce H. Krogh, editors, *Lecture Notes in Computer Science, Hybrid Systems: Computation and Control*, pages 282–295, Berlin, 2000. Springer-Verlag.
8. Pieter J. Mosterman. *Hybrid Dynamic Systems: A hybrid bond graph modeling paradigm and its application in diagnosis* PhD dissertation, Vanderbilt University, 1997.
9. Pieter J. Mosterman and Gautam Biswas. Diagnosis of continuous valued systems in transient operating regions. *IEEE Transactions on Systems, Man, and Cybernetics*, 29(6):554–565, November 1999.
10. Pieter J. Mosterman and Gautam Biswas. A Java Implementation of an Environment for Hybrid Modeling and Simulation of Physical Systems In *International Conference on Bond Graph Modeling (ICBGM '99)*, pages 157–162, San Francisco, January 1999.
11. Pieter J. Mosterman, Ravi Kapadia, and Gautam Biswas. Using Bond Graphs for Diagnosis of Dynamic Physical Systems In *Sixth International Workshop on Principles of Diagnosis*, pages 81–85, Goslar, Germany, October 1995.
12. Pieter J. Mosterman, Eric J. Manders, and Gautam Biswas. Qualitative Dynamic Behavior of Physical System Models With Algebraic Loops In *Eleventh International Workshop on Principles of Diagnosis*, pages 155–162, Morelia, Mexico, 2000.
13. Sriram Narasimhan, Gautam Biswas, Gabor Karsai, Tal Pasternak, and Feng Zhao. Building observers to address fault isolation and control problems in hybrid dynamic systems. In *Proceedings of the 2000 IEEE International Conference on Systems, Man, and Cybernetics*, pages 2393–2398, Nashville, TN, 2000.
14. Sriram Narasimhan, Feng Zhao, Gautam Biswas, and Elmer Hung. An integrated framework for combining global and local analyses in diagnosing hybrid systems. In *Eleventh International Workshop on Principles of Diagnosis*, pages 163–170, Morelia, Mexico, June 2000.
15. M. Sampath, R. Sengupta, S. Lafortune, K. Sinnamohideen, and D.C. Teneketzis. Failure diagnosis using discrete-event models. *IEEE Transactions on Automatic Control*, 40(9):1555–1575, September 1995.
16. M. Sampath, R. Sengupta, S. Lafortune, K. Sinnamohideen, and D.C. Teneketzis. Failure diagnosis using discrete-event models. *IEEE Transactions on Control Systems Technology*, 4(2):105–124, March 1996.
17. Marc Torrens, Rainer Weigel, and Boi Faltings. Java constraint library: bringing constraint technology on the internet using the java language. In *AAAI-97*, Providence, Rhode Island, 1997. Workshop on Constraints and Agents.

Addressing Multiobjective Control: Safety and Performance through Constrained Optimization*

Meeko Oishi[1], Claire J. Tomlin[1], Vipin Gopal[2], and Datta Godbole[2]

[1] Hybrid Systems Lab, Stanford University, Stanford, CA
{moishi,tomlin}@stanford.edu
[2] Honeywell Technology Center, Minneapolis, MN
{vipin.gopal,datta.godbole}@htc.honeywell.com

Abstract. We address systems which have multiple objectives: broadly speaking, these objectives can be thought of as *safety* and *performance* goals. Guaranteeing safety is our first priority, satisfying performance criteria our second. In this paper, we compute the system's safe operating space and represent it in closed form, and then, within this space, we compute solutions which optimize a given performance criterion. We describe the methodology and illustrate it with two examples of systems in which safety is paramount: a two-aircraft collision avoidance scenario and the flight management system of a VSTOL aircraft. In these examples, performance criteria are met using mixed-integer nonlinear programming (MINLP) and nonlinear programming (NLP), respectively. Optimized trajectories for both systems demonstrate the effectiveness of this methodology on systems whose safety is critical.

1 Introduction

Aircraft collision avoidance maneuvers and flight management systems are safety critical systems for which one would like to guarantee a certain level of performance: controllers for such systems must address potentially conflicting goals of hierarchical importance [1]. The safety of a system is determined by its ability to remain within an allowable subset of the state space. For example, in collision avoidance maneuvers, the aircraft must remain separated by a minimum distance, while in flight management systems, the state of the aircraft must remain inside its aerodynamic flight envelope. Performance goals can be specified in terms of costs of deviations from desired routes, or in minimizing fuel usage. Combining controllers to meet these objectives is an important and difficult problem: conflicting objectives can result in chattering and other undesirable effects [2]. In [1], the authors proposed a scheme for combining multiobjective controllers for systems with safety and performance objectives. The safe region

---

* Research supported by a National Science Foundation Graduate Research Fellowship, by DARPA under the Software Enabled Control Program (administered by AFRL under contract F33615-99-C-3014), and by a Stanford University Terman Faculty Award.

M.D. Di Benedetto, A. Sangiovanni-Vincentelli (Eds.): HSCC 2001, LNCS 2034, pp. 459–472, 2001.

of operation and the controller necessary to guarantee that the system remain within the safe region is first determined, and the designer is given the freedom to choose a controller that satisfies performance constraints within this safe region. This controller must be overridden whenever the system reaches the boundary of the safe space. In this paper, we address the design of the performance controller under the restrictions of the safety controller. Our methodology combines the Hamilton-Jacobi approach of [3] (for systems in which we can find *closed-form representations* of the safe space) and nonlinear optimization techniques [4,5], by viewing the restrictions necessary for safety as inequality constraints in a nonlinear optimization problem. A similar problem of incorporating state and control restrictions has been addressed for linear hybrid systems with linear constraints by using a model predictive control framework [6,7].

By designing our controller in two steps, we assure that the most important criteria, safety, is always met, and that the controller optimizes the performance of the system over the safe region of operation for any specified time horizon. This two-step process assumes that the analytical solution for the safe region is known; however, in cases for which there is no analytical solution, an analytical underapproximation can be used. By contrast, a one-step method in which safety and performance are optimized in a single cost function over a fixed time horizon guarantees safety only over that time horizon – although the system will remain outside of the unsafe set for the time over which performance is optimized, it could potentially enter unsafe set at the next time-step.

We demonstrate our method to generate safe, yet optimal, trajectories on two nonlinear, safety-critical systems. The collision avoidance scenario involves the lateral dynamics of two cooperative aircraft in free flight [8]. Collision avoidance has been an active area of research for contributors who have approached the problem in a variety of ways, including probabilistic [9,10], optimal [11,12,13], and hybrid [14,1] frameworks. The focus of the probabilistic and hybrid work has been on the computation of safe operating regions for groups of aircraft, while the focus of the optimal work has been to optimize performance criteria over a finite horizon while maintaining a 5 nmi radial separation between aircraft. The safety of the latter solution depends on appropriate choice of time horizon. The flight management system presented involves the longitudinal dynamics of a Vertical and/or Short Take-Off and Landing (VSTOL) aircraft. The safe region of operation for each mode of the hybrid system was derived in [2], and the stability of switched feedback linearizing control laws analyzed in [15]. The naive combination of these two controllers results in chattering and large tracking errors.

In this paper, we compute optimal control laws which smoothly guide the system through the safe region of operation. Our methodology for multiobjective controller synthesis involves three steps: analyzing the safety of the system, representing the safe region of operation in a form suitable for a nonlinear program, and then optimizing a desired performance goal constrained to lie within the safe region of operation. We demonstrate our methodology for each of the above steps with the collision avoidance and VSTOL examples. We then discuss our optimization results and conclude with directions for further research.

2   Problem Description

We address the problem of combining safety and performance goals for a hybrid system in a single discrete mode, that is, for the nonlinear continuous dynamics:

$$\dot{x} = f(x, u) \tag{1}$$

with state $x \in X$, and control input $u \in U$. Given an initial unsafe region $G \subset X$, we follow the method of [3] to compute the maximal controlled invariant set contained in G^c, which is denoted $W^* \subset X$. W^* represents those states from which there exists a control input $u \in U$ such that the system can remain in W^* for all future time. We also compute the set valued feedback control law $U_{\text{safe}}(x)$ which guarantees that the system remains in W^*. Next, we determine a closed-form representation for the safety constraints $x \in W^*$, which we represent as $c_W(x) \leq 0$. We then optimize the desired performance goal by minimizing $J_{\text{perf}}(x, u)$ over $x \in W^*$ subject to discretized dynamics.

$$
\begin{aligned}
\text{Minimize } \quad & J_{\text{perf}}(x_k, u_k) \\
\text{subject to: } \quad & x_{k+1} = f_d(x_k, u_k) \\
& X_{\min} \leq x_k \leq X_{\max}, U_{\min} \leq u_k \leq U_{\max} \\
& c_W(x_k) \leq 0
\end{aligned}
\tag{2}
$$

The control law which results from this optimization will, by construction, keep the discretized system within the safe region W^* for the time horizon over which it is optimized. As with any discretization process, the discretized model does differ from the continuous model, allowing for unaccounted-for discrepancies in the performance of these controllers on the actual continuous system. Discretization in hybrid systems is further complicated due to the interaction of the continuous dynamics with transitions. In this paper we use a forward Euler discretization method and neglect any discrepancies.

2.1   Collision Avoidance

We consider the lateral dynamics of a two-aircraft scenario with full cooperation between aircraft (safety concerns arise due to finite control input). The two aircraft travel at a constant speed V in the (x, y) plane with heading angles ψ_1 and ψ_2, respectively. The lateral dynamics of the two aircraft are $\underline{\dot{x}} = f(\underline{x}, u)$, where $\underline{x} = [x_1 \ y_1 \ \psi_1 \ x_2 \ y_2 \ \psi_2]^T$ and $u = [u_1 \ u_2]^T$, the roll angles of the two vehicles. For $i \in \{1, 2\}$, $\dot{x}_i = V \sin \psi_i$, $\dot{y}_i = V \cos \psi_i$, $\dot{\psi}_i = \frac{g}{V} \tan u_i$, and $u_i \in [-\phi_{\max}, \phi_{\max}]$, where $\phi_{\max} = 2\pi/9$ due to allowable aircraft roll. Since the relative orientation of the aircraft is of main interest, we transform the inertial two-aircraft system into a right-handed relative frame of reference by defining the relative position and heading of aircraft 2 with respect to the inertial position and heading of aircraft 1: (x_r, y_r, θ_r), where $\theta_r = \psi_1 - \psi_2$ and $[x_r \ y_r]^T = R^T(\pi/2 - \psi_1)[(x_2 - x_1)\ (y_2 - y_1)]^T$, $R(\beta)$ a standard rotation matrix through the angle β. The relative dynamics are therefore $\dot{\underline{x}}_r = f_r(\underline{x}_r, u)$, where

$$\begin{aligned} \dot{x}_r &= -V + V\cos\theta_r - \tfrac{g}{V}y_r\tan u_1 \\ \dot{y}_r &= V\sin\theta_r + \tfrac{g}{V}x_r\tan u_1 \\ \dot{\theta}_r &= -\tfrac{g}{V}(\tan u_2 - \tan u_1) \end{aligned} \qquad (3)$$

with $\underline{x}_r = [x_r \ y_r \ \theta_r]^T$. The minimum aircraft separation is defined as 5 nautical miles. To be safe, therefore, the state must remain in G^c, where

$$G^c = \{(x_r, y_r, \theta_r) : x_r^2 + y_r^2 \geq 5^2\} \ . \qquad (4)$$

2.2   VSTOL FMS

Consider the longitudinal axis dynamics of the VSTOL aircraft in the TRANSITION mode, or the mode in which the thrust can be vectored from the body axis through 90°, resulting in a wide range of dynamic behaviors [2]. The inertial coordinates of the aircraft's center of mass are (x, z) along the horizontal and vertical axes, respectively, and the pitch angle θ is the angle between the aircraft body axis and the inertial x axis. The flight path angle γ, the angle of attack α, and the ground speed V are defined as $\gamma = \tan^{-1}(\tfrac{\dot{z}}{\dot{x}})$, $\alpha = \theta - \gamma$, and $V = \sqrt{\dot{x}^2 + \dot{z}^2}$, respectively. The aerodynamic equations for lift (L) and drag (D) are given by $L = a_L V^2(1 + c\alpha)$, $D = a_D V^2(1 + b(1 + c\alpha)^2)$, with constants $b = 0.02$, $c = 11.42$, $a_L = 2.72$, $a_D = 2.54$ determined from actual Harrier flight data [16] as well as our own estimates. Further details on the model development are available in [2]. The aircraft nozzles rotate from the body axis through the angle δ with rate $\dot{\delta}$. We assume that the autopilot has direct control over both the forward thrust $u_1 = T$, the pitch acceleration $u_2 = J\ddot{\theta}$ (through the elevators), and the nozzle acceleration $u_3 = \ddot{\delta}$. We obtain the longitudinal dynamics from the Newton-Euler equations

$$M\begin{bmatrix} \ddot{x} \\ \ddot{z} \end{bmatrix} = R(\theta)\left(R^T(\alpha)\begin{bmatrix} -D \\ L \end{bmatrix} + \begin{bmatrix} u_1\cos\delta \\ u_1\sin\delta - \epsilon u_2 \end{bmatrix} \right) - \begin{bmatrix} 0 \\ Mg \end{bmatrix} \qquad (5)$$

where ϵ is a small positive constant. The aircraft has mass $M = 16280\,\mathrm{lb}$ and moment of inertia about the pitch axis $J = 32000\,\mathrm{slug\text{-}ft}^2$. Safety regulations for the aircraft dictate that the aircraft state must remain within specified limits, called the aerodynamic flight envelope, given by $V \in [V_{\min}, V_{\max}]$, $\gamma \in [\gamma_{\min}, \gamma_{\max}]$, $\theta \in [\theta_{\min}, \theta_{\max}]$, $\dot{\theta} \in [\dot{\theta}_{\min}, \dot{\theta}_{\max}]$, $\delta \in [\delta_{\min}, \delta_{\max}]$, and $\dot{\delta} \in [\dot{\delta}_{\min}, \dot{\delta}_{\max}]$. The set G includes all states which are not inside these bounds.

3   Safety Analysis

We obtain the maximal controlled invariant set by first specifying a cost function $J_{\text{safe}}(x, t)$ whose initial condition $J_{\text{safe}}(x, 0) = l(x)$ encodes the boundary of the allowable states ∂G. (The function $l(x)$ is negative inside G, zero on ∂G, and positive outside G). We pose the problem as an optimal control problem and solve two coupled Hamilton-Jacobi equations as in [3,17], whose solution describes the boundary of the maximal controlled invariant set W^* and the safe set of control inputs $U_{safe}(x)$. For the collision avoidance scenario, we can find a closed-form solution for the representation of W^*. In the flight management system, due to the system's high dimension, we analyze the safety of the system by projecting the system onto two-dimensional subspaces and then analyzing the safety of the system within each projection. The safety of the entire system is guaranteed by specifying that the aircraft remain within the intersection of these two-dimensional safe regions, which is a subset of the maximal controlled invariant set.

3.1   Collision Avoidance

Due to finite control input, there are certain initial configurations of the two aircraft for which, despite their best efforts, the aircraft will eventually violate G. To find this region, we use the method of [14], but obtain an analytical solution due to the cooperation between aircraft. An analytic solution arises because the computation of the safe control law results in $u_{safe}(\underline{x}_r) = [u_{safe1}, u_{safe2}]$ where $u_{safe1} = u_{safe2}$, meaning that, along optimal trajectories $\theta_r = \theta_{rsafe}$ is constant and thus (3) becomes an affine system:

$$
\underline{\dot{x}}_r = \begin{bmatrix} 0 & -\frac{g}{V}\tan u_{safe1} & 0 \\ \frac{g}{V}\tan u_{safe1} & 0 & 0 \\ 0 & 0 & 0 \end{bmatrix} \underline{x}_r + \begin{bmatrix} -V + V\cos\theta_{rsafe} \\ V\sin\theta_{rsafe} \\ 0 \end{bmatrix}. \tag{6}
$$

The boundary of the usable part on ∂G is given by $BUP = \{(x_p, y_p), (-x_p, -y_p)\}$, where $x_p = \frac{5}{\sqrt{2}}\frac{\sin\theta_r}{\sqrt{1-\cos\theta_r}}, \theta_r \neq 0$ and $y_p = \frac{5}{\sqrt{2}}\sqrt{1-\cos\theta_r}$. Integrating (6) directly from the BUP, and eliminating time:

$$
\begin{aligned}
(x_r(t) + c\sin\theta_r)^2 + (y_r(t) + c(1-\cos\theta_r))^2 &= \left(5 + c\sqrt{2(1-\cos\theta_r)}\right)^2 \\
(x_r(t) - c\sin\theta_r)^2 + (y_r(t) - c(1-\cos\theta_r))^2 &= \left(5 + c\sqrt{2(1-\cos\theta_r)}\right)^2
\end{aligned} \tag{7}
$$

where $c = \frac{V^2}{g\tan\phi_{max}}$. The maximal controlled invariant set $W^* = \{(X_1^c \cup X_2^c \cup X_3^c) \cap X_4^c\}$ is a function of $\underline{x}_r$, where the sets $X_j = \{\underline{x}_r \mid h_j(\underline{x}_r) \leq 0\}$, and

$$
\begin{aligned}
h_1(\underline{x}_r) &= (x_r + c\sin\theta_r)^2 + (y_r + c(1-\cos\theta_r))^2 - \left(5 + c\sqrt{2(1-\cos\theta_r)}\right)^2 \\
h_2(\underline{x}_r) &= (x_r - c\sin\theta_r)^2 + (y_r - c(1-\cos\theta_r))^2 - \left(5 + c\sqrt{2(1-\cos\theta_r)}\right)^2 \\
h_3(\underline{x}_r) &= -x_r(1-\cos\theta_r) + y_r\sin\theta_r \\
h_4(\underline{x}_r) &= x_r^2 + y_r^2 - 25 \\
h_5(\underline{x}_r) &= x_r\sin\theta_r + y_r(1-\cos\theta_r) .
\end{aligned} \tag{8}
$$

These sets are depicted in Figure 1 (projected onto (x_r, y_r) for a given θ_r) and Figure 2. The control law on the boundary of W^* is given by

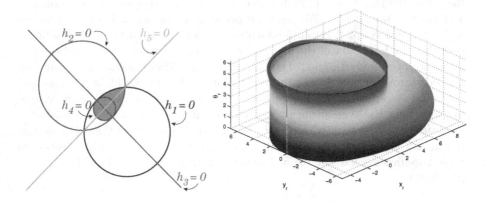

Fig. 1. Unsafe region for a given θ_r **Fig. 2.** Maximal Controlled Invariant Set W^*

$$u_{\text{safe}}(\underline{x}_r) = \begin{cases} \begin{bmatrix} \phi_{\max} \\ \phi_{\max} \\ -\phi_{\max} \\ -\phi_{\max} \end{bmatrix} & \{\underline{x}_r \mid (h_1(\underline{x}_r) = 0 \land h_3(\underline{x}_r) \leq 0 \land h_5(\underline{x}_r) \leq 0)\} \\ & \{\underline{x}_r \mid (h_2(\underline{x}_r) = 0 \land h_3(\underline{x}_r) \leq 0 \land h_5(\underline{x}_r) > 0)\} \end{cases} . \quad (9)$$

Details of this analysis are presented in [18].

3.2   VSTOL FMS Model

The safety analysis for the VSTOL FMS in TRANSITION mode follows [2]. Due to the high dimensionality of the system, we analyze the safety of the system in two-dimensional projections onto the (V, γ), $(\theta, \dot{\theta})$, and $(\delta, \dot{\delta})$ spaces. We then intersect these results to form the controlled invariant set $W^* = \{W_{(V,\gamma)} \cap W_{(\theta,\dot{\theta})} \cap W_{(\delta,\dot{\delta})}\}$, where

$$\begin{aligned} W_{(V,\gamma)} &= \{\underline{x} \mid (V_{\min} \leq V \leq V_{\max}) \land (\gamma_{\min} \leq \gamma \leq \gamma_{\max})\} \\ W_{(\theta,\dot{\theta})} &= \Big\{\underline{x} \mid (\theta_{\min} \leq \theta \leq \theta_{\max}) \land (\dot{\theta}_{\min} \leq \dot{\theta} \leq \dot{\theta}_{\max}) \land \\ &\qquad \Big(-\sqrt{2(\theta - \theta_{\min})u_{2\max}/J} \leq \dot{\theta} \leq \sqrt{2(\theta - \theta_{\max})u_{2\min}/J}\Big)\Big\} \\ W_{(\delta,\dot{\delta})} &= \Big\{\underline{x} \mid (\delta_{\min} \leq \delta \leq \delta_{\max}) \land (\dot{\delta}_{\min} \leq \dot{\delta} \leq \dot{\delta}_{\max}) \land \\ &\qquad \Big(-\sqrt{2(\delta - \delta_{\min})u_{3\max}} \leq \dot{\delta} \leq \sqrt{2(\delta - \delta_{\max})u_{3\min}}\Big)\Big\} . \end{aligned} \quad (10)$$

The set valued control law $U_{\text{safe}}(\underline{x})$ restricts the control along certain boundaries of W^*. With $\theta_1 = \frac{\dot{\theta}_{\max}^2}{2u_{2\min}} + \theta_{\max}$, $\theta_2 = \frac{\dot{\theta}_{\min}^2}{2u_{2\max}} + \theta_{\min}$, $\delta_1 = \frac{\dot{\delta}_{\max}^2}{2u_{3\min}} + \delta_{\max}$, and $\delta_2 = \frac{\dot{\delta}_{\min}^2}{2u_{3\max}} + \delta_{\min}$, $U_{\text{safe}}(\underline{x})$ is defined as:

$$\begin{cases} u_1 = T(\alpha, \delta, V_{\min}, \gamma) & \text{s.t.} \quad (T\cos(\alpha + \delta) \geq a_D V_{\min}^2 (1 + b(1 + c\alpha)^2) \\ & \qquad + mg \sin\gamma) \\ u_1 = T(\alpha, \delta, V_{\max}, \gamma) & \text{s.t.} \quad (T\cos(\alpha + \delta) \leq a_D V_{\max}^2 (1 + b(1 + c\alpha)^2) \\ & \qquad + mg \sin\gamma) \\ u_1 = T(\alpha, \delta, V, \gamma_{\min}) & \text{s.t.} \quad (T\sin(\theta - \gamma_{\min} + \delta) \geq -a_L V^2 (1 + c(\theta - \gamma_{\min})) \\ & \qquad + mg \cos\gamma_{\min}) \\ u_1 = T(\alpha, \delta, V, \gamma_{\max}) & \text{s.t.} \quad (T\sin(\theta - \gamma_{\max} + \delta) \leq -a_L V^2 (1 + c(\theta - \gamma_{\max})) \\ & \qquad + mg \cos\gamma_{\max}) \\ u_2 = u_{2\min} & \text{when } (\dot\theta = -\sqrt{2(\theta - \theta_{\min})u_{2\max}/J}) \wedge (\theta \geq \theta_1) \\ u_2 = u_{2\max} & \text{when } (\dot\theta = \sqrt{2(\theta - \theta_{\max})u_{2\min}/J}) \wedge (\theta \leq \theta_2) \\ u_2 \leq 0 & \text{when } (\dot\theta = \dot\theta_{\max}) \wedge (\theta < \theta_1) \\ u_2 \geq 0 & \text{when } (\dot\theta = \dot\theta_{\min}) \wedge (\theta > \theta_2) \\ u_3 = u_{3\min} & \text{when } (\dot\delta = -\sqrt{2(\delta - \delta_{\min})u_{3\max}}) \wedge (\delta \geq \delta_1) \\ u_3 = u_{3\max} & \text{when } (\dot\delta = \sqrt{2(\delta - \delta_{\max})u_{3\min}}) \wedge (\delta \leq \delta_2) \\ u_3 \leq 0 & \text{when } (\dot\delta = \dot\delta_{\max}) \wedge (\delta < \delta_1) \\ u_3 \geq 0 & \text{when } (\dot\delta = \dot\delta_{\min}) \wedge (\delta > \delta_2) \; . \end{cases}$$

$$(11)$$

4 Nonlinear Constrained Optimization

We now seek to solve the nonlinear constrained optimization problem (2). In the case of the flight management system, this is fairly straightforward, as the controlled invariant set is already written as an intersection of inequality constraints. The collision avoidance scenario, however, results in an expression for the maximal controlled invariant set which is represented as a combination (not just the intersection) of many inequalities. In order to use the optimization framework above, we introduce a mixed-integer programming framework to represent the maximal controlled invariant set as an intersection of inequality constraints.

4.1 Collision Avoidance

Binary variables $\delta_1, \delta_2, \delta_3$ are introduced for each of the regions X_1, X_2 and X_3 (see Figure 1) [6]. By adding constraints which involve the binary variables, we can reformulate the inequalities which express W^* as $c_W(\underline{x}_r) \leq 0$ from (2).

$$\begin{aligned} \delta_1(\underline{x}_r) = 1 &\Leftrightarrow h_1(\underline{x}_r) \leq 0, \quad m_1\delta_1(\underline{x}_r) \leq h_1(\underline{x}_r) \leq M_1(1 - \delta_1(\underline{x}_r)) \\ \delta_2(\underline{x}_r) = 1 &\Leftrightarrow h_2(\underline{x}_r) \leq 0, \quad m_2\delta_2(\underline{x}_r) \leq h_2(\underline{x}_r) \leq M_2(1 - \delta_2(\underline{x}_r)) \\ \delta_2(\underline{x}_r) = 1 &\Leftrightarrow h_3(\underline{x}_r) \leq 0, \quad m_3\delta_3(\underline{x}_r) \leq h_3(\underline{x}_r) \leq M_3(1 - \delta_3(\underline{x}_r)) \end{aligned} \qquad (12)$$

$$\delta_1(\underline{x}_r) + \delta_2(\underline{x}_r) + \delta_3(\underline{x}_r) \leq 2 \qquad (13)$$

Inequalities (12) express the sets X_1, X_2, X_3 with $m_j = \min_{\underline{x}_r} X_j$ and $M_j = \max_{\underline{x}_r} X_j$. Figure 3 shows the possible $(\delta_1, \delta_2, \delta_3)$ for a given θ_r. Thus (13) in conjunction with the constraint that the system remain outside of G ($x_r^2 + y_r^2 \geq 25$) can be used to represent W^*. The continuous system is now a differential

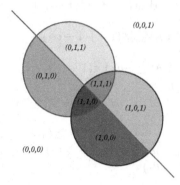

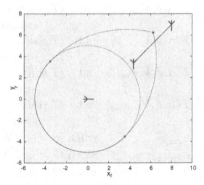

Fig. 3. Possible $(\delta_1, \delta_2, \delta_3)$ combinations for a given θ_r

Fig. 4. Optimization without safety constraints over a shortened time horizon

algebraic system, with nonlinear dynamics subject to algebraic inequality constraints involving the states and control.

The continuous dynamics in inertial coordinates are discretized with the explicit Euler formula over N time-steps of size Δt. We wish to minimize the cost function

$$J_{\text{perf}} = \sum_{k=1}^{N} \left((\psi_{1,k} - \psi_{1,0})^2 + (\psi_{2,k} - \psi_{2,0})^2 + u_{1,k}^2 + u_{2,k}^2 \right) \tag{14}$$

which penalizes deviations from the aircrafts' original headings while minimizing control effort. This minimization is subject to the following constraints, which involve the inertial and relative equations of motion, safety constraints, and final state constraints which return both aircraft to their original headings.

$$
\begin{aligned}
x_{1,k} &= x_{1,k-1} + V\Delta t \sin \psi_{1,k} & x_{r,k} &= \sin \psi_{1,k}(x_{2,k} - x_{1,k}) \\
y_{1,k} &= y_{1,k-1} + V\Delta t \cos \psi_{1,k} & &\quad + \cos \psi_{1,k}(y_{2,k} - y_{1,k}) \\
\psi_{1,k} &= \psi_{1,k-1} + \tfrac{g}{V}\Delta t \tan u_{1,k} & y_{r,k} &= -\cos \psi_{1,k}(x_{2,k} - x_{1,k}) \\
x_{2,k} &= x_{2,k-1} + V\Delta t \sin \psi_{2,k} & &\quad + \sin \psi_{1,k}(y_{2,k} - y_{1,k}) \\
y_{2,k} &= y_{2,k-1} + V\Delta t \cos \psi_{2,k} & \theta_{r,k} &= \psi_{1,k} - \psi_{2,k} \\
\psi_{2,k} &= \psi_{2,k-1} + \tfrac{g}{V}\Delta t \tan u_{2,k} & r_k &= 5 + c\sqrt{2(1 - \cos \theta_r)}
\end{aligned}
\tag{15}
$$

$$
\begin{aligned}
h_{1,k} &= (x_{r,k} + c\sin \theta_{r,k})^2 & m_1\delta_{1,k} &\leq h_{1,k} \leq M_1(1 - \delta_{1,k}) \\
&\quad + (y_{r,k} + c(1 - \cos \theta_{r,k}))^2 - r_k^2 & & \\
h_{2,k} &= (x_{r,k} - c\sin \theta_{r,k})^2 & m_2\delta_{2,k} &\leq h_{2,k} \leq M_2(1 - \delta_{2,k}) \\
&\quad + (y_{r,k} - c(1 - \cos \theta_{r,k}))^2 - r_k^2 & & \\
h_{3,k} &= -x_{r,k}(1 - \cos \theta_{r,k}) + y_{r,k} \sin \theta_{r,k} & m_3\delta_{3,k} &\leq h_{3,k} \leq M_3(1 - \delta_{3,k}) \\
& 2 \geq \delta_{1,k} + \delta_{2,k} + \delta_{3,k} & &
\end{aligned}
\tag{16}
$$

$$25 \leq x_{r,k}^2 + y_{r,k}^2 \qquad \psi_{1,N} = \psi_{1,0} \qquad \psi_{2,N} = \psi_{2,0} \tag{17}$$

■

4.2   VSTOL FMS

Unlike the collision avoidance scenario, the restrictions for safety in the VSTOL FMS are already represented as the intersection of inequalities. We discretize the continuous system (5) through an explicit Euler formulation over N time steps of length Δt. We wish to minimize the cost function

$$J_{\text{perf}} = \sum_{k=1}^{N} \left(\left(\frac{u_{1,k}}{u_{1\max}} \right)^2 + \left(\frac{u_{2,k}}{u_{2\max}} \right)^2 + \left(\frac{u_{3,k}}{u_{3\max}} \right)^2 \right) \tag{18}$$

which penalizes large control inputs. This minimization is subject to the equations of motion, initial, and final constraints. The initial state constraints fix inertial positions and velocities at x_0, $\dot{x}_0$, z_0, $\dot{z}_0$. Final constraints force the aircraft to reach a minimum desired velocity V_f and desired altitude z_f by the final time t_N. Additionally, final state constraints on δ and $\dot{\delta}$ maintain continuity of the hybrid system across the switch from TRANSITION mode to CTOL (Conventional Take-Off and Landing) mode. (The system's continued trajectory in CTOL mode is not presented here).

$$
\begin{aligned}
x_k &= x_{k-1} + \Delta t \dot{x}_k & V_k &= \sqrt{\dot{x}_k^2 + \dot{z}_k^2} & V_N &\geq V_f \\
z_k &= z_{k-1} + \Delta t \dot{z}_k & \gamma_k &= \tan^{-1}(\dot{z}_k/\dot{x}_k) & z_N &\geq z_f \\
\theta_k &= \theta_{k-1} + \Delta t \dot{\theta}_k & \alpha_k &= \theta_k - \gamma_k & \delta_N &= 0 \\
\dot{\theta}_k &= \dot{\theta}_{k-1} + \Delta t u_{2,k}/J & D_k &= a_D V_k^2 (1 + b(1 + c\alpha_k)^2) & \dot{\delta}_N &= 0 \\
\delta_k &= \delta_{k-1} + \Delta t \dot{\delta}_k & L_k &= a_L V_k^2 (1 + c\alpha_k) & & \\
\dot{\delta}_k &= \dot{\delta}_{k-1} + \Delta t u_{3,k} & & & &
\end{aligned}
\tag{19}
$$

$$
\begin{bmatrix} \dot{x}_k \\ \dot{z}_k \end{bmatrix} = \begin{bmatrix} \dot{x}_{k-1} \\ \dot{z}_{k-1} \end{bmatrix} + \frac{\Delta t}{M} \left(R(\gamma_{k-1}) \begin{bmatrix} -D_{k-1} \\ L_{k-1} \end{bmatrix} + \right.
$$
$$
\left. R(\theta_{k-1}) \begin{bmatrix} u_{1,k-1} \cos \delta_{k-1} \\ u_{1,k-1} \sin \delta_{k-1} - \epsilon u_{2,k-1} \end{bmatrix} - \begin{bmatrix} 0 \\ Mg \end{bmatrix} \right)
\tag{20}
$$

$$
\begin{aligned}
-\sqrt{2(\theta_k - \theta_{k\min})u_{2,k\max}/J} &\leq \dot{\theta}_k \leq \sqrt{2(\theta_k - \theta_{k\max})u_{2,k\min}/J} \\
-\sqrt{2(\delta_k - \delta_{k\min})u_{3,k\max}} &\leq \dot{\delta}_k \leq \sqrt{2(\delta_k - \delta_{k\max})u_{3,k\min}}
\end{aligned}
\tag{21}
$$

■

5   Results

We modeled both examples in GAMS, a programming environment which invokes prescribed solvers for mixed-integer nonlinear programs (MINLPs) and nonlinear programs (NLPs) [19]. The MINLP solver, DICOPT [20], successively solves NLPs and mixed-integer linear programs (MIPs) until the solution converges to its optimum value. DICOPT used two nonlinear solvers, CONOPT [21] and rSQP [22], as well as the MIP solver CPLEX [23]. The plain NLP problems used the nonlinear solver CONOPT. The three collision avoidance scenarios all begin at the same initial state $\underline{x}_0 = [0\ 0\ \pi/2\ 8\ 7\ \pi]^T$, but utilize different controllers to address (1) optimization with safety restrictions, (2) tracking with safety restrictions (no optimization), and (3) optimization without safety restrictions. The two optimizations were computed in approximately 140 seconds and 4809 iterations, and 1 second and 3 iterations, respectively, on a Dell 400 MHz single processor with 128MB RAM. The two VSTOL scenarios compare optimization with safety restrictions and tracking with safety restrictions. The nonlinear optimization completed in 330 seconds and 2356 iterations on a SunUltra60Creator3D with 384MB RAM.

5.1   Collision Avoidance

Optimization with Safety Constraints. The entire system (14)-(17) was optimized, constraining the optimal solution to lie within the range of allowable controls U_{safe} as well as within W^* at each time point. The optimal trajectory smoothly navigates both aircraft in W^*, and the resultant control does not chatter (Figure 5). This method produces a well-behaved control law and smooth trajectories for the aircraft.

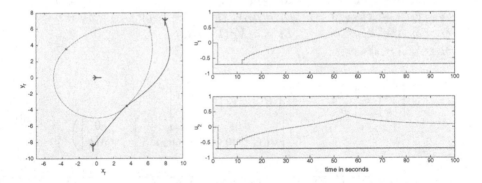

Fig. 5. Optimization with safety constraints: Trajectory in relative coordinates and control history

Tracking with Safety Override. We contrast the results from the above method with a simple method used in [2] for longitudinal envelope protection. In this method, a tracking control law is overridden when necessary with the control law to enforce safety. The continuous system is subject to actuator saturation, and the state of the system is continually examined, enabling the safety controller (9) to override the tracking controller when the system encounters the boundary of W^*.

$$U_{\text{perf}}(\underline{x}) = \begin{cases} \frac{V}{g} \begin{bmatrix} \tan^{-1}(-\lambda(\psi_1 - \psi_1(0))) \\ \tan^{-1}(-\lambda(\psi_2 - \psi_2(0))) \end{bmatrix} & \underline{x} \in W^* \\ u_{\text{safe}}(\underline{x}) & \text{otherwise} \end{cases} \qquad (22)$$

The nonlinear inversion tracking control law places the poles of the error dynamics on the negative real axis at $-\lambda = -1.5$. While this approach is appealing in its simplicity, in practice it is problematic due to the chattering in the control law when the system switches from the tracking control law to the safety control law (Figure 6). The chattering results from the fact that the control law chosen for tracking is often completely contradictory to the control law necessary for safety.

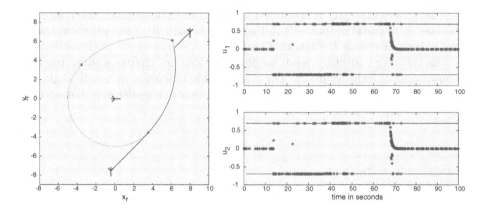

Fig. 6. Tracking with safety override: Trajectory in relative frame and control history

Optimization Without Safety Constraints. For completeness, the system is also compared to the one-step nonlinear optimization method used in [12]. The system (14,15,17) is optimized, maintaining aircraft separation and constraining $u \in U$. This requires only an NLP (not MINLP) solver since the maximal controlled invariant set is ignored.

For generic initial conditions and time horizons, there is no guarantee of safety, of remaining within W^*. As shown in Figure 4, the optimal control law leads the aircraft right to the boundary of G. While maintaining aircraft separation for the time over which the system is optimized, the aircraft are left in an orientation which will inevitably result in a violation of the minimum aircraft separation (4), demonstrating the advantage of two-step controller synthesis. Separating the safety and performance goals into a two-stage optimization problem enforces safety over any time horizon.

The computational difficulties associated with MINLPs make the NLP scenario, with minimum separation inequality (4) but no safety restrictions W^*, appealing for cases in which we know ahead of time that the time horizon we optimize over is "long enough" to complete the conflict avoidance maneuver. For a time horizon of 100 seconds CONOPT solved the system in 23 seconds and 676 iterations, considerably less than the MINLP solver used in the optimization with safety constraints.

5.2   VSTOL FMS

We perform a similar comparison of two multiobjective methods for the flight management system. The aircraft begins at $[x_0\ \dot{x}_0\ z_0\ \dot{z}_0]^T = [0\ 40\ 18\ 0]^T$ in both cases. We compare the two-step controller synthesis, optimizing perfor-mance within the safety restrictions, with the method used in [2], overriding a tracking control law with the safety control law when necessary.

The system (18)-(21) is optimized and plotted (solid) against the trajectory obtained from tracking (dashed) in Figures 7 through 10. The optimized trajec-tory is smoother than the tracking trajectory, does not cause pitch oscillations (as the tracking trajectory tends to do), and does not chatter despite reaching saturation in the thrust input. The considerable difference in nozzle angle tra-jectories (Figure 8) could result from the fact that our model does not account for interactions with the ground.

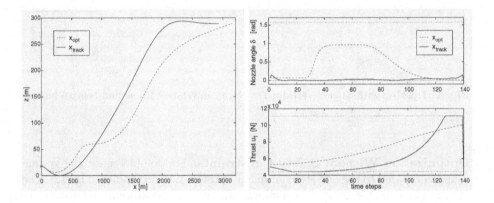

Fig. 7. Trajectories in longitudinal plane

Fig. 8. Nozzle angle and thrust time his-tories

6   Conclusion

The results of this paper serve to motivate the problem of developing computa-tionally efficient methods for multiobjective controller synthesis in hybrid sys-tems. We have shown that for nonlinear continuous state systems, it is feasible to combine safe set computation with constrained nonlinear programming in order

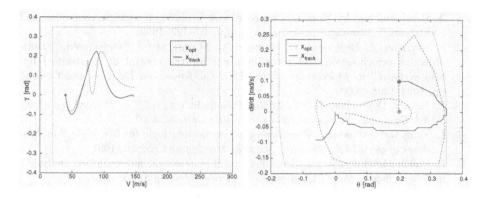

Fig. 9. Trajectories in (V, γ) Projection   **Fig. 10.** Trajectories in $(\theta, \dot{\theta})$ Projection

to compute solutions which satisfy both safety and performance goals. However, there are a number of issues which need to be addressed. The current solvers are very sensitive to the initial values of the state and control trajectories, so if these solvers were to be used in practice today, good intuition is needed to provide an initial iterate. Our results from the collision avoidance scenario could be readily extended to a higher number of aircraft by examining the relative separation between each aircraft pair. However, for this to be a feasible method to obtain optimal trajectories, solving a mixed-integer nonlinear program for nonlinear, trigonometric functions needs to become a simpler process. The representation of the maximal controlled invariant set in closed form is also required: currently, we can do this only for systems for which we can solve Hamilton's equations analytically. For more complicated systems, an underapproximation of the safe set with a simpler representation is required. Finally, we are now extending these techniques to systems with multiple discrete modes (the full hybrid model of the VSTOL aircraft), which requires optimization across the mode switch as well as within each mode.

References

1. J. Lygeros, C. Tomlin, and S. Sastry, "Multiobjective hybrid controller synthesis," in *Hybrid and Real-Time Systems* (O. Maler, ed.), LNCS 1201, pp. 109–123, Grenoble: Springer Verlag, 1997. UCB/ERL Memo M97/59.
2. M. Oishi and C. Tomlin, "Switched nonlinear control of a VSTOL aircraft," in *Proceedings of the IEEE Conference on Decision and Control*, (Phoenix, AZ), 1999.
3. C. Tomlin, *Hybrid Control of Air Traffic Management Systems*. PhD thesis, University of California, Berkeley, CA, September 1998.
4. L. Biegler, "Efficient solution of dynamic optimization and MPC problems," in *Progress in Systems and Control Theory*, vol. 26, pp. 219–243, Birkhauser Springer Verlag, 2000.
5. V. Gopal and L. Biegler, "Large scale inequality constrained optimization and control," *IEEE Control Systems Magazine*, vol. 18, pp. 59–68, December 1998.

6. A. Bemporad and M. Morari, "Control of systems integrating logic, dynamics, and constraints," *Automatica*, vol. 35, no. 3, pp. 407–427, 1999.

7. E. Kerrigan, A. Bemporad, D. Mignone, M. Morari, and J. Maciejowski, "Multi-objective prioritisation and reconfiguration for the control of constrained hybrid systems," in *Proceedings of the IEEE Conference on Decision and Control*, pp. 1694–1698, 2000.

8. R. Schulz, D. Shaner, and Y. Zhao, "Free-flight concept," in *Proceedings of the AIAA Guidance, Navigation, and Control Conference*, 1997.

9. L. Yang and J. Kuchar, "Prototype conflict alerting logic for free flight," in *Proceedings of the AIAA Aerospace Sciences Meeting and Exhibit*, 1997.

10. R. Paielli and H. Erzberger, "Free flight conflict detection and resolution analysis," in *Proceedings of the AIAA Aerospace Sciences Meeting and Exhibit*, 1997.

11. R. Schulz and Y. Zhao, "Deterministic resolution of two aircraft conflict in free-flight," in *AIAA Guidance, Navigation, and Control Conference*, 1997.

12. V. Gopal and R. Schulz, "Interior point methods for aircraft conflict resolution problems," *Proceedings of the SIAM Conference on Optimization*, December 1999.

13. P. Menon, G. Sweriduk, and B. Sridhar, "Optimal strategies for free-flight air traffic conflict resolutions," *Journal of Guidance, Control, and Dynamics*, vol. 22, no. 2, pp. 202–211, 1999.

14. C. Tomlin, G. J. Pappas, and S. Sastry, "Conflict resolution for air traffic management: A case study in multi-agent hybrid systems," *IEEE Transactions on Automatic Control*, vol. 43, pp. 509–521, April 1998.

15. M. Oishi and C. Tomlin, "Switching in nonminimum phase systems: Applications to a VSTOL aircraft," in *Proceedings of the American Control Conference*, 2000.

16. "YAV-8B Simulation and Modeling," Tech. Rep. CR-170397, NASA, March 1983.

17. I. Mitchell and C. Tomlin, "Level set methods for computation in hybrid systems," in *Hybrid Systems: Computation and Control* (B. Krogh and N. Lynch, eds.), LNCS, Springer Verlag, 2000.

18. M. Oishi, "Safe collision avoidance maneuvers using constrained optimization," Tech. Rep. SUDAAR 730, Stanford University, 2001.

19. A. Brooke, D. Kendrick, A. Meeraus, and R. Raman, *GAMS: A User's Guide*. GAMS Development Corporation, Washington, DC, 1998.

20. J. Viswanathan, I. Grossman, and E. Kalvelagen, *GAMS/DICOPT Solver Manual*. Engineering Design Research Center, Carnegie Mellon University, and GAMS Development Corp. http://www.gams.com.

21. A. Drud, "CONOPT – A large scale GRG code," *Operations Research Society of America Journal on Computing*, no. 6, pp. 207–216, 1994.

22. L. Biegler, C. Schmid, and D. Ternet, "A multiplier-free, reduced Hessian method for process optimization," in *Large-Scale Optimization with Applications, Part II: Optimal Design and Control, in IMA Volumes in Mathematics and Applications*, Springer Verlag, 1997.

23. CPLEX Optimization Inc. http://www.cplex.com.

Representation of Quantised Systems by the Frobenius-Perron Operator

Jochen Schröder and Jan Lunze

Technical University Hamburg-Harburg,
Institute of Control Engineering,
D-21071 Hamburg, Germany
{j.schroeder, lunze}@tu-harburg.de
http://www.tu-harburg.de/rts

Abstract. The paper concerns the representation of continuous-variable discrete-time systems with quantised input and state. It shows that the autonomous quantised system is represented by the Frobenius-Perron operator and the non-autonomous by the Foias operator. A finite and complete approximation of the Frobenius-Perron operator is given by an automaton which turns out to be identical to the discrete abstraction of the quantised system that is currently studied in the literature on verification or diagnosis of hybrid systems. Hence, the paper shows a connection between the mathematical literature and hybrid systems research. As a result of this connection it is shown that the abstraction converges to the continuous system for finer quantisation. The paper ends with presenting a method for the computation of abstractions that guarantees the completeness of the resulting model.

1 Introduction

This paper concerns quantised systems (Figure 1), which are a specific type of hybrid systems. The injector and the quantiser are interfaces between the numerical signals of the continuous-variable system and the symbolical values that serve as input or output of the quantised system. The motivation for considering such systems comes from process supervision, where the controller of a continuous system has only access to discrete input and outputs.

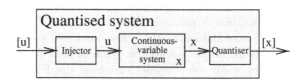

Fig. 1. Quantised system.

Quantised systems have been studied recently in the literature on verification of discrete control algorithms or on process diagnosis where the quantised

M.D. Di Benedetto, A. Sangiovanni-Vincentelli (Eds.): HSCC 2001, LNCS 2034, pp. 473–486, 2001.
© Springer-Verlag Berlin Heidelberg 2001

system is replaces by a discrete-event model, which refers only to the symbolic signals $[u]$ and $[x]$ but does no longer include continuous-variable elements. This model is called a *qualitative model* of the continuous-variable system or a *discrete abstraction* of the quantised system.

The main aim of this paper is to show that quantised systems can also be dealt with as a nonlinear system and studied by means of methods that have been developed in mathematical systems theory. The main idea is to consider the set of all states x of the continuous-variable system that have the same quantised value $[x]$ and to follow the ensemble of all trajectories that start from this set. Such trajectory ensembles can be described by the Frobenius-Perron operator (FPO), which has been introduced in the analysis of chaotic systems. This paper shows that autonomous quantised systems can be represented by the FPO. Hence, results from mathematical systems theory can be directly applied to quantised systems. First, it is shown that discrete-event models of quantised systems that are used in the hybrid system literature are discrete approximations of the FPO. Hence, well-known properties of discrete approximations of the FPO can be used to prove the convergence of the discrete abstraction for increasing resolution of the quantiser. Second, a method for computing *complete* qualitative models is derived by using the idea of hyperbox cell-to-cell mapping.

Relevant literature. There are two lines of research relevant for this study. The first concerns the modelling of hybrid systems and their application to control tasks. In order to overcome the difficulties brought about by the complexity of hybrid systems automata-theoretic descriptions have been proposed in [9] and [11] for quantised discrete-time continuous systems and [2], [5] or [10] for discrete-event quantised systems. The other line of research concerns the mathematical study of nonlinear and chaotic systems. The FPO has been studied to analyse the evolution of densities of nonlinear transformations throughout the last decades. About 40 years ago a finite approximation method for the FPO has been suggested in [13]. Several years later it was shown in [7] for scalar systems and in [1] for multi-dimensional systems that the approximate operator converges to the FPO.

This paper combines both lines of research and applies results on the FPO to the quantised system.

Structure of the paper. The main idea of the presented approaches is to consider probability density functions in the state-space rather than single states. In Section 2 the temporal evolution of such density functions is considered. It is shown that this evolution is precisely described by the FPO. Section 3 deals with the approximation of the behaviour of the quantised system. The resulting qualitative model is a stochastic automaton given in Section 4. It is shown that this automaton is the result of a discretisation of the FPO. Section 5 deals with computational aspects of this discretisation. A fundamental requirement in process supervision is to obtain a complete model, which requires a sound approximation of the FPO. A method is presented that guarantees soundness for Lipschitz-constrained systems.

2   Evolution of Probability Densities in the State–Space

2.1   Results from Measure Theory

For a description of the behaviour of the quantised system essential concepts from measure theory are needed. For a more detailed introduction the reader is referred to the textbook [6].

Consider a set Ω, which is usually the $\mathbb{R}^n$, and a family $\sigma(\Omega)$ of subsets of Ω. This family is called a σ-algebra, if

1. $\Omega \in \sigma(\Omega)$, and $A \in \sigma(\Omega) \Rightarrow \Omega \backslash A \in \sigma(\Omega)$,
2. for every sequence $\{A_k\}$, $A_k \in \sigma(\Omega) \Rightarrow \bigcup_k A_k \in \sigma(\Omega)$

hold. A measure is a function $\mu : \Omega \to \mathbb{R}^+$ that satisfies $\mu(\emptyset) = 0$ and:

$$\mu(\bigcup_k A_k) = \sum_k \mu(A_k) \quad \text{if } A_i \cap A_j = \emptyset, \ i \neq j .$$

The triple $(\Omega, \sigma(\Omega), \mu)$ is called a measure space and all $A \in \sigma(\Omega)$ measurable sets. A commonly used measure space is the Borel measure space $(\mathbb{R}, \mathcal{B}, \mu)$, where the Borel σ-algebra is by definition the smallest σ-algebra containing all intervals $[a, b]$ on $\mathbb{R}$ and the Borel measure is given by $\mu([a, b]) = b - a$. Its extension to higher dimension yields the space $(\mathbb{R}^n, \mathcal{B}^n, \mu^n)$, which contains all hypercubes with their hypervolume as measure. For $\Omega \subset \mathbb{R}^n$ the corresponding Borel σ-algebra is denoted as $\mathcal{B}(\Omega)$.

Given a measure space $(\Omega, \sigma(\Omega), \mu)$, a function $p \colon \Omega \to \mathbb{R}$ satisfying $p^{-1}(\Delta) \in \sigma(\Omega)$ or equivalently $\{A : p(A) \in \Delta\} \in \sigma(\Omega)$ for every interval $\Delta \subset \mathbb{R}$ is called measurable. The Lebesgue integral is defined for every measurable function and is denoted by $\int_\Omega p(\omega)\mu(d\omega)$. For a set $A \in \sigma(\Omega)$ the Lebesgue integral is defined as $\int_A p(\omega)\mu(d\omega) = \int_\Omega 1_A(\omega)p(\omega)\mu(d\omega)$ with the indicator function $1_A(x)$ that is 1 for $x \in A$ and 0 otherwise. The Borel measure of every Borel measurable set A can be expressed as the Lebesgue integral: $\mu(A) = \int_A \mu(d\omega)$.

In a measure space $(\Omega, \sigma(\Omega), \mu)$ the family of all measurable functions $p :$ $\Omega \to \mathbb{R}$ for which $||p||_1 = \int_\Omega |p(\omega)|\mu(d\omega) < \infty$ holds, is called $L^1(\Omega, \sigma(\Omega), \mu)$ (abbreviated as L^1 space). A sub-space of L^1 is the space

$$D(\Omega, \sigma(\Omega), \mu) = \{p \in L^1 \ : \ p \geq 0, \ ||p||_1 = 1\}$$

of all density functions, i.e. those L^1 functions that satisfy the properties of density functions in probability theory.

2.2   Problem Statement

For simplicity of presentation, the theory is developed now for autonomous quantised systems and extended to non-autonomous systems in Section 2.5. The continuous–variable system is described for a given measure space $(\Omega, \sigma(\Omega), \mu)$ by

$$x(k+1) = f(x(k)) \tag{1}$$

with $x \in \Omega$ and $f : \Omega \to \Omega$. The initial state $x(0)$ is unknown. Instead only an initial density function $p_0(x) \in D(\Omega, \sigma(\Omega), \mu)$ is given.

The aim is to find the probability with which the symbols $[x(k)]$ describing the quantised state appear at the output of the quantised system in two steps:

1. The evolution of the initial density function is described as sequence $p(x, k)$ of density functions over the discrete time k, with $p(x, 0) = p_0(x)$ and $p(x, k) \in D$, $\forall k$. This problem will be solved in in Section 2.3.
2. From the sequence of density functions $p(x, k)$ the discrete conditional probability distribution $\mathbf{Prob}([x(k)] \,|\, p_0(x))$ of the state symbols for given quantiser is derived. This problem will be investigated in Section 2.4.

2.3   The Frobenius-Perron Operator

Definition 1. *Given a measure space $(\Omega, \sigma(\Omega), \mu)$ and a non-singular measureable transformation $f : \Omega \to \Omega$, for which for every $A \in \sigma(\Omega)$ with $\mu(A) = 0$ the relation $\mu(f^{-1}(A)) = 0$ holds. Then the Frobenius-Perron operator $P : L^1 \to L^1$ associated with f is defined by:*

$$\int_A Pp(\omega)\mu(d\omega) = \int_{f^{-1}(A)} p(\omega)\mu(d\omega) \,, \quad \text{for all } A \in \sigma(\Omega) \,. \tag{2}$$

Note that P is implicitly defined by eqn. (2) as an operator which $p \in L^1$ into $Pp \in L^1$.

If $f : \mathbb{R}^n \to \mathbb{R}^n$ in $(\mathbb{R}^n, \mathcal{B}^n, \mu^n)$ is a diffeomorphism, i.e. if f is bijective and both f and f^{-1} are differentiable, the FPO is explicitly given by

$$Pp(x) = p(f^{-1}(x)) \cdot \left| \left(\frac{\partial f^{-1}}{\partial x} \right) \right| \,, \tag{3}$$

where $|(\partial f^{-1}/\partial x)|$ denotes the determinant of the Jacobian of f^{-1} [6].

The FPO P is a linear operator. One of its most important properties is that it is a density operator, i.e. $Pp(x) \in D$, whenever $p(x) \in D$. Hence, the FPO solves the first problem given in Section 2.2. With $p(x, 0) = p_0(x) \in D$ eqn. (3) is used to determine the evolution of this density function recursively by: $p(x, k+1) = Pp(x, k)$.

Examples. From eqn. (3) the FPO of $f : \mathbb{R}^+ \to \mathbb{R}^+$, $f(x) = x^2$ is given by $Pp(x) = p(\sqrt{x})/(2\sqrt{x})$. For the initial density $p_0(x) = 5 \cdot 1_{[0.6,\, 0.8]}$, which describes a uniform distribution of the system state in the interval $[0.6,\, 0.8]$, the FPO yields

$$p(x, 1) = Pp(x, 0) = \frac{5}{2\sqrt{x}} \cdot 1_{[0.6^2,\, 0.8^2]} \quad \text{and}$$

$$p(x, k) = P^k p(x, 0) = \frac{5}{(2\sqrt{x})^k} \cdot 1_{[0.6^{2k},\, 0.8^{2k}]} \,.$$

As another example the FPO of a linear system $x(k+1) = Ax$ with non-singular matrix A is given by $Pp(x) = p(A^{-1}x) \cdot |\det A^{-1}|$.

2.4   Representation of the Autonomous Quantised Systems

In the following the measure space $(\Omega, \mathcal{B}(\Omega), \mu^n)$, $\Omega \subset \mathbb{R}^n$ is considered. The quantiser introduces a partition of Ω into N regions $\mathcal{Q}_x(1), \ldots, \mathcal{Q}_x(N)$ such that $\mu^n(\mathcal{Q}_x(i)) > 0$, $i = 1, \ldots, N$ holds. According to this partition the quantiser assigns to each value $\boldsymbol{x}(k)$ a discrete value $[\boldsymbol{x}(k)] \in \mathcal{N}_x$ with $\mathcal{N}_x = \{1, 2, \ldots, N\}$ such that $\boldsymbol{x}(k) \in \mathcal{Q}_x(i) \Leftrightarrow [\boldsymbol{x}(k)] = i$ holds.

In terms of a L^1 function $p(\boldsymbol{x})$ the quantiser defines a projection to the subset

$$\Delta_N = \{p(\boldsymbol{x}) : p(\boldsymbol{x}) = \sum_{i=1}^{N} \alpha_i \cdot b^i(\boldsymbol{x}), \ \alpha_i \in \mathbb{R}\} \subset L^1 , \quad b^i(\boldsymbol{x}) = \frac{1_{\mathcal{Q}_x(i)}}{\mu^n(\mathcal{Q}_x(i))} \quad (4)$$

of all L^1 functions that can be written as finite sum of some L^1 functions $b^i(\boldsymbol{x})$.

Definition 2. *A projector is an operator* $Q_N : L^1 \to \Delta_N$ *with:*

$$Q_N p = \sum_{i=1}^{N} \lambda_i b^i , \quad \lambda_i = \int_{\mathcal{Q}_x(i)} p(\boldsymbol{\omega}) \mu^n(d\boldsymbol{\omega}) , \quad (5)$$

According to this definition, the projection is such that the weight $\lambda_i/\mu^n(\mathcal{Q}_x(i))$ of each simple function $1_{\mathcal{Q}_x(i)}$ is the mean value of $p(\boldsymbol{x})$ in the region $\mathcal{Q}_x(i)$.

A discretiser is associated with the projector which maps a density function $p(\boldsymbol{x})$ to an N-dimensional discrete probability distribution $\mathbf{Prob}([\boldsymbol{x}(k)]) \in \mathcal{W}^N$ with $\mathcal{W}^N = \{\boldsymbol{p}_D \in [0, 1]^N : \sum_{i=1}^{N} p_D^i = 1\}$, where p_D^i is the i-th element of the N-vector $\boldsymbol{p}_D$.

Definition 3. *The operator* $D_N : D \to \mathcal{W}^N$, $D_N p = (\lambda_1, \ldots, \lambda_N)'$ *with* λ_i *given by eqn. (5) is called (density) discretiser.*

Hence, the autonomous quantised system is described by

$$p(\boldsymbol{x}, k+1) = Pp(\boldsymbol{x}, k), \quad p(\boldsymbol{x}, 0) = p_0(\boldsymbol{x}) \quad (6)$$
$$\mathbf{Prob}([\boldsymbol{x}(k)] \,|\, p_0(\boldsymbol{x})) = D_N p(\boldsymbol{x}, k) , \quad (7)$$

with initial density function $p_0(\boldsymbol{x})$. That is, it is represented by the FPO P of the continuous-variable system and by the discretiser D_N associated with the quantiser.

Example. Consider again $f(x) = x^2$ in $(\mathbb{R}^+, \mathcal{B}, \mu)$ with $p_0(x) = 5 \cdot 1_{[0.6, \, 0.8]}$ and the partition $\mathcal{Q}_x(1) = [0, 0.5)$, $\mathcal{Q}_x(2) = [0.5, 1)$, $\mathcal{Q}_x(3) = [1, \infty)$. Then eqns. (6) and (7) yields (Figure 2):

$$D_N p(x, 0) = (0\ 1\ 0)' \quad D_N p(x, 0) = (0.4645\ 0.5355\ 0)' \quad \text{etc.}$$

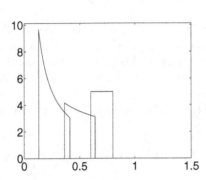

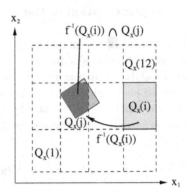

Fig. 2. Sequence of density functions.   **Fig. 3.** Explanation of Ulam's method.

2.5   Extension to Non-autonomous Systems

The aim of this section is to define an operator similar to the FPO for non-autonomous systems. As this operator is formulated as an operator acting on measures, first the FPO on measures is given.

In Section 2.1 the Borel measure has been written as $\mu(A) = \int_A \mu(d\omega)$. An important result of measure theory, the Radon-Nikodym theorem, says that for any measure ν in $(\Omega, \sigma(\Omega), \mu)$ satisfying $\mu(A) = 0 \Rightarrow \nu(A) = 0$ there exists a non-negative, integrable function $p : \Omega \to \mathbb{R}$ such that

$$\nu(A) = \int_A p(\omega)\mu(d\omega) . \tag{8}$$

Such a measure ν is said to be absolute continuous to μ. This result means that in a certain sense a density corresponds to a measure and vice-versa. Not every measure can be represented by a density function, but every density leads to a measure that is absolute continuous to the Borel measure. As a consequence, the FPO can be formulated as an operator transforming one measure into another instead of an operator transforming one density into another as done in the previous sections.

Consider all finite measures on $(\Omega, \sigma(\Omega))$, i.e. all measures for which $\mu(A) < \infty$ holds for all $A \in \sigma(\Omega)$, and denote the space of all these measures by $\mathcal{M}$. Then the FPO $\hat{P} : \mathcal{M} \to \mathcal{M}$ on measures is given by

$$\hat{P}\nu(A) = \int_\Omega 1_A(\boldsymbol{f}(\omega))\nu(d\omega) . \tag{9}$$

For measures in the form (8) and non-singular transformations $\boldsymbol{f}$ the FPO on measures becomes the FPO in the form of eqn. (2) [6].

Consider now the non-autonomous system

$$\boldsymbol{x}(k+1) = \boldsymbol{f}(\boldsymbol{x}(k), \boldsymbol{u}(k)) \tag{10}$$

with $x \in \Omega$, $u \in \Psi$ and $f : \Omega \times \Psi \to \Omega$ together with the quantiser and injector as shown in Figure 1. In the following it is assumed that $\Omega \subset \mathbb{R}^n$, $\Psi \subset \mathbb{R}^m$ and both Ω and Ψ are closed and Borel measurable. Furthermore, for every fixed $u \in \Psi$ the transformation $f(x, u)$ is assumed to be continuous in x and for every fixed $x \in \Omega$ measurable in u. Borel measures used in the following are denoted by μ^n for $\mathcal{B}(\Omega)$ and μ^m for $\mathcal{B}(\Psi)$.

The injector is defined similar to the quantiser by a partition of Ψ into M regions $\mathcal{Q}_u(1), \ldots, \mathcal{Q}_u(M)$ such that $\mu^m(\mathcal{Q}_u(l)) > 0$, $l = 1, \ldots, M$ holds. For given discrete input $l \in \mathcal{N}_u$ with $\mathcal{N}_u = \{1, \ldots, M\}$ the injector chooses a value $u(k)$ from $\mathcal{Q}_u(l)$ randomly according to a given time-invariant distribution. That is, for every $l \in \mathcal{N}_u$ a probability measure

$$\nu^l(B) = \int_B p^l(\psi)\mu^m(d\psi) \quad \text{for } B \in \mathcal{B}(\mathcal{Q}_u(l)) \tag{11}$$

is given which is the same for all k.

Under the assumption that the random vectors $x(0), u(0), u(1), \ldots$ are independent of each other, for each $l \in \mathcal{N}_u$ the following operator can be defined:

Definition 4. *[6] The operator $\hat{P}^l : \mathcal{M} \to \mathcal{M}$ associated with the system (10) for given measure ν^l is defined by*

$$\hat{P}^l\mu(A) = \int_\Omega \left\{ \int_\Psi 1_A(f(\omega, \psi))\nu^l(d\psi) \right\} \mu(d\omega) \tag{12}$$

with $\mu \in \mathcal{M}$ and $A \in \mathcal{B}(\Omega)$. This operator is called Foias operator.

Remark. In controlled systems the independence assumption concerning the initial states and the inputs is usually not satisfied. It has not yet been investigated whether the Foias operator can be extended avoiding the use of a product of measures as in eqn. (12) requiring the independence assumption.

By means of the Foias operator the non-autonomous quantised system with initial state measure $\mu_0(A) = \int_A p_0(\omega)\mu^n(d\omega)$ is described by

$$\mu_{k+1}(A) = \hat{P}^{[u(k)]}\mu_k(A), \quad \mu_k(A) = \int_A p(\omega, k)\mu^n(d\omega) \tag{13}$$

$$\mathbf{Prob}([x(k)] \,|\, p_0(x), [u(0)], \ldots, [u(k)]) = D_N p(x, k) \,, \tag{14}$$

for any $A \in \mathcal{B}(\Omega)$ assuming that the transformation $f(x, u)$ is such that all measures obtained by application of eqn. (13) are absolute continuous to the Borel measure μ^n. According to eqns. (13), (14) the non-autonomous quantised system is represented by the set of Foias operators $\hat{P}^{[u]}$ obtained for $[u] \in \mathcal{N}_u$ each depending on the corresponding measure $\nu^{[u]}$ introduced by the injector and the discretiser D_N associated with the quantiser.

The difficulty is that the representation of the non-autonomous system (13)–(14) is described by a transformation of measures rather than by a transformation of densities. The Foias operator can be transformed into an operator on densities similar to the FPO in eqn. (3) but, in contrast to the FPO, this representation still depends upon the given densities.

3 Approximate Representation of Quantised Systems

3.1 Approximation of the FPO

In the previous section the FPO and the Foias operator as representations of the quantised system were introduced. However, a closed form of the FPO as given in the examples in Sections 2.3 and 2.4 can only be found for simple systems, and the Foias operator cannot even for simple systems be given explicitly.

Hence, if the FPO should be used to solve process supervision tasks, an approximation of the FPO is needed that can be found explicitly for arbitrary transformation f. The approximation presented in this section is based on the restriction that the FPO should not be applicable to all L^1 functions but only to those which can be represented by a finite sum of indicator functions (so-called simple functions). More precisely, as before, the measure space $(\Omega, \mathcal{B}(\Omega), \mu^n)$, $\Omega \subset \mathbb{R}^n$ is considered with a partition of Ω into N regions $\mathcal{Q}_x(1), \ldots, \mathcal{Q}_x(N)$ and the subset Δ_N of all L^1 functions as in eqn. (4) is used. In order to apply the FPO to the quantised system, this partition is set to the partition introduced by the quantiser (cf. Section 2.4).

Definition 5. *The* quantised Frobenius-Perron operator *with respect to f is defined as the operator $P_N : \Delta_N \to \Delta_N$ with:*

$$P_N b^j(x) = \sum_{i=1}^{N} \text{Prob}(i|j) \cdot b^i(x) , \quad \text{Prob}(i|j) = \frac{\mu^n(f^{-1}(\mathcal{Q}_x(i)) \cap \mathcal{Q}_x(j))}{\mu^n(\mathcal{Q}_x(j))} . \quad (15)$$

The quantised FPO has been introduced in [13] and is also called Ulam's piecewise constant approximation of the FPO. The conditional probabilities $\text{Prob}(i|j)$ define a Markov chain with the state set $\{1, \ldots N\}$ or, in terms of qualitative modelling, an autonomous stochastic automaton (cf. [9], Section 4.2).

Figure 3 explains the meaning of eqn. (15). The conditional probability $\text{Prob}(i|j)$ describes the probability that the successor state of the continuous-variable system (1) is in $\mathcal{Q}_x(i)$ if it is known that the system state is currently in $\mathcal{Q}_x(j)$. It is given by the ratio between the measures of the set $f^{-1}(\mathcal{Q}_x(i)) \cap \mathcal{Q}_x(j)$ and of the entire region $\mathcal{Q}_x(j)$.

The following theorem describes the relation between the FPO and the quantised FPO using the projector Q_N of Definition 2.

Theorem 1. *[1] For all $p(x) \in \Delta_N$ the relation $P_N p(x) = Q_N P p(x)$ holds.*

According to this theorem, the map $P_N p(x)$ of any function $p(x) \in \Delta_N$ determined with the quantised FPO P_N is the same as the projection of the precise map $P p(x)$ by the continuous FPO to Δ_N. Note that the theorem only holds in terms of the projection to Δ_N. Hence, the theorem means that the weights of the $b^i(x)$ determined by P_N are the same as the λ_i obtained by application of eqn. (5) to $P p(x)$.

Theorem 2. *[7] For all $p(x) \in \Delta_N$ the relation $P_N p(x) \xrightarrow[N \to \infty]{} P p(x)$ holds.*

This important result means that for increasingly finer partition the quantised FPO converges to the FPO, for any transformation f.

3.2   Extension to Non-autonomous Systems

As before the measure spaces $(\Omega, \mathcal{B}(\Omega), \mu^n)$ with $\Omega \subset \mathbb{R}^n$ and $(\Psi, \mathcal{B}(\Psi), \mu^m)$ with $\Psi \subset \mathbb{R}^m$ are considered. In addition to the partition introduced in the previous section, further partitions of each $\mathcal{Q}_u^l$ could be introduced to approximate the Foias operators. Instead, as the input set Ψ is already partitioned, each input distribution $p^l(\boldsymbol{u})$ as introduced in eqn. (11) is approximated by a single indicator function using the projector of Definition 2:

$$Q_1 p^l(\boldsymbol{u}) = \frac{\int_{\mathcal{Q}_u(l)} p^l(\psi) \mu^m(d\psi)}{\mu^m(\mathcal{Q}_u(l))} = \frac{1_{\mathcal{Q}_u(l)}}{\mu^m(\mathcal{Q}_u(l))} \; .$$

After partitioning the state set Ω as before the following operator can be defined:

Definition 6. *The* quantised Foias operator *with respect to the transformation* $\boldsymbol{f}$ *is defined as the operator* $P_N^l : \Delta_N \to \Delta_N$ *with:*

$$P_N^l b^j(\boldsymbol{x}) = \sum_{i=1}^{N} Prob(i|j,l) \cdot b^i(\boldsymbol{x}), \; Prob(i|j,l) = \frac{\mu^{n+m}(\boldsymbol{f}^{-1}(\mathcal{Q}_x(i)) \cap \mathcal{Q}_{xu}(j,l))}{\mu^{n+m}(\mathcal{Q}_{xu}(j,l))}$$

$$\tag{16}$$

and $\mathcal{Q}_{xu}(j,l) := \mathcal{Q}_x(j) \times \mathcal{Q}_u(l)$.

Figure 3 can also be used to explain the quantised Foias operator. $\boldsymbol{f}^{-1}(\mathcal{Q}_x(i))$ defines a set of states and inputs in the compound state and input set $\Omega \times \Psi$. Eqn. (16) is the relation of the measures of the subset of $\boldsymbol{f}^{-1}(\mathcal{Q}_x(i))$ lying in $\mathcal{Q}_{xu}(j,l)$ and the entire region $\mathcal{Q}_{xu}(j,l)$.

Theorems 1 and 2 seem to hold for the quantised Foias operator, although this has not yet been proved in literature.

4   Qualitative Modelling

4.1   Modelling Aim

The methods described in the previous section were developed in the literature on nonlinear, especially chaotic systems. Hence, they were applied with partitions as fine as necessary for obtaining numerically precise solutions for stationary densities etc. (cf. e.g. [3], [12]).

In contrast to this, the aim of this paper is to obtain a model for process supervision purposes while leaving the partition as rough as possible or by using partitions that are given by measurement devices. Nonetheless, the models used in this section turn out to be identical to the quantised FPO for autonomous systems or to the set of quantised Foias operators for non-autonomous systems. Hence, the results of the previous sections show the connection between the qualitative modelling approach and nonlinear systems theory though the field of application is completely different. The main difference is that the application to process supervision requires completeness:

Definition 7. *Denote the variable of the qualitative model corresponding to* $[\boldsymbol{x}(k)]$ *by* $z(k)$. *A qualitative model is* complete *if*

$$\mathbf{Prob}([\boldsymbol{x}(k)] \mid p_0(\boldsymbol{x}), [\boldsymbol{u}(0)], ..., [\boldsymbol{u}(k)]) > 0$$
$$\Rightarrow \quad \mathbf{Prob}(z(k) \mid p_0(\boldsymbol{x}), [\boldsymbol{u}(0)], ..., [\boldsymbol{u}(k)]) > 0 \tag{17}$$

holds for any input symbol sequence and for any initial density $p_0(\boldsymbol{x})$.

4.2   Qualitative Model of the Quantised System

A stochastic automaton $\mathcal{S}(\mathcal{N}_z, \mathcal{N}_v, F, \boldsymbol{p}_z(0))$ is used as qualitative model of the system (13)–(14). The set $\mathcal{N}_z = \{1, \ldots, N\}$ is the finite set of automaton states, $\mathcal{N}_v = \{1, \ldots, M\}$ the set of input symbols, and $\boldsymbol{p}_z(0) \in \mathcal{W}^N$ the initial state probability distribution. The transition relation F

$$F : \mathcal{N}_z \times \mathcal{N}_z \times \mathcal{N}_v \rightarrow [0,\ 1], \quad F(z', z, v) = \mathrm{Prob}(z'|z, v)$$

describes the conditional probability that the automaton state changes from z to the successor state z' for input symbol v.

In order to approximate the quantised system, the automaton $\mathcal{S}$ is used with $\mathcal{N}_z = \mathcal{N}_x$ and $\mathcal{N}_v = \mathcal{N}_u$. The stochastic automaton defines the set of operators $\tilde{P}^v : \mathcal{W}^N \rightarrow \mathcal{W}^N$ given by

$$\tilde{P}^v \boldsymbol{p} = \sum_{z=1}^{N} (\tilde{p}^z P^v \boldsymbol{\delta}^z), \quad \text{with} \quad \tilde{P}^v \boldsymbol{\delta}^z = \sum_{z'=1}^{N} F(z', z, v) \cdot \boldsymbol{\delta}^{z'}, \tag{18}$$

where $\boldsymbol{\delta}^z \in \mathcal{W}^N$ denotes the unit vector $(0 \ldots 1 \ldots 0)$ whose z-th element is equal to one, and p^z the z-th component of the vector $\boldsymbol{p} \in \mathcal{W}^N$.

The set of all quantised states i that can be reached by the quantised system from the quantised state j for the quantised input l is denoted by

$$\mathcal{T}_{\mathrm{QS}}(j, l) = \{i \ : \ \mathrm{Prob}(i|j, l) > 0\} \tag{19}$$

with $\mathrm{Prob}(i|j, l)$ defined by eqn. (16). Similarly, $\mathcal{T}_F(z, v)$ denotes the set of states reached from automaton state z for input v: $\mathcal{T}_F(z, v) = \{z' \ : \ F(z', z, v) > 0\}$.

Definition 8. *A stochastic automaton* $\mathcal{S}(\mathcal{N}_z, \mathcal{N}_v, F, \boldsymbol{p}_z(0))$ *is called* sound *with respect to a given quantised system, if the following relations hold:*

$$\mathcal{T}_F(z, v) \supseteq \mathcal{T}_{\mathrm{QS}}(j = z, l = v) \qquad \forall z \in \mathcal{N}_z, \ v \in \mathcal{N}_v \tag{20}$$
$$D_N p_0(\boldsymbol{x}) > 0 \ \Rightarrow \ \boldsymbol{p}_z(0) > 0 \quad \textit{(componentwise)} \tag{21}$$

Theorem 3. *A stochastic automaton is a complete model of the quantised system if and only if it is sound.*

Proof. The necessity is obvious because if the automaton is not sound there is at least one transition occurring in the quantised system that cannot occur in the automaton, which violates the completeness (17) for $k = 1$. The proof that soundness is sufficient is given in [8].   □

According to this result, eqns. (13)-(14) representing the non-autonomous quantised system can be approximated by the simpler equations

$$\boldsymbol{p}_z(k+1) = \tilde{P}^{[\boldsymbol{u}(k)]}\boldsymbol{p}_z(k) \tag{22}$$

$$\mathbf{Prob}(z(k) \,|\, p_0(\boldsymbol{x}), [\boldsymbol{u}(0)], ..., [\boldsymbol{u}(k)]) = \boldsymbol{p}_k^z \tag{23}$$

where the operators $\tilde{P}^{[\boldsymbol{u}]}$ contains a transition relation F fulfilling condition (20), and $\boldsymbol{p}_0^z$ fulfils condition (21). Eqns. (22) and (23) approximate the quantised system and fulfil the modelling aim (17).

Remark. The best sound model is obtained, if the transition relation is set according to the transition probabilities of the quantised Foias operator

$$F^*(z', z, v) = \frac{\mu^{n+m}(\boldsymbol{f}^{-1}(\mathcal{Q}_x(z')) \cap \mathcal{Q}_{xu}(z, v))}{\mu^{n+m}(\mathcal{Q}_{xu}(z, v))} \tag{24}$$

(cf. eqn. (16)) and, if the initial probability distribution $\boldsymbol{p}_0^z = D_N p_0(\boldsymbol{x})$ is used. F^* is the best transition relation, i.e. it contains the smallest possible set of transitions necessary for soundness.

5   Sound Abstraction of Qualitative Models

Whereas it is easy to fulfil the soundness condition (21) it is difficult to practically compute a transition relation F for given quantised system such that condition (20) is satisfied. In this section a method for computing F is presented that guarantees soundness and converges to F^* for increasing approximation accuracy. Furthermore it is explained why the "classical" point mapping does not guarantee that the resulting models are sound and, hence, cannot be used to compute qualitative models for process supervision.

Both methods presented in this section use a "forward" way to determine the transition probabilities (16):

$$\mathrm{Prob}(i|j, l) = \frac{\mu^{n+m}(\{(\boldsymbol{x}, \boldsymbol{u}) \in \mathcal{Q}_{xu}(j, l) \,:\, \boldsymbol{f}(\boldsymbol{x}, \boldsymbol{u}) \in \mathcal{Q}_x(i)\})}{\mu^{n+m}(\mathcal{Q}_{xu}(j, l))} \,.$$

The set described in the numerator of this fraction is the same as in eqn. (16) but it is described by using the transformation $\boldsymbol{f}(\boldsymbol{x}, \boldsymbol{u})$ instead of its inverse.

5.1   Point-Based Cell-to-Cell Mapping

The classical method to compute transition probabilities from one cell of a partitioned space to another is point mapping [4]. It is widely used for the analysis of nonlinear dynamical systems and originally formulated only for autonomous systems. In the following the method is briefly summarised and applied to compute an estimate of the transition relation.

The main idea is to take a selection of points of each region $\mathcal{Q}_{xu}(j, l)$

$$\tilde{\mathcal{Q}}_{xu}(j, l) = \{(\boldsymbol{x}_1, \boldsymbol{u}_1), (\boldsymbol{x}_2, \boldsymbol{u}_2), ..., (\boldsymbol{x}_K, \boldsymbol{u}_K)\},$$
$$\text{with} \quad (\boldsymbol{x}_\kappa, \boldsymbol{u}_\kappa) \in \mathcal{Q}_{xu}(j, l), \kappa = 1, ..., K \,,$$

such that they are uniformly distributed over $\mathcal{Q}_{xu}(j,l)$. For each point $(\boldsymbol{x}_\kappa, \boldsymbol{u}_\kappa)$ of $\tilde{\mathcal{Q}}_{xu}(j,l)$ eqn. (10) is used to construct the map $\boldsymbol{f}(\boldsymbol{x}_\kappa, \boldsymbol{u}_\kappa)$. The partition of Ω is used to determine the successor state i. Doing this for all points $\kappa = 1, \ldots, K$ the sets

$$\tilde{\mathcal{Q}}_{xu}(i,j,l) = \{(\boldsymbol{x}, \boldsymbol{u}) \mid (\boldsymbol{x}, \boldsymbol{u}) \in \tilde{\mathcal{Q}}_{xu}(j,l), \boldsymbol{f}(\boldsymbol{x}, \boldsymbol{u}) \in \mathcal{Q}_x(i)\}, \quad i = 1, \ldots, N \quad (25)$$

can be constructed. Then the transition relation is approximated by

$$F^-(z', z, v) = \frac{\Lambda(\tilde{\mathcal{Q}}_{xu}(z', z, v))}{\Lambda(\tilde{\mathcal{Q}}_{xu}(z, v))}, \quad i = 1, \ldots, N$$

where $\Lambda(\cdot)$ denotes the number of points contained in the set and F^- denotes the obtained transition relation. According to the law of large numbers this estimate of the transition probabilities converges to F^* for $K \to \infty$.

This method can directly be implemented on a computer. As the sets $\tilde{\mathcal{Q}}_{xu}(j,l)$ are finite and, therefore, a finite number of mappings with eqn. (10) leads to $\tilde{\mathcal{Q}}_{xu}(i,j,l)$, all sets can be stored in a computer memory. Furthermore the implementation is very simple as only partition and mapping functions are required. However, the problem of point mapping is that the soundness of the obtained model cannot be guaranteed. More precisely, for F^- the relation

$$\mathcal{T}_{F^-}(z, v) \subseteq \mathcal{T}_{F^*}(z, v) \quad \forall \, (z, v) \in \mathcal{N}_z \times \mathcal{N}_v \quad (26)$$

rather than the soundness condition (20) holds. This means that only in the ideal case that $\mathcal{T}_{F^-}(z, v) = \mathcal{T}_{F^*}(z, v)$ holds for all z, v a complete model is obtained. Practically the number of points to be mapped must be so high that with reasonable computational effort even for simple systems only an incomplete model with $\mathcal{T}_{F^-}(z, v) \subset \mathcal{T}_{F^*}(z, v)$ can be obtained.

5.2   Hyperbox Cell-to-Cell Mapping

In this section a method is presented that guarantees soundness. It is assumed that $\boldsymbol{f}$ satisfies a Lipschitz condition, i.e. a number $\phi \in \mathbb{R}^+$ exists such that

$$||(\boldsymbol{f}(\boldsymbol{x}_1, \boldsymbol{u}_1) - \boldsymbol{f}(\boldsymbol{x}_2, \boldsymbol{u}_2))||_\infty \leq \phi \cdot \left\| \begin{pmatrix} \boldsymbol{x}_1 - \boldsymbol{x}_2 \\ \boldsymbol{u}_1 - \boldsymbol{u}_2 \end{pmatrix} \right\|_\infty \quad (27)$$

holds where the infinity norm $|| \cdot ||_\infty$ is used. For simplicity reasons it is assumed that all partitions are orthogonal resulting in hyperboxes $\mathcal{Q}_x$ and $\mathcal{Q}_u$ (cf. Figure 4).

The idea will be described by using Figure 4. On the left–hand side of the figure the state-input-space $\Omega \times \Psi$ is shown. The dashed lines symbolise the partition bounds and the cell $\mathcal{Q}_{xu}(j,l)$ to be mapped, depicted in light gray, is assumed to be quadratic with a sidelength of $2r^0$. Initially only the black centre point $(\boldsymbol{x}^0, \boldsymbol{u}^0)$ is positioned used. The cell can be described by:

$$\mathcal{Q}_{xu}(j,l) = \{(\boldsymbol{x}, \boldsymbol{u}) \mid ||(\boldsymbol{x}, \boldsymbol{u}) - (\boldsymbol{x}^0, \boldsymbol{u}^0)||_\infty \leq r^0\} . \quad (28)$$

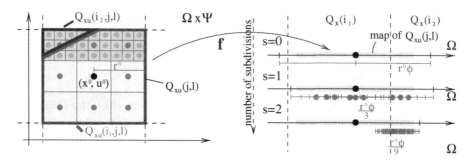

Fig. 4. Hyperbox mapping.

The point $(\boldsymbol{x}^0, \boldsymbol{u}^0)$ is mapped to the state-space Ω by eqn. (10) resulting in the black point $\boldsymbol{f}(\boldsymbol{x}^0, \boldsymbol{u}^0)$ depicted on the right-hand side of Figure 4 (for $s = 0$). Due to the Lipschitz constraint (27) the map of the box $\mathcal{Q}_{xu}(j, l)$ can be overapproximated by the box

$$\mathcal{Q}_{x'}^{\text{approx}} = \{\boldsymbol{x} \mid ||\boldsymbol{x} - \boldsymbol{f}(\boldsymbol{x}^0, \boldsymbol{u}^0)||_\infty \leq r^0 \cdot \phi\}\,.$$

which degenerates to an interval in Figure 4. If, as in the figure the set $\mathcal{Q}_{x'}^{\text{approx}}$ overlaps with more than one partition of Ω, it is not known whether this overlap results from the overapproximation of the map of $\mathcal{Q}_{xu}$. Therefore, the box in the state-input-space $\Omega \times \Psi$ is subdivided into $3^{n+m} = 9$ boxes. The additional grey points are mapped, resulting in grey intervals in Figure 4, for $s = 1$ with length $r^0 \phi/3$. A corner check reveals whether or not the boxes lie completely within one region i of the partitioned state set. Mapped boxes that cover more than one partition region of Ω have to be further subdivided in the state-input-space. The subdivision can be stopped when the size of the mapped approximation boxes with radius $r^0 \phi/3^s$ became smaller than the partition of Ω, where s is the number of subdivisions. Then the quantisation of the corners of the mapped boxes cover all possible successor states i that could possibly be reached by the map of $\mathcal{Q}_{xu}(j, l)$. This guarantees soundness. The subdivision can also be continued to further increase the accuracy of the approximation. In Figure 4 the subdivision can be stopped at $s = 1$ to guarantee soundness. However it is continued to determine the areas of $\mathcal{Q}_{xu}(i_1, j, l)$ and $\mathcal{Q}_{xu}(i_2, j, l)$ more precisely.

Theorem 4. *The hyperbox cell-to-cell mapping yields a sound automaton. The estimate of the transition probabilities converges to $F^*(z', z, v)$ for all z', z, v for increasing number of subdivisions.*

Due to space limitations the method cannot be formally introduced and proved in this paper. However, the soundness becomes clear from the Lipschitz condition, as the map of each box is conservatively approximated and the whole partition region $\mathcal{Q}_{xu}(j, l)$ of the state-input space is covered by boxes. Figure 4 shows that the relevant Borel measures in the state-input-space are approximated with increasing accuracy if more and more subdivisions of the boxes are used. Simultaneously the estimate of the transition probabilities converges to the corresponding value of F^*.

6   Conclusions

It has been shown that quantised systems can be represented by the Frobenius-Perron operator for autonomous or the Foias operator for non-autonomous systems. As a consequence, results of the FPO theory can be applied to quantised systems. It is shown that a finite approximation of the FPO is identical to the abstraction of the quantised system in form of a stochastic automaton. With this it has been shown that the abstraction converges to the FPO with finer quantisation. Furthermore, methods have been presented to compute abstractions of the quantised system. A hyperbox cell mapping method has been presented to guarantee the completeness of the abstraction.

References

1. Ding, J., A. Zhou: Finite approximations of Frobenius-Perron operators. A solution of Ulam's conjecture to multi-dimensional transformations. Physica D **92** (1996) 61–68
2. Förstner, D., J. Lunze: A discrete-event abstraction of continuous-variable systems with asynchronous inputs. Proc. 3rd IMACS Symposium on Math. Mod., Vienna (2000) 449-452
3. Guder, R., E. Kreuzer: Using generalized cell mapping to approximate invariant measures on compact manifolds. Int. J. of Bifurcation and Chaos **7** (1997) 2487-2499
4. Hsu, C.S.: Cell-to-cell mapping. Springer-Verlag, New York (1987)
5. Krogh, B.H., A. Chutinan: Hybrid systems: modelling and supervisory control. Advances in Control, Springer-Verlag, London (1999) 227-246
6. Lasota, A., M.C. Mackey: Chaos, fractals, and noise. Springer-Verlag, New York (1994)
7. Li, T.Y.: Finite approximation of the Frobenius-Perron operator. A solution to Ulam's conjecture. J. Approx. Theory **17** (1976) 177–186
8. Lunze, J., B. Nixdorf, J. Schröder: A unified approach to the representation of discrete-time and discrete-event quantised systems. Proc. European Control Conf., Karlsruhe (1999)
9. Lunze, J.: Qualitative modelling of linear dynamical systems with quantised state measurements. Automatica **30** (1994) 417–432
10. Preisig, H. A., M. J. H. Pijpers, M. Weiss: A discrete modelling procedure for continuous processes based on state–discretisation. Proc. 2nd IMACS Symposium on Math. Mod., Vienna (1997) 189–194
11. Raisch, J.: Nondeterministic automata as approximations for continuous systems – an approach with an adjustable degree of accuracy. Proc. 2nd IMACS Symposium on Math. Mod., Vienna (1997) 195–202
12. Schwarz, W., M. Götz, K. Kelber, A. Abel, T. Falk, F. Dachselt: Statistical analysis and design of chaotic systems. Technical Report, TU-Dresden (2000)
13. Ulam, S.M.: A collection of mathematical problems. Interscience, New York, (1960)

Semi-decidable Synthesis for Triangular Hybrid Systems

Omid Shakernia[1], George J. Pappas[2], and Shankar Sastry[1]

[1] Department of EECS, University of California at Berkeley, Berkeley, CA 94704
{omids,sastry}@eecs.berkeley.edu
[2] Department of EE & CIS, University of Pennsylvania, Philadelphia, PA 19104
pappasg@ee.upenn.edu

Abstract. The algorithmic design of least restrictive controllers for hybrid systems that satisfy reachability specifications has received much attention recently. Despite the importance of algorithmic approaches to controller design for hybrid systems, results that guarantee termination of the algorithms have been limited. In this paper, we extend recent decidability results on controller synthesis for classes of linear hybrid systems to semi-decision procedures for *triangular hybrid systems* which can be used to model nonholonomic systems after a transformation. Our results are then applied to verification of a conflict resolution maneuver from air traffic control.

1 Introduction

Safety criticality in motivating applications [13] of hybrid systems has resulted in much research on computing reachable sets for hybrid systems in order to ensure that these systems avoid unsafe regions of the state space [2,3,4]. Furthermore, much research has recently focused on controller synthesis of hybrid systems where the safety property is ensured by design [1,6,7,12].

The complexity of the motivating applications makes algorithmic approaches to controller synthesis very desirable, whenever possible. However, termination guarantees for algorithmic approaches to synthesis have been limited. In particular, the game theoretic framework for controller synthesis introduced in [6] was only recently shown to result in decision procedures for various classes of linear systems [9], and semi-decision procedures for classes of linear hybrid systems [10].

In this paper, we proceed along the same spirit of [9,10] but we increase the complexity of the continuous dynamics to capture *triangular hybrid systems*, which are defined as hybrid control systems whose continuous dynamics in each discrete state are nonlinear with a triangular structure. Triangular nonlinear systems is a rich class of nonlinear systems that capture the so-called *chained systems*, which can be used to model nonholonomic systems after a state transformation. Nonholonomic systems have been very useful kinematic models of aircraft, robots, space robots, etc [5]. In this paper, we consider the following controller synthesis problem: *Given a triangular hybrid system, compute the maximal control invariant set of initial conditions and least restrictive controller*

M.D. Di Benedetto, A. Sangiovanni-Vincentelli (Eds.): HSCC 2001, LNCS 2034, pp. 487–500, 2001.
© Springer-Verlag Berlin Heidelberg 2001

such that for all disturbances the state will avoid an unsafe set. In particular, we present a semi-decision procedure which, if it terminates, exactly solves the above problem.

The solution of the above problem depends critically on state of the art techniques from controller synthesis of hybrid systems. In particular, we adopt the general framework for controller synthesis of nonlinear hybrid systems [6], while we follow in spirit the approach taken in [9]. In particular, we focus on continuous games for triangular nonlinear systems. Application of the maximum principle leads to bang-bang optimal controls and a triangular structure in the co-state equations. Rather than solving the Hamilton-Jacobi partial differential equations for reachability computations, we abstract the bang-bang nature of the optimal control to a hybrid system. The piece-wise constant nature of the optimal inputs and disturbances, and the triangular structure of the state and co-state dynamics leads to polynomial flows for the states and co-states. This allows us to use quantifier elimination in each discrete state of the abstracted game to perform reachability computations. The above sequence of steps results in a semi-decision procedure for controller synthesis for triangular hybrid systems. However, unlike classes of linear systems where the number of switchings is uniformly finite [9], no such guarantee exists for triangular systems, making very difficult any claims for a decision procedure.

The structure of this paper is as follows: In Section 2 we review the synthesis framework of [6]. In Section 3 we present a semi-decision procedure for reach set computation in triangular nonlinear systems, which is lifted in Section 4 to triangular hybrid systems. These results are then applied in Section 5 to a verification of a conflict resolution maneuver from air traffic control.

2   Controller Synthesis for Nonlinear Hybrid Systems

In this section we review the framework for computing the maximum controlled invariant safe set for general nonlinear hybrid systems [6,12].

Definition 1 (Hybrid system).
A hybrid system H is a collection (X, V, I, f, E, ϕ), with:

- **State and input variables:** *X and V are disjoint collections of state and input variables. We assume that $X = X_D \cup X_C$ and $V = V_D \cup V_C$, where X_C and V_C contain continuous, and X_D and V_D discrete variables. We refer to valuations $x \in \mathbf{X}$ and $v \in \mathbf{V}$ as the state and the input of the hybrid system.*
- **Initial states:** *$I \subseteq \mathbf{X}$ is a set of initial valuations of the state variables.*
- **Continuous evolution:** *$f : \mathbf{X} \times \mathbf{V} \to T\mathbf{X_C}$ is a vector field.*
- **Discrete transitions:** *$E \subseteq \mathbf{X} \times \mathbf{V} \times \mathbf{X}$ is a set of discrete transitions.*
- **Admissible inputs:** *$\phi : \mathbf{X} \to 2^{\mathbf{V}}$ gives the set of admissible inputs at a given state $x \in \mathbf{X}$.*

It is customary to use the notation $(q, x) = (x|_{X_D}, x|_{X_C}) \in \mathbf{X}$. The meaning of the variable x will be clear from the context.

For any input $v = (u, d) \in \mathbf{V}$, define the set:

$$Inv(v) \triangleq \{x \in \mathbf{X} \mid v \in \phi(x) \land (x, v, x) \in E\}.$$

For a state $x \in \mathbf{X}$ and input $v = (u, d)$, define:

$$Next(x, v) \triangleq \begin{cases} \{y \in \mathbf{X} \mid (x, v, y) \in E\} & \text{if } v \in \phi(x) \\ \emptyset & \text{if } v \notin \phi(x). \end{cases}$$

$Inv(v)$ is the set of states from which continuous evolution is possible under input v, while $Next(x, v)$ is the set of states that can be reached from x under input v through a discrete transition. For any set $K \subseteq \mathbf{X}$ and input $v = (u, d)$ the *successor* of K under v is given by $Next(K, v) = \bigcup_{x \in K} Next(x, v)$.

For any set $K \subseteq \mathbf{X}$ define the *controllable predecessor* of K, $Pre_u(K)$, and the *uncontrollable predecessor* of K, $Pre_d(K)$, by:

$$Pre_u(K) \triangleq \{x \in \mathbf{X} \mid \exists u \in \mathbf{U} \ \forall d \in \mathbf{D} \ x \notin Inv(v) \land \ Next(K, v) \subseteq K\} \cap K,$$
$$Pre_d(K) \triangleq \{x \in \mathbf{X} \mid \forall u \in \mathbf{U} \ \exists d \in \mathbf{D} \ Next(K, v) \cap K^c \neq \emptyset\} \cup K^c.$$

where $v = (u, d)$. $Pre_u(K)$ contains all states in K for which u can force a transition back into K. $Pre_d(K)$ contains all states outside K together with those states for which it is possible to transition outside K regardless of the action of u. Whereas Pre_u and Pre_d capture information about regions of the state space that can be reached through discrete transitions of the system, the following operator [12] captures continuous reachability information.

Definition 2 (Reach-Avoid). *Given a hybrid system H and disjoint sets K, $G \subseteq \mathbf{X}$, the operator $Reach : 2^{\mathbf{X}} \times 2^{\mathbf{X}} \to 2^{\mathbf{X}}$ is defined as:*

$$Reach(K, G) \triangleq \{x_0 \mid \forall u \in \mathcal{U} \exists d \in \mathcal{D} \exists t \geq 0 : x(t) \in K \land \forall s \in [0, t] \ x(s) \notin G\},$$

were $\mathcal{U}, \mathcal{D}$ denote the set of piecewise continuous functions from the $\mathbb{R}$ to $\mathbf{U}, \mathbf{D}$ respectively, and $x(\cdot)$ is the unique state trajectory starting from initial condition $x(0) = x_0$ under the input (u, d).

The set $Reach(K, G)$ contains the states from which for all controls there exists a disturbance such that the state trajectory can be driven to K while avoiding the escape set G. The following algorithm uses the *Reach* operator to compute the maximal controlled invariant subset of F (see [12]).

Algorithm 1 (Maximum Controlled Invariant Safe Set)
initialize
$\quad W^0 = F; \quad W^{-1} = \emptyset; \quad i = 0$
while $W^i \neq W^{i-1}$
$\quad\quad W^{i-1} = W^i \setminus Reach(Pre_d(W^i), Pre_u(W^i))$
$\quad\quad i = i - 1$
end while
$W^* := W^i$
end

Algorithm 1 iteratively removes from the safe set F all states for which there is a disturbance which either through continuous evolution or discrete transition can bring the system outside F regardless of the control action. In order to implement Algorithm 1, one needs to encode sets of states, perform set intersection, union, test for emptiness, and *exactly* compute $Reach(\cdot, \cdot)$. If all these conditions hold for a class of systems, then the problem is *semi-decidable* for that class of systems. Even though there is no *guarantee* of termination, if the algorithm terminates, then it exactly computes the unique maximal controlled invariant set W^*. If in addition, Algorithm 1 is guaranteed to terminate after a finite number of iterations for a class of systems, then we say the problem is *decidable* for that class.

The main difficulty in the implementation of Algorithm 1 is the computation of the *Reach* operator. For general nonlinear hybrid systems, the computation of *Reach* relies on the numerical solution of a pair of coupled Hamilton-Jacobi partial differential equations [7,12]. *In this paper, we show that for a certain class of nonlinear hybrid systems with triangular continuous dynamics each step of Algorithm 1 is symbolically computable.* This class is rich enough to capture hybrid systems with chained nonlinear dynamics, which model nonholonomic kinematics for aircraft, cars, and robots.

3   Computing Safe Sets for Triangular Nonlinear Systems

In this section, we address the problem of computing maximal controlled invariant safe sets for a class of nonlinear control systems subject to disturbances. The computation of maximal safe sets is a fundamental step in the least restrictive controller synthesis problem [6]. In this section, we extend the methodology of symbolic controller synthesis for classes linear systems described in [9] to a class of nonlinear systems.

For a differential game $\dot{x} = f(x, u, d)$ between inputs $u \in U \subset \mathbb{R}^{n_u}$ and disturbances $d \in D \subset \mathbb{R}^{n_d}$, the solution to the controller synthesis problem requires the computation of the set of initial states for which there exists a disturbance that can eventually drive the system to some unsafe set regardless of the actions of the control. Therefore the controller synthesis problem for continuous time system requires the computation of the continuous system version of the Reach-Avoid set.

Definition 3 (Reach-Avoid). *Given a differential game* $\dot{x} = f(x, u, d)$ *and disjoint sets* $K, G \subseteq \mathbb{R}^n$, *the operator Reach* $: 2^{\mathbb{R}^n} \times 2^{\mathbb{R}^n} \to 2^{\mathbb{R}^n}$ *is defined as:*

$$Reach(K, G) \triangleq \{x_0 \mid \forall u \in \mathcal{U} \; \exists d \in \mathcal{D} \; \exists t \geq 0 \; : \; x(t) \in K \wedge \forall s \in [0, t] \; x(s) \notin G\},$$

where $\mathcal{U}$, $\mathcal{D}$ *denote the set of piecewise continuous functions from the* $\mathbb{R}$ *to* U, D *respectively, and* $x(\cdot)$ *is the unique state trajectory of* $\dot{x} = f(x, u, d)$ *starting from initial condition* $x(0) = x_0$ *under the input* (u, d).

The set $Reach(K, G)$, which is graphically depicted in Figure 1, contains the states from which for all controls there exists a disturbance such that the state

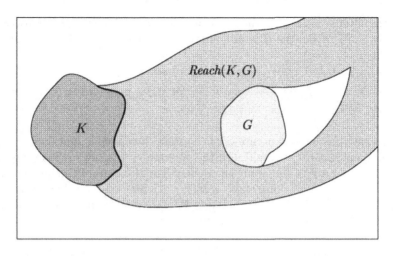

Fig. 1. Showing a graphical depiction of $Reach(K, G)$.

trajectory can be driven to K while avoiding the escape set G. It was shown recently that the computation of $Reach$ is decidable for certain classes of linear systems [10]. Here we extend the result to a class of nonlinear systems. As a motivating example, consider the following nonlinear system in so-called *chain form*:

$$
\begin{aligned}
\dot{x}_j^0 &= u_j & j &= 1, \ldots, m \\
\dot{x}_{ij}^1 &= x_i^0 u_j & j &= 1, \ldots, m \text{ and } i < j \\
\dot{x}_{ij}^k &= x_{ij}^{k-1} u_j & j &= 1, \ldots, m \text{ and } i < j \text{ and } k = 2, \ldots, n_j.
\end{aligned}
\tag{1}
$$

Control systems of the class shown in equation (1) are quite important because they can be used to model many types of nonholonomic and under-actuated systems including unicycles, cars, multi-steering trucks with N-trailers, space robots, etc. [8]. We now apply the symbolic controller synthesis methodology described in [9,10] to this chain form system.

3.1   Computation of Optimal Control

For the chain form system (1), suppose we wish to compute the set of initial conditions $W \subset \mathbb{R}^n$ for which there exists a control $u(\cdot)$, constrained to a compact rectangular feasible control set $U \subset \mathbb{R}^m$, that can steer the state to the goal $G \subset \mathbb{R}^n$ while avoiding states $B \subset \mathbb{R}^n$. This problem is closely related to the problem of nonholonomic motion planning in the presence of obstacles [5] and is equivalent to computing $W = Reach(G, B)$.

To solve the reachability problem, we first introduce the *co-state* $p \in \mathbb{R}^n$ and construct the Hamiltonian:

$$
H(x, p, u) = p^T f(x, u) = \sum_{j=1}^m \left(p_j^0 + \sum_{i=1}^{j-1} \left(p_{ij}^1 x_i^0 + \sum_{k=2}^{n_j} p_{ij}^k x_{ij}^{k-1} \right) \right) u_j.
$$

The Hamiltonian satisfies the state and co-state differential equations $\dot{x} = \frac{\partial H}{\partial p}$, $\dot{p} = -\frac{\partial H}{\partial x}$. From the Hamiltonian, we compute the co-state dynamics:

$$\dot{p}_{ij}^{n_j} = 0 \qquad\qquad j = 1,\dots,m \text{ and } i < j$$

$$\dot{p}_{ij}^{k-1} = -p_{ij}^k u_j \qquad\qquad j = 1,\dots,m \text{ and } i < j \text{ and } k = 2,\dots,n_j$$

$$\dot{p}_i^0 = -\sum_{j=1}^m p_{ij}^1 u_j \qquad i = 1,\dots,m.$$

Notice that the chain structure of the system dynamics is inherited by the co-state dynamics. Next, we initialize the co-state as the inward-pointing normal on the boundary of G and apply the Pontryagin Maximum Principle to compute the optimal control $u^* = \arg\max_{u \in U} H(x,p,u)$. Since the feasible control set is a compact rectangle $U = \prod_{i=1}^m [\underline{U}_j, \overline{U}_j] \subset \mathbb{R}^m$, we may decompose the Maximum Principle for each component of the input:

$$u_j^* = \arg\max_{u_j \in [\underline{U}_j, \overline{U}_j]} \left(p_j^0 + \sum_{i=1}^{j-1} \left(p_{ij}^1 x_i^0 + \sum_{k=2}^{n_j} p_{ij}^k x_{ij}^{k-1} \right) \right) u_j. \qquad (2)$$

3.2   Construction of Hybrid System

The Maximum Principle calls for *bang-bang* controls: the optimal controls will always lie on the vertices on the feasible control set U. From equation (2), it is direct to see that u_j^* is either $\underline{U}_j$ or $\overline{U}_j$ depending on the sign of the "switching function" of the state and co-state which multiplies u_j. Thus, as proposed in [9, 10] we can construct a hybrid system which has $2^m + 1$ discrete states: One discrete state for each vertex of the rectangle U, and one discrete state for stopping the reachability computation on the obstacle set B (see [10]). The guards and invariants for the constructed hybrid system are defined by the "switching functions" in the optimal control shown in equation (2).

3.3   Reach Set Computation

For each discrete state of the constructed hybrid system we need to solve a reachability computation for a system of the form:

$$\begin{aligned}
\dot{x}_j^0 &= u_j^* & j &= 1,\dots,m \\
\dot{x}_{ij}^1 &= x_i^0 u_j^* & j &= 1,\dots,m \text{ and } i < j \\
\dot{x}_{ij}^k &= x_{ij}^{k-1} u_j^* & j &= 1,\dots,m \text{ and } i < j \text{ and } k = 2,\dots,n_j \\
\dot{p}_{ij}^{n_j} &= 0 & j &= 1,\dots,m \text{ and } i < j. \\
\dot{p}_{ij}^{k-1} &= -p_{ij}^k u_j^* & j &= 1,\dots,m \text{ and } i < j \text{ and } k = 2,\dots,n_j \\
\dot{p}_i^0 &= -\sum_{j=1}^m p_{ij}^1 u_j^* & i &= 1,\dots,m,
\end{aligned} \qquad (3)$$

where u_j^* is a constant rational number. It is easily shown that the problem of computing the reachable set of this system is decidable. Indeed, due to the chain form of the state and co-state dynamics, we may iteratively compute the flow of the system by symbolic integration and substitution starting from x_i^0 and proceeding down the chain. By symbolic integration the flow of this system is computed to be:

$$x_i^0(t) = x_i^0(0) + u_i^* t \qquad\qquad i = 1, \ldots, m$$
$$x_{ij}^1(t) = x_{ij}^1(0) + x_i^0(0)u_j^* t + \tfrac{1}{2}u_i^* u_j^* t^2$$
$$\vdots$$
$$p_{ij}^{n_j}(t) = p_{ij}^{n_j}(0) \qquad\qquad j = 1, \ldots, m \text{ and } i < j$$
$$p_{ij}^k(t) = \sum_{l=0}^{n_j - k} \frac{(-u_j^* t)^l}{l!} p_{ij}^{k+l}(0) \qquad j = 1, \ldots, m \text{ and } i < j \text{ and } k = 1, \ldots, n_j$$
$$p_i^0(t) = p_i^0(0) + \sum_{l=1}^{n_j - 1} \frac{(-u_j^* t)^l}{l!} p_{ij}^l(0) \quad i = 1, \ldots, m.$$

We use the notation $x(t) = \phi(x_0, u, t)$ to denote the state $x(t)$ which is a result of flowing for t seconds along the dynamics of the system with input u starting at the initial condition $x(0) = x_0$. Since the flow of this system is polynomial, it admits quantifier elimination [11], and hence the computation of the set of points which can reach a semi-algebraic set K, $\{x_0 \in \mathbb{R}^n \mid \exists t > 0 \; : \; \phi(x_0, u_j^*, t) \in K\}$ for each discrete state of the constructed hybrid system is decidable.

The only remaining condition of interest for the constructed hybrid system is an upper bound on the number of switchings between the discrete states. For the case of linear systems with dynamic matrices that are either nilpotent or diagonalizable with real rational eigenvalues, a result of Pontryagin provides that the number of switchings of the optimal control is no greater than the dimension of the system. For these classes of systems, we are able to show decidability of the least restrictive controller synthesis problem [9]. We can make no such claim in the case of chain form systems of the type in equation (1). In general there is no upper bound on the number of switchings on the optimal control defined in (2). Hence we conclude that controller synthesis problem for the class of chain form systems is *semi-decidable*.

3.4 Triangular Systems

Upon examination, we realize that there are essentially two features in the structure of chain form systems that allow the above methodology to work:

1. The vector field has linear terms in u.
    - Thus the Hamiltonian has linear terms in u, and applying the Maximum Principle, we see that the optimal input u^* is piecewise constant on the vertices of the feasible control set.
    - This allows us to construct a hybrid system out of the switching logic of the optimal control, where for each discrete state there is a constant u^*.
2. The time derivative of each state is a polynomial in the input and the *preceding* states of the chain.
    - For a constant u^* the flow can be computed iteratively by symbolic integration and substitution starting from the beginning of the chain.
    - Since u^* is constant and the vector field depends polynomially in states, the flow of the system is polynomial in u^*, t and the state.

– This structure is inherited by the co-state dynamics and hence the flow of the co-state can also be symbolically integrated.

The observation above suggests that the methodology for symbolic reachability computation will also work on the following larger class of *triangular nonlinear systems*.

Definition 4 (Triangular nonlinear system).
A nonlinear system $\dot{x} = f(x, u)$ is called triangular if it can be written as:

$$\dot{x}_0 = a + \sum_{j=1}^{m} b_j u_j$$
$$\dot{x}_1 = f_1(x_0) + \sum_{j=1}^{m} g_{1j}(x_0)u_j$$
$$\dot{x}_2 = f_2(x_0, x_1) + \sum_{j=1}^{m} g_{2j}(x_0, x_1)u_j$$
$$\vdots$$
$$\dot{x}_n = f_n(x_0, \dots, x_{n-1}) + \sum_{j=1}^{m} g_{nj}(x_0, \dots, x_{n-1})u_j,$$

where a, $b_j \in \mathbb{Q}$ and f_i, $g_{ij} \in \mathbb{Q}[x_0, \dots, x_{i-1}]$ for $i = 1, \dots, n$ and $j = 1, \dots, m$.

Moreover, it is direct to see that the methodology is also applicable to the class of triangular *differential games* between inputs $u \in \mathbb{R}^{n_u}$ and disturbances $d \in \mathbb{R}^{n_d}$.

Definition 5 (Triangular differential game).
A differential game $\dot{x} = f(x, u, d)$ is called triangular if it can be written as:

$$\dot{x}_{0j} = a_j + \sum_{k=1}^{n_u} b_{jk}u_k + \sum_{k=1}^{n_d} c_{jk}d_k$$
$$\dot{x}_{1j} = f_{1j}(x_{01}, \dots, x_{0L}) + \sum_{k=1}^{n_u} g_{1jk}(x_{01}, \dots, x_{0L})u_j +$$
$$\sum_{k=1}^{n_d} h_{1jk}d_k(x_{01}, \dots, x_{0L})$$
$$\vdots$$
$$\dot{x}_{ij} = f_{ij}(x_{01}, \dots, x_{0L}, \dots, x_{(i-1)1}, \dots x_{(i-1)L}) +$$
$$\sum_{k=1}^{n_u} g_{ijk}(x_{01}, \dots, x_{0L}, \dots, x_{(i-1)1}, \dots x_{(i-1)L})u_j +$$
$$\sum_{k=1}^{n_d} h_{ijk}(x_{01}, \dots, x_{0L}, \dots, x_{(i-1)1}, \dots x_{(i-1)L})d_k$$

for $j = 1, \dots, L$, and $i = 1, \dots, n_j$, and where a_j, b_{jk}, $c_{jk} \in \mathbb{Q}$ and f_{ij}, g_{ijk}, h_{ijk} are polynomials with rational coefficients.

Theorem 1 (Semi-decidable reach for triangular differential games).
For a triangular differential game $\dot{x} = f(x, u, d)$, if the inputs and disturbances are constrained to compact rectangles with rational coefficients, then for any disjoint semi-algebraic sets $K, G \subset \mathbb{R}^n$, the problem of computing Reach(K, G) is semi-decidable.

Proof. We need to show that the methodology for symbolic reach set computation proposed in [9,10] can be applied to triangular differential games and that each step in the methodology is computable.

1. **Compute Optimal Control.** Since the vector field can be written as $\dot{x} = f_1(x, u) + f_2(x, d)$, the Hamiltonian $H = p^T f(x, u, d)$ is *separable*, which implies that there exists a *saddle solution* (u^*, d^*) of optimal control and disturbance:

$$u^* = \arg\max_{u \in U} p^T f_1(x, u), \qquad d^* = \arg\min_{d \in D} p^T f_2(x, d). \qquad (4)$$

Moreover, since the Hamiltonian has linear terms in u and d, and the sets of feasible controls and disturbances are compact rectangles $U = \prod_{i=1}^{n_u}[\underline{U}_j, \overline{U}_j] \subset \mathbb{R}^{n_u}$, $D = \prod_{i=1}^{n_d}[\underline{D}_j, \overline{D}_j] \subset \mathbb{R}^{n_d}$, we may decompose equation (4) to get:

$$u_j^* = \arg\max_{u_j \in [\underline{U}_j, \overline{U}_j]} s_j^u(x, p) \, u_j, \qquad d_j^* = \arg\max_{d_j \in [\underline{D}_j, \overline{D}_j]} s_j^d(x, p) \, d_j, \qquad (5)$$

where $s_j^u(\cdot)$ and $s_j^d(\cdot)$ are "switching functions" which are polynomial in the state and co-state (x, p). The Maximum Principle calls for *bang-bang* optimal controls and disturbances: Depending on the signs of the switching functions, the optimal controls and disturbances will always lie on a vertex of the feasible control and disturbance set.

2. **Construct Hybrid System.** Construct a hybrid system with 2^{n_u} discrete states for each possible optimal control, 2^{n_d} discrete states for each possible disturbance, and one discrete state for stopping the reachability computation on the avoid set G (see [10]). The switching functions $s_j^u(\cdot)$, $s_j^d(\cdot)$ determine the discrete transitions of the constructed hybrid system, and continuous dynamics are the co-state dynamics $\dot{p} = -\frac{\partial H}{\partial x}$ appended to $\dot{x} = f(x, u^*, d^*)$ where (u^*, d^*) are constant.

3. **Calculate Reach Set.** In each discrete state, the triangular structure of the state dynamics and the fact that the optimal control and disturbance (u^*, d^*) are constant allows the flow of the state dynamics to can be computed by symbolic integration. Moreover, it is direct to check that the co-state dynamics inherit the triangular structure of the state dynamics and that the flow of the co-state dynamics can also be integrated symbolically. Since the flow in each discrete state of the constructed hybrid system is polynomial, we may perform quantifier elimination to compute the reachable set for each discrete state of the hybrid system.

We have constructed a hybrid system for which the problem of computing the reach set of each discrete state is decidable. By initializing the hybrid system with the usable part of the unsafe set K (see [9]), we have a semi-decision procedure for computing $Reach(K, G)$. However, since in general there is no bound on the number of times the switching functions change sign, there is no bound on the number of discrete transitions the hybrid system takes, and hence we cannot guarantee that the reach set computation will terminate.   □

4 Controller Synthesis for Triangular Hybrid Systems

The results of the previous section naturally inspire the following definition.

Definition 6 (Triangular hybrid system).
A hybrid system $H = (X, V, I, f, E, \phi)$ is called a triangular hybrid system if $\forall q \in \mathbf{X}_D$ the set of feasible inputs $\phi(q, x)|_{V_C} = \mathbf{U}_q \times \mathbf{D}_q$, where $\mathbf{U}_q$ and $\mathbf{D}_q$ are compact rectangles with rational vertices, the reset relation $E \subseteq \mathbf{X} \times \mathbf{V} \times \mathbf{X}$ is semi-algebraic, and for each discrete state q the vector field $f(q, x, u, d)$ is triangular with rational coefficients.

The results of the previous section provide that for each discrete state of the hybrid system, the computation of *Reach* is semi-decidable. Hence if the discrete transition Pre_d and Pre_u are computable (they are when the reset relation $E \subseteq \mathbf{X} \times \mathbf{V} \times \mathbf{X}$ is semi-algebraic), then each iteration of Algorithm 1 is computable, and hence we conclude that the problem of computing the maximum controlled invariant set is *semi-decidable*.

Theorem 2 (Semi-decidable controller synthesis for triangular hybrid systems). *For a triangular hybrid system H and a semi-algebraic safe set F, the problem of computing the maximum controlled invariant set $W^* \subseteq F$ is semi-decidable.*

If the computation of maximal safe set W^* terminates, we would like to provide a least restrictive controller that renders W^* invariant. Since the continuous dynamics of triangular hybrid systems are polynomial, the definition of the least restrictive controller can be written as a quantified first order formula in the theory of reals. Hence the least restrictive controller can be computed by quantifier elimination and is given in the following proposition [10].

Proposition 1 (Least restrictive controller). *Given a triangular hybrid system H and a semi-algebraic maximal controlled invariant set*

$$W^* = \left\{ x \in \mathbb{R}^n \mid \bigvee_{j=1}^{K} \left(\bigwedge_{k=1}^{L_j} h_{j_k}(x) \leq 0 \right) \right\},$$

the least restrictive controller $g(x) : \mathbf{X} \to 2^{\mathbf{U}}$ that renders W^* invariant is computable and is given by:

$$g(x) = \begin{cases} \{u \in \phi(x)|_U \mid \forall d \in \phi(x)|_D : Next(x, (u, d)) \subseteq W^*\} & \text{if } x \in (W^*)^o \\ \{u \in \phi(x)|_U \mid [\bigvee_{j=1}^{K}(\bigwedge_{k=1}^{L_j}(h_{j_k}(x) = 0) \Rightarrow \forall d \in \phi(x)|_D : \\ \quad (\frac{\partial h_{j_k}(x)}{\partial x})^T f(x, (u, d)) \leq 0) \wedge x \in Inv(u, d)] \vee \\ \quad [\forall d \in \phi(x)|_D : Next(x, (u, d)) \subseteq W^* \wedge x \notin Inv(u, d)]\}, & \text{if } x \in \partial W^* \\ \phi(x)|_U, & \text{if } x \in (W^*)^c. \end{cases}$$

Triangular hybrid systems is the first known class of nonlinear hybrid systems which has a semi-decidable controller synthesis problem. In the following section we apply our methodology to a conflict resolution example from air traffic control.

5   Conflict Resolution Example

In this section we present an application of our methodology towards verification of maneuvers for multi-agent hybrid systems. As an example application we verify a conflict resolution maneuver for air traffic control similar to the one described in [13]. Consider the following conflict resolution maneuver for two aircraft:

1. Cruise until aircraft are α_1 miles apart;
2. Change heading by $\Delta\phi$; fly until lateral displacement of d miles achieved;
3. Change to original heading; fly until aircraft are α_2 miles apart;
4. Change heading by $-\Delta\phi$; fly until lateral displacement of $-d$ miles achieved;
5. Change to original heading.

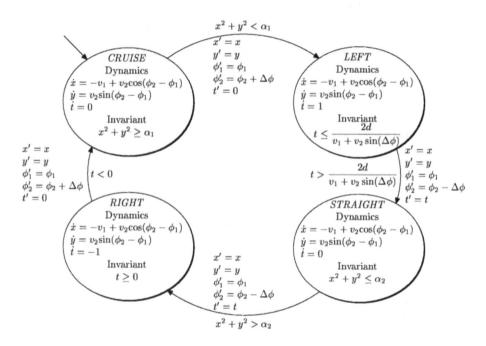

Fig. 2. Hybrid system model of aircraft conflict resolution maneuver.

The hybrid automaton modeling this maneuver has discrete states {$CRUISE$, $LEFT$, $STRAIGHT$, $RIGHT$} and is depicted in Figure 2. The continuous dynamics in each discrete state is the relative flow of the aircraft given a fixed velocity and heading, (v_i is the velocity and ϕ_i is the heading of aircraft i). The aircraft are considered to be at a safe distance if they are at least 5 miles apart. In the relative coordinate frame, the *unsafe* set is given by {$(x, y) \in \mathbb{R}^2 \mid x^2 + y^2 \leq 5$}.

Aircraft 1 is assumed to fly at a fixed velocity v_i and heading ϕ_1, while aircraft 2 can switch "modes" and rotate left or right a fixed angle of $\pm\Delta\phi$. It is clear that the hybrid automaton modeling the conflict resolution maneuver belongs to the class of triangular hybrid systems described in the previous sections.

Using the quantifier elimination package of MATHEMATICA 4.0, we computed the minimal unsafe sets for each discrete state of the automaton for the scenario where two aircraft are approaching each other with velocities $v_1 = 4$, $v_2 = 5$, with initial heading difference of $\phi_2 - \phi_1 = \frac{\pi}{2}$, and aircraft 2 allowed to change directions at an angle of $\pm\Delta\phi$ such that $\sin(\pm\Delta\phi) = \pm\frac{4}{5}$. Equations (6)-(8) show the results of the computation.

$$v_1 = 4; v_2 = 5; \lambda = 0$$
$$\texttt{unsafeCruise} = \texttt{Resolve}\left[\exists t > 0 \wedge (x - v_1 t + \lambda v_2 t)^2 + (y + \sqrt{1 - \lambda^2} v_2 t)^2 \leq 25\right]$$
$$= \left(y < -\tfrac{20}{\sqrt{41}} \wedge -\sqrt{41} - \tfrac{4y}{5} \leq x \leq \sqrt{41} - \tfrac{4y}{5}\right) \vee$$
$$\left(y = -\tfrac{20}{\sqrt{41}} \wedge -\sqrt{41} - \tfrac{4y}{5} < x \leq \sqrt{41} - \tfrac{4y}{5}\right) \vee$$
$$\left(y = \tfrac{20}{\sqrt{41}} \wedge -\sqrt{25 - y^2} < x < \sqrt{41} - \tfrac{4y}{5}\right) \vee \qquad (6)$$
$$\left(\tfrac{20}{\sqrt{41}} \leq y < 5 \wedge -\sqrt{25 - y^2} < x < \sqrt{25 - y^2}\right) \vee$$
$$\left(-\tfrac{20}{\sqrt{41}} < y < \tfrac{20}{\sqrt{41}} \wedge -\sqrt{25 - y^2} < x \leq \sqrt{41} - \tfrac{4y}{5}\right)$$

$$v_1 = 4; v_2 = 5; \lambda = \tfrac{3}{5}$$
$$\texttt{unsafeLeft} = \texttt{Resolve}\left[\exists t > 0 \wedge (x - v_1 t + \lambda v_2 t)^2 + (y + \sqrt{1 - \lambda^2} v_2 t)^2 \leq 25\right]$$
$$= \left(y < -\tfrac{5}{\sqrt{17}} \wedge -\tfrac{5\sqrt{17}}{4} - \tfrac{y}{4} \leq x \leq \tfrac{5\sqrt{17}}{4} - \tfrac{y}{4}\right) \vee$$
$$\left(y = -\tfrac{5}{\sqrt{17}} \wedge -\tfrac{5\sqrt{17}}{4} - \tfrac{y}{4} < x \leq \tfrac{5\sqrt{17}}{4} - \tfrac{y}{4}\right) \vee$$
$$\left(y = \tfrac{5}{\sqrt{17}} \wedge -\sqrt{25 - y^2} < x < \tfrac{5\sqrt{17}}{4} - \tfrac{y}{4}\right) \vee \qquad (7)$$
$$\left(\tfrac{5}{\sqrt{17}} < y < 5 \wedge -\sqrt{25 - y^2} < x < \sqrt{25 - y^2}\right) \vee$$
$$\left(-\tfrac{5}{\sqrt{17}} < y < \tfrac{5}{\sqrt{17}} \wedge -\sqrt{25 - y^2} < x \leq \tfrac{5\sqrt{17}}{4} - \tfrac{y}{4}\right)$$

$$v_1 = 4; v_2 = 5; \lambda = -\tfrac{3}{5}$$
$$\texttt{unsafeRight} = \texttt{Resolve}\left[\exists t > 0 \wedge (x - v_1 t + \lambda v_2 t)^2 + (y + \sqrt{1 - \lambda^2} v_2 t)^2 \leq 25\right]$$
$$= \left(y < -7\sqrt{\tfrac{5}{13}} \wedge -\tfrac{5\sqrt{65}}{4} - \tfrac{7y}{4} \leq x \leq \tfrac{5\sqrt{65}}{4} - \tfrac{7y}{4}\right) \vee$$
$$\left(y = -7\sqrt{\tfrac{5}{13}} \wedge -\tfrac{5\sqrt{65}}{4} - \tfrac{7y}{4} < x \leq \tfrac{5\sqrt{65}}{4} - \tfrac{7y}{4}\right) \vee$$
$$\left(y = 7\sqrt{\tfrac{5}{13}} \wedge -\sqrt{25 - y^2} < x < \tfrac{5\sqrt{65}}{4} - \tfrac{7y}{4}\right) \vee \qquad (8)$$
$$\left(7\sqrt{\tfrac{5}{13}} < y < 5 \wedge -\sqrt{25 - y^2} < x < \sqrt{25 - y^2}\right) \vee$$
$$\left(-7\sqrt{\tfrac{5}{13}} < y < 7\sqrt{\tfrac{5}{13}} \wedge -\sqrt{25 - y^2} < x \leq \tfrac{5\sqrt{65}}{4} - \tfrac{7y}{4}\right)$$

Since the relative heading and velocity of the two aircraft is same for the *CRUISE* and *STRAIGHT* flight modes, then $\texttt{unsafeCruise=unsafeStraight}$.

The result of the symbolic computation of the minimal unsafe sets is shown in Figure 3. The set unsafeCruise\unsafeLeft contains the set of states which are made safe by the aircraft turning left, and the set unsafeCruise \ unsafeRight contains the set of states which are made safe by the aircraft turning right. The set unsafeCruise \ (unsafeLeft ∪ unsafeRight) contains the states which are made safe by turning either left or right, and the set unsafeCruise ∩ unsafeLeft ∩ unsafeRight shown in Figure 3(d) is the set of states which is unsafe regardless of the action the aircraft takes.

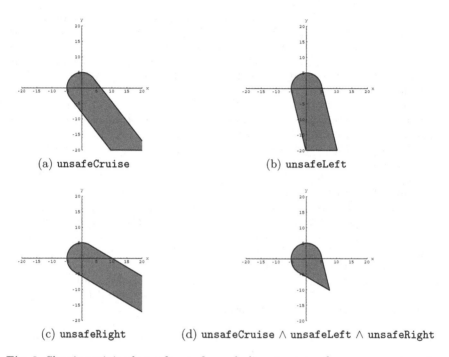

(a) unsafeCruise   (b) unsafeLeft

(c) unsafeRight   (d) unsafeCruise ∧ unsafeLeft ∧ unsafeRight

Fig. 3. Showing minimal unsafe sets for each discrete state of maneuver automaton.

6   Conclusion

In this paper, we have presented the first class of nonlinear hybrid systems with a semi-decidable controller synthesis problem. This class of *triangular hybrid systems* is rich enough to capture hybrid models that include kinematic models of aircraft, robots, and cars. Our results were illustrated on a conflict resolution example from air traffic control.

Acknowledgments. The work by O. Shakernia was supported by ONR under grants N00014-97-1-0946 and N00014-00-1-0621, and by DARPA under grant

F33615-98-C-3614. The work of G. J. Pappas was partially supported by DARPA Grant F33615-00-C-1707, and the University of Pennsylvania Research Foundation.

References

1. E. Asarin, O. Bournez, T. Dang, O. Maler, and A. Pnueli. Effective controller synthesis of switching controllers for linear systems. *Proceedings of the IEEE*, 88(7):1011–1025, July 2000.
2. A. Chutinam and B. Krogh. Verification of polyhedral-invariant hybrid automata using polygonal flow pipe approximations. In *Hybrid Systems : Computation and Control*, volume 1569 of *LNCS*. Springer Verlag, 1999.
3. T. Dang and O. Maler. Reachability analysis via face lifting. In *Hybrid Systems : Computation and Control*, volume 1386 of *LNCS*, pages 96–109. Springer Verlag, Berlin, 1998.
4. G. Lafferriere, G. J. Pappas, and S. Yovine. A new class of decidable hybrid systems. In *Hybrid Systems : Computation and Control*, volume 1569 of *Lecture Notes in Computer Science*, pages 137–151. Springer Verlag, 1999.
5. Z. Li and J.F. Canny, editors. *Nonholonomic Motion Planning*. Kluwer Academic Publishers, 1993.
6. J. Lygeros, C. Tomlin, and S.S. Sastry. Controllers for reachability specifications for hybrid systems. *Automatica*, 35(3):349–370, March 1999.
7. I. Mitchell and C. Tomlin. Level set methods for computation in hybrid systems. In *Proceedings of Hybrid Systems: Computation and Control*, LNCS 1790, pages 310–323. Springer-Verlag, March 2000.
8. R.M. Murray, Z. Li, and S.S. Sastry. *A Mathematical Introduction to Robotic Manipulation*. CRC Press, 1994.
9. O. Shakernia, G. Pappas, and S. Sastry. Decidable controller synthesis for classes of linear systems. In *Hybrid Systems: Computation and Control*, LNCS 1790, pages 407–420. Springer-Verlag, March 2000.
10. O. Shakernia, G. Pappas, and S. Sastry. Semidecidable controller synthesis for classes of linear hybrid systems. In *Proceedings of the 39th IEEE Conference on Decision and Control*, Sydney, AU, December 2000.
11. A. Tarski. *A decision method for elementary algebra and geometry*. University of California Press, second edition, 1951.
12. C. Tomlin, J. Lygeros, and S. Sastry. Computing controllers for nonlinear hybrid systems. In *Proceedings of Hybrid Systems: Computation and Control*, LNCS 1569. Springer-Verlag, March 1999.
13. C. Tomlin, G. J. Pappas, and S. Sastry. Conflict resolution for air traffic management : A study in muti-agent hybrid systems. *IEEE Transactions on Automatic Control*, 43(4):509–521, April 1998.

Hybrid Abstractions
that Preserve Timed Languages

Paulo Tabuada[1] and George J. Pappas[2]

[1] Instituto de Sistemas e Robótica, Instituto Superior Técnico
1049-001 Lisboa - Portugal, tabuada@isr.ist.utl.pt
[2] Department of Electrical Engineering, University of Pennsylvania
Philadelphia, PA 19104, pappasg@ee.upenn.edu

Abstract. In this paper we consider the problem of extracting an abstraction from a hybrid control system while preserving timed languages. Such consistent abstractions are clearly useful as the abstracted, higher level model could be used for controller synthesis or verification of the more complicated lower level model. The class of abstracting maps we consider in this paper compress only the continuous states without aggregating any discrete states. Given such an abstracting map, we determine natural conditions that determine when trajectories of the original hybrid system can be generated by the abstracted hybrid system. Conversely, we determine conditions under which the two hybrid systems generate exactly the same timed language.

1 Introduction

The analysis and synthesis of hybrid control systems has received tremendous attention recently. The scale of the motivating applications, such as air traffic management systems [15] or automotive engine control systems [4], require that the resulting analysis and control methodologies scale up efficiently, in order to facilitate the realistic application of computational methods to real-scale examples.

One of the fundamental approaches to reducing the complexity of large scale system analysis and design is the process of *abstraction*. From an analysis perspective, given a model and a property of interest, one tries to extract a simpler model, an abstraction, that preserves the property of interest while ignoring irrelevant details. This approach has been used successfully in extracting discrete abstractions of hybrid systems while preserving many properties that can be expressed in various temporal logics [3].

From a design perspective, given a hybrid control system, one would like to extract an abstracted hybrid system, perform the design at the higher level abstraction, and then *refine* the design at the lower level. In this hierarchical setting, a methodology which extracts a hierarchy of hybrid system models at various levels of abstraction is critical.

Due to the complexity of combinatorial problems, the notion of abstraction is more mature in theoretical computer science than control theory. For purely discrete systems, the notions of language equivalence, simulation, and bisimulation

M.D. Di Benedetto, A. Sangiovanni-Vincentelli (Eds.): HSCC 2001, LNCS 2034, pp. 501–514, 2001.

are established [10]. For purely continuous systems, however, these concepts are only recently beginning to emerge. In particular, in [12], a notion of abstraction for continuous systems was formalized. In [11] reachability preserving abstractions of continuous linear systems were characterized, leading to hierarchical reachability algorithms for linear control systems. In [13], these results where generalized for nonlinear analytic systems. A general theory of abstraction for hybrid systems will clearly merge the continuous and discrete approaches.

In this paper, we address the problem of extracting a hybrid abstraction from a hybrid control model while preserving timed languages. Given a hybrid system, the timed language is simply the timed trajectory of the discrete states. Therefore, the timed language maintains the discrete state the system is in as well as relevant timing information.

This problem is important for a variety for reasons. For scheduling multiple physical processes (such as air traffic management systems), the higher level may be simply interested in which discrete mode each process is in (landing, holding, etc.) and when. Therefore the higher level (air traffic control) would like then to use the simplest possible model of an aircraft that is compatible with the original aircraft dynamics but also with the scheduling operation. Furthermore, the results of this paper can be easily adapted to properly extract hybrid abstractions from purely continuous systems [14]. Finally, the results of the paper are the fist steps towards a more general abstraction methodology for hybrid systems.

In order for the abstracted model to generate the same discrete symbols, we consider aggregating only the continuous dynamics. Abstracting the continuous dynamics while preserving the timed language requires the abstraction process to be done in manner that allows us to detect all the discrete transitions. This places a natural condition between the abstracting maps, guards and invariants of the discrete transitions. Assuming that our aggregating maps satisfy these conditions, we show that hybrid trajectories of the original model can be simulated by the abstracted model. Consequently, the abstracted model also generates the same timed language. In general, the abstracted system is *not* a timed automaton [2], as we may need to preserve richer continuous dynamics in order to properly detect the discrete transitions.

In order to ensure that timed trajectories of the abstracted model are feasible by the original hybrid model, we rely heavily on the abstraction results for continuous systems [13]. These results give us *constructive* methods for extracting hierarchies of nonlinear control systems while preserving exact time controllability. Exact time controllability allows us to preserve a form of *timed* reachability. Using these results, we can place additional conditions on our abstracting maps in order to ensure that in each discrete location, the ability to reach a certain guard at the same time can be done at both levels of abstraction. This allows us to show that the timed language generated at the high level can be implemented at the lower level.

This paper is organized as follows : In Section 2, we review the continuous abstraction methodology as presented in [11,13]. In Section 3, we define hybrid systems, and determine conditions under which the hybrid abstraction and the original hybrid system model can generate the same timed language. Our constructions are briefly illustrated by a simple example in Section 4, but the reader is referred to a more detailed application in [14]. Section 5 contains interesting issues for further research.

2   Abstractions of Continuous Systems

Contrary to differential equations whose abstractions are characterized by very strict conditions, abstractions of control systems involve only moderate conditions due to the nondeterministic nature of control systems. In subsequent discussion, we assume the reader is familiar with differential geometric concepts at the level presented in [1].

2.1   Abstractions of Control Systems

We begin with an abstract definition of a control system:

Definition 1 (Control System). *A control system $S = (U, F)$ consists of a fiber bundle $\pi : U \longrightarrow M$ called the control bundle and a smooth map $F : U \longrightarrow TM$ which is fiber preserving, that is $\pi' \circ F = \pi$ where $\pi' : TM \longrightarrow M$ is the tangent bundle projection. Given a control system $S = (U, F)$, the control distribution $\mathcal{D}$ of control system S, is naturally defined pointwise by $\mathcal{D}(x) = F(\pi^{-1}(x))$ for all $x \in M$.*

The control space U is modeled as a fiber bundle since in general the control inputs available may depend on the current state of the system. On a local coordinate chart, Definition 1 can be read as $\frac{d}{dt}x = f(x, u)$ with $u \in \pi^{-1}(x)$, therefore recovering the traditional form of the control system. Before introducing the notion of abstraction for continuous control systems, the concept of trajectories of control systems is required:

Definition 2 (Trajectories of Control Systems). *A curve $c : I \longrightarrow M$, $I \subseteq \mathbb{R}_0^+$ is called a trajectory of control system $S = (U, F)$ if there exists a curve $c^U : I \longrightarrow U$ satisfying:*

$$\pi \circ c^U = c$$
$$\frac{d}{dt}c(t) = c_*(\frac{d}{dt}) = c_*(1) = F(c^U)$$

Again in local coordinates, the above definition simply says that $x(t)$ is a solution to a control system if there exists an input $u(t) \in U(x(t)) = \pi^{-1}(x(t))$ satisfying $\frac{d}{dt}x(t) = f(x(t), u(t))$. Our goal is to construct a map $\phi : M \longrightarrow N$, the *abstraction map* or *aggregation map*, that will induce a new control system (U_N, F_N) on the lower dimensional manifold N having as trajectories $\phi(c)$, where c are S trajectories. The concept of abstraction map for continuous control systems is defined as follows:

Definition 3 (Abstraction Map). *Let $S_M = (U_M, F_M)$ and $S_N = (U_N, F_N)$ be two control systems on manifolds M and N, respectively. A map $\phi : M \longrightarrow N$ is called an abstraction or aggregation map iff for every trajectory c^M of S_M, $\phi(c^M)$ is a trajectory of S_N. Control system S_N is called a ϕ-abstraction of S_M.*

The above definition is clearly inspired from the notions of language equivalence and simulation of transition systems [10]. From Definition 3, it is clear that an abstraction captures all the trajectories of the original system, but may also contain redundant trajectories. These redundant trajectories are not feasible by the original system and are therefore undesired.

Since Definition 3 defines abstractions at the level of trajectories, it is difficult to determine whether a control system is an abstraction of another one, since this would require integration of the control systems. One is then interested in a characterization of abstractions which is equivalent to Definition 3 but easily checkable. To pursue this, one needs to introduce the notion of ϕ-related control systems.

Definition 4 (ϕ-related control systems). *Let $S_M = (U_M, F_M)$ and $S_N = (B_N, F_N)$ be two control systems defined on manifolds M and N, respectively. Let $\phi : M \longrightarrow N$ be a smooth map. Then control systems S_M and S_N are ϕ-related iff for every $x \in M$*

$$\phi_* \left(F_M \left(\pi_M^{-1}(x) \right) \right) \subseteq F_N \left(\pi_N^{-1}(\phi(x)) \right) \tag{1}$$

The notion of ϕ-related control systems is a generalization of ϕ-related vector fields commonly found in differential geometry as explained in [11]. It is evident that given two systems that are ϕ-related to a control system their intersection is also ϕ-related. This immediately suggests that given a control system and a map ϕ, there is a *minimal* ϕ-related control system, in which case the inclusion (1) can be replaced by equality[1]. We can now provide the connection between abstractions and ϕ-related control systems:

Theorem 1 ([12,11]). *Let S_M and S_N be control systems on manifolds M and N, respectively, and $\phi : M \longrightarrow N$ a smooth map. Then S_M and S_N are ϕ-related if and only if S_N is a ϕ-abstraction of S_M.*

The control system S_N is called the *minimal ϕ-abstraction* of a control system S_M iff S_N is the minimal system that is ϕ-related to S_M.

For analytic control systems there is a constructive method which given a control system S_M and a map $\phi : M \longrightarrow N$, generates a ϕ-abstraction S_N. This construction, which generalizes the construction for linear systems described in [11], is now briefly reviewed. The reader is referred to [13] for more details.

Given two distributions $\mathcal{A}$ and $\mathcal{B}$ on manifold M, define a distribution $[\mathcal{A}, \mathcal{B}]$ by declaring $[\mathcal{A}, \mathcal{B}](p)$ to be the subspace of $T_p M$ generated by vectors of the form $[X, Y](p)$, where X, Y are any two analytic vector fields in $\mathcal{A}$ and $\mathcal{B}$ respectively,

---

[1] Note that this minimal element is unique up to a change of coordinates.

and $[X, Y]$ is their Lie bracket. By resorting to this constructive method, define the distribution $\overline{\mathcal{D}}_M$ as:

$$\overline{\mathcal{D}}_M = \mathcal{K} \cup \mathcal{D}_M \cup [\mathcal{K}, \mathcal{D}_M] \cup [\mathcal{K}, [\mathcal{K}, \mathcal{D}_M]] \cup \dots \tag{2}$$

where $\mathcal{K}$ is the integrable distribution $Ker(\phi_*)$, ϕ_* is the push forward map of ϕ, and $\mathcal{D}_M$ the distribution associated with control system S_M. Distribution $\overline{\mathcal{D}}_M$ allows us to construct the minimal ϕ-abstraction on N as:

$$\mathcal{D}_N(y) = \phi_* \left(\overline{\mathcal{D}}_M(x) \right) \tag{3}$$

for any $x \in \phi^{-1}(y)$. If S_N is extracted from S_M using this canonical construction, then control system S_N will be referred to as *canonically ϕ-related* to S_M.

2.2   Controllability Equivalence

In general, since the abstracted system is less constrained, the abstracted model may allow evolutions that might not be implementable on the original system. However the original system and its abstraction can still be rendered equivalent regarding some properties of interest. In this paper, we will focus on exact time controllability which is defined using the reachable sets of control system S_M:

Definition 5 (Reachable set [7]). *For each $T > 0$, and each x in M, the set of points reachable from x at time T, denoted by $Reach(x, T)$, is equal to the set of terminal points $c^M(T)$ of S_M trajectories that originate at x.*

Definition 6 (Exact Time Controllability). *A control system is said to be exact time controllable if for any $T > 0$, $Reach(x, T) = M$ for any $x \in M$.*

Consider two systems S_M and S_N and a surjective map $\phi : M \longrightarrow N$. Control systems S_M and S_N are equivalent from an exact time controllability point of view if the following property holds: there exists an S_M trajectory connecting $x_1 \in M$ to $x_2 \in M$ in time T if and only if there exists a S_N trajectory connecting $\phi(x_1) \in N$ to $\phi(x_2) \in N$ also in time T. This property is clearly reminiscent of timed-bisimulations [10].

If we assume that the control system is affine in the control, that is, on local charts it can be written as:

$$F(x, u) = f(x) + \sum_{i=1}^{k} g_i(x) u_i \tag{4}$$

then we can characterize exact time controllability through the Lie algebra generated by $\{g_1(x), g_2(x), \dots, g_k(x)\}$ and denoted by $Lie_g(S_M)$.

Theorem 2 ([7]). *An analytic control system S_M affine in control, as defined in (4), is exact time controllable if $Lie_g(S_M(x)) = T_x M$ for every $x \in M$.*

We defer the reader to [6,7] for further details regarding the various notions and concepts of controllability. The main theorem regarding controllability equivalence of abstractions (see [13]) can now be restated as follows:

Theorem 3 (Exact Time Controllability Equivalence). *Let S_M and S_N be two analytic control systems on analytic manifolds M and N, respectively, and let N be an embedded submanifold of M. Let $\phi : M \to N$ be an analytic surjective submersion. If S_N is canonically ϕ-related to S_M and*

$$Ker(\phi_*) \subseteq Lie_g(S_M) \tag{5}$$

then S_N is exact time controllable iff S_M is.

Equations (2,3) and Theorem 3 provide a constructive way of building continuous abstractions that propagate reachable sets, and in particular exact time controllability. When additional properties must be propagated, additional constraints must be imposed on the abstracting maps.

3   Hybrid Control Abstractions

Although hybrid abstractions follow the same conceptual ideas of discrete and continuous abstractions, their study is somewhat more involved due to the complicated nature of hybrid trajectories. We start with a hybrid system model that allows different continuous spaces in each discrete location.

Definition 7 (Hybrid Control System). *A hybrid control system is a tuple $H = (X, X_0, S, Inv, R)$ with the following components:*

- *X is the state space of the hybrid control system and is given by a family of smooth manifolds $X = \{M_q\}_{q \in Q}$ indexed[2] by a finite set Q. Each state thus has the form (x, q), where $x \in M_q$ is the continuous part of the state, and $q \in Q$ is the discrete part.*
- *$X_0 = \{M_q^0\}_{q \in Q_0} \subseteq X$ is the set of initial states.*
- *$S: Q \to \{(U_q, F_q) : (U_q, F_q)$ is a control system on $M_q\}$ assigns to each discrete state $q \in Q$ a control system (U_q, F_q) which governs the evolution of the continuous part of the state. Thus in discrete location q, the continuous part of the state satisfies $\frac{d}{dt}x = f(x, q, u)$ with $u \in \pi^{-1}(x, q)$.*
- *$Inv: Q \to 2^X$ assigns to each location $q \in Q$ an invariant set $Inv(q) \subseteq M_q$.*
- *$R \subseteq X \times X$ is a relation capturing the discrete jumps.*

Hybrid systems are typically represented as finite graphs with vertices Q, and edges E defined by

$$E = \{(q, q') \in Q \times Q \mid ((x, q), (x', q')) \in R \text{ for } x \in Inv(q) \text{ and } x' \in Inv(q')\}.$$

---

[2] When all the manifolds M_q are equal, then the state space X is $X = M \times Q$.

With each edge $e = (q, q') \in E$ we associate a *guard* set defined as

$$Guard(e) = \{x \in Inv(q) \mid ((x, q), (x', q')) \in R \text{ for some } x' \in Inv(q')\}$$

and a set-valued *reset* map

$$Reset(e, x) = \{x' \in Inv(q') \mid ((x, q), (x', q')) \in R\}.$$

Trajectories of the hybrid system H originate at any initial state $(x, q) \in X_0$ and consist of concatenations of *continuous flows* and *discrete jumps*. Continuous flows keep the discrete part of the state constant at q, and the continuous part evolves over time according to the control system $\frac{d}{dt}x = f(x, q, u)$, as long as x remains inside the invariant set $Inv(q)$. If during the continuous flow, it happens that $x \in Guard(e)$ for some $e = (q, q') \in E$, then the edge e becomes *enabled*. The state of the hybrid system may then instantaneously jump from (x, q) to any (x', q') with $x' \in Reset(e, x)$. Then the process repeats, and the continuous part of the state evolves according to the control system $\frac{d}{dt}x = f(x, q', u)$. We shall therefore assume that a trajectory of an hybrid control system is a map[3] ξ from a time set $\mathbb{T}$ to the state space $X = \{M_q\}_{q \in Q}$ of H, that is:

$$\begin{aligned} \xi : \mathbb{T} &\longrightarrow \{M_q\}_{q \in Q} \\ \tau &\mapsto (x(\tau), q(\tau)) \end{aligned} \tag{6}$$

An abstracting map for hybrid systems can now be defined in the same way it was defined for continuous systems.

Definition 8 (Abstraction Map). *Let* $H_X = (X, X_0, S_X, Inv_X, R_X)$ *and* $H_Y = (Y, Y_0, S_Y, Inv_Y, R_Y)$ *be two hybrid control systems with* $X = \{M_q\}_{q \in Q}$ *and* $Y = \{N_p\}_{p \in P}$. *A map* $\phi : X \longrightarrow Y$ *is called an abstraction or aggregation map iff for every trajectory* c^{H_X} *of* H_X, $\phi(c^{H_X})$ *is a trajectory of* H_Y.

Even though, we are interested in general abstracting maps, we now focus on a subclass of abstracting maps that are suitable for preserving timed languages.

3.1   Timed Language Generated by a Hybrid System

In this paper we shall focus on abstractions that render the original system and its abstraction equivalent regarding the timed language they can generate. The timed string corresponding to a trajectory $\xi(\tau) = (x(\tau), q(\tau))$ of an hybrid control system is simply given by $q(t)$. Naturally $q(t)$ can be regarded as a timed string[4] since it can be written in the more usual form $\{(t, q(t))\}_{t \in \mathbb{R}_0^+}$. The timed language generated by an hybrid control system is therefore defined as:

---

[3] When multiple discrete jumps in zero time are allowed, a more complex notion of time is required to regard an hybrid trajectory as a map, see for example [9].

[4] The string $s = q(t)$ can be transformed to retain only the discrete states, and the first instance of time at which the system has changed discrete state. The results presented in this paper are however independent of that transformation.

Definition 9 (Timed language of a hybrid system). *Let H be a hybrid control system. The timed language generated by H and denoted by Σ_H is given by all the strings $q(t)$, where $q(t)$ is the discrete part of an hybrid trajectory $\xi(\tau) = (x(\tau), q(\tau))$ of H.*

With this notion of timed language, timed language equivalence between two hybrid system requires the discrete behavior of the hybrid abstraction to be *equal* to the discrete behavior of the original system. Therefore aggregation can only happen on the continuous part of the hybrid system. We will therefore restrict the class of abstracting maps to the following form:

$$\phi : \{M_q\}_{q \in Q} \longrightarrow \{N_q\}_{q \in Q}$$
$$\phi(x, q) = (\phi(x), q) \qquad (7)$$

that is, if ϕ is written as $\phi = (\phi_M, \phi_Q)$, then ϕ_Q is the identity map on $Q = P$.

Even though for continuous systems we can always extract abstractions that preserve trajectories, for hybrid control systems additional constraints must be imposed on the abstracting map to ensure timed language equivalence. This is because the discrete dynamics rely heavily on certain sets, such as the guards and the invariants, and we have to ensure that these sets are abstracted correctly at the higher level.

3.2   Propagating Guards and Invariants

Let us zoom into a discrete state and consider the relevant sets which trigger the discrete dynamics, namely the guards and the invariants. Timed language equivalence requires that these sets must be aggregated in a consistent way.

Figure 1 represents the state space of the original system with the guard defined by a relation of the type $x_2 > const$. When performing an abstraction using the map $\phi(x_1, x_2) = x_2$, in the abstracted system it is still possible to determine if the continuous part of the trajectory belongs or not on the guard. No information required by the discrete dynamics was lost in the abstracting process. However if the abstracting map is $\phi(x_1, x_2) = x_1$ it is no longer possible to determine if the continuous part of the trajectory belongs or not to the guard, therefore it is not possible to generate the same timed language.

The essential property to be propagated is therefore the ability to distinguish between sets $\phi(A)$ and $\phi(B)$ in the abstracted system if and only if it is possible to distinguish between relevant sets A and B in the original system. The relevant sets can be encoded in a partition of the state space, where each equivalence class of the partition corresponds to a possible combination of guards and invariants. The required partition can be modeled as a map Ψ_M defined as:

$$\Psi_M : M \longrightarrow D \qquad (8)$$

where D is a finite set. We assume that the map Ψ_M results in a topologically well behaved partition[5]. Partition propagation can now be defined as:

---

[5] For example, the partition can be a subanalytic stratification [8].

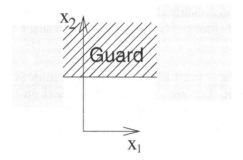

Fig. 1. Detecting a guard.

Definition 10 (Partition Propagation). *An abstracting map $\phi : M \rightarrow N$ propagates a partition Ψ_M iff there exists a partition on N defined by a map $\Psi_N : N \rightarrow D$ such that the following diagram commutes.*

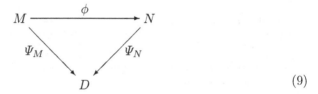

(9)

or equivalently iff $\Psi_M(x) = \Psi_N \circ \phi(x)$.

Note that propagating the partitions is stronger than preserving the partition which only requires that $\Psi_M(x_1) = \Psi_M(x_2) \Rightarrow \Psi_N \circ \phi(x_1) = \Psi_N \circ \phi(x_2)$ and allows, for example, merging two Ψ_M equivalence classes into a single equivalence class in Ψ_N. This is not a desirable situation since the ability to distinguish between the two equivalence classes is lost.

Although Definition 10 captures the fundamental property that the abstracting map should possess it does not characterize it directly. A characterization is given in the following proposition:

Proposition 1. *An abstracting map $\phi : M \rightarrow N$ propagates a partition Ψ_M iff the preimage under ϕ of a point $y \in N$ is totally contained in a single Ψ_M equivalence class, equivalently, if for all $y \in N$ there exists one and only one $d \in D$ such that $\Psi_M \circ \phi^{-1}(y) = \{d\}$.*

Proof. (Sufficiency) We proceed by contradiction. Suppose that $\Psi_M(x) = \Psi_N \circ \phi(x)$ and there exist two different elements $a, b \in M$ that belong to two different Ψ_M equivalence classes, that is $\Psi_M(a) \neq \Psi_M(b)$. Admit further that they are mapped into the same point in N, $\phi(a) = \phi(b)$. We have that $\Psi_M(a) = \Psi_N \circ \phi(a)$, but since $\phi(a) = \phi(b)$, $\Psi_N \circ \phi(a) = \Psi_N \circ \phi(b) = \Psi_M(b)$. Therefore $\Psi_M(a) = \Psi_M(b)$, a contradiction.

(Necessity) We define explicitly the map Ψ_N as $\Psi_N(y) = \Psi_M(x)$ for all $x \in \phi^{-1}(y)$ which is well defined since $\phi^{-1}(y)$ is contained in a single Ψ_M equivalence class. $\square$

Proposition 1 states partition propagation conditions explicity on the abstracting map ϕ, but they are very difficult to check in general. However it is rather intuitive that a sufficient condition for partition propagation is symmetry, as expressed in the next proposition.

Proposition 2. *Suppose that the partition Ψ_M on manifold M is invariant under the action of a group G, then the abstracting map ϕ defined as the projection from the manifold M to the orbit space M/G propagates the partition Ψ_M.*

Proof. If the Ψ_M equivalence classes are invariant under G action, then the orbit through the point x_0, namely $O_{x_0} = \{x \in M : x = gx_0 \; \forall_{g \in G}\}$ is contained in a Ψ_M equivalence class. Since the preimages under ϕ are precisely the sets O_{x_0} the conditions of Proposition 1 are satisfied. $\square$

In fact, symmetry is also a necessary condition when more structure is imposed on the set M and the map ϕ. To study general nonlinear abstracting maps we consider that M and N are smooth manifolds and that the abstracting map ϕ is a smooth surjective submersion. Resorting to this differentiable structure, Proposition 1 specializes to:

Proposition 3. *A smooth surjective submersion $\phi : M \longrightarrow N$ between smooth manifolds propagates a partition Ψ_M if and only if the partition equivalence classes are invariant under $Ker(\phi_*)$.*

Proof. (Sufficiency) The vectors in $Ker(\phi_*)$ span an involuntive distribution which has constant rank at every $x \in M$ since the map ϕ is a submersion. By Frobenius theorem [1] there exists an integrating manifold that can be described as the action of $\mathbb{R}^p$, with $p = dim(\mathcal{K})$, on M given by $\gamma = \phi_1(t_1) \circ \phi_2(t_2) \circ \ldots \circ \phi_p(t_p)$. Each $\phi_i(t_i)$ is the flow of the vector field Z^i from the generators of $\mathcal{K}$, that is $\mathcal{K} = Span\{Z^1, Z^2, \ldots, Z^p\}$. The partition equivalence classes are therefore invariant under this action and by Proposition 2 the partition is propagated.

(Necessity) The preimage of a point $y \in N$ by ϕ is a smooth submanifold of M when the derivative of ϕ, is surjective, which is the case since ϕ is an submersion. The tangent space of the submanifold $\phi^{-1}(y)$ is given by the vectors $X \in TM$ that belong to $Ker(\phi_*)$. Since the partition is propagated the preimage of a point $y \in N$ by ϕ is totally contained inside a partition equivalence class and therefore the partition equivalence classes are invariant under $Ker(\phi_*)$. $\square$

The above characterizations of the abstracting maps are critical in order to propagate discrete trajectories from the original hybrid control system to the abstracted one while ensuring timed language equivalence.

3.3 Hybrid Abstractions

Given a hybrid system, H_X and an abstracting map ϕ, we now present a construction that generates an hybrid abstraction H_Y. The abstraction process depends on the observation that the continuous dynamics in a particular discrete state is essentially decoupled from the continuous dynamics in the other discrete state, the only link being given by the *Reset* map. It is therefore possible to use a different abstracting map ϕ_q in each discrete state $q \in Q$ of the hybrid system H_X. More formally:

Definition 11 (Construction of hybrid abstractions). *Consider hybrid control system $H_X = (X, X_0, S_X, Inv_X, R_X)$ with $X = \{M_q\}_{q \in Q}$ and consider the collection of maps $\Phi = \{\phi_q\}_{q \in Q}$, $\phi_q : M_q \longrightarrow N_q$. The resulting hybrid abstraction $H_Y = (Y, Y_0, S_Y, Inv_Y, R_Y)$ is a tuple consisting of:*

- *For all $q \in Q$, $N_q = \phi_q(M_q)$, therefore the state space is $Y = \{N_q\}_{q \in Q}$.*
- *$Y_0 = \{N_q^0\}_{q \in Q_0}$ where $N_q^0 = \phi_q(M_q^0)$.*
- *S_Y is a function that maps each $q \in Q$ to the minimal ϕ_q-abstraction of the corresponding control system $S_X(q)$ using the canonical construction (2,3).*
- *$Inv_Y(q) = \phi_q(Inv_X(q))$.*
- *$R_Y = \{((y, q), (y', q')) \in Y \times Y : (y, q) = \phi_q(x, q) \land (y', q') = \phi_{q'}(x', q') \land ((x, q), (x', q')) \in R_X\}$. More specifically we have*
  - *$Guard_Y(e) = \phi_{q_i}(Guard_X(e))$*
  - *$Reset_Y(e, x_i) = \phi_{q_j} \circ Reset_X(e, \phi_{q_i}^{-1}(x_i))$ for all $e = (q_i, q_j) \in E$, $x \in M$.*

Therefore the discrete state space remains unaltered and only the continuous state space is aggregated from M_q to N_q is each discrete location $q \in Q$, and similarly for the set of initial conditions. The continuous control system $S_X(q)$ is replaced by its minimal ϕ_q-abstraction. The new invariant on each location $q \in Q$ is the image of the initial invariant under ϕ_q, that is $\phi_q(Inv_X(q))$. The reset relation R_Y is the image of the reset relation R_X by the abstracting map resulting in the new guards being the image of the initial guards by the abstracting map. The reset maps $Reset_Y$ are given by the image under ϕ_{q_j} of the reset maps $Reset_X$ evaluated at every point of the set valued map $\phi_{q_i}^{-1}$. The main result relating hybrid abstraction constructed through Definition 11 and timed language equivalence can now be stated as follows:

Theorem 4 (Timed language equivalent hybrid abstractions). *Let H_X and H_Y be hybrid control systems and suppose H_Y is obtained from H_X using Definition 11. If the family of maps $\Phi = \{\phi_q\}_{q \in Q}$ is such that the invariants and guards in each discrete location $q \in Q$ are invariant under $Ker(\phi_{q*})$ then H_Y is a Φ-abstraction of H_X.*

If furthermore $Ker(\phi_{q*}) \subseteq Lie_g(S_M(q))$ for each $q \in Q$ then H_X and H_Y generate the same timed language.

Proof. To show that H_Y is a Φ-abstraction of H_X we need to show that for every trajectory $c^{H_X} = (x(\tau), q(\tau))$, $\Phi(c^{H_X})$ is a trajectory of H_Y. For any trajectory $(x(\tau), q(\tau))$ of H_X, $(x(0), q(0)) \in X_0$, therefore $\Phi(x(0), q(0)) = (\phi_{q(0)}, q(0)) \in Y_0$

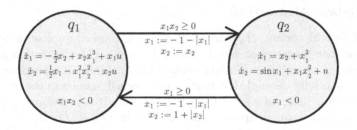

Fig. 2. Hybrid control system H_X.

since $N_q^0 = \phi_q(M_q^0)$. As long as the trajectory c^{H_X} flows continuously on a state $q \in Q$, $x(\tau)$ is a trajectory of $S_X(q)$, therefore $y(\tau)$ is a trajectory of $S_Y(q)$ since $S_Y(p)$ is ϕ_q-related to $S_X(q)$ and $x(\tau) \in Inv_X(q)$ implies $y(\tau) \in Inv_Y(q)$ by construction and partition propagation. When $x(\tau)$ enters a guard $Guard_X(e)$, $y(\tau)$ enters $Guard_Y(e)$ by construction and partition propagation. If the hybrid control system H_X jumps from location q_i to location q_j then H_Y can also take the same transition since the finite graphs of H_Y and H_X are equal and the corresponding transitions become enabled at the same time. After the jump $x(\tau) \in Reset_X(e, x')$ and therefore $y(\tau) \in Reset_Y(e, y')$ by construction of $Reset_Y$. Since the trajectory c^{H_X} is composed of continuous flows and jumps and H_Y simulates both, a finite induction argument on the number of jumps concludes the proof.

To show timed language equivalence it suffices to show that hybrid control system H_X is capable of simulating the continuous part of every H_Y trajectory since both systems have the same finite graph. This is now a direct consequence of using the minimal control abstraction $S_N(q)$ of control system $S_M(q)$ in each discrete location $q \in Q$ as Theorem 3 asserts that both control systems are exact time controllability equivalent. $\qquad\square$

4 Example

We illustrate our results by a simple example. Consider the hybrid control system H_X displayed in Figure 2. Using as abstracting maps $\phi_{q_1} = x_1 x_2$ and $\phi_{q_2} = x_1$ we extract the timed language equivalent abstraction presented in Figure 3. Due to space restrictions, we shall present the details regarding state q_2. We start by noting that $Inv(q_2)$ is invariant under $Ker(\phi_{q_2*}) = K = \frac{\partial}{\partial x_2}$ since K is everywhere tangent to the surfaces $x_1 = const$. The guard is given by the complement of the invariant and is, therefore, also invariant under K. The next step is to determine if ϕ_{q_2} satisfies Theorem 3 conditions, but this is automatically true since $K = g_1(x)$, and therefore $K \in Lie_g\{g_1(x)\} = \{g_1(x)\}$. The new dynamics in each location can be determined through the construction (2, 3). Writing the dynamics as $\dot{x} = f(x) + g(x)u$ we compute $[K, f] = X_1 = \frac{\partial}{\partial x_1} + 2x_1 x_2 \frac{\partial}{\partial x_2}$ and

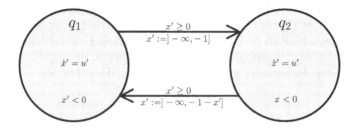

Fig. 3. Hybrid abstraction H_Y of the hybrid control system H_X.

$[K, X_1] = X_2 = 2x_1 \frac{\partial}{\partial x_2}$. However X_2 in linearly dependent on g so that:

$$\overline{\mathcal{D}}_M = \{f, g, X_1\} \tag{10}$$

Computing the pushforward by ϕ_{q_2} of $\overline{\mathcal{D}}_M(x)$ we get:

$$\phi_{q_2 *}(\overline{\mathcal{D}}_M(x)) = \{(x_2 + x_1^2)\frac{\partial}{\partial x_1}, \frac{\partial}{\partial x_1}\} \tag{11}$$

In N coordinates, (given by x'), x_1 equals x' and x_2 is now regarded as a control input v. The new dynamics is then given by $\dot{x}' = 1 + x'^2 + v$ and after introducing a new control input given by $u' = v + 1 + x'^2$ we get finally $\dot{x}' = u'$. The invariant on N becames $x_1 = x' < 0$ and the guard reads $x' \geq 0$. To determine the new reset map one computes $\phi_{q_2}^{-1}(x') = \{(x_1, x_2) \in M : x_1 = x' \wedge x_2 \in \mathbb{R}\}$. Using this data the reset map of the hybrid automaton H_X is $x_1 := -1 - |x'| = -1 - x'$ (since the guard is only enable for $x_1 \geq 0$) and $x_2 := 1 + [0, +\infty[= [1, +\infty[$. Aplying ϕ_{q_1} to this reset maps gives the new reset map $x' := (-1 - x')([1, +\infty[) =]-\infty, -1 - x']$.

Note how in this case the nonlinear dynamics could be simplified in such a way that HYTECH [5] or other similar tool can be used to analyze the resulting abstraction. For a more complicated example which extracts a hybrid abstraction from a purely continuous system, the reader is referred to [14].

5 Conclusions

In this paper, we have considered the problem of extracting hybrid abstractions from hybrid control systems while preserving timed languages. Generalizing the results of this paper to more general abstracting maps and more general properties is clearly important. Different properties may require different conditions on the abstracting maps, as well as different compatibility conditions between the abstracting maps and the guards, invariants, and continuous dynamics.

Acknowledgment. This work was performed while the first author was visiting the University of Pennsylvania. This research is partially supported by DARPA MoBIES grant F33615-00-C-1707, DARPA JFACC Grant N66001-99-C-8510, the University of Pennsylvania Research Foundation, and by Fundação para a Ciência e Tecnologia under grant PRAXIS XXI/BD/18149/98.

References

1. R. Abraham, J. Marsden, and T. Ratiu. *Manifolds, Tensor Analysis and Applications.* Applied Mathematical Sciences. Springer-Verlag, 1988.
2. R. Alur and D.L. Dill. A theory of timed automata. *Theoretical Computer Science,* 126:183-235, 1994.
3. Rajeev Alur, Tom Henzinger, Gerardo Lafferriere, and George J. Pappas. Discrete Abstractions of Hybrid Systems. *Proceedings of the IEEE,* 88(7):971-984, July 2000.
4. A. Balluchi, L. Benvenuti, M. D. Di Benedetto, C. Pinello, and A. L. Sangiovanni-Vicentelli. Automotive engine control and hybrid systems: Challenges and opportunities. *Proceedings of the IEEE,* 88(7):888-912, July 2000.
5. T. A. Henzinger, P. H. Ho, and H. Wong-Toi. A user guide to HYTECH. In E. Brinksma, W. R. Cleaveland, K. G. Larsen, T. Margaria, and B. Steffen, editors, *TACAS 95: Tools and Algorithms for the Construction and Analysis of Systems,* volume 1019 of *Lecture Notes in Computer Science,* pages 41-71. Springer-Verlag, 1995.
6. A. Isidori *Nonlinear Control Systems.* Springer-Verlag, second edition, 1989.
7. Velimir Jurdjevic. *Geometric Control Theory.* Cambridge University Press, 1997.
8. Gerardo Lafferriere, George J. Pappas, and Shankar Sastry. Subanalytic Stratifications and Bisimulations. In T. Henzinger and S. Sastry, editors, *Hybrid Systems: Computation and Control,* volume 1386 of *Lecture Notes in Computer Science,* pages 205-220. Springer Verlag, Berlin, 1998.
9. John Lygeros, Claire Tomlin, and Shankar Sastry. Controllers for Reachability Specifications for Hybrid Systems. *Automatica,* 35(3):349-370, 1999.
10. R. Milner. *Communication and Concurrency.* Prentice Hall, 1989.
11. George J. Pappas, Gerardo Lafferriere, and Shankar Sastry. Hierarchically Consistent Control Systems. *IEEE Transactions on Automatic Control,* 45(6):1144-1160, June 2000.
12. George J. Pappas and Shankar Sastry. Towards Continuous Abstractions of Dynamical and Control Systems. In P. Antsaklis, W. Kohn, A. Nerode, and S. Sastry, editors, *Hybrid Systems IV,* volume 1273 of *Lecture Notes in Computer Science,* pages 329-341. Springer-Verlag, Berlin, Germany, 1997.
13. George J. Pappas and Slobodan Simic. Consistent Hierarchies of Nonlinear Abstractions. In *Proceedings of the 39th IEEE Conference in Decision and Control.* Sydney, Australia, December 2000.
14. Paulo Tabuada, George J. Pappas, and Pedro Lima. Hybrid abstractions: A search and rescue case study. In *Proceedings of the 2001 European Control Conference.* Porto, September 2001. Submitted.
15. Claire Tomlin, George J. Pappas, and Shankar Sastry, Conflict Resolution for Air Traffic Management: A Study in Muti-Agent Hybrid Systems. *IEEE Transactions on Automatic Control,* 43(4):509-521, April 1998.

Author Index

Lecture Notes in Computer Science

For information about Vols. 1–1931
please contact your bookseller or Springer-Verlag

Vol. 1969: D.T. Lee, S.-H. Teng (Eds.), Algorithms and Computation. Proceedings, 2000. XIV, 578 pages. 2000.

Vol. 1970: M. Valero, V.K. Prasanna, S. Vajapeyam (Eds.), High Performance Computing – HiPC 2000. Proceedings, 2000. XVIII, 568 pages. 2000.

Vol. 1971: R. Buyya, M. Baker (Eds.), Grid Computing – GRID 2000. Proceedings, 2000. XIV, 229 pages. 2000.

Vol. 1972: A. Omicini, R. Tolksdorf, F. Zambonelli (Eds.), Engineering Societies in the Agents World. Proceedings, 2000. IX, 143 pages. 2000. (Subseries LNAI).

Vol. 1973: J. Van den Bussche, V. Vianu (Eds.), Database Theory – ICDT 2001. Proceedings, 2001. X, 451 pages. 2001.

Vol. 1974: S. Kapoor, S. Prasad (Eds.), FST TCS 2000: Foundations of Software Technology and Theoretical Computer Science. Proceedings, 2000. XIII, 532 pages. 2000.

Vol. 1975: J. Pieprzyk, E. Okamoto, J. Seberry (Eds.), Information Security. Proceedings, 2000. X, 323 pages. 2000.

Vol. 1976: T. Okamoto (Ed.), Advances in Cryptology – ASIACRYPT 2000. Proceedings, 2000. XII, 630 pages. 2000.

Vol. 1977: B. Roy, E. Okamoto (Eds.), Progress in Cryptology – INDOCRYPT 2000. Proceedings, 2000. X, 295 pages. 2000.

Vol. 1978: B. Schneier (Ed.), Fast Software Encryption. Proceedings, 2000. VIII, 315 pages. 2001.

Vol. 1979: S. Moss, P. Davidsson (Eds.), Multi-Agent-Based Simulation. Proceedings, 2000. VIII, 267 pages. 2001. (Subseries LNAI).

Vol. 1983: K.S. Leung, L.-W. Chan, H. Meng (Eds.), Intelligent Data Engineering and Automated Learning – IDEAL 2000. Proceedings, 2000. XVI, 573 pages. 2000.

Vol. 1984: J. Marks (Ed.), Graph Drawing. Proceedings, 2001. XII, 419 pages. 2001.

Vol. 1985: J. Davidson, S.L. Min (Eds.), Languages, Compilers, and Tools for Embedded Systems. Proceedings, 2000. VIII, 221 pages. 2001.

Vol. 1987: K.-L. Tan, M.J. Franklin, J. C.-S. Lui (Eds.), Mobile Data Management. Proceedings, 2001. XIII, 289 pages. 2001.

Vol. 1988: L. Vulkov, J. Waśniewski, P. Yalamov (Eds.), Numerical Analysis and Its Applications. Proceedings, 2000. XIII, 782 pages. 2001.

Vol. 1989: M. Ajmone Marsan, A. Bianco (Eds.), Quality of Service in Multiservice IP Networks. Proceedings, 2001. XII, 440 pages. 2001.

Vol. 1990: I.V. Ramakrishnan (Ed.), Practical Aspects of Declarative Languages. Proceedings, 2001. VIII, 353 pages. 2001.

Vol. 1991: F. Dignum, C. Sierra (Eds.), Agent Mediated Electronic Commerce. VIII, 241 pages. 2001. (Subseries LNAI).

Vol. 1992: K. Kim (Ed.), Public Key Cryptography. Proceedings, 2001. XI, 423 pages. 2001.

Vol. 1993: E. Zitzler, K. Deb, L. Thiele, C.A.Coello Coello, D. Corne (Eds.), Evolutionary Multi-Criterion Optimization. Proceedings, 2001. XIII, 712 pages. 2001.

Vol. 1995: M. Sloman, J. Lobo, E.C. Lupu (Eds.), Policies for Distributed Systems and Networks. Proceedings, 2001. X, 263 pages. 2001.

Vol. 1997: D. Suciu, G. Vossen (Eds.), The World Wide Web and Databases. Proceedings, 2000. XII, 275 pages. 2001.

Vol. 1998: R. Klette, S. Peleg, G. Sommer (Eds.), Robot Vision. Proceedings, 2001. IX, 285 pages. 2001.

Vol. 1999: W. Emmerich, S. Tai (Eds.), Engineering Distributed Objects. Proceedings, 2000. VIII, 271 pages. 2001.

Vol. 2000: R. Wilhelm (Ed.), Informatics: 10 Years Back, 10 Years Ahead. IX, 369 pages. 2001.

Vol. 2003: F. Dignum, U. Cortés (Eds.), Agent Mediated Electronic Commerce III. XII, 193 pages. 2001. (Subseries LNAI).

Vol. 2004: A. Gelbukh (Ed.), Computational Linguistics and Intelligent Text Processing. Proceedings, 2001. XII, 528 pages. 2001.

Vol. 2006: R. Dunke, A. Abran (Eds.), New Approaches in Software Measurement. Proceedings, 2000. VIII, 245 pages. 2001.

Vol. 2007: J.F. Roddick, K. Hornsby (Eds.), Temporal, Spatial, and Spatio-Temporal Data Mining. Proceedings, 2000. VII, 165 pages. 2001. (Subseries LNAI).

Vol. 2009: H. Federrath (Ed.), Designing Privacy Enhancing Technologies. Proceedings, 2000. X, 231 pages. 2001.

Vol. 2010: A. Ferreira, H. Reichel (Eds.), STACS 2001. Proceedings, 2001. XV, 576 pages. 2001.

Vol. 2013: S. Singh, N. Murshed, W. Kropatsch (Eds.), Advances in Pattern Recognition – ICAPR 2001. Proceedings, 2001. XIV, 476 pages. 2001.

Vol. 2015: D. Won (Ed.), Information Security and Cryptology – ICISC 2000. Proceedings, 2000. X, 261 pages. 2001.

Vol. 2018: M. Pollefeys, L. Van Gool, A. Zisserman, A. Fitzgibbon (Eds.), 3D Structure from Images – SMILE 2000. Proceedings, 2000. X, 243 pages. 2001.

Vol. 2021: J. N. Oliveira, P. Zave (Eds.), FME 2001: Formal Methods for Increasing Software Productivity. Proceedings, 2001. XIII, 629 pages. 2001.

Vol. 2024: H. Kuchen, K. Ueda (Eds.), Functional and Logic Programming. Proceedings, 2001. X, 391 pages. 2001.

Vol. 2027: R. Wilhelm (Ed.), Compiler Construction. Proceedings, 2001. XI, 371 pages. 2001.

Vol. 2028: D. Sands (Ed.), Programming Languages and Systems. Proceedings, 2001. XIII, 433 pages. 2001.

Vol. 2029: H. Hussmann (Ed.), Fundamental Approaches to Software Engineering. Proceedings, 2001. XIII, 349 pages. 2001.

Vol. 2030: F. Honsell, M. Miculan (Eds.), Foundations of Software Science and Computation Structures. Proceedings, 2001. XII, 413 pages. 2001.

Vol. 2031: T. Margaria, W. Yi (Eds.), Tools and Algorithms for the Construction and Analysis of Systems. Proceedings, 2001. XIV, 588 pages. 2001.

Vol. 2034: M.D. Di Benedetto, A. Sangiovanni-Vincentelli (Eds.), Hybrid Systems: Computation and Control. Proceedings, 2001. XIV, 516 pages. 2001.